AUTOIMMUNITY: EXPERIMENTAL AND CLINICAL ASPECTS

ANNALS OF THE NEW YORK ACADEMY OF SCIENCES
Volume 475

AUTOIMMUNITY: EXPERIMENTAL AND CLINICAL ASPECTS

Edited by Robert S. Schwartz and Noel R. Rose

The New York Academy of Sciences
New York, New York
1986

Cover: The cover shows T-cell activation by alloantigen (see page 308).

Library of Congress Cataloging-in-Publication Data

Autoimmunity: experimental and clinical aspects.

(Annals of the New York Academy of Sciences, ISSN 0077-8923; v. 475)
"The papers in this volume were presented at a conference . . . which was held by the New York Academy of Sciences on June 17–19, 1985 in New York City"— Contents p.
Includes bibliographies and index.
1. Autoimmune diseases—Congresses. 2. Autoanti-bodies—Congresses. I. Schwartz, Robert S., 1928– II. Rose, Noel R. III. New York Academy of Sciences. IV. Series. [DNLM: 1. Autoantibodies—congresses. 2. Autoimmune Diseases—congresses. W1 AN626YL v.475/ WD 305 A9396 1985]
Q11.N5 vol. 475   500 s   86-16309
[RC600]   [616.97]
ISBN 0-89766-345-4
ISBN 0-89766-346-2 (pbk.)

SP
Printed in the United States of America
ISBN 0-89766-345-4 (cloth)
ISBN 0-89766-346-2 (paper)
ISSN 0077-8923

ANNALS OF THE NEW YORK ACADEMY OF SCIENCES

Volume 475
July 30, 1986

AUTOIMMUNITY: EXPERIMENTAL AND CLINICAL ASPECTS[a]

Editors
ROBERT S. SCHWARTZ and NOEL R. ROSE

CONTENTS

[a]The papers in this volume were presented at a conference entitled Autoimmunity: Experimental and Clinical Aspects, which was held by the New York Academy of Sciences on June 17–19, 1985, in New York City.

Part V. New Forms of Therapy
Irun R. Cohen, *Chair*

Poster Papers

Financial assistance was received from:

- BURROUGHS WELLCOME CO.
- COOPER BIOMEDICAL INC.
- E. I. du PONT de NEMOURS & COMPANY/CENTRAL RESEARCH AND DEVELOPMENT DEPARTMENT
- IMREG INC.
- NATIONAL INSTITUTE OF ALLERGY AND INFECTIOUS DISEASES/NATIONAL INSTITUTES OF HEALTH
- A. H. ROBINS COMPANY
- SCHERING-PLOUGH CORPORATION
- SQUIBB CORPORATION
- STUART PHARMACEUTICALS/DIVISION OF ICI AMERICAS INC.
- UPJOHN DIAGNOSTICS/DIVISION OF THE UPJOHN COMPANY
- WAMPOLE LABORATORIES AND WALLACE LABORATORIES/ CARTER-WALLACE, INC.

Introduction

ROBERT S. SCHWARTZ

Department of Medicine
New England Medical Center
Boston, Massachusetts 02111

The usual kind of introductory note to a volume like this one summarizes the main points of the meeting and gives its principal conclusions. That would not be possible for so rich and varied a meeting as the one on autoimmune diseases sponsored by the New York Academy of Sciences in March 1985. Instead, I will recount, in the form of a remembered dialogue between Ian Mackay and myself, the origins of the meeting. I sat next to Ian at one of the sessions of the Kyoto International Congress of Immunology in August 1983. The speaker was tedious. We spoke *sotto voce*:

Ian, I haven't seen you in a long time. How are you?
Fine, Bob, but you know how far Boston is from Melbourne.
What *is* that fellow getting at?
Something that was published last year, actually.
Not like the old days.
Well, but these international congresses are all alike. Nothing new.
Except one.
Yeah?
Remember New York?
Which?
The one on autoimmunity.
Oh, yeah.
That was vintage stuff.
Remember Witebsky?
You mean. . . .
Right, he finally satisfied himself that autoantibodies against red cells were real.
He did the obvious experiment.
Yeah, but *he* did it!
Remember the best part of his presentation?
You mean. . . .
When he turned to Dameshek.
He was sitting in the front row.
And said, "Bill, you were right!"
I could see Dameshek's head glowing.
Those two finally came together.
But they were really on good terms, despite the posturing.
That meeting was historic.
New York Academy.
Right.
Do you realize that it will be twenty years soon?
Good God!
It was 1965.
I can't. . . .
Why don't you put on another one?
I can't. . . .

You and Noel.

I can't. . . .

After all, you and Noel, the "sons" of Dameshek and Witebsky.

I can't. . . .

Look, it would be a marvellous thing, and the time is ripe.

I can't. . . .

After this meeting I'm going to Baltimore. Noel and I are writing a book on autoimmunity.

I can't. . . .

I'll talk to Noel, I'm sure he'll want to do it.

I can't. . .

(Voice from the podium): The next speaker is. . . .

HLA Class II Variants: Structural Studies and Disease Associations[a]

GERALD T. NEPOM

Division of Immunology
Virginia Mason Research Center
Seattle, Washington 98101
and
University of Washington School of Medicine
Seattle, Washington 98195

Understanding the genetic basis of disease susceptibility presents a complex and multifaceted challenge. Recent advances in understanding the biology and biochemistry of the human major histocompatibility complex, called HLA, now permit us to specifically address questions of genetic predisposition in a number of autoimmune diseases. One approach to understanding the genetic basis of immune dysfunction is to analyze the role of MHC-enclosed molecules in disease expression. A number of autoimmune diseases are known to be associated with HLA antigens, specifically by virtue of the reactivity of alloantisera recognizing certain HLA specificities with a disproportionate number of patients as compared to normal individuals. The link between such phenotypic associations and molecular immune mechanisms should provide a key for understanding disease susceptibility: When a disease is HLA-associated, which precise genetic elements within the HLA complex contribute the associated risk?

A RECONSIDERATION OF THE ASSOCIATION BETWEEN HLA-DR4 AND RHEUMATOID ARTHRITIS

HLA-DR4 Is Not a Single Haplotype

The HLA-DR specificities, DR1-w14, are defined serologically by clustering cells of similar reactivity using selected alloantisera as typing reagents. Accordingly, each specificity corresponds to a particular epitope recognized by alloantisera that is present on cell surface molecules encoded in the HLA-D region. Over the last two years, we have reported a number of studies[1-4] in which we have analyzed the relationship between HLA-DR specificities and individual class II molecules expressed on homozygous typing cells. These studies have clearly shown that structurally distinct molecules may cross-react with alloantiserum to define a given HLA-DR specificity that results in typing responses that are phenotypically identical. For example, we identified 6 electrophoretically distinct DR-like Ia molecules among a panel of 17 HLA-DR4 homozygous typing cells tested. Detailed analysis of these structural variants reveals that the HLA-DR specificities, including HLA-DR4, are broad public serologic specificities that are present on structurally distinct class II molecules from multiple different haplotypes.[1,2] The implication of these findings is that what DR4+ cells have

[a]This work was supported by Genetic Systems Corporation.

in common is that the DR4 epitope carried by at least one of their D-region gene products will react with the DR4 alloantiserum to give the positive typing reaction. However, beyond this cross-reactive epitope, each cluster of cells possesses a unique collection of class II antigens such that "DR4" encompasses multiple distinct haplotypes. Therefore, in order to investigate genetic haplotypes that potentially account for HLA-DR4 associations with disease, the DR4 specificity alone is neither an adequate nor the most specific marker to follow.

The HLA class II genetic region consists of approximately five α genes and seven β genes clustered within three loci (DR, DQ, and DP) that could potentially encode seven or more different Ia molecules per haplotype.[5] Since, as mentioned above, the DR4 specificity is an epitope on at least one of these Ia molecules, it is plausible to presume that other class II specificities linked to DR4, such as DQw3, might be expressed on distinct molecules that vary among different haplotypes. This is, in fact, the case. Using sequential immune precipitation with monoclonal antibodies directed to two different class II loci, we demonstrated structural variability among not only DR molecules, but also DQ molecules among different DR4+, DQw3+ homozygous typing cells (HTC).[2] Recently, we have observed electrophoretic variation among products of a related class II locus expressed on DR4+, DQw3+ cells, which we call DQβ2, using the monoclonal antibody 17.15 (unpublished results). In additional studies analyzing immunoprecipitated β-chain polypeptides from other HTC, Groner et al.,[6] Maeda et al.,[7] Giles et al.,[8] Ishikawa et al.,[9] and Suzuki et al.[10] have reported similar variations among different DR4+, DQw3+ haplotypes. Thus, products of at least two class II genes are structurally polymorphic not only among different HLA-DR specificities, but within the DR4 specificity itself. FIGURE 1 illustrates this point. Each of these loci, therefore, encodes molecules that potentially account for structural variants expressed as class II functional differences in immune regulation.

The finding that several distinct haplotypes share a common HLA-DR specificity indicates that the use of the typing specificity itself is inadequate to determine the extent of class II molecular variation. The technique of two-dimensional gel electrophoresis following immunoprecipitation of class II molecules, which was used in the studies outlined above, is itself potentially underestimating the total extent of diversity in the class II region. This is because molecules that are distinct by amino acid sequence, but do not differ in overall charge (i.e., neutral amino acid substitutions), might remain undetected by protein electrophoretic techniques. In addition, when considering models for the association of HLA with disease, we might also consider models in which the genetic basis of disease association is actually related to a DNA noncoding region; that is, it is conceivable that genetic elements outside the coding regions contribute through regulatory mechanisms to altered class II expression or other phenotypic differences. For both these reasons, we have begun to investigate the genotypic differences among different DR4-positive haplotypes.

In a recent study, we identified a number of polymorphic restriction endonuclease fragments (RFLP) that demonstrate considerable genotypic diversity among 17 HLA-DR4-positive homozygous cell lines.[11] Using the enzymes, Pst I and Hind III, major differences were seen between many of the cell lines for fragments homologous to DQα and DQβ cDNA probes. Rarely, RFLP distinguished among DR4 HTC using DRβ probes. Thus, restriction endonuclease recognition sequences among DRβ alleles within DR4+ haplotypes were apparently generally conserved, whereas nucleotide variations among DQβ alleles were quite extensive. The restriction enzyme patterns observed correlated precisely neither with serological DR typing, HLA-D typing as defined by MLC, nor electrophoretic polypeptide profiles. For example, we detected at least three different RFLP among Dw4 HTC that are all mutually nonreactive by MLC. Analysis of our data on RFLP patterns among DR4+ cells suggested that some observed differences represent allelic variation within DQβ genes, some represent cross-hybridization with related loci such as DP, indicating haplotype variability at linked loci, while some indicate differences at restriction endonuclease sites unrelated to the coding regions. FIGURE 2 illustrates the extremely high degree of diversity observed among DR4 HCL when genomic DNA digested with Msp I is hybridized to a DQβ probe.

These findings imply that what the DR4-positive cells have in common is the DR4 epitope, carried by at least one of their D-region gene products, that reacts with the DR4 alloantiserum to give a positive typing reaction. Beyond this cross-reactive epitope, however, each cluster of cells possesses a unique collection of class II antigens that are products of multiple class II loci. In other words, the DR4-positive population

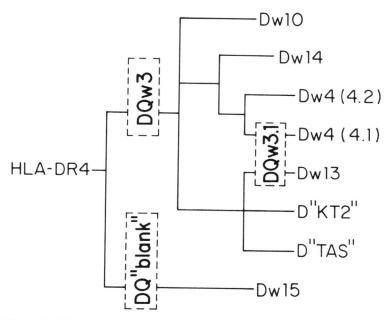

FIGURE 1. The DR4-associated family of haplotypes. Each cluster in the DR4 "family tree" denotes haplotypes that express different class II variants. Clusters are distinct by virtue of variant DRβ chains, variant DQβ chains, or both (see text for details). Within the broad DR4 allospecificity, three broad DQ allospecificities are illustrated. The DQw3 and DQw"blank" subsets encompass two arms of the tree, while the DQw3.1 subset represents an epitope shared by more than one HLA-D cluster within the DQw3 group of haplotypes.

consists of several discrete haplotypes that are actually quite diverse. If specific haplotypes account for HLA associations with disease, then the serologic HLA specificity alone is not a sufficient specific marker to optimally predict disease risk.

Patients with Seropositive Juvenile Rheumatoid Arthritis Express Specific HLA Molecules Defining Rare Haplotypes

Many investigators have reported associations between adult rheumatoid arthritis and the HLA-DR4 and/or Dw4 typing specificities with relative risk ratios from

3.5–6.[12–16] The comparable pediatric condition, seropositive JRA, is characterized by positive serum rheumatoid factor (usually in high titer) and severe, symmetrical polyarticular disease with frequent subcutaneous nodules (occurring predominantly in females).[17] Seropositive JRA is also associated with the DR4 typing specificity,[18] an analysis that we have extended by using more specific biochemical haplotypic markers. Using HLA-D analysis by mixed lymphocyte culture and two-dimensional polypeptide gel electrophoresis of immunoprecipitated DR and DQ class II molecules, we analyzed 17 HLA-DR4-positive patients with seropositive JRA. In contrast to the wide variety of DR4-associated polypeptides expressed on different HCL, the patients expressed a very limited selection of DR4-associated class II molecules. Only two DR4-associated

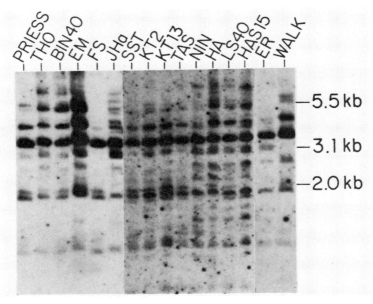

FIGURE 2. Genomic polymorphisms among HLA-DR4-positive homozygous cell lines. Msp I restriction endonuclease digestion of genomic DNA from 16 DR4 homozygous cell lines is illustrated, blotted and hybridized with a DQβ cDNA probe. A large number of polymorphic fragments are apparent, emphasizing the high degree of genotypic diversity within the DQ region present on different DR4-positive haplotypes.

haplotypes were found among the JRA patients: one carries the Dw4 specificity and appears to be similar to a prevalent DR4-associated haplotype in normal individuals; the other, carrying a Dw14 specificity, is much more rare in the general population. Of considerable interest was the observation that over half of the patients were homozygous for DR4; furthermore, 7 out of 12 homozygous DR4 patients were actually heterozygous for the combination of one Dw4 haplotype and another Dw14 haplotype. This is an extremely rare incidence, providing a relative risk for disease of approximately 120.[18]

    This heterozygous predisposition associated with juvenile rheumatoid arthritis (Dw4/Dw14) is reminiscent of the reported heterozygous DR3/DR4 predisposition associated with juvenile-onset diabetes (IDDM).[19] Since a DR4-positive haplotype is associated with each disease, we compared genomic patterns in JRA with those in IDDM. In order to directly test the hypothesis that specific DR4 haplotypes, not the DR4 specificity itself, predispose to disease, we analyzed DR4-associated DQβ and DQα genes in a population of IDDM patients who typed as DR4.

DR4$^+$ HAPLOTYPES DIFFER BETWEEN IDDM PATIENTS AND JRA PATIENTS

Genotypic Variation at DQβ Identifies Two DQw3-Associated Variants

Restriction endonuclease digestion of genomic DNA can be used to identify specific nucleotide sequences that function as markers for individual genes or gene segments.[20-25] FIGURE 3 illustrates the complexities of blotting genomic DNA using probes for different loci that are partially homologous, such as DR and DQ. Fragments that hybridize to a single probe can frequently be assigned to specific genes; when such a fragment is variably expressed in different individuals, it is referred to as "polymorphic" and can potentially relate to functional differences. Several investigators have previously reported RFLP that correlated with diabetes, notably the presence of a 12.0-kb Bam HI fragment and a Taq I 1.8-kb fragment,[26] along with the absence of a Bam HI 3.7-kb fragment,[27] as compared to normal individuals, all hybridizing to DQβ probes. On the basis of the findings listed above, namely, that genotypic polymorphism identifies multiple distinct DQ alleles within DR4-positive haplotypes, and that specific haplotypes, rather than the serologic markers, identify disease susceptibility markers, we analyzed the DQ polymorphisms of normal and diabetic DR4-positive individuals.

Among normal individuals, these findings can be summarized as follows: One of the DQβ genes, which we call DQβ1, is relatively nonpolymorphic among individuals with similar DQ typing specificities; for instance, DQw3$^+$ individuals share characteristic RFLP, such as 10.2-kb Bam HI and 3.2-kb Hind III fragments. The other DQβ locus, which we call DQβ2, is polymorphic among individuals who share identical HLA typing specificities; that is, DQw3-positive individuals have either a Bam HI 12-kb fragment or its allelic variant, Bam HI 6.9/3.7-kb fragments.[28] This DQβ2 gene has an interesting and somewhat restricted polymorphism within the DQw3 population. Two stable variants exist (which are allelic forms of each other) that encode polypeptides carrying DQw3 specificities. These two DQβ2 allelic variants differ from each other throughout a large portion of their genomic DNA, as evaluated by restriction mapping using a locus-specific synthetic oligonucleotide probe specific for the β2 exon.[29] Six different restriction endonucleases, including Bam HI, Pvu II, Hind III, Xba I, Taq I, and Sst I, are all capable of recognizing this allelic difference (although they have different nucleotide recognition sequences), indicating that the variation among these two alleles is quite extensive. In our mapping studies to date, we have localized much of the variation to the intron between the β1 and β2 exons of the DQβ2 genes, but the extension of the polymorphism through the β1 and β2 coding regions is not yet mapped.

A Specific DQβ Variant Identifies DR4-Positive Patients with IDDM

A large number of studies have associated HLA-DR4 with insulin-dependent diabetes mellitus.[30] Of 17 unrelated HLA-DR4-positive IDDM patients analyzed for

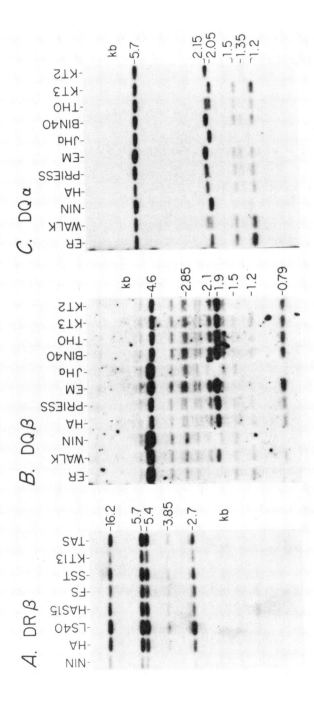

FIGURE 3. HLA-DR4-associated RFLP using different cDNA probes. Genomic DNA from DR4-positive homozygous cell lines was digested with Taq I restriction endonuclease, separately blotted, and hybridized to three class II cDNA probes. DNA fragments that hybridize with one probe, but not the others, such as the 16.2-kb fragment hybridizing to DRβ or the 1.9-kb fragment hybridizing to DQβ, permit probable assignment of these fragments to the homologous genes. Some fragments, such as the 5.7-kb bands hybridizing to DRβ and DQα probes, probably represent coincidental comigration. Other bands with similar fragment sizes possibly represent cross-hybridization with weakly homologous probes. Assignment of a polymorphic fragment to a specific allele, such as the 1.9-kb DQβ hybridizing fragment or the 2.1- and 2.0-kb DQα hybridizing fragments, is made by family segregation analysis and/or deletion mutant analysis.

genomic DQβ polymorphisms, 16 contained characteristic RFLP for one of these specific DQβ2 allelic variants and not the other.[31] This variant, which we call DQw3.2, therefore serves as a specific genomic marker for DQβ2 genes on haplotypes carrying the DR4 specificity that is associated with IDDM. FIGURE 4 is an example of restriction endonuclease digestion of genomic DNA from IDDM patients, using Taq I and hybridizing with a DQβ probe to illustrate this point. Fragments such as the 0.8- and 1.9-kb bands are markers for the DQw3.2 allele at DQβ2; several DR4 cells represented in FIGURE 3B (ER, NIN, JHa), as well as the first lane in FIGURE 4, represent the alternate DQw3.1 allele lacking these bands. Of interest is the observation that RFLP such as the 12-kb Ban HI and 1.9-kb Taq I fragments associated with diabetes by other investigators (see above) actually identify this same DQβ2 variant. Thus, we are able to map such nucleotide variation to a specific region of an expressed

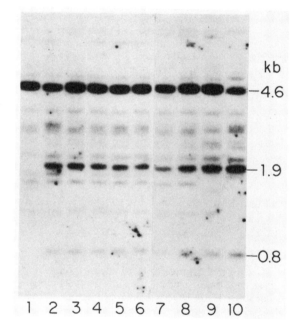

FIGURE 4. Detection of the DQw3.2 allele in IDDM genomic DNA. Genomic DNA from ten IDDM patients is shown, digested with Taq I and hybridized with the DQβ probe. The presence of the 1.9- and 0.8-kb hybridizing fragments denotes the presence of the DQw3.2 allele in nine out of ten patients.

DQβ gene, strongly implicating this gene product or a closely linked product directly in disease susceptibility.

Although the specificity HLA-DR4 is associated both with JRA and with IDDM, it is quite clear that the specific haplotypes that subdivide the DR4 family of haplotypes contain the disease-associated elements that serve as the most specific markers for the disease risk. Since we have identified a particular genomic variant associated with DR4 in IDDM, we directly tested for the presence of this variant in the population with DR4-positive seropositive JRA. In contrast to the preponderance of the DQw3.2 allele in IDDM, the DQw3 seropositive JRA patients expressed either the DQw3.1 or the DQw3.2 allele, and sometimes both, without apparent association with disease expression.[31] Our interpretation of this finding is that the DQβ2 locus, while specifically implicated in IDDM, is not equally implicated in susceptibility to JRA.

Indeed, the variation among JRA patients at DQβ2 is what one would expect in the normal population. If a specific HLA locus is to be implicated in seropositive JRA, very likely it will require additional analysis of subtle allelic complexities throughout the class II region. TABLE 1 summarizes these observations.

ALLELIC VARIATION AS A MARKER OF DISEASE

Since specific genomic variants within class II are extremely highly correlated with disease expression, it is tempting to speculate that the allelic marker itself is a functional disease marker. However, in the examples so far identified, this is not the case. For example, HLA identical siblings of patients with IDDM share both the DR serotyping and the particular DQβ2 allelism implicated as a disease marker as mentioned above.[31] Many of these siblings in multiple families studied to date are not diabetic. Our interpretation of this observation is that either both sibs contain the same genetic risk and only one incurred the necessary environmental risk or, alternatively, that additional genomic differences persist among apparently HLA identical sibs not detected by these techniques. In either event, the identification of specific HLA variants does not invariably predict disease.

TABLE 1. DR4-Related Allelic Markers for DQ Locus Polymorphisms Associated with Disease

Locus:	DQβ2		DQα	
Allele:	DQw3.1	DQw3.2	2.1	2.2
Informative RFLP:	6.9/3.7-kb Bam HI 3.4-kb Hind III	12-kb Bam HI 1.9-kb Taq I	2.1-kb Taq I	2.2-kb Taq I
Disease Association:				
IDDM	0–8%	92–100%	33%	100%
JRA (seropositive)	64%	91%	90%	70%

As with the example of DQβ allelic variants, specific allelic variants at other loci such as DQα can also be identified by genomic blotting analysis. FIGURE 3 and TABLE 1 demonstrate HLA-DQα hybridizing fragments from Taq I digested genomic DNA of DR4$^+$, DQw3$^+$ individuals that show bands at either 2.2- or 2.1-kb; heterozygotes show both. Thus, this RFLP is a specific marker of allelism for a DQα-related gene. Following a similar argument as that developed above for allelism defined for the DQβ2 gene, one might expect that specific DQα allelic variants, functioning as haplotypic markers, would correlate with disease susceptibility phenotype. As illustrated in TABLE 1, all IDDM patients tested contain the Taq I 2.2-kb fragment; JRA patients contain either or, in many cases, both fragments. Thus, although the specific DQα allele marked by a Taq I 2.2-kb RFLP is not disease-specific, it too is indicative of specific haplotypes conferring disease risk for IDDM.

Viewed within a molecular evolutionary context, such experimental observations are suggestive of a model in which the accumulation of nucleotide variation has several effects: First, apparently sporadic nucleotide shifts can occur, which are detected by frequent RFLP that do not directly correlate with any obvious phenotype. Second, some nucleotide shifts are quite stable, conserved throughout recent generations, and serve as specific haplotypic markers for inheritance of linked traits. Detected by specific RFLP, such markers may indicate similarity at one locus (e.g., DQβ) independent of other loci (e.g., DRβ), as illustrated by the presence of specific DQw3.1 RFLP on cells carrying either the DR4, 5, or 8 specificities.[28] Third, additional nucleotide variation can occur that leads to expression of disease susceptibility traits. When this variation occurs in evolutionary terms later than the generation of haplotypic markers detected by RFLP, then the specific nucleotides identifying the haplotype are inclusive genetic markers for disease risk. If similar disease-associated nucleotide shifts occur prior to the accumulation of particular haplotypic markers, then such genetic haplotype markers are not specifically predictive for risk.

As summarized above, each of the components of this model has been observed experimentally. The observation of a specific genomic polymorphism in patients with autoimmune disease is not itself sufficient to identify a precise linkage or causation. A particular variant such as DQw3.2 identifies a specific allelic polymorphism at a single gene locus. Thus, we now have a specific structural definition for polymorphisms implicated in some element of disease risk: such markers identify haplotypes at increased risk for disease susceptibility, allowing for additional unknown environmental or genetic factors. They effectively rule out many serologically identical HLA phenotypes as being implicated in disease suceptibility. Finally, they direct further scientific inquiry into specific genes and their products in order to understand the molecular basis for the associated disease.

ACKNOWLEDGMENTS

My collaborators in the original studies cited are acknowledged for their substantial contributions to this project, including Barbara Nepom, John A. Hansen, Se Jong Kim, Susan Holbeck, Erik Mickelson, Jane Schaller, Jerry Palmer, Jack Silver, and Christine Seyfried.

REFERENCES

1. NEPOM, B. S., G. T. NEPOM, E. MICKELSON, P. ANTONELLI & J. A. HANSEN. 1983. Electrophoretic analysis of human HLA-DR antigens from HLA-DR4 homozygous cell lines: Correlation between β-chain diversity and HLA-D. Proc. Natl. Acad. Sci. USA 80: 6962–6966.
2. NEPOM, G. T., B. S. NEPOM, P. ANTONELLI, E. MICKELSON, J. SILVER, S. A. GOYERT & J. A. HANSEN. 1984. The HLA-DR4 family of haplotypes consists of a series of distinct DR and DS molecules. J. Exp. Med. 159: 394–404.
3. NEPOM, G. T., B. S. NEPOM, M. E. WILSON, E. MICKELSON, P. ANTONELLI & J. A. HANSEN. 1984. Multiple Ia-like molecules characterize HLA-DR2-associated haplotypes which differ in HLA-D. Hum. Immunol. 10: 143–151.
4. BALDWIN, G. C., E. M. MICKELSON, J. A. HANSEN, B. NISPEROS, P. ANTONELLI, B. S. NEPOM & G. T. NEPOM. 1985. Electrophoretic variation between class II molecules expressed on HLA-DRw8 homozygous typing cells reveals multiple distinct haplotypes. Immunogenetics 21: 49–60.
5. NOMENCLATURE FOR FACTORS OF THE HLA SYSTEM 1984. 1984. Tissue Antigens 24: 73–80.
6. GRONER, J. P., A. J. WATSON & F. H. BACH. 1983. Dw/LD-related molecular polymorphism of DR4 β-chains. J. Exp. Med. 157: 1687–1691.
7. MAEDA, H. & R. HIRATA. 1984. Molecular identifications of HLA-DR4, MT3, and TB21 antigens on HLA-DR4 homozygous B cell lines. J. Immunol. 132: 574–577.
8. GILES, R.C., C. K. HURLEY & J. D. CAPRA. 1984. Primary structural variation among

serologically indistinguishable DS antigens. The MB3-bearing molecule in DR4 cells differs from the MB3 bearing molecule in DR5 cells. J. Immunol. **133:** 1–3.

9. ISHIKAWA, H., M. KASAHARA, H. IKEDA, K. OGASAWARA, S. HAWKINS, T. TAKENOUCHI, A. WAKISAKA, Y. KIKUCHI & M. AIZAWA. 1985. Demonstration of structural polymorphism among MB3 light chains by two-dimensional gel electrophoresis. J. Immunol. **134:** 417–422.

10. SUZUKI, M., T. YABE, M. SATAKE, T. JUJI & H. HAMAGUCHI. 1984. Two-dimensional gel electrophoretic analysis of the MT3 and DR4 molecules from different D-typed cells. J. Exp. Med. **160:** 751–758

11. HOLBECK, S. L., S. J. KIM, J. SILVER, J. A. HANSEN & G. T. NEPOM. 1985. HLA-DR4-associated haplotypes are genotypically diverse within HLA. J. Immunol. **135:** 637–641.

12. STASTNY, P. 1978. Association of the B-cell alloantigen DRw4 with rheumatoid arthritis. N. Engl. J. Med. **298:** 869–871.

13. DOBLOUG, J. H., O. FØRRE & E. THORSBY. 1979. HLA-DRw4 and rheumatoid arthritis. Lancet **1:** 548–549.

14. KARR, R. W., G. E. RODEY, T. LEE & B. D. SCHWARTZ. 1980. Association of HLA-DRw4 with rheumatoid arthritis in black and white patients. Arthritis Rheum. **23:** 1241–1245.

15. MCMICHAEL, A. J., T. SASAZUKI, H. O. MCDEVITT & R. O. PAYNE. 1977. Increased frequency of HLA-Cw3 and HLA-Dw4 in rheumatoid arthritis. Arthritis Rheum. **20:** 1037–1042.

16. JARAQUEMADA, D., C. PACHOULA-PAPASTERIADIS, H. FESTENSTEIN, J. A. SACHS, I. M. ROITT, M. CORBETT & B. ANSELL. 1979. HLA-D and DR determinants in rheumatoid arthritis. Transplant. Proc. **XI:** 1306.

17. SCHALLER, J. G. 1980. Juvenile rheumatoid arthritis. Pediatr. Rev. **2:** 163–174.

18. NEPOM, B. S., G. T. NEPOM, E. MICKELSON, J. G. SCHALLER, P. ANTONELLI & J. A. HANSEN. 1984. Specific HLA-DR4-associated histocompatibility molecules characterize patients with seropositive juvenile rheumatoid arthritis. J. Clin. Invest. **74:** 287–291.

19. SVEJGAARD, A. & L. P. RYDER. 1981. HLA genotype distribution and genetic models of insulin-dependent diabetes mellitus. Ann. Hum. Genet. **45:** 293–298.

20. SOUTHERN, E. M. 1975. Detection of specific sequences among DNA fragments separated by gel electrophoresis. J. Mol. Biol. **98:** 503–517.

21. WAKE, C. T., E. O. LONG & B. MACH. 1982. Allelic polymorphism and complexity of the genes for HLA-DR β chains—direct analysis of DNA-DNA hybridization. Nature **300:** 372–374.

22. OWERBACH, D., A. LERNMARK, L. RASK, P. A. PETERSON, P. PLATZ & A. SVEJGAARD. 1983. Detection of HLA-D/DR-related DNA polymorphism in HLA-D homozygous typing cells. Proc. Natl. Acad. Sci. USA **80:** 3758–3761.

23. TROWSDALE, J., J. LEE, J. CAREY, F. GROSVELD, J. BODMER & W. BODMER. 1983. Sequences related to HLA-DR α chain on human chromosome 6: Restriction enzyme polymorphism detected with DCα chain probes. Proc. Natl. Acad. Sci. USA **80:** 1972–1976.

24. AUFFRAY, C., A. BEN-NUN, M. ROUX-DOSSETO, R. N. GERMAIN, J. G. SEIDMAN & J. L. STROMINGER. 1983. Polymorphism and complexity of the human DC and murine I-A α chain genes. EMBO J. **2:** 121–124.

25. COHEN, D., I. LEGALL, A. MARCADET, M. P. FONT, J. M. LALOVEL & J. DAUSSET. 1984. Clusters of HLA class II restriction fragments describe allelic series. Proc. Natl. Acad. Sci. USA **81:** 7870–7874.

26. COHEN, D., O. COHEN, A. MARCADET, M. P. FONT, C. MASSART, J. HORS, I. DESCHAMPS & J. DAUSSET. 1984. Association of class I and class II MHC restriction fragment polymorphism with HLA-related diseases. In Histocompatibility Testing 1984. E. D. Albert *et al.*, Eds: 557–558. Springer-Verlag. Heidelberg.

27. OWERBACK, D., A. LERNMARK, P. PLATZ, L. P. RYDER, L. RASK, P. A. PETERSON & J. LUDVIGSSON. 1983. HLA-D region β-chain DNA endonuclease fragments differ between HLA-DR identical healthy and insulin-dependent diabetic individuals. Nature **303:** 815–817.

28. KIM, S. J., S. L. HOLBECK, B. NISPEROS, J. A. HANSEN, H. MAEDA & G. T. NEPOM. 1985.

Identification of a polymorphic variant associated with HLA-DQw3 characterized by specific restriction sites within DQβ. Proc. Natl. Acad. Sci. USA **82:** 8139–8143.

29. NEPOM, G. T. & S. HOLBECK. 1985. A locus-specific oligodeoxynucleotide probe specific for HLA class II DQ β genes. *In* Advances in Gene Technology: Molecular Biology of the Immune System, pp. 259–260. ICSU Press. Cambridge, United Kingdom.

30. BERTRAMS, J. & M. P. BAUR. 1984. Insulin-dependent diabetes mellitus. *In* Histocompatibility Testing 1984. E. D. Albert *et al.*, Eds.: 348–358. Springer-Verlag. Berlin.

31. NEPOM, B., S-J. KIM, J. PALMER, J. HANSEN, S. HOLBECK & G. T. NEPOM. 1986. The HLA DR4 specificity represents different haplotypes in IDDM and JRA. Submitted for publication.

DISCUSSION OF THE PAPER

B. SINGH (*University of Alberta, Edmonton, Canada*): In what domain of the DRβ protein does the polymorphism occur?

G. T. NEPOM (*University of Washington School of Medicine, Seattle, WA*): By HPLC analysis, it is predominantly in the $\beta 1$ domain. There are multiple peptide differences between the different allelic polypeptides, but most of them are in DR$\beta 1$.

C. G. FATHMAN (*Stanford University School of Medicine, Stanford, CA*): One diabetic patient had the 6.7-kb band, but did not type as DR3. Do you have an explanation for this finding?

NEPOM: That is due to coincidental comigration. Both DR3 and some haplotypes of DR4 produce bands at 6.7 kb, so they superimpose on the gels and this makes identification of the 3 and 4 heterozygote tricky.

H. O. McDEVITT (*Stanford University, Stanford, CA*): Have you tried AVA-1 with the DRβ probe on DR4?

NEPOM: No.

McDEVITT: We tested ten restriction enzymes and found two (AVA-1 and one other) that give good evidence for polymorphism. Unfortunately, the bands do not correlate with either DW type or any other split that has been made of DR4.

NEPOM: One would anticipate finding such enzymes because there is quite a bit of polypeptide variation there.

Molecular Genetics and T Cells in Autoimmunity[a]

PETER STASTNY, LINDA K. MYERS, GABRIEL NUÑEZ,
MARIE L. HOOVER, J. DONALD CAPRA,
AND EDWARD J. BALL

Departments of Internal Medicine and Microbiology
The University of Texas
Health Science Center at Dallas
Southwestern Medical School
Dallas, Texas 75235

GENETIC SUSCEPTIBILITY

It is generally accepted that susceptibility for development of certain autoimmune diseases such as Type I diabetes or rheumatoid arthritis is, at least in part, genetically determined. The discovery, in recent years, of associations of these diseases with the major histocompatibility complex has provided even more convincing evidence of this fact. About one-half of identical twins of diabetic patients have been found to develop the disease.[1] The data in rheumatoid arthritis is not as well defined. This is due, at least in part, to imprecision in diagnosis in earlier studies.[2] However, it is estimated that 40–50% of monozygotic twins are concordant. From the data obtained from monozygotic twins, the magnitude of the genetic component can be estimated. It can also be inferred that there is a considerable role for environmental factors. However, given a considerable genetic component in susceptibility, one wonders how much of it is directly related to the inheritance of factors linked to the HLA complex. In Type I diabetes, the highest risk has been associated with the heterozygote genotype of DR3, DR4. Interestingly, even in monozygotic twins, this HLA type appears to be associated with more frequent development of disease in the second twin.[3]

The role of HLA alone in disease susceptibility can best be evaluated by performing family studies and subsequent analyses of HLA identical sibs. A number of such studies have already been performed in both Type I diabetes and rheumatoid arthritis. In Type I diabetes, we have studied 24 random families (TABLE 1). One hundred and seven family members were investigated clinically and complete HLA typing was performed. Among the 83 first-degree relatives of the probands, 8 were affected, giving a frequency of 10%. Among the sibs, of those sharing two haplotypes with the first affected subject, 22% developed disease. Sibs sharing one haplotype were next (14%). Only 2 of the 48 parents had the disease (4%). When the distribution of HLA-DR genotypes was analyzed, it was found that all of the DR3, DR4 sibs had developed diabetes (TABLE 2). The increase in this genotype among affected offspring was highly significant ($p < 0.002$). None of the other genotypes were significantly different from the numbers expected on the basis of Hardy-Weinberg assumptions and using the gene frequencies observed in the parents.

In rheumatoid arthritis, Payami and co-workers[4] have recently analyzed data from

[a]This work was supported in part by NIH grant no. 1-R01-AI21278.

12

TABLE 1. Type I Diabetes in Members of 24 Families of Random Diabetic Patients

		Affected	
First-Degree Relatives[a]	No.	No.	Percent
All	83	8	10
Sharing one HLA haplotype—all	70	5	7
—parents	48	2	4
—sibs	22	3	14
Sharing two HLA haplotypes	9	2	22

[a]This study included 107 family members. The oldest affected child was taken as proband in each case.

82 multiplex families compiled from 14 separate studies. In a subset of their data, consisting of 66 cases in which two sibs were affected, there was a definite difference between the observed sharing of haplotypes and that expected (TABLE 3). Thus, in addition to the association with Dw4/DR4 in population studies, the analysis of multiplex families has demonstrated the presence of an RA susceptibility gene in the HLA region.[4] In all of these studies, however, many HLA-identical sibs of the probands are disease-free, indicating that other genes and environmental factors are important.

Juvenile arthritis has been studied by us and others.[5–11] It is a heterogeneous group of conditions causing chronic inflammatory arthritis in childhood. In a study of 183 random JA patients at our institution, we initially divided the patients into seven groups. The results of histocompatibility testing, though, suggested that four groups should be recognized. Boys with onset after nine years of age (12% of the patients) are almost all (80%) B27-positive. Patients with systemic onset (15% of the patients) and those with polyarthritis and positive rheumatoid factor (6% of the patients) are clearly distinct groups. All the rest, including pauciarticular with or without iritis and polyarticular rheumatoid factor-negative, can be combined. As will be discussed below, this group of patients has an association with DRw52 with certain unusual features.

TABLE 2. Distribution of HLA Genotypes in 24 Families of Diabetic Patients

HLA-DR Genotype	Nonaffected Sibs N = 28			Patients N = 29		
	Exp.[a]	Obs.	χ^2	Exp.	Obs.	χ^2
DR3, DR3	0.9	1	0.0	0.9	1	0.0
DR3, DRX	5.5	10	2.1	5.7	5	0.1
DR4, DR4	2.1	6	7.6[c]	2.1	4	1.6
DR4, DRX	8.4	8	0.6	8.7	8	0.0
DR3, DR4	2.7	0	2.7	2.8	8	9.8[d]
DR4, DRX	8.5	3	5.4[b]	8.8	3	3.8[b]
3 d.f.			18.3[d]			13.9[c]

[a]Expected genotypes from Hardy-Weinberg assumptions based on observed gene frequencies in 48 parents. Gene frequencies were DR3 = 0.177, DR4 = 0.271, and DRX = 0.552.
[b]$p < 0.05$.
[c]$p < 0.01$.
[d]$p < 0.002$.

TABLE 3. HLA Haplotype Sharing in 66 Families with Two Affected Sibs of RA Patients[a]

Results	HLA Haplotypes Shared		
	2	1	0
Observed	22	36	8
	(61)	(55)	(12)
Expected	16.5	33	16.5
	(25)	(50)	(25)

[a]Modified from H. Payami et al.[4]

IMMUNOLOGICAL MECHANISMS

Since the associations between disease susceptibility and HLA point to the HLA-D region (which is involved in the immune response), it is a reasonable working hypothesis that the effect of these genetic factors is related to immunoregulation. Most likely it involves communication between cells. Antigen presentation by accessory cells to T cells is probably a good *in vitro* model of the kind of functional process most likely to be involved. Much has been learned about this process in the last two years from the study of T-cell clones, the analysis of the role of various cell surface molecules, and the recent characterization of the antigen-specific T-cell receptor.

HLA-D REGION DETERMINANTS

The HLA-D region can be subdivided into the HLA-DR, -DQ, and -DP subregions. Since the subregions encode more than one polypeptide (alpha and beta chains), the genetic organization includes multiple loci within each subregion. The loci of the HLA-DR and -DQ subregions are closely linked and recombination between them appears to be extremely rare. Further complexity comes from the contribution of multiple antigenic epitopes in each of several beta chains. Moreover, in the DQ subregion in which both alpha and beta chains are polymorphic, neoantigens may be generated by transassociation of molecules. Because of this, considerable confusion exists in the interpretation of serologic data. The traditional method of analysis of patterns of panel distribution fails to distinguish between determinants expressed on different molecules.

RESTRICTION FRAGMENT POLYMORPHISMS

An approach that has become recently available is based on hybridization of specific cDNA probes with restriction-enzyme-digested genomic DNA. Southern blotting analysis with DR-beta, DQ-beta, and DQ-alpha probes has already been shown to yield polymorphisms that correlate with the different serologically defined class II specificities.[12-17] In FIGURE 1, there are shown the results obtained with genomic DNA digested with the enzyme, Pst I, and hybridized with a DQ-alpha probe. The panel was selected to include many cells positive for DRw52 in order to study the association with juvenile arthritis. It is of interest that a fragment of approximately 4.5 kb was found in most of the DRw52-positive samples, but was absent in two subjects also known to be DRw52-positive. Thus, a polymorphism detected with a DQ-alpha probe resembles the serologically defined specificity DRw52, but does not match this antigen completely. One possible explanation of these results is that this is a DQ-related polymorphism that resembles DRw52 because of linkage disequilibrium. At the protein level, a specificity partially resembling DRw52 (including mostly DR3 and DR5) and associated with the DQ-alpha chain was recently described by Tosi and co-workers.[18] We have also observed DR-like DQ-associated specificities recognized with typing sera.[19] Using monoclonal antibodies to determine the molecular localization of determinants recognized by cytotoxic typing sera, we have recently reported that certain human alloantisera recognize determinants on HLA-DQ molecules that are distinct from DQw1, DQw2, and DQw3. These DQ-associated determinants were found to segregate with HLA in family studies and were found to have a more restricted cellular distribution than the DR antigens.[20]

FINE SPECIFICITY OF RESTRICTION DETERMINANTS

Studies with T-cell clones have yielded a considerable amount of information about the restriction determinants that trigger either antigen-specific or allogeneic T

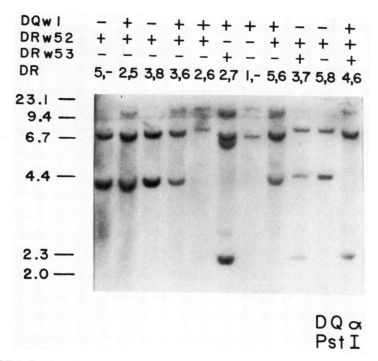

FIGURE 1. Southern blot of genomic DNA digested with Pst I and hybridized with a DQ-alpha probe. A fragment of approximately 4.5 kb appears to correlate with DRw52. For details, see text.

TABLE 4. Restriction Determinant Preference

MHC Haplotype: HLA-DR4, DRw53, DQw3		
Antigen	Restriction Determinant	Molecule
Mumps	DRw53-like	DR
GAT	DQw3 subset	DQ

cells.[21-23] In our laboratory, T-cell lines of either type have been developed by primary stimulation followed by isolation of T-cell blasts on percoll gradients. The lines are then grown in IL-2-rich medium and cloned by limiting dilution. Clones specific for products of each of the D subregions have been demonstrated. In many cases, the clones were found to recognize antigenic determinants distinct from those currently recognized by serologic methods. In addition, it was observed that cellularly defined determinants with very similar panel distributions may nonetheless be shown to be distinct on the basis of blocking with monoclonal antibodies against D-region products. The similar population distribution of these determinants is presumably due to the strong linkage disequilibrium exhibited within the D region.

RESTRICTION DETERMINANT PREFERENCE

A series of experiments are being conducted to determine whether T-cell clones responding to a certain antigen preferentially utilize some restriction determinants more often than others. These experiments are still in progress, but two points can already be made. When responder T cells from donors having the haplotype HLA-DR4, DRw53, DQw3 are stimulated with mumps antigen, the restriction determinants recognized are usually borne by molecules encoded by the DR subregion. When T cells having the same haplotype are stimulated with the polypeptide antigen GAT, the predominant restriction determinants appear to be carried by molecules encoded by the DQ subregion (TABLE 4). In addition, a majority of the resulting T-cell lines after stimulation with mumps viral antigen appears to correspond, by panel distribution, to DRw53 rather than DR4. There are certain limitations to these studies because mumps antigen presumably is composed of multiple antigenic epitopes. However, a possible explanation of the preponderance of DRw53-like restriction determinants recognized might be that an immunodominant mumps determinant is recognized predominantly in the context of DRw53-like determinants. Alternatively, DR-subregion class II molecules may express relatively more DRw53-like epitopes than DR4-like epitopes and T cells may utilize these determinants with a frequency similar to their expression.

It is also of interest that the DQw3-like determinants that restrict the GAT-specific T cells are not identical to DQw3. Rather, they resemble some of the new antigens on DQ molecules that we have recently described in observing lysostripping with monoclonal antibodies and cytotoxicity with human alloantisera.[19] In fact, the first of these specificities detected in our laboratory[24] was initially recognized by correlation with the reactions of a GAT-specific T-cell line. Since these DQ polymorphisms have thus far gone largely undetected, it is quite possible that diseases thought to be associated with DR are in reality related primarily to a product of the DQ subregion. Furthermore, the possibility of transassociation of DQ molecules (for example, in DR3, DR4 heterozygotes) should be kept in mind.

ALLOSTIMULATING EPITOPES ON A DRw11, DRw52, DQw3 HAPLOTYPE

Allogeneic T-cell clones were developed to better evaluate the specificites associated with DRw52. Normally, DRw52 defined with alloantisera includes virtually all individuals having DR3, DR5 (including DRw11 and DRw12), DRw6 (including DRw13 and DRw14), and DRw8. However, in juvenile arthritis, the association includes DR5, DRw6, and DRw8, while DR3 is not increased in frequency compared to controls. Three of the T-cell clones selected for this study showed an excellent panel correlation with DRw11 ($r = 0.65$, 0.74, and 0.83, respectively). The other three reacted with subsets of the DRw52-positive cells and each was unique in its panel distribution. Murine monoclonal antibodies against human class II antigens were then used to characterize the epitopes recognized by these T-cell clones (FIGURE 2). The same stimulating cell was used for all the T cells. The patterns of monoclonal antibody inhibition indicated that several distinct epitopes were being defined. T cell 925.5E11 was inhibited only by the DQ-specific monoclonal antibodies, TU22 and IVD12 (FIGURE 2). Thus, this T-cell clone reacts with a DRw11-like epitope expressed on a DQ molecule. T-cell clones 938(.5)B17 and 938.1.C6 were inhibited by the monoclonal antibodies, I-LR2 and MCS7; T-cell clones 938(.25)H6 and 31.5.G5 were inhibited by 7.3.19.1 and by L22.7. These two groups appear to define epitopes on separate DR-beta chains. We have arbitrarily called them DR-beta-1 and DR-beta-2. Finally, the cell line 938(.25)H2 was not inhibited by either I-LR2 or 7.3.19.1; it was blocked,

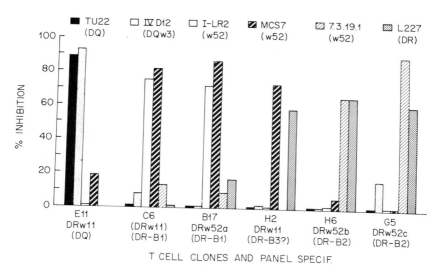

FIGURE 2. T-cell clones recognize different epitopes on a DRw11, DRw52, DQw3-positive stimulating cell. Inhibition of T-cell proliferation was assayed by addition of monoclonal antibodies to the cultures. The *r* values for correlation of T-cell clones with DRw11 were: E11 = 0.65, C6 = 0.74, H2 = 0.83. DRw52a, DRw52b, and DRw52c are arbitrary designations of panel reactivity patterns of the T-cell clones, B17, H6, and G5. The specificities of the monoclonal antibodies, TU22, IVD12, I-LR2, MCS7, 7.3.19.1, and L227, are shown in parentheses. For interpretation, see text.

however, by MCS7 and L227. We have tentatively assigned this epitope to DR-beta-3, but additional work is needed before this can be established with certainty.

Of interest is the fact that two T-cell clones with a DRw52-like specificity resemble the pattern that characterizes patients with juvenile arthritis. That is, they react with a subset of DRw8, DR5, and DRw6 cells and do not react (or react only rarely) with DR3 cells. Both of these clones have been tested with about 25 juvenile arthritis patients so far and they are showing a striking association, with a higher relative risk than any other reagents thus far tested.

DQ AND DR ANTIGENS ON ANTIGEN-PRESENTING CELLS

Considerable variation can be observed in the quantity of class II molecules expressed on the surface of monocytes obtained from human peripheral blood. While virtually all the monocytes express DR and DP, detectable amounts of DQ molecules are found in less than half of the adherent monocytes.[25-27] Two-color immunofluorescence experiments in the FACS showed that the DQ-rich cells were also characterized by a higher density of DR on their surface. This relationship between DR and DQ molecules expressed was found not to apply to other cell surface molecules such as Leu/M3 and LFA-3.[28] We have taken advantage of these quantitative variations in class II antigen expression to investigate the effect they might have on the capacity of accessory cells to stimulate T cells in MLR reactions and in antigen-specific HLA-restricted responses. To study the contribution of DR-enriched and DQ-depleted subsets in the MLR, adherent cells were sorted after staining with the monoclonal antibody, TU22.[29] The DQ-enriched population elicited strong allogeneic responses. The DQ-depleted cells were less effective at all stimulator/responder ratios. In other experiments, the cells were sorted on the basis of density of expression of DR using the monoclonal antibody, I-LR2. It was found that there was a correlation between the intensity of DRw52 staining and the primary MLR stimulation of T cells.

Next, the relationship between the expression of DR and DQ and the ability to support T-cell proliferation to antigen was examined. It was found that the subset of cells expressing DQ and increased density of DR was more efficient in antigen presentation of mumps or tetanus toxoid antigen than the DQ-negative, DR-dim adherent cells. Similar results were obtained with cloned antigen-specific T-cell lines restricted by a single DR-subregion specificity. Taken together, the results indicate that quantitative variation in DR/DQ molecules on antigen-presenting cells influences their ability to support T-cell responses.

OTHER CELLS WITH ABUNDANT SURFACE CLASS II ANTIGENS FUNCTION POORLY AS ACCESSORY CELLS

While these relationships hold when monocytes isolated from peripheral blood are compared on the basis of Ia antigen expression, other cells have been found to function poorly as accessory cells, despite having large amounts of DR. A summary of a number of different experiments demonstrating this phenomenon is shown in TABLE 5. Lung macrophages have been studied most extensively. These cells are rich in both DR and DQ and yet their ability to stimulate in the primary MLR and in the response of PBL to mumps has been uniformly poor.[30] They have also been found to be rather ineffective accessory cells for most mumps-specific T-cell lines. Experiments are in progress to elucidate the mechanism. Thus far, it does not appear to be due to an inhibitory effect and it does not appear to be due to a defect in antigen processing. The results could be due to other surface molecules, such as LFA-1, LFA-2, or LFA-3. Possibly, fibroblasts may lack the ligand for LFA-1 as has been recently suggested.[31]

Fibroblasts are normally Ia-negative, but after incubation with gamma-interferon, they express large amounts of DR. These cells also have been found to be very poor stimulators of the primary MLR. Their ability to activate T-cell lines has varied from poor to good. Work is in progress to determine the reason for these differences.

POLYMORPHISMS OF T-CELL RECEPTOR GENES

In addition to HLA-linked disease genes, it is very likely that other genetic factors will be identified that contribute to susceptibility. Recent work in a number of laboratories has brought us to the point of being able to analyze the potential role of the T-cell receptor genes in disease predisposition. Clone-specific murine monoclonal antibodies have identified a 90-kDa membrane glycoprotein associated with the T3 complex. The receptor was found to be composed of two disulfide-linked peptides, both

TABLE 5. Cells with Abundant Surface Class II MHC Antigens That Function Poorly as Accessory Cells

Cell Type	T Cells	Antigen	Response
Lung $m\phi$	PBL	Mumps	Poor or neg.
	PBL	MLR	Poor or neg.
	Lines	Mumps	Usually poor
Fibroblasts $+ \gamma - $ IFN	PBL	MLR	Poor or neg.
	Lines	MLR	Poor to good

of which have variable and constant regions that resemble immunoglobulin. The genes encoding the alpha and beta chains that comprise the T-cell receptor have been characterized. Polymorphism of the human T beta gene has been described by Robinson and Kindt.[32] We have recently demonstrated[33] that the human T alpha gene, as well as the beta gene, is polymorphic.

In these studies, genomic DNA was isolated from B-cell lines and peripheral blood from members of several families. It was digested with various restriction enzymes and then after Southern blotting, it was hybridized with the T-cell alpha probe, pGA5. A polymorphism was found using the enzyme, Bgl II. When DNA was digested with this enzyme, seven fragments were found to hybridize with the pGA5 probe. Five of the fragments were the same among all individuals tested. Two fragments varied. A 3.2-kb fragment was found in about 97% of the tested population. An additional 2.9-kb fragment was observed in about 23%. In one cell line, apparently homozygous for the 2.9-kb fragment, the larger piece was absent. The gene frequencies were 0.87 for the 3.2-kb fragment and 0.13 for the 2.9-kb band. When families were studied, segregation of the polymorphic RFLP was demonstrated. Studies are in progress to determine whether haplotyping for the T-cell receptor genes in multiplex disease families with the markers now available will allow detection of a contribution of this genetic system to susceptibility for development of autoimmune disease.

CONCLUSION

In vitro T-cell responses have been used as a model to study the role of various factors that might influence the development of autoimmunity. T cells recognize antigens in association with MHC determinants. This fact appears to provide a good working hypothesis for the role of class II antigens in various autoimmune diseases. T cells appear to display a preference for products of one or another subregion when responding to different nominal antigens. The epitopes of class II molecules recognized by T cells often appear to be distinct from those defined by conventional typing. Monoclonal antibodies have been used to define the epitopes of a DRw11, DRw52, DQw3 haplotype. Of particular interest were several T-cell clones that were stimulated by epitopes associated with DRw52-like specificities and which gave three distinct patterns of monoclonal antibody inhibition correlating with their location on different subsets of molecules encoded within the DR subregion. It is not yet known how many related, but distinct epitopes can be recognized using the same approach of panel studies and inhibition with monoclonal antibodies. It is of interest that two of the T-cell clones developed in the course of these studies recognized determinants associated with juvenile arthritis.

The quantity of class II antigens expressed on the surface of accessory cells may be an important factor in determining T-cell activation. Peripheral blood monocytes selected in the FACS on the basis of high-level expression of DQ and DR were much better stimulators and accessory cells than those having low levels of these antigens. In addition to HLA, other factors need to be considered in accessory cell activity. It has been observed that certain types of cells have poor accessory cell function even though they express abundant DR. They may be lacking surface molecules distinct from Ia that are expressed on antigen-presenting cells and that appear to play a role in T-cell activation.

Among the molecules that participate in T-cell–accessory-cell interactions, the T-cell receptor is of major importance. It confers the nominal antigen-MHC restriction specificity and its binding to antigen triggers T-cell activation. The genes that encode T receptor alpha and beta chains function in a manner similar to the immunoglobulin genes that generate specific antibodies. The isolation of probes for the genes of the alpha and beta chains of the T-cell receptor has made it possible to search for polymorphisms associated with these genes. Recent experiments have demonstrated that both of these genes are polymorphic and that variants identified by Southern blotting can be shown to segregate in families. Experiments are in progress to determine whether T-cell receptor genes are in linkage with susceptibility for development of autoimmune disease.

ACKNOWLEDGMENTS

The authors would like to thank James Marks and Chester Fink for making available their patients and Ronald Levy, Lee Nadler, Timothy Springer, and Andrew Ziegler for generous supply of monoclonal antibodies. The authors would also like to thank Debbie Hui and Chris Danielson for excellent secretarial help.

REFERENCES

1. BARNETT, A. H., C. EFF, R. D. G. LESLIE & D. A. PYKE. 1981. Diabetes in identical twins. A study of 200 pairs. Diabetologia **20:** 87–93.

2. LAWRENCE, J. S. 1970 (Heberden Oration, 1979). Rheumatoid arthritis—nature or nurture? Ann. Rheum. Dis. **29:** 357–379.
3. JOHNSTON, C., D. A. PYKE, A. G. CUDWORTH & E. WOLF. 1983. HLA-DR typing in identical twins with insulin-dependent diabetes: difference between concordant and discordant pairs. Br. Med. J. **286:** 253–255.
4. PAYAMI, H., G. THOMSON, M. A. KHAN, D. M. GRENNAN, P. SANDERS, P. DYER & C. DOSTAL. 1986. Genetics of rheumatoid arthritis. Tissue Antigens **27:** 57.
5. STASTNY, P. & C. FINK. 1979. Different HLA-D associations in adult and juvenile rheumatoid arthritis. J. Clin. Invest. **63:** 124.
6. NEPOM, B. S., G. T. NEPOM, E. MICKELSON, J. G. SHCALLER, P. AUTONELLI & J. A. HANSEN. 1984. Specific HLA-DR4-associated histocompatibility molecules characterize patients with seropositive juvenile rheumatoid arthritis. J. Clin. Invest. **4:** 287.
7. GLASS, D., D. LITVIN, K. WALLACE, L. CHYLAK, M. GAROVOY, C. B. CARPENTER & P. H. SCHUR. 1980. Early-onset pauciarticular juvenile rheumatoid arthritis associated with human leukocyte antigen-DRw5, iritis, and antimolecular antibodies. J. Clin. Invest. **66:** 426.
8. SUCIU-FOCA, N., M. GODFREY, J. JACOBS, R. KHAN, C. ROHOWSKY, A. FOCA-RODI, K. WOODWARD & M. HARDY. 1980. Increased frequency of DRw5 in pauciarticular JRA. *In* Histocompatibility Testing 1980. P. I. Terasaki, Ed. Los Angeles.
9. SCHALLER, J. G. & J. HANSEN. 1982. Early childhood pauciarticular juvenile rheumatoid arthritis: clinical and immunogenetics studies. Arthritis Rheum. **25:** 563 (abstract).
10. REEKERS, P., E. D. A. M. SCHRETLEN & L. B. A. VAN DE PULTE. 1983. Increase of HLA-"DRw6" in patients with juvenile chronic arthritis. Tissue Antigens **22:** 382.
11. ANSELL, B. M. & E. ALBERT. 1985. Joint report on juvenile chronic arthritis, pauciarticular type. *In* Histocompatibility Testing 1984. E. D. Albert, M. P. Baur & W. R. Mayr, Eds. Springer-Verlag. Heidelberg.
12. WAKE, C. T., E. O. LONG & B. MACH. 1982. Allelic polymorphism and complexity of the genes for HLA-DR beta chains—direct analysis by DNA-DNA hybridization. Nature **300:** 372–374.
13. AUFFRAY, C., A. BEN-NUN, M. ROUX-DOSSESTO, R. N. GERMAIN, J. G. SEIDMAN & J. L. STROMINGER. 1983. Polymorphism and complexity of the human DC and murine I-A α chain genes. EMBO J. **2:** 121–124.
14. COHEN, D., I. LE GALL, A. MARCADET, M. P. FONT, J. M. LALOUEL & J. DAUSSET. 1984. Clusters of HLA class II β restriction fragments describe allelic series. Proc. Natl. Acad. Sci. USA **81:** 7870–7874.
15. WALLIN, J., J. BOHME, B. CARLSSON, E. MOLLER, P. A. PETERSON & L. RASK. 1984. HLA class II polymorphism: Restriction fragment patterns correlated to Ninth Workshop serology and function. *In* Histocompatibility Testing 1984. E. D. Albert, M. P. Baur & W. R. Mayr, Eds.: 572–576. Springer-Verlag. Heidelberg.
16. TILANUS, J. G. J., M. L. BOSCH, R. GERRETS & M. J. GIPHART. 1984. Molecular analysis of HLA: Haplotype-specific DNA hybridization patterns using class II cDNA probes. *In* Histocompatibility Testing 1984. E. D. Albert, M. P. Baur & W. R. Mayr, Eds.: 577–581. Springer-Verlag. Heidelberg.
17. HUI, K. M., A. V. GROVES, D. JARAQUEMADA, G. GROSVELD, J. AWAD, C. NAVARRET, J. TROWSDALE, E. MURRAY & H. FESTENSTEIN. 1984. DNA restriction fragment length polymorphism of the human class II genes as analyzed by Southern blotting technique. *In* Histocompatibility Testing 1984. E. D. Albert, M. P. Baur & W. R. Mayr, Eds.: 590–594. Springer-Verlag. Heidelberg.
18. TOSI, R., N. TANIGAKI, R. SORRENTINO, D. CENTIS & G. B. FERRARA. 1984. Serologically detectable polymorphism of the HLA-DC α-subunit. J. Immunol. **132:** 277–282.
19. NUÑEZ, G., M. L. LATIMER, E. J. BALL, L. K. MYERS & P. STASTNY. 1984. Serologic detection of new polymorphisms on DQ molecules distinct from the DQw1, 2, and 3 specificities. *In* Histocompatibility Testing 1984. E. D. Albert, M. P. Baur & W. R. Mayr, Eds.: 421–422. Springer-Verlag. Heidelberg.
20. NUÑEZ, G. & P. STASTNY. 1985. Detection of serologically defined HLA-DQ polymorphisms distinct from DQw1, DQw2, and DQw3. Submitted for publication.
21. BALL, E. J. & P. STASTNY. 1984. Antigen-specific HLA-restricted human T cell lines. I. An MT3-like restriction determinant distinct from HLA-DR. Immunogenetics **19:** 13–26.

22. BALL, E. J. & P. STASTNY. 1984. Antigen-specific HLA-restricted human T cell lines. II. A GAT-specific T-cell line restricted by a determinant carried by an HLA-DQ molecule. Immunogenetics 20: 547–564.

23. MYERS, L. K., E. J. BALL & P. STASTNY. 1984. Different specificities of an HLA-DRw6 haplotype detected by alloreactive lymphocytes. Hum. Immunol. 11: 193–205.

24. BALL, E. J., L. K. MYERS, G. NUÑEZ & P. STASTNY. 1984. Private specificities of human Ia-like molecules detected by T cell lines. In Histocompatibility Testing 1984. E. D. Albert, M. P. Baur & W. R. Mayr, Eds.: 474–475. Springer-Verlag. Heidelberg.

25. GONWA, T. A., L. J. PICKER, H. V. RAFF, S. M. GOYERT, J. SILVER & J. B. STOBO. 1983. Antigen-presenting capabilities of human monocytes correlate with their expression of HLA-DS, an Ia determinant distinct from HLA-DR. J. Immunol. 130: 706–711.

26. NUÑEZ, G., R. C. GILES. E. J. BALL, C. K. HURLEY, J. D. CAPRA & P. STASTNY. 1984. Expression of HLA-DR, MB, MT, and SB antigens on human mononuclear cells: identification of two phenotypically distinct monocyte populations. J. Immunol. 133: 1305.

27. CHEN, Y. X., R. L. EVANS, M. S. POLLACK, L. L. LANIER, J. H. PHILLIPS, C. ROUSSO, N. L. WARNER & F. M. BRODSKY. 1984. Characterization and expression of the HLA-DC antigens defined by anti-Leu 10. Hum. Immunol. 10: 221–235.

28. NUÑEZ, G., E. J. BALL & P. STASTNY. Quantitative variation in HLA-DQ and HLA-DR determinants expressed on antigen-presenting cells influences antigen-induced T cell activation. Submitted for publication.

29. NUÑEZ, G., E. J. BALL, L. K. MYERS & P. STASTNY. 1985. Allostimulating cell in man. Quantitative variation in the expression of HLA-DR and HLA-DQ molecules influences T-cell activation. Immunogenetics 22: 85.

30. LIPSCOMB, M. F., C. R. LYONS, L. M. MILLER, G. NUÑEZ, P. STASTNY, W. VIAL, V. LEM, J. WEISSLER & G. TOEWS. 1986. Human alveolar macrophages: HLA-DR positive macrophages that are poor stimulators of the mixed leukocyte reaction. J. Immunol. 136: 497.

31. GOLDE, W. T., J. W. KAPPLER, J. GREENSTEIN, B. MALISSEN, L. HOOD & P. MARRACK. 1985. Major histocompatibility complex-restricted antigen receptor on T cells. VIII. Role of the LFA-1 molecule. J. Exp. Med. 161: 635–640.

32. ROBINSON, M. A. & T. J. KINDT. 1985. Segregation of polymorphic T cell receptor genes in human families. Proc. Natl. Acad. Sci. USA 82: 3804.

33. HOOVER, M. L., J. MARKS, J. CHIPMAN, E. PALMER, P. STASTNY & J. D. CAPRA. 1985. Restriction fragment length polymorphism of the gene encoding the alpha chain of the human T cell receptor. J. Exp. Med. 162: 1087.

DISCUSSION OF THE PAPER

J. F. BACH (*Hopital Necker, Paris, France*): Can your work explain why about 50% of juvenile diabetics are not HLA-DR3?

P. STASTNY (*University of Texas Health Science Center, Dallas, TX*): That question has not been addressed in our laboratory. We are investigating the difference between HLA identical siblings and monozygotic twins. Perhaps, T-cell receptor polymorphisms will explain the difference.

H. O. McDEVITT (*Stanford University, Stanford, CA*): Was it DRW-52 that showed the correlation with juvenile rheumatoid arthritis or a particular T-cell clone?

STASTNY: It was an epitope recognized by a particular T-cell clone that was inhibited by the monoclonal antibody I-LR2.

S. FERRONE (*New York Medical College, Valhalla, NY*): In the blocking experiments, you showed that the anti-DQ antibody blocked the cytotoxicity of the anti-DR clone. Do you know whether the anti-DQ antibody cross-reacts with DR5?

STASTNY: You have got it wrong. First of all, these are not cytotoxicity experiments. These were proliferative experiments. These T-cell clones proliferate when incubated with antigen-presenting cells. Secondly, the DR specificity was assigned by panel study. In other words, the majority of cells that stimulated this particular T-cell clone were DR5. What I am trying to show is that a panel study, which has been very useful in HLA serology for so many years, is no longer useful because even though by panel the epitope appears to be DR5, by monoclonal antibody studies, it is on DQ.

FERRONE: How then do you exclude that the anti-DQ does not cross-react with DR5?

STASTNY: Both of the anti-DQs have been studied extensively in a variety of serologic methods and they do not react with DR5.

UNIDENTIFIED DISCUSSANT: Do you think that T-cell clones will be better reagents to define the epitope?

STASTNY: T-cell clones have one attractive feature. They represent function. On the other hand, the chemical studies are very elegant, but eventually you will have to look at function to know what is happening. That basically is what the T-cell clones are doing for us.

Gene Conversion

A Mechanism to Explain HLA-D Region and Disease Association[a]

C. GARRISON FATHMAN, JORG GORONZY, AND
CORNELIA WEYAND

Division of Immunology
Department of Medicine
Stanford University School of Medicine
Stanford, California 94305

INTRODUCTION

It is our hypothesis that the association of certain autoimmune disorders with products of the major histocompatibility complex, the HLA-D region class II molecules, is the result of a pathogenic immune response against an environmental antigen. This immune response is induced by the formation of the ternary complex of antigen, MHC class II molecule, and T-cell receptor required for T-cell activation (FIGURE 1). Data from our laboratory and elsewhere support our hypothesis that such ternary complex formation is regulated by the polymorphic hypervariable regions of the class II HLA-D region molecules.[1-3]

The association of seropositive rheumatoid arthritis with HLA-DR4 is well established.[4,5] This association has previously been interpreted as demonstration of a susceptibility factor that might be inherited within or in strong linkage to the HLA-D region. Techniques previously used to analyze MHC class II antigens of patients with rheumatoid arthritis included conventional HLA-DR serological typing and cellular typing for HLA-D determinants.[6,7] Although the association is reproducibly demonstrable, only two-thirds of the patients with rheumatoid arthritis type as HLA-DR4.[5] Why don't all patients type as HLA-DR4? Our hypothesis suggests that conventional serologic typing is not indicative of the immune response gene products that lead to pathogenic responses with resultant autoimmune sequelae. Rather, the hypervariable regions of the HLA-D products that regulate immune response are T-cell interaction sites and can be recognized using T-cell clones.

MHC CLASS II HYPERVARIABLE REGIONS: GENE CONVERSION

The human and murine major histocompatibility complex is comprised of a cluster of closely linked genes that encode polymorphic cell surface proteins important in mediating immune responses to a wide variety of immunological stimuli.[8] Recent molecular data have suggested that the allelic protein polymorphism of the subunits comprising the Ia molecules is clustered in short stretches of hypervariability within

[a]This work was supported by NIH grant support no. AI 18716 and the Stanford Arthritis Center grant no. AM 20610. JG is a fellow of the DFG. CW is a fellow of the Arthritis Foundation.

24

the first external protein domain.[1-3] The observed regions of allelic hypervariability in the first domain are similar for the α and β chains of products of both the I-A and I-E subregions of the murine MHC[3] and for HLA-DR β products.[1] The stretches of sequence between such hypervariable regions are conserved, both among alleles at a particular locus and among loci.[1-3]

This pattern of allelic polymorphism that has clusters of polymorphism separated by stretches of nucleotide sequence homology among the alleles and between the class II α and β loci has suggested the possibility that such polymorphism might be generated, at least in part, by gene-conversion-like events.[9] In support of this hypothesis are data from our laboratory.[2] We reported the isolation of a murine alloreactive T-cell clone that was equally stimulated by B10.A(5R), (B6A)F$_1$, and the A$_\beta^b$ mutant B6.C-H-2^{bm12} (bm12) spleen cells, but not by the bm12 parental B6 cells.[2] Data obtained using monoclonal antibodies suggested that this clone, 4.1.4., recognized an epitope carried both by the A$_\beta^{bm12}$ and the E$_\beta^b$ chains. We localized this shared sequence recognized by clone 4.1.4 and defined the molecular basis for the bm12 mutation as follows: we isolated a cDNA clone for the E$_\beta^b$ gene and determined its nucleotide sequence.[2] A$_\beta^{bm12}$ differed from the A$_\beta^b$ parent allele by only three nucleotides in a clustered region of fourteen nucleotides between amino acid residue 67–71 of the mature A$_\beta$ polypeptide.[10] This clustering of mutations within a short stretch of

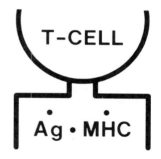

FIGURE 1. The ternary complex of MHC class II molecule, antigen, and T-cell receptor, whose interaction is required for T-cell activation.

nucleotide sequence suggested the possibility that the bm12 mutation was generated by a single event and by comparing this sequence to that of the E$_\beta^b$ gene, it was revealed that the bm12 mutation is identical to the E$_\beta^b$ genome in the corresponding region. We suggested that this mutation arose by a gene-conversion-like event in which a stretch of sequence from the E$_\beta^b$ locus was inserted appropriately in the A$_\beta^b$ locus with resultant production of a mutant molecule recognized by clone 4.1.4 as if the epitope that it recognized in the native I-E molecule was transferred intact into the new I-A framework (FIGURE 2).

Perhaps more importantly for our hypothesis, the bm12 mutation cluster spans one of the previously described hypervariable regions of the β chain.[3] Recognition of this region by clone 4.1.4 provided the first direct evidence of the functional importance of such hypervariable regions in T-cell stimulation. Additional data generated by studying immunological reactivity of bm12 and its parent B6 have suggested that this mutation is involved in a variety of immunologic phenomena including skin graft rejection[11] and Ir gene control of response to various protein antigens such as the species variants of insulin.[12] If this intergenic transfer of a hypervariable region sequence in the generation of the bm12 mutation is just one example of a more generalized mechanism, it would implicate conversion-like events in conjunction with

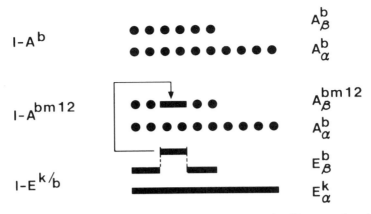

FIGURE 2. A diagrammatic representation of the gene-conversion-like event that shifted a portion of E_β^b into A_β^b, which resulted in the mutant A_β^{bm12} molecule.

phenotypic selection in the evolution of the clustered patterns of polymorphisms observed among the class II alleles.[3] If such a mechanism is operable in man,[9] as well as in the mouse, it might suggest an alternate hypothesis for the less than stringent associations of serologically defined HLA-D region products with diseases such as rheumatoid arthritis. Our hypothesis suggests that in man, as in mouse, such shuffling of hypervariable regions might occur with resultant changes of immune response phenotype in the absence of any detectable serologic changes of the framework molecule in which the relevant T-cell restriction site has been inserted. This would suggest that patients with seropositive rheumatoid arthritis that are not typed serologically as HLA-DR4 might still possess "DR4 derived" hypervariable regions expressed in the class II molecules that are recognized by T cells in association with environmental antigens in a pathogenic way as if they were still in the HLA-DR4 framework.

ALLOREACTIVE T-CELL CLONES DEFINE HLA-D ENCODED EPITOPES

In order to test this hypothesis, we have generated human alloreactive T-cell clones to dissect the HLA-D specificities.[13] Using such clones, we have been able to demonstrate that all patients tested with seropositive rheumatoid arthritis ($N = 23$), irrespective of the patients' HLA-D or HLA-DR type, expressed at least one of the T-cell epitopes recognized by a panel of four human alloreactive T-cell clones.[14] These data, presented below, suggest the possibility that such alloreactive human T-cell clones might recognize MHC class II T-cell interaction sites that are etiologically involved in the pathogenesis of rheumatoid arthritis.

Human class II molecules are defined and characterized both by conventional serologic techniques (as HLA-DR specificities) and by mixed lymphocyte reactions (as HLA-D specificities). By cellular typing, the serotype HLA-DR4, previously demonstrated to be associated with seropositive rheumatoid arthritis, has been divided into five subgroups: Dw4, Dw10, Dw13, Dw14, and Dw15.[15,16] The fact that the serotype HLA-DR4 has been differentiated by cellular typing into five subgroups suggests that the polymorphic structures of the HLA-D region seen by alloantisera are different from determinants recognized by T lymphocytes. Using human alloreactive T-cell clones, we have been able to show that typing responses and mixed lymphocyte reactions, which are the basis for HLA-D typing responses, are elicited by the recognition of a combination of different T-cell epitopes.[13] Thus, conventional cellular typing for HLA-D specificities does not reflect the presence of single allodeterminants. Due to the functional role of class II molecules in immune response,[8] T lymphocytes should be better probes to analyze the immunologically relevant fine specificities of HLA-D molecules for HLA and disease association.

SHARED T-CELL EPITOPES AMONG PATIENTS WITH SEROPOSITIVE RA

The T-cell clones used in this study were established by stimulation of peripheral blood lymphocytes from normal donors against a B lymphoblastoid cell line from a patient with seropositive rheumatoid arthritis. The class II molecules on the stimulator cell had been previously characterized by detailed cellular typing and biochemical analysis as HLA-DR4 homozygous and HLA-Dw4/HLA-Dw14 heterozygous.[16] T-cell clones were established from five different donors and clones were selected by analysis of their reactivity profile on a panel of homozygous typing cell lines (HTC). The four clones selected for study, T4-31, CB1-15, C2-1, and C2-6, were responsive to Dw14, but not to Dw4 homozygous typing cells, as is demonstrated in TABLE 1. Clone CB1-15 also recognized homozygous typing cells of the HLA-Dw10 specificity, thus suggesting the possibility that there is a shared T-cell epitope on HLA-Dw14 and HLA-Dw10 homozygous typing cells. All four clones were alloreactive and did not respond to autologous controls.

Proliferative responses of these four alloreactive T-cell clones were tested on cells from 23 patients with classical seropositive rheumatoid arthritis.[13] These patients were characterized clinically by a severe and progressive form of arthritis and most had failed disease-remitting therapy. Two-thirds of the patients typed HLA-DR4, which is in accord with the known HLA-DR4 association of seropositive rheumatoid arthritis.[4,5]

TABLE 1. Responses of Four Alloreactive Clones to DR4 Homozygous Typing Cells[a]

		Clone			
HTC	HLA-D	T4-31	CB1-15	C2-1	C2-6
JAH	4,4	0	0	333	126
BSM	4,4	520	574	7	596
BOD	4,4	752	290	156	710
AL 10	10,10	520	15413	40	0
TS 10	10,10	160	18557	0	419
KT 2	13,13	22	310	30	45
JHA	13,13	563	404	0	0
BIN 40	14,14	16887	42021	570	4393
LS 40	14,14	21107	53447	5615	17857
IST	14,14	12077	17370	5266	247
HAS 15	15,15	1490	21	0	309

[a]In this study, 1×10^4 cloned T cells were stimulated with 3×10^4 irradiated stimulator cells. Cultures were pulsed after 48 hours with 1 μCi ^{3}H-thymidine and harvested after an additional 12 hours. Results are expressed as net cpm, defined by the proliferative response of the clone in the presence of stimulator cells minus cpm incorporated by stimulator cells alone.

Additionally, the patients' cells were typed for the HLA-D specificity, Dw14, using primed lymphocyte typing reagents. Only 2 of the 15 DR4$^+$ patients and none of the 8 DR4$^-$ patients were HLA-Dw14 by these PLT reagents. Although these four clones were Dw14 reactive on the panel of HTC and only 2 of the 23 RA patients were Dw14, data presented in TABLE 2 show that these four clones recognized all of the patients with seropositive rheumatoid arthritis. Interestingly, the epitopes recognized by the individual clones are randomly distributed among the patients. Although the specificities seen by these four clones were clearly associated with the HLA-Dw14$^+$ homozygous typing cells, the allodeterminants recognized by these clones were present on cells from patients that did not type HLA-Dw14 or HLA-DR4.

In addition to examining the 23 seropositive rheumatoid arthritis patients, 18 DR4$^+$ normal nonrheumatoid donors were tested for the presence of determinants recognized by this panel of four alloreactive T-cell clones. Approximately half of these DR4$^+$ nonrheumatoid donors expressed determinants recognized by these four clones (TABLE 3). T-cell epitopes defined by these four clones were, however, rare among DR4$^-$ individuals and only 2 of the 23 nonrheumatoid patients who were HLA-DR4$^-$ were recognized by this panel of four alloreactive T-cell clones. Thus, although rare in nonrheumatoid DR4$^-$ control patients, one-third of the rheumatoid arthritis patients who were HLA-DR4$^-$ were identified by at least one of this panel of four clones. Epidemiological studies of identical twins and family studies of patients with rheuma-

TABLE 2. Percent Relative Response of Clones[a]

Patient	HLA-D	T4-31	CB1-15	C2-1	C2-6
1	4,7	<10	58	<10	26
2	1,4	46	76	<10	<10
3	4,–	60	86	<10	<10
4	4,–	72	41	<10	<10
5	4,5	30	43	<10	<10
6	4,5	32	62	<10	<10
7	4,w8	40	100	<10	<10
8	4,w9	32	40	<10	<10
9	4,1	64	<10	93	28
10	4,1	32	<10	62	96
11	4,1	58	<10	<10	<10
12	4,w10	38	<10	12	<10
13	4,3	<10	<10	90	<10
14	4,–	<10	<10	36	<10
15	4,w10	<10	<10	39	98
16	2,w8	<10	48	<10	<10
17	5,w8	<10	86	<10	<10
18	1,–	24	<10	<10	<10
19	1,7	23	<10	<10	<10
20	2,7	<10	<10	85	<10
21	2,7	<10	<10	<10	98
22	w6,–	<10	<10	62	<10
23	5,w10	<10	<10	<10	32

[a]Reactivity of four alloreactive T-cell clones stimulated with cells from patients with RA. Culture conditions are as in TABLE 1. Relative response is the proliferation induced by individual stimulator responder combinations divided by the maximal thymidine uptake of the highest responder stimulator combination in each assay (usually induced by BIN 40) × 100%. A relative response of less than 20% was considered negative. These data are maximum percent relative response of three or more assays for each combination.

TABLE 3. Distribution Pattern of Four T-Cell Clones on a Panel of Unrelated DR4$^+$ Donors[a]

HLA-DR	T4-31	CB1-15	C2-1	C2-6
3,4	−	−	−	−
2,4	−	−	−	−
4,4	−	−	−	−
2,4	−	−	−	−
4,w6	−	−	−	−
2,4	−	−	−	−
4,7	−	−	−	−
2,4	−	−	−	−
4,4	±	−	−	−
4,w9	−	−	+	−
3,4	−	−	+	−
4,7	+	+	−	−
2,4	−	+	−	−
4,4	+	+	−	−
4,−	+	+	−	−
4,w6	−	−	+	+
4,−	−	+	−	−
4,w6	−	+	+	+

[a]Responses of the four alloreactive clones assayed on nonrheumatoid DR4$^+$ stimulator cells. Pluses correspond to a percent relative response greater than 20%; minuses to less than 10% (see legend to TABLE 2).

toid arthritis have shown that affected and unaffected siblings share HLA-DR4 haplotypes.[18,19] These findings predict that genetic markers that are associated with rheumatoid arthritis must also be present in nonrheumatoid individuals. Thus, in a manner analogous to the HLA-B27 typing for ankylosing spondylitis, these data suggest the possibility that there will be genetic markers of predisposition for the development of classical seropositive rheumatoid arthritis and that such markers might be recognized by human alloreactive T-cell clones.

SUMMARY

In speculating about mechanisms that might give rise to T-cell epitopes appearing within different HLA-DR frameworks, we return to the hypothesis expressed above that suggests that gene-conversion-like events might be involved in shuffling the hypervariable segments of HLA-D region exons into alternative HLA-D region frameworks where they will still be recognized by the T cell (but not typed by conventional serology or mixed lymphocyte typing) as the "disease associated" HLA product. This might well explain the lack of stringent association between rheumatoid arthritis and HLA-DR4. It is possible, through the use of such alloreactive T-cell clones, that we might eventually define subgroups based upon presumed genetic susceptibility markers, which might allow therapeutic or prognostic assignment of patients with seropositive rheumatoid arthritis.

REFERENCES

1. BELL, J. I., P. ESTESS, T. ST. JOHN, R. SAIKI, D. L. WATLING, H. A. ERLICH & H. O. MCDEVITT. 1985. Proc. Natl. Acad. Sci. USA **82:** 3405–3409.

2. MENGLE-GAW, L., S. CONNER, H. O. MCDEVITT & C. G. FATHMAN. 1984. J. Exp. Med. **150:** 1184–1194.
3. MENGLE-GAW, L. & H. O. MCDEVITT. 1985. Annu. Rev. Immunol. **3:** 367–396.
4. STASTNY, P. 1978. N. Engl. J. Med. **298:** 869–871.
5. MILLER, M. L. & D. N. GLASS. 1981. Bull. Rheum. Dis. **31:** 21–25.
6. STASTNY, P. 1980. Joint report on rheumatoid arthritis. *In* Histocompatibility Testing. P. I. Terasaki, Ed.: 681–686. UCLA Tissue Typing Laboratory. Los Angeles.
7. YOUNG, A., D. JARAQUEMADA, J. AWAD, H. FESTENSTEIN, M. CORBETT, F. C. HAY & I. M. ROITT. 1984. Arthritis Rheum. **27:** 20–25.
8. SCHWARTZ, R. A. 1985. Annu. Rev. Immunol. **3:** 237–261.
9. AUFFRAY C., J. W. LILLIE, D. ARNOT, D. GROSSBERGER, D. KAPPES & J. L. STROMINGER. 1984. Nature **308:** 327–333.
10. MCINTYRE, K. & J. SEIDMAN. 1984. Nature **308:** 551–553.
11. MCKENZIE, I. F. C., G. M. MORGAN, M. S. SANDRIN, M. M. MICHAELIDES, R. W. MELVOLD & H. I. KOHN. 1979. J. Exp. Med. **150:** 1323–1331.
12. HOCHMAN, P. S. & B. T. HUBER. J. Exp. Med. **160:** 1925–1930.
13. WEYAND, C., J. GORONZY & C. G. FATHMAN. 1986. Proc. Natl. Acad. Sci. USA **83:** 762–766.
14. GORONZY, J., C. WEYAND & C. G. FATHMAN. 1986. J. Clin. Invest. **77:** 1042–1049.
15. REINSMOEN, N. & F. H. BACH. 1982. Hum. Immunol. **4:** 249–258.
16. NEPOM, B. S., G. T. NEPOM, E. MICKELSON, P. ANTONELLI & J. A. HANSEN. 1983. Proc. Natl. Acad. Sci. USA **80:** 6962–6966.
17. NEPOM, B. S., G. T. NEPOM, E. MICKELSON, J. G. SCHALLER, P. ANTONELLI & J. A. HANSEN. 1984. J. Clin. Invest. **74:** 287–291.
18. NUÑEZ, G., S. MOORE, G. V. BALL, E. R. HURD & P. STASTNY. 1984. J. Rheum. **11:** 129–135.
19. KHAN, M. A., I. KUSHNER & L. R. WEITKAMP. 1983. Tissue Antigens **22:** 182–185.

DISCUSSION OF THE PAPER

B. H. HAHN (*University of California, Los Angeles, CA*): Can any of these T-cell clones, when cocultured with an MHC-compatible B cell, drive rheumatoid factor production?

C. G. FATHMAN (*Stanford University School of Medicine, Stanford, CA*): It is a very interesting possibility, but we have not addressed it.

B. SINGH (*University of Alberta, Edmonton, Canada*): Have you selected for autoreactive T-cell clones from normal subjects?

FATHMAN: Autoreactive T-cell clones are a quite interesting phenomenon, but we do not select for them. We select against them. We find them frequently, as does everyone who clones T cells. Most interestingly, when you start with an antigen-specific or alloreactive T-cell clone and carry it in culture, we almost invariably end up with autoreactive contaminants, which we can subclone. This may mean that the repertoire of T cells is continually changing and the selective pressure of self-reactivity in culture selects these sorts of mutants.

E. A. CLARK (*University of Washington, Seattle, WA*): I want to come back to the question of the use of T-cell clones versus serology with monoclonal antibody. Do you have any information on whether or not the reactivity patterns of any of your T-cell clones correlate with the reactivity pattern of G. Nepom's monoclonal antibody?

FATHMAN: G. Nepom and I have not yet collaborated on the use of that antibody. However, I think the way that we are going to solve this question ultimately is to generate monoclonal antibodies that uniquely recognize human DR products expressed by transfected cells. That experiment will give us the polymorphisms required to answer the question. There are so few good antipolymorphic DR antibodies that we have not seen the sorts of associations that G. Nepom showed for his one antibody, A-10-83.

UNIDENTIFIED DISCUSSANT: Can you provide a possible mechanism for the antibodies that block the non-DR4 antigens?

FATHMAN: That refers to the gene conversion mechanism. The possibility exists that when a gene segment converts into a different DRβ, the T cell still recognizes it (as if it were in its original configuration), but serologically, the molecule has another spatial orientation. Thus, the ability of the monoclonal antibodies to interact with the converted DRβ will be slightly different. That is our model, but we have no evidence to support it. We would, though, like to think that it is the transfer of a hypervariable region from a DR4-like precursor into, for example, DR1 or DW8 that the T-cell clone uniquely recognizes.

R. S. SCHWARTZ (*Tufts University School of Medicine, Boston, MA*): I would like to propose an extension of your bad-luck hypothesis and to bring the B cell into the discussion. I do not believe that the B cell is a passive bystander in any of the responses you have discussed. Not only can it function as an antigen-presenting cell, but it has a hypermutable antigen receptor. If we think about that in the context of what you have proposed, we can imagine another aspect of the potential for "bad luck" if you encounter an antigen with multiple epitopes.

FATHMAN: I would agree with you. We have found that B cells (which express DR antigen) function very effectively to present antigen to T-cell clones. Therefore, it is possible that the B cell can trap the antigen, process it, and then present carrier epitopes to the T cell.

P. STASTNY (*University of Texas Health Science Center, Dallas, TX*): I do not think that we need gene conversion to explain all the phenomena.

FATHMAN: I agree with you. We have no evidence that gene conversion is a generally applicable process.

Genetics of the Complement System[a]

CHESTER A. ALPER

The Center for Blood Research;
Department of Pediatrics
Harvard Medical School;
and
Department of Medicine
The Children's Hospital
Boston, Massachusetts 02115

It is now over 65 years since "the first record of the inheritance of a single non-sex-linked character affecting the blood serum of a mammal."[1] That character was the deficiency of a complement component in laboratory guinea pigs at the Vermont State Agricultural Experiment Station. Since that time, inherited deficiency states of almost all of the approximately 20 proteins that constitute the mammalian complement system have been described in patients or in laboratory animals. Essentially all of this knowledge is the product of the past 25 years of intensive investigation paralleling the unravelling of the complement system, its components, its reaction mechanisms, and the biological activities associated with its activation. The transfer of knowledge has been reciprocal with contribution by the study of deficiency states and genetic polymorphisms to this general unravelling.

GENETIC POLYMORPHISM IN COMPLEMENT PROTEINS

Inherited structural polymorphism has been identified in a majority of complement proteins since the first descriptions of common inherited C3 variants.[2,3] TABLE 1 gives a summary of the described genetic polymorphisms within the serum complement system of man.[4] In all instances, expression is codominant and inheritance of the variants is autosomal. In FIGURE 1, we see the electrophoretic patterns of some of the known variants of C3. The patterns are produced by electrophoresis of fresh serum in agarose gel under conditions that allow separation of C3 from other protein bands. Patterns are produced by simple protein staining, taking advantage of the relatively high normal serum concentration of this complement component. The C3 variants are, in general, shown in heterozygotes who also have C3 S (for slow), which is the most common variant in all ethnic groups thus far studied. The single-banded pattern near the center of the figure is given by the protein from the homozygote for C3 S. In general, genetic polymorphism in other complement proteins is detected by agarose gel electrophoresis or isoelectric focusing. This reveals differences in net surface charge, which reflects amino acid substitutions presumably involving one or at most a few base alterations in the DNA sequence of the coding portions of the complement genes. Specific complement protein patterns are developed after separation either by immunofixation[5] or by use of an overlay agarose gel containing antibody-sensitized sheep red

[a]Principal support for the original work was provided by NIH grant nos. AM-26844, AM-16392, AI-14157, HD-17461, CA-19589, CA-20531, and CA-06516, and Clinical Research Center grant no. FR-128 at The Children's Hospital.

cells and all components needed for complement-mediated lysis, except for the component to be analyzed.[6] Although the diagram in FIGURE 1 suggests that the product of each *C3* gene is a single homogeneous band, this is an oversimplification. All complement components, like all serum proteins, show charge heterogeneity and form multiple bands on electrophoresis or isoelectric focusing. For recognition of variants, it is sufficient to utilize a homologous band, preferably the most prominent, as in the factor B (BF) patterns shown in FIGURE 2.

Recently, restriction fragment length polymorphisms in DNA (RFLP) in or very close to genes encoding complement proteins have been detected. In the case of C4, one such DNA polymorphism appears to correlate absolutely with a specific structural

TABLE 1. Approximate Frequencies of Common Alleles of Human Complement Genetic Loci[a]

Locus[b]	Race	Common Alleles and Their Frequencies				
C3	Whites	S 0.78	F 0.22			
	Orientals	S 0.99				
	Blacks	S 0.93	F 0.06			
C5[c]	Melanesians	1 0.93	2 0.07			
C6	Whites	A 0.61	B 0.37			
	Orientals	A 0.59	B 0.35			
	Blacks	A 0.56	B 0.38			
C81(α-γ)	Orientals	A 0.65	B 0.35			
	Blacks	A 0.70	B 0.25	A1 0.05		
	Whites	A 0.65	B 0.35			
C82(β)	Whites	A 0.95	B 0.44			
C3BRM	Whites	A(F)0.83	B(S)0.16	C 0.01		
FH	Whites	1 0.69	2 0.30	3 0.01		
C4BP	Whites	1 0.98	2 0.02			
C2	Whites	C 0.96	B 0.03			
BF	Blacks	F 0.51	S 0.44	F1 0.05		
	Orientals	S 0.89	F 0.11			
	Whites	S 0.80	F 0.18	F1 0.01	S1 0.01	
C4A	Whites	2 0.064	3 0.638	4 0.078	6 0.034	Q0 0.176
C4B	Whites	1 0.747	2 0.111	3 0.026	Q0 0.116	

[a]Only alleles with frequencies of approximately 0.01 or more are listed. Almost all loci have rare variants in one or more populations.
[b]*C3BRM* is the locus for the C3b-C4b receptor. The polymorphism is in the different molecular sizes of its variants. *FH* is the locus for factor H (β_{1H}-globulin), *C4BP* is that of C4 binding protein, and *BF* is that for factor B.
[c]*C5* shows no variation in whites, blacks, or Orientals.

variant found in the protein,[7] but in another instance, the DNA polymorphism serves to distinguish individuals who have the same C4 variant proteins.[8]

INHERITED COMPLEMENT DEFICIENCIES

Deficiency states for human complement proteins are now known for most complement proteins. In most instances, individuals with specific component deficiencies are homozygotes for null alleles at the structural loci for the respective complement proteins.[9-11] This is also true of complement deficiencies in experimental animals

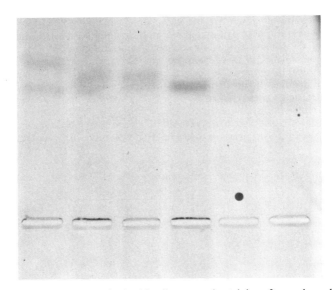

FIGURE 1. C3 variant patterns obtained by direct protein staining after prolonged agarose gel electrophoresis in calcium-containing buffer at pH 8.6 of fresh serum samples. The anode was at the top. Except for the homozygous C3 S pattern (fourth from left), the samples were from individuals heterozygous for common *C3*S* and a variant *C3* allele. Among the variants, only *C3*F* is common in Caucasians at a frequency of around 0.25. Rare variants are designated by electrophoretic mobility relative to C3 S to F1 as 1.0. From left to right, the patterns are F1S, F0.55, FS, S, SS0.4, and SS0.6.

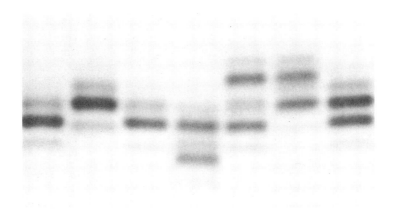

FIGURE 2. Electrophoretic patterns of factor B (BF) in fresh serum after specific immunofixation. The anode was at the top. There are four common alleles for *BF* with *S* most common in Caucasians and *F* with a frequency of around 0.2. *F1* and *S1* have frequencies in Caucasians of around 0.01. Phenotypes of individual samples are (from left to right): S, F1S, SS1, F1S, F1F, and FS.

for which there are known structural polymorphisms, as in guinea pig C4 and C2 deficiency.[13] FIGURE 3 illustrates a family with several members who are heterozygous for C3 deficiency. It can be seen from the figure that all such persons (who have C3 serum concentrations approximately 50% of normal and who are indicated in the figure by half-blackened symbols) express only one C3 variant. In some cases, an affected parent and child have totally different C3 variants. For example, individual II-2 is C3 S and has an affected child and an affected father who are both C3 F. The only explanation for these findings is that affected individuals have one expressed C3 structural gene and an allelic silent or near-silent C3 gene.[9] Thus, II-2 is C3 SQ0, where Q0 denotes "quantity zero." That some C3 is produced by $C3*Q0$ is evidenced by the presence of very low concentrations of C3 (less than 0.1% of normal as detected by radioimmunoassay) in the serum of several unrelated homozygous C3-deficient patients.[14] Of some interest is the fact that peripheral blood monocytes from homozygous C3-deficient patients produce about 25% of the normal amount of C3 with normal

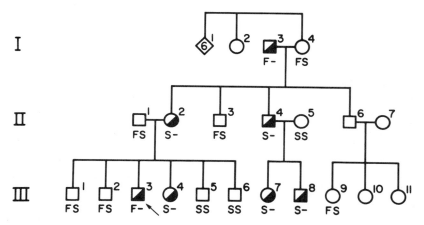

FIGURE 3. The HUB family with a C3 null (Q0) gene. Affected persons are shown by half-blackened symbols and have approximately half-normal C3 levels. C3 types, given below each symbol, show that the affected persons express only one typeable C3 structural allele and this may differ from that of their (affected) parent or child (I-3 versus II-2 versus III-3). (Reprinted by permission from *The Journal of Clinical Investigation.*[9])

subunit size and number.[15] It should be kept in mind that most serum C3 derives from the hepatocyte, as shown by a complete change of C3 genetic type to that of the donor following orthotopic transplantation of the liver.[16]

For several of the complement proteins, the situation appears to be more complex. For example, deficiency of C8 activity occurs in two forms reflecting the fact that the C8 molecule consists of an alpha-gamma chain disulfide-linked subunit loosely bound to beta chains.[17,18] One form involves deficiency of the alpha-gamma subunit[19,20] and the other of the beta subunit.[21,22] Analysis of the inheritance of genes for structural variants of these subunits reveals that the two loci controlling them are unlinked (i.e., not close to one another in the genome).[23] Perhaps in similar fashion, there are two distinct forms of deficiency of C1q,[24,25] which is a protein that consists of three disulfide-linked subunits for which no genetic structural variation is known. The situation is complex, however. Despite the fact that mature circulating C3, C4, and C5 consist of two, three, and two subunits each, respectively, the proteins are synthesized as single polypeptide chains[26,27] under control of single cistrons. The multichain mature proteins are produced by postsynthetic processing involving limited proteolysis.[28]

C4 and its deficiency state present a different kind of problem. In man[29,30] and in the mouse[31] (but not, apparently, in the guinea pig), the C4 locus is duplicated. Although in the mouse the duplicated locus produces a protein, Slp, without C4 function, in man, the products of both loci are functional although of different hemolytic activity[32] and chemical reactivity.[33] The locus for the more active product, *C4B*, also encodes a protein with an apparently slightly lighter alpha chain,[34] with different alloantigenicity (Chido versus Rodgers)[35] and with less overall negative

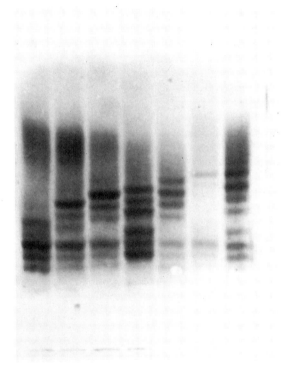

FIGURE 4. Agarose gel electrophoretic patterns of C4 in neuraminidase-treated fresh EDTA plasma visualized by immunofixation. The anode was at the top. Each allele produces three protein bands, the most anodal of which is usually darkest. C4 types (with Q0 for null alleles), from left to right: C4A1,Q0 C4B1,1; C4A2,2 C4B1,1; C4A3,3 C4B1,Q0; C4A4,4 C4B2,2; C4A5,3 C4B1,Q0; C4A6,Q0 C4B1,1; C4A6,3 C4B2,1.

charge than *C4A*. There are multiple amino acid differences between C4A and C4B, chiefly in the alpha chains. *C4A* and *C4B* are very closely linked, there are common half-null *C4A-C4B* haplotypes,[29,30] and there is extensive genetic structural polymorphism at both C4 loci,[32] as shown in FIGURE 4. Presumably, the duplication facilitated unequal crossing-over with the subsequent generation of half-null haplotypes, as well as duplications of *C4A* and *C4B*, which have also been found and are rather common.[36,37] The complete deficiency state for C4 is the consequence of homozygosity for a rare double-null *C4A-C4B* haplotype, *C4A*Q0, C4B*Q0*.[38]

There is evidence that the null C4 genes on some half-null haplotypes involve deletions of a C4 gene.[39] In the guinea pig, a structural gene for C4 is present in the deficient animal, but the mRNA is larger than normal.[40] No C4 can be detected in the serum of homozygous deficient humans[41,42] or guinea pigs,[43] and antiserum to C4 is easily made in deficient animals on the injection of normal guinea pig serum. There is a form, though, of C4 deficiency in man in which 4–20% of the normal serum concentration of C4 is present in affected persons, in which inheritance is autosomal dominant, and in which there is no apparent connection whatsoever to structural C4 genes.[44]

An exception to the general autosomal recessive inheritance of severe complement deficiency states is that of P (properdin).[45] In several families, deficiency of properdin appears to be inherited as an X-linked recessive trait.

Deficiencies of inhibitors in the complement system result in spontaneous complement activation *in vivo* and consumption of the natural substrates of the target proteases (or proteases for which the deficient proteins are cofactors). Thus, in $C\overline{1}$ inhibitor deficiency (hereditary angioneurotic edema), there is a marked reduction in the serum concentrations of C4 and C2, the natural substrates of activated C1.[46] In similar fashion, deficiencies of I (the C3b-C4b inactivator) and H (a cofactor for I) result in cleavage and consumption of C3 and B.[47,48]

Inherited defects in the $C\overline{1}$ inhibitor (hereditary angioneurotic edema) present a number of unusual genetic features. Inheritance is autosomal dominant and there are two forms: some 85% of families have patients who have markedly reduced serum levels of apparently normal $C\overline{1}$ inhibitor, whereas the remaining 15% have normal or supernormal concentrations of functionally defective $C\overline{1}$ inhibitor.[50] Serum levels of $C\overline{1}$ inhibitor are 5–31% of normal in the low protein form of the disease[51] and there are a number of different forms of the rarer dysfunctional form in which the $C\overline{1}$ inhibitor proteins differ from one another in net surface charge, in apparent molecular size,[52] and in their ability to inhibit $C\overline{1}s$ and other proteases with different substrates.[53] Little or no normal $C\overline{1}$ inhibitor can be detected in the serum of patients with dysfunctional protein.[51]

Remarkably, patients with either the protein-deficient or dysfunctional forms of hereditary angioneurotic edema respond to therapy with androgens with an amelioration of symptoms.[54–56] Even more remarkably, androgen administration results in a reversal of the basic biochemical and immunochemical abnormalities in the plasma of these patients.[54–57] Those with low concentrations of normal $C\overline{1}$ inhibitor protein experience a rise in level toward half-normal; in those with dysfunctional proteins, normal $C\overline{1}$ inhibitor appears in serum and also rises in concentration toward half-normal. As one might expect, the concentrations of the natural substrates of $C\overline{1}$, C2, and C4 also rise into the normal range.

From the metabolic study of isotopically labeled purified normal and dysfunctional $C\overline{1}$ inhibitor proteins in patients and normal subjects,[58] it is clear that the normal protein is more rapidly catabolized in patients than in normal subjects. Dysfunctional $C\overline{1}$ inhibitors may be catabolized at normal, subnormal, or supernormal rates in patients. In general, synthesis rates for normal $C\overline{1}$ inhibitor (when measurable) are approximately half-normal in patients as predicted from their heterozygosity for the normal and abnormal states. It may therefore be that at half-normal synthesis of $C\overline{1}$ inhibitor, there is some activation of C1 and other proteases, and this leads to hyperconsumption of normal $C\overline{1}$ inhibitor and a fall in serum level in all patients well below 50%.[59]

MAJOR HISTOCOMPATIBILITY COMPLEX (MHC) COMPLEMENT GENES (COMPLOTYPES)

The chromosomal localization is known for five complement genes in man and mouse. *C3* in man is on chromosome 19[60] and is linked to the genes for the Lewis blood group antigen, for apolipoprotein B, and for the secretor status of ABH substances. In the mouse, $C3$ is on chromosome 17, located some 11 centimorgans telomeric to the H-2 complex.[61,62] In both species, $C2, BF$ (the gene for factor B), and the two genes for C4-like proteins are located within the major histocompatibility complex.[63-67] However, in the mouse, the complement genes are between H-2K and H-2D (both class I), whereas in man, they are between HLA-B and HLA-DR (class I and class II). In man, the $C2, BF, C4A, C4B$ complex occupies about 120 kb of genomic DNA[68] and the orientation with respect to HLA-B/DR is unknown. The analogous complex in the mouse is more extensive at 240 kb.[69] In man, $C2$ and BF are very close to one another, separated by less than 2 kb, but BF and $C4A$ are separated by about 30 kb. $C4A$ and $C4B$ are about 10 kb apart. Immediately 3' to each C4 gene, there is a gene for the steroid-metabolizing enzyme, 21-hydroxylase, in mice and humans,[70,71] one of which may be unexpressed. Because the human genes, $C2, BF,$ and $C4,$ are so close to one another, they are inherited as single genetic units and no recombinations have been detected in many thousands of meioses.[72] Specific allelic sets can thus be recognized from family studies and they have been termed complotypes. These are designated arbitrarily as BF, C2, C4A, C4B variants. For example, BF S, C2 C, C4A Q0, C4B 1 is abbreviated as SC01. TABLE 2 gives complotypes that occur on chromosomes from Caucasians in frequencies of 0.01 or higher. As can be seen, there are at least 14 such complotypes.[72]

EXTENDED MHC HAPLOTYPES

When alleles at closely linked genetic loci occur together on the same chromosome at a frequency significantly greater than (or less than) that predicted by their individual frequencies, they are said to be in significant linkage disequilibrium. Sets of HLA-A, B and HLA-B, D/DR alleles in significant linkage disequilibrium have been known for some years.[73,74] Although linkage disequilibrium between individual BF, C2, and C4 alleles and other MHC alleles (particularly HLA-D/DR and HLA-B) can be shown, the most striking and significant linkage disequilibrium is demonstrable between whole

TABLE 2. Common Extended Haplotypes in Whites[a]

Haplotype[b]	Haplotype Frequency (per 1000)	Significance P
HLA-(A1), B8, DR3, SC01	93	1.4×10^{-5}
(A3), B7, DR2, SC31	59	0.048
(A2), B12(w44), DR7, FC31	37	0.002
(A2), B12(w44), DR4, SC30	34	0.012
(A1), B17(w57), DR7, SC61	28	2.8×10^{-4}
(A2), B40(w61), DRw6, SC02	11	0.026
(A2 or A3), B14, DR1, SC2(1,2)[c]	11	0.0063
(A1 or A2), B15(w62), DR4, SC33	9	0.015
(A3), Bw35, DR1, FC(3,2)0[c]	9	1×10^{-4}
(A25), B18, DR2, S042	9	0.001
(A26), Bw38, DR4, SC21	5	0.006
(Aw30), B18, DR3, F1C30	5	0.001

[a]Data updated from Awdeh et al.[75] for Boston whites.
[b]The most common HLA-A types for each extended haplotype are given in parentheses. Complotypes are given as BF, C2, C4A, C4B types, with "0" standing for null or Q0 genes.
[c]These have C4 duplications: C4A2, C4B1, C4B2 and C4A3, C4A2, C4BQ0, respectively.

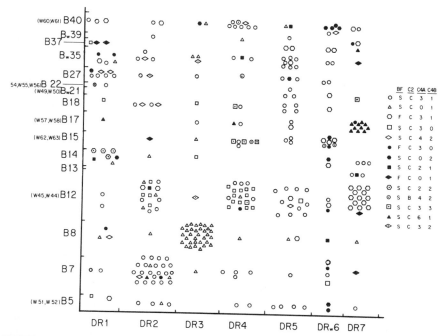

FIGURE 5. Distribution of complotypes with respect to HLA-B and HLA-DR. Note that the width of the columns and rows representing individual HLA-specificities is proportional to allele frequency in our population of normal chromosomes from Caucasians. (Reprinted by permission from *The Proceedings of The National Academy of Sciences.*[75])

complotypes and HLA-B and HLA-D/DR. A way to visualize three-point linkage disequilibrium between complotypes, HLA-B, and HLA-DR is shown in FIGURE 5.[75] In this graph, the width of the columns and rows representing HLA-B and HLA-DR alleles is proportional to the frequencies of these alleles in the population of chromosomes. Complotypes are shown by individual symbols. In the absence of linkage disequilibrium, there should be even scatter of each of the symbols throughout the diagram. Clustering of symbols in any HLA-B-DR "box" suggests positive linkage disequilibrium. Perhaps the most striking cluster in FIGURE 5 is that in the HLA-B8, DR3 box. Not only are most SC01 in this box, but no other complotype is found there. Other clusters are also obvious: SC31 with HLA-B7, DR2; SC61 with HLA-B57, DR7; and so forth. On formal analysis for three-point linkage disequilibrium (taking into account lower order pairwise linkage disequilibrium), a number of significantly positive linkage disequilibrium sets on chromosomes from Caucasians can be identified (TABLE 2). They account for around 30% of haplotypes, with the remainder consisting of randomly associating alleles. We have referred to the HLA-B, DR, complotype sets in significant linkage disequilibrium as "extended haplotypes."[75] In most instances, these extended haplotypes show limited variation at HLA-A and in some at GLOI (a locus some 5 centimorgans or recombination units from HLA-DR). They appear to have fixed alleles at other closely linked loci such as HLA-C and HLA-DP.[76] Thus, the concept emerges of stretches of chromosome 6 fixed at some past time in human evolution.[77]

The mechanisms by which linkage disequilibrium and extended haplotypes are generated are unknown, but they certainly include selection, which is probably for immune response genes important in resistance to infectious diseases.[78] In addition, some extended haplotypes may be analogs of mouse *t*-mutants.[75,77] The latter are found in wild mouse populations and show suppression of crossing-over with wild chromosomes (leading to extensive linkage disequilibrium of alleles, including those of the MHC), which is probably due to massive DNA inversions,[79–81] homozygous lethality, and male segregation distortion. In the latter phenomenon, the male bearer of a *t*-mutant and a wild chromosome 17 passes the *t*-bearing chromosome preferentially to all or nearly all his offspring. In this regard, it is fascinating that the extended haplotype [HLA-B8, DR3, SC01] when marked by GLO2 (but not GLO1) is transmitted to about 85–90% of children if it occurs in families with type 1 diabetes mellitus or gluten-sensitive enteropathy.[75,82]

DISEASES ASSOCIATED WITH COMPLEMENT GENES

It appears likely that many of the MHC alleles found to be increased among patients with a variety of diseases (including complement alleles) are increased because of the increase in frequency among these patients of certain extended haplotypes carrying these alleles. [HLA-B8, DR3, SC01] is increased in a number of diseases, including type 1 diabetes and gluten-sensitive enteropathy. Of particular interest is the finding that it is only the [HLA-B8, DR3, SC01, GLO2] haplotype (not the same haplotype with GLO1) that is increased among diabetics.[83] Similarly, the reason *BF*F1* is increased among type 1 diabetics[84] is that it is almost always part of the extended haplotype [B18, DR3, F1C30] increased among patients. From these observations, it seems probable that if a disease susceptibility gene is on an extended haplotype, the latter and the alleles it bears will be increased among patients. If the extended haplotype does not carry a susceptibility gene, it will appear to be protective and its alleles will be reduced in frequency in patients.

In a related manner, C2 deficiency, a disease exclusively of Caucasians, often occurs in the extended haplotype [HLA-B18, DR2, S042], often with A25(10) at the HLA-A locus.[64,85,86] In this case, the extended haplotype may have arisen from a recent single mutation in *C2* on a chromosome with HLA-A25, B18, DR2 and BFS, C4A4, C4B2. That this is likely is suggested by the fact that HLA-A is fairly variable when it is not HLA-A25 and GLO is mixed. C4 deficiency is found on several completely different chromosomes.

The association of complement deficiency diseases with autoimmune disorders and phenomena, particularly systemic lupus erythematosus, is intriguing. On the one hand, the classical and alternative pathways of complement activation are clearly involved in dissolution of immune complexes.[87] Therefore, it may be that complete or severe deficiency of the relevant complement components contributes to autoimmune phenomena via this route. There is always the possibility that complement deficiency results in defective resistance to microorganisms that may cause some of these diseases, such as systemic lupus or rheumatoid arthritis. Finally, for C2 and C4 deficiency, we must consider the possibility of linkage disequilibrium with aberrant immune response genes, which, in turn, can be responsible for autoimmune disorders.

In addition to an increased frequency of autoimmune diseases, patients with complement deficiencies have increased susceptibility to bacterial infections. This is particularly true of C3[88] and I[89] deficiency in which a wide variety of pyogenic organisms may be involved. In addition, patients deficient in one of the late-acting complement components (C5, C6, C7, C8, or C9) have increased susceptibility to systemic neisserial infection with recurrent meningitis or systemic gonorrhea.[90,91]

The symptoms of hereditary angioneurotic edema are dramatic, with episodic painless, nonerythematous, nonpruritic swelling of the skin. The edema may also involve the gastrointestinal tract with vomiting and severe watery diarrhea. If it affects the upper respiratory tract, laryngeal edema and asphyxiation may ensue.

CONCLUSION

In conclusion, our knowledge of the genetics of the complement system has increased explosively over the past decade or two. In many ways, complement genetics illustrates general mammalian genetic principles in a straightforward way. In some instances, as in hereditary angioneurotic edema, special features related to the complement system lend special nuances and perplexities. Those complement genes that are in the MHC have to be viewed within the context of the MHC and its peculiarities. At the same time, the study of complement genetics has provided clues to the structure and function of complement proteins and more recently to the structure and function of that most fascinating of chromosomal regions, the major histocompatibility complex.

ACKNOWLEDGMENTS

The original work from our laboratories cited in this review is the result of collaborative efforts with many investigators. In addition, Louise Viehmann provided superb secretarial assistance.

REFERENCES

1. HYDE, R. R. 1932. The complement deficient guinea pig: A study of an inheritable factor in immunity. Am. J. Hyg. **15:** 824–836.
2. ALPER, C. A. & R. P. PROPP. 1968. Genetic polymorphism of the third component of human complement (C'3). J. Clin. Invest. **47:** 2181–2191.
3. AZEN, E. A. & O. SMITHIES. 1968. Genetic polymorphism of C'3 (beta-1C-globulin) in human serum. Science **162:** 905–907.
4. RAUM, D., V. H. DONALDSON, F. S. ROSEN & C. A. ALPER. 1980. Genetics of complement. Curr. Top. Hematol. **3:** 111–174.
5. ALPER, C. A. & A. M. JOHNSON. 1969. Immunofixation electrophoresis: A technique for the study of protein polymorphism. Vox Sang. **17:** 445–452.
6. HOBART, M. J., P. J. LACHMANN & C. A. ALPER. 1975. Polymorphism of human C6. *In* Prot. Biol. Fluids, vol. 22. H. Peeters, Ed.: 575–580. Pergamon. New York.
7. PALSDOTTIR, A., S. J. CROSS, J. H. EDWARDS & M. C. CARROLL. 1983. Correlation between a DNA restriction frequent length polymorphism and the C4A 6 protein. Nature **306:** 615–616.
8. WHITEHEAD, A. S., D. E. WOODS, E. FLEISCHNICK, J. E. CHIN, E. J. YUNIS, A. J. KATZ, P. S. GERALD, C. A. ALPER & H. R. COLTEN. 1984. DNA polymorphisms of the C4 genes: A new marker for analysis of the major histocompatibility complex. N. Engl. J. Med. **310:** 88–94.

9. ALPER, C. A., R. P. PROPP, M. R. KLEMPERER & F. S. ROSEN. 1969. Inherited deficiency of the third component of human complement (C'3). J. Clin. Invest. **48:** 553–557.

10. PARISER, K. M., D. RAUM, E. M. BERKMAN, C. A. ALPER & V. AGNELLO. 1978. Evidence for a silent or null gene in hereditary C2 deficiency. J. Immunol. **121:** 2580–2581.

11. GLASS, D., D. RAUM, D. BALAVITCH, E. KAGAN, A. RABSON, P. H. SCHUR & C. A. ALPER. 1978. Inherited deficiency of the sixth component of complement: A silent or null gene. J. Immunol. **120:** 538–541.

12. KRÖNKE, M., A. F. GECZY, U. HADDING & D. BITTER-SUERMANN. 1977. Linkage of C4 and C4 deficiency to Bf and GPLA. Immunogenetics **5:** 461–466.

13. HADDING, U., T. HOFFMANN & D. BITTER-SUERMANN. 1980. C2 deficiency in guinea pigs. J. Immunol. **124:** 1521 (abstract).

14. DAVIS, A. E., III, J. S. DAVIS IV, A. R. RABSON, S. G. OSOFSKY, H. R. COLTEN, F. S. ROSEN & C. A. ALPER. 1977. Homozygous C3 deficiency: Detection of C3 by radioimmunoassay. Clin. Immunol. Immunopathol. **8:** 543–550.

15. EINSTEIN, L. P., P. J. HANSEN, M. BALLOW, A. E. DAVIS III, J. S. DAVIS IV, C. A. ALPER, F. S. ROSEN & H. R. COLTEN. 1977. Biosynthesis of the third component of complement (C3) *in vitro* by monocytes from both normal and homozygous C3-deficient humans. J. Clin. Invest. **60:** 963–969.

16. ALPER, C. A., A. M. JOHNSON, A. G. BIRTCH & F. D. MOORE. 1969. Human C'3: Evidence for the liver as the primary site of synthesis. Science **163:** 286–288.

17. KOLB, W. P. & H. J. MÜLLER-EBERHARD. 1976. The membrane attack mechanism of complement: The three polypeptide chain structure of the eighth component. J. Exp. Med. **143:** 1131–1139.

18. STECKEL, E. W., R. G. YORK, J. B. MONAHAN & J. M. SODETZ. 1980. The eighth component of human complement: Purification and physiochemical characterization of its unusual subunit structure. J. Biol. Chem. **255:** 11,997–12,005.

19. PETERSEN, B. H., J. A. GRAHAM & G. F. BROOKS. 1976. Human deficiency of the eighth component of complement. The requirement of C8 for serum *Neisseria gonorrhoeae* bactericidal activity. J. Clin. Invest. **57:** 283–290.

20. RAUM, D., M. A. SPENCE, D. BALAVITCH, S. TIDEMAN, A. D. MERRITT, R. T. TAGGART, B. H. PETERSEN, N. K. DAY & C. A. ALPER. Genetic control of the eighth component of complement. J. Clin. Invest. **64:** 858–865.

21. TEDESCO, F., S. M. BARDARE, A. M. GIOVANETTI & G. SIRCHIA. 1980. A familial dysfunction of the eighth component of complement (C8). Clin. Immunol. Immunopathol. **16:** 180–191.

22. TEDESCO, F., P. DENSEN, M. A. VILLA, B. H. PETERSEN & G. SIRCHIA. 1983. Two types of functional eighth component of complement (C8) molecules in C8 deficiency in man. J. Clin. Invest. **71:** 188–191.

23. ALPER, C. A., D. MARCUS, D. RAUM, B. H. PETERSEN & T. J. SPIRA. 1983. Evidence for two unlinked genetic loci for the eighth component of human complement (C8). J. Clin. Invest. **72:** 1526–1531.

24. BERKEL, A. I., M. LOOS, Ö. SANAL, G. MAUFF, Y. GÜNGEN, Ü. ÖRS, F. ERSOY & O. YEGIN. 1979. Clinical and immunological studies in a case of selective complete C1q deficiency. Clin. Exp. Immunol. **38:** 52–63.

25. THOMPSON, R. A., M. HAENEY, K. B. M. REID, J. G. DAVIS, R. H. R. WHITE & A. H. CAMERON. 1980. A genetic defect of the C1q subcomponent of complement associated with childhood (immune complex) nephritis. N. Engl. J. Med. **303:** 22–24.

26. HALL, R. E. & H. R. COLTEN. 1977. Molecular size and subunit structure of the fourth component of guinea pig complement. J. Immunol. **118:** 1903–1905.

27. COLTEN, H. R., C. A. ALPER & F. S. ROSEN. 1981. Current concepts in immunology. Genetics and biosynthesis of complement proteins. N. Engl. J. Med. **304:** 653–656.

28. GOLDBERGER, G. & H. R. COLTEN. 1980. Precursor complement protein (Pro-C4) is converted *in vitro* to native C4 by plasmin. Nature **286:** 514–516.

29. O'NEILL, G. J., S. Y. YANG & B. DUPONT. 1978. Two HLA-linked loci controlling the fourth component of human complement. Proc. Natl. Acad. Sci. USA **75:** 5165–5169.

30. AWDEH, Z., D. RAUM & C. A. ALPER. 1979. Genetic polymorphism of the fourth component of human complement: Detection of heterozygotes. Nature **282:** 205–207.

31. SHREFFLER, D. C. 1976. The S region of the mouse major histocompatibility complex (H-2): Genetic variations and functional role in the complement system. Transplant. Rev. **32:** 140–167.

32. AWDEH, Z. L. & C. A. ALPER. 1980. Inherited structural polymorphism of the fourth component of human complement (C4). Proc. Natl. Acad. Sci. USA **77:** 3576–3580.

33. ISENMAN, D. E. & J. R. YOUNG. 1984. The molecular basis for the difference in immunohemolysis activity of the Chido and Rodgers isotypes of human complement component C4. J. Immunol. **132:** 3019–3027.

34. ROOS, M. H., E. MOLLENHAUER, P. DÉMANT & C. RITTNER. 1982. A molecular basis for the two locus model of human complement component C4. Nature **298:** 854–855.

35. O'NEILL, G. J., S. Y. YANG, J. TEGOLI, R. BERGER & B. DUPONT. 1978. Chido and Rodgers blood groups are distinct antigenic components of human complement C4. Nature **273:** 668–670.

36. BRUUN-PETERSEN, G., L. U. LAMM, B. K. JACOBSEN & T. KRISTENSEN. 1982. Genetics of human complement C4. Two homoduplication haplotypes *C4S, C4S* and *C4F, C4F* in a family. Hum. Genet. **61:** 36–38.

37. RAUM, D., Z. AWDEH, J. ANDERSON, L. STRONG, J. GRANADOS, L. PEVAN, E. GIBLETT, E. J. YUNIS & C. A. ALPER. 1984. Human C4 haplotypes with duplicated *C4A* or *C4B*. Am. J. Hum. Genet. **36:** 72–79.

38. AWDEH, Z., H. D. OCHS & C. A. ALPER. 1981. Genetic analysis of C4 deficiency. J. Clin. Invest. **67:** 260–263.

39. CARROLL, M. C., A. PALSDOTTIR, K. T. BELT & R. R. PORTER. 1985. Deletion of complement C4 and steroid 21-hydroxylase genes in the HLA class III region. EMBO J. **4:** 2547–2552.

40. WHITEHEAD, A. S., G. GOLDBERGER, D. E. WOODS, A. F. MARKHAM & H. R. COLTEN. 1983. Use of a cDNA clone for the fourth component of human complement (C4) for analysis of genetic deficiency of C4 in guinea pig. Proc. Natl. Acad. Sci. USA **80:** 5387–5391.

41. HAUPTMANN, G., E. GROSSHANS & E. HEID. 1974. Lupus érythémateux aigus et déficits héréditaires en complément. A propos d'un cas par déficit complêt en C4. Ann. Dermatol. Syphiligr. **101:** 479–496.

42. OCHS, H. D., S. I. ROSENFELD, E. D. THOMAS, E. R. GIBLETT, C. A. ALPER, B. DUPONT, J. SCHALLER, B. C. GILLILAND, J. A. HANSEN & R. J. WEDGWOOD. 1977. Linkage between the gene (or genes) controlling the synthesis of the fourth component of complement and the major histocompatibility complex. N. Engl. J. Med. **296:** 470–475.

43. ELLMAN, L., I. GREEN & M. FRANK. 1970. Genetically controlled total deficiency of the fourth component of complement in the guinea pig. Science **170:** 74–75.

44. MUIR, W. A., S. HEDRICK, C. A. ALPER, O. D. RATNOFF, B. SCHACTER & J. J. WISNIESKI. 1984. Inherited incomplete deficiency of the fourth component of complement (C4) determined by a gene not linked to human histocompatibility leukocyte antigens. J. Clin. Invest. **74:** 1509–1514.

45. SJÖHOLM, A. G., J-H. BRACONIER & C. SÖDERSTRÖM. 1982. Properdin deficiency in a family with fulminant meningococcal infections. Clin. Exp. Immunol. **50:** 291–297.

46. DONALDSON, V. H. & F. S. ROSEN. 1964. Action of complement in hereditary angioneurotic edema: The role of C'1 esterase. J. Clin. Invest. **43:** 2204–2213.

47. ALPER, C. A., N. ABRAMSON, R. B. JOHNSTON, JR., J. H. JANDL & F. S. ROSEN. 1970. Studies *in vivo* and *in vitro* on an abnormality in the metabolism of C3 in a patient with increased susceptibility to infection. J. Clin. Invest. **49:** 1975–1985.

48. THOMPSON, R. A. & M. H. WINTERBORN. 1981. Hypocomplementaemia due to a genetic deficiency of beta$_{1H}$-globulin. Clin. Exp. Immunol. **46:** 110–119.

49. DONALDSON, V. H. & R. R. EVANS. 1963. A biochemical abnormality in hereditary angioneurotic edema: Absence of serum inhibitor of C'1-esterase. Am. J. Med. **35:** 37–44.

50. ROSEN, F. S., P. CHARACHE, J. PENSKY & V. H. DONALDSON. 1965. Hereditary angioneurotic edema: Two genetic variants. Science **148:** 957–958.

51. ROSEN, F. S., C. A. ALPER, J. PENSKY, M. R. KLEMPERER & V. H. DONALDSON. 1971. Genetically determined heterogeneity of the C'1-esterase inhibitor in patients with hereditary angioneurotic edema. J. Clin. Invest. **50:** 2143–2149.

52. HARRISON, R. A. & F. S. ROSEN. 1982. Structural characterization of Cl-esterase inhibitor (C$\overline{1}$-INH) and comparison with dysfunctional proteins from individuals with H.A.N.E. Mol. Immunol. **19:** 1374.

53. DONALDSON, V. H., R. A. HARRISON, F. S. ROSEN, D. H. BING, G. KINDNESS, J. CANAR, C. J. WAGNER & S. AWAD. 1985. Variability in purified dysfunctional C$\overline{1}$-inhibitor proteins from patients with hereditary angioneurotic edema. Functional and analytical gel studies. J. Clin. Invest. **75:** 124–132.

54. SPAULDING, W. B. 1960. Methyltestosterone therapy for hereditary episodic edema (hereditary angioneurotic edema). Ann. Intern. Med. **53:** 739–745.

55. GELFAND, J. A., R. J. SHERINS, D. W. ALLING & M. M. FRANK. 1976. Effective prophylaxis of hereditary angioedema by an impeded androgen, danazol. Clin. Res. **24:** 446A (abstract).

56. ROSSE, W. F., G. L. LOGUE & H. R. SILBERMAN. 1976. The effect of synthetic androgens on the clinical course and C1 esterase inhibitor (C1 INH) levels in hereditary angioneurotic edema (H.A.N.E.). Clin. Res. **24:** 482A (abstract).

57. GELFAND, J. A., R. J. SHERINS, D. W. ALLING & M. M. FRANK. 1976. Treatment of hereditary angioedema with danazol. N. Engl. J. Med. **295:** 1444–1448.

58. QUASTEL, M., R. A. HARRISON, M. CICARDI, C. A. ALPER & F. S. ROSEN. 1983. Behavior *in vivo* of normal and dysfunctional C$\overline{1}$-inhibitor in normal subjects and patients with hereditary angioneurotic edema. J. Clin. Invest. **71:** 1041–1046.

59. LACHMANN, P. J. & F. S. ROSEN. 1984. The catabolism of C$\overline{1}$-inhibitor and the pathogenesis of hereditary angio-edema. Acta Pathol. Microbiol. Scand. Sect. **C92** (suppl. 284): 35–39.

60. WHITEHEAD, A. S., E. SOLOMON, S. CHAMBERS, W. F. BODMER, S. POVEY & G. FEY. 1982. Assignment of the structural gene for the third component of human complement to chromosome 19. Proc. Natl. Acad. Sci. USA **79:** 5021–5025.

61. DA SILVA, F. P., G. F. HOECKER, N. K. DAY, K. VIENNE & P. RUBINSTEIN. 1978. Murine complement component 3: Genetic variation and linkage to H-2. Proc. Natl. Acad. Sci. USA **79:** 963–965.

62. NATSUUME-SAKAI, S., J. HAYAKAWA & M. TAKAHASHI. 1978. Genetic polymorphism of murine C3 controlled by a single codominant locus on chromosome 17. J. Immunol. **121:** 491–498.

63. ALLEN, F. H., JR. 1974. Linkage of HL-A and GBG. Vox Sang. **27:** 382–384.

64. FU, S. M., H. G. KUNKEL, H. P. BRUSMAN, F. H. ALLEN, JR. & M. FOTINO. 1974. Evidence for linkage between HLA histocompatibility genes and those involved in the synthesis of the second component of complement. J. Exp. Med. **140:** 1108–1111.

65. ALPER, C. A. 1976. Inherited structural polymorphism in human C2: Evidence for genetic linkage between *C2* and *Bf.* J. Exp. Med. **144:** 1111–1115.

66. SHREFFLER, D. C. 1976. The S region of the mouse major histocompatibility complex (H-2): Genetic variations and functional role in the complement system. Transplant. Rev. **32:** 140–167.

67. DÉMANT, P., J. CAPKOVÁ, E. HINZOVÁ & B. VORÁCOVÁ. 1973. The role of the histocompatibility-2-linked *Ss-Slp* region in the control of mouse complement. Proc. Natl. Acad. Sci. USA **70:** 863–864.

68. CARROLL, M. C., R. D. CAMPBELL, D. R. BENTLEY & R. R. PORTER. 1984. A molecular map of the major histocompatibility complex class III region of man linking complement genes C4, C2, and factor B. Nature **307:** 237–241.

69. CHAPLIN, D. D., D. E. WOODS, A. S. WHITEHEAD, G. GOLDBERGER, H. R. COLTEN & J. G. SEIDMAN. 1983. Molecular map of the murine S region. Proc. Natl. Acad. Sci. USA **80:** 6947–6951.

70. WHITE, P. C., D. D. CHAPLIN, J. H. WEIS, B. DUPONT, M. I. NEW & J. G. SEIDMAN. 1984. Two steroid 21-hydroxylase genes are located in the murine S region. Nature **312:** 465–470.

71. CARROLL, M. C., R. D. CAMPBELL & R. R. PORTER. 1985. The mapping of 21-hydroxylase genes adjacent to complement component C4 genes in HLA, the major histocompatibility complex. Proc. Natl. Acad. Sci. USA **82:** 521–525.

72. ALPER, C. A., D. RAUM, S. KARP, Z. L. AWDEH & E. J. YUNIS. 1983. Serum complement "supergenes" of the major histocompatibility complex in man (complotypes). Vox Sang. **45:** 62–67.

73. BODMER, W. F. & J. G. BODMER. 1978. Evolution and function of the HLA system. Br. Med. Bull. **34:** 309–316.

74. AMOS, D. B. & D. D. KOSTYU. 1980. HLA—A central immunological agency of man. *In* Advances in Human Genetics, vol. 10. H. Harris & K. Hirschhorn, Eds.: 137–208. Plenum. New York.

75. AWDEH, Z. L., D. RAUM, E. J. YUNIS & C. A. ALPER. 1983. Extended HLA/complement allele haplotypes: Evidence for T/t-like complex in man. Proc. Natl. Acad. Sci. USA **80:** 259–263.

76. MATSUI, Y., S. M. ALOSCO, Z. AWDEH, R. J. DUQUESNOY, P. L. PAGE, R. J. HARTZMAN, C. A. ALPER & E. J. YUNIS. 1984. Linkage disequilibrium of *HLA-SB1* with *HLA-A1, B8, DR3, SC01* and of *HLA-SB4* with the *HLA-A26, Bw38, DW10, DR4, SC21* extended haplotypes. Immunogenetics **20:** 623–631.

77. ALPER, C. A., Z. L. AWDEH, D. D. RAUM & E. J. YUNIS. 1982. Extended major histocompatibility complex haplotypes: Role of alleles analogous to murine *t* mutants. Clin. Immunol. Immunopathol. **24:** 276–285.

78. BODMER, W. F. 1980. Models and mechanisms for HLA and disease associations. J. Exp. Med. **152**(suppl.): 353s–357s.

79. ARTZT, K., H-S. SHIN & D. BENNETT. 1982. Gene mapping within the T/t complex of the mouse. II. Anomalous position of *H-2* complex in *t* haplotypes. Cell **28:** 471–476.

80. SILVER, L. M. 1982. Genomic analysis of the *H-2* complex region associated with mouse *t*-haplotypes. Cell **29:** 961–968.

81. SHIN, H-S., L. FLAHERTY, K. ARTZT, D. BENNETT & J. RAVETCH. 1983. Inversion in the *H-2* complex of *t*-haplotypes in mice. Nature **306:** 380–383.

82. AWDEH, Z., D. RAUM, E. J. YUNIS, A. KATZ, K. H. GABBAY & C. A. ALPER. 1983. Male transmission bias of a human chromosome 6p (abstract). Am. Assoc. Clin. Histocompatibility Testing, Ninth Annual Meeting. Chicago, Illinois.

83. RAUM, D., Z. AWDEH, E. J. YUNIS, C. A. ALPER & K. H. GABBAY. 1984. Extended major histocompatibility complex haplotypes in type I diabetes mellitus. J. Clin. Invest. **74:** 449–454.

84. RAUM, D., C. A. ALPER, R. STEIN & K. H. GABBAY. 1979. Genetic marker for insulin-dependent diabetes mellitus. Lancet **i:** 1208–1210.

85. FU, S. M., R. STERN, H. G. KUNKEL, B. DUPONT, J. A. HANSEN, N. K. DAY, R. A. GOOD, C. JERSILD & M. FOTINO. 1975. MLC determinants and C2 deficiency: LD-7a associated with C2 deficiency in four families. J. Exp. Med. **142:** 495–496.

86. AWDEH, Z. L., D. D. RAUM, D. GLASS, V. AGNELLO, P. H. SCHUR, R. B. JOHNSTON, JR, E. W. GELFAND, M. BALLOW, E. YUNIS & C. A. ALPER. 1981. Complement-human histocompatibility antigen haplotypes in C2 deficiency. J. Clin. Invest. **67:** 581–583.

87. MILLER, L. H. & V. NUSSENZWEIG. 1975. A new complement function: solubilization of antigen-antibody aggregates. Proc. Natl. Acad. Sci. USA **72:** 418–422.

88. ALPER, C. A., H. R. COLTEN, F. S. ROSEN, A. R. RABSON, G. M. MACNAB & J. S. S. GEAR. 1972. Homozygous deficiency of C3 in a patient with repeated infections. Lancet **ii:** 1179–1181.

89. ALPER, C. A., N. ABRAMSON, R. B. JOHNSTON, JR, J. H. JANDL & F. S. ROSEN. 1970. Increased susceptibility to infection associated with abnormalities of complement mediated functions and of the third component of complement (C3). N. Engl. J. Med. **282:** 349–354.

90. LIM, D., A. GEWURZ, T. F. LINT, M. GHAZE, B. SEPHERI & H. GEWURZ. 1976. Absence of the sixth component of complement in a patient with repeated episodes of meningococcal meningitis. J. Pediatr. **89:** 42–47.

91.   PETERSEN, B. H., T. J. LEE, R. SNYDERMAN & G. F. BROOKS. 1979. *Neisseria meningitidis* and *Neisseria gonorrhoeae* bacteremia associated with C6, C7, or C8 deficiency. Ann. Intern. Med. **90:** 917–920.

DISCUSSION OF THE PAPER

H. O. MCDEVITT (*Stanford University, Stanford, CA*): In one of your earlier studies, you showed that there was one particular DR3 extended haplotype that tended to show segregation distortion. Have you gone any further with that?

C. A. ALPER (*The Center for Blood Research, Boston, MA*): Yes. If you look in families of patients with type I diabetes or gluten enteropathy and remove the proband to eliminate ascertainment bias, there is about an 85% segregation distortion from the male.

MCDEVITT: For which haplotype?

ALPER: B8, DR3, SC01, GLO2, but not GLO1. In other words, it is the same one that is increased in diabetes.

N. F. TALAL (*University of Texas Health Science Center, San Antonio, TX*): A number of genes related to sex hormones also map to the class III region. S. A. Ahmed in my laboratory has been looking at the ability of androgen to suppress the response to PPD as a function of H2 type. PPD was selected because the response to it is not under H2 control. The effect of androgen on this system appears to segregate with H2 type.

ALPER: In that connection, many of the murine class III antigens are under androgen regulation, particularly levels of C4.

MCDEVITT: In the mouse, it has been found that segregation distortion and suppression of crossing-over is due to an altered chromosomal order. In other words, the tufted and the *t*-allele loci are inverted. Has anybody looked at the extended haplotypes that show segregation distortion and found that the gene order is inverted on the chromosomes?

ALPER: We are very interested in that question, but we have no data yet.

Origins of Pathogenic Anti-DNA Idiotypes in the NZB × SWR Model of Lupus Nephritis[a]

SYAMAL K. DATTA AND JERRIE GAVALCHIN

Department of Medicine (Hematology/Oncology Division)
and Cancer Research Center
New England Medical Center
and
Tufts University School of Medicine
Boston, Massachusetts 02111

INTRODUCTION

The New Zealand strains of mice, notably NZB and (NZB × NZW)F$_1$ hybrids, have served as informative models for the study of systemic lupus erythematosus (SLE) in humans.[1] These mice and the NZB × SWR crosses that we shall describe here resemble humans with respect to the sex distribution and immunopathologic characteristics of SLE. Recently, two additional strains, MRL-*lpr/lpr* and BXSB, have been vigorously investigated as models of SLE.[2] In the MRL-*lpr/lpr* strain, a recessive gene, *lpr*, accelerates the development of SLE.[3] No human counterpart of such a model exists. Moreover, the *lpr* gene produces full-blown SLE only in the genetic background of the "normal" congeneic partner, MRL-(+/+), but not in the background of other normal nonautoimmune mouse strains.[4,5] The "normal" MRL-(+/+) mouse strain, however, does develop nephritis and produce high levels of autoantibodies later in life.[6,7] Thus, the extensive investigations in the MRL-*lpr/lpr* strain have so far dealt with secondary factors that can accelerate and increase the severity of SLE. The primary mechanism of autoimmunity in the MRL model lies in the "normal" MRL-(+/+) background and this strain has yet to be systematically studied. Similarly, in the BXSB model, Y-chromosome linked genes accelerate the development of SLE in male mice of a SLE-prone genetic background. Although many studies have been carried out on the secondary effects of the Y-chromosome accelerating genes, almost nothing is known about the primary underlying defects in this model.[8]

The NZB × SWR cross, on the other hand, has unique features that enable a genetic dissection of various components that may be primarily involved in autoimmune disease. Unlike the NZB parents or crosses of NZB with other normal strains, the F$_1$ hybrids of NZB and the normal SWR mouse strain uniformly develop lethal glomerulonephritis. In addition, as in human SLE, the incidence of lupus nephritis is higher in the female (NZB × SWR)F$_1$ hybrids.[9,10] The only other cross of NZB that regularly develops a high incidence of lupus nephritis is the (NZB × NZW)F$_1$ hybrid. NZW mice, however, are not normal; they produce anti-DNA antibodies and develop nephritis later in life.[11] They also share background genes with the NZB strain, and

[a]These studies were supported by National Institutes of Health grant no. RO1-CA-31789. JG received a fellowship from the Arthritis Foundation.

both NZB and NZW strains have the same virologic abnormalities, i.e., production of exceptionally high levels of retroviruses and retroviral antigen (gp70) throughout life.[12] By contrast, mice of the SWR strain do not produce any infectious retroviruses and they have extremely low serum levels of gp70.[9,13] Moreover, they do not develop any manifestations of autoimmune disease nor do they produce autoantibodies spontaneously.[9,10] Therefore, because of their contrasting virologic and immunologic phenotypes from both the NZB and NZW strains, the SWR mice are valuable genetic tools that can be used to define the role of various NZB abnormalities in the etiology of autoimmune disease. Furthermore, the NZB × SWR crosses are also helping us to identify the factors contributed by a completely normal strain in the development of lupus nephritis.

EARLIER STUDIES WITH NZB × SWR CROSSES

Studies to Determine the Role of Retroviruses in SLE

NZB and NZB × NZW mice have two distinctive features: the uniform development of autoimmune disease and the high level expression of xenotropic retroviruses throughout life. Viral antigens (the viral envelope glycoprotein, gp70) and antiviral antibodies, together with antibodies to DNA, are detected in the renal lesions of NZB × NZW mice.[12] These observations suggested a cause and effect relationship between the virus and the autoimmune disease.[14–19] The virus was thought both to initiate the disease and provide antigens that generated nephritogenic immune complexes. The presence of virus particles and the detection of viral antigens and antiviral antibodies in lesions did not, however, constitute proof that xenotropic viruses caused the disease of NZB mice. Transmission of autoimmunity could not be achieved with cell-free filtrates from NZB mice.[20] The reason for this became evident later. The xenotropic variety of retroviruses expressed by NZB mice could not infect mouse cells; they could infect only cells of heterologous species.[14] Thus, a traditional microbiological approach could not be applied to the solution of the problem. However, with the NZB × SWR cross, the relevance of the virus to autoimmunity could be ascertained by genetic techniques.

The genetic analysis became feasible by the identification of two autosomal dominant genes that governed the expression of xenotropic virus in NZB mice.[21,22] One of these genes, *Nzv-1*, specified high-grade expression of the virus and the other, *Nzv-2*, specified low-grade expression of the virus. Homozygosity for recessive alleles at both loci resulted in a virus-negative mouse strain, such as the SWR.[22] Matings between NZB and virus-negative SWR mice resulted in three kinds of progeny in F_2 and (F_1 × SWR) backcross generations: high-virus, low-virus, and virus-negative. These virologic phenotypes were stable and thus permitted a test of the hypothesis that development of autoimmunity requires the expression of xenotropic virus. The results were clear-cut: the virological phenotype of the progeny of NZB × SWR crosses was independent of the presence of autoantibodies or glomerulonephritis. Crosses that were virologically identical to NZB mice failed to develop any signs of autoimmunization. In fact, the progeny mice that were virus-negative were able to produce autoantibodies to erythrocytes and DNA and develop severe immune-deposit glomerulonephritis in the absence of deposits of viral gp70 antigens.[9,13] Moreover, the other NZB traits, namely, high levels of circulating gp70 antigen and gp70 immune complexes, could also be dissociated from the development of glomerulonephritis in the NZB × SWR crosses.[13] The dissociation between virus expression and the development of autoimmune disease was not a peculiar feature of NZB × SWR crosses; similar results were found in crosses between NZB and B10.A, C57Bl/6, and AKR mice and they were also found in recombinant inbred lines derived from NZB and C58 progenitor strains.[9,23]

The above results indicated that the xenotropic virus and gp70 antigen are *endogenous* and thus potential autoantigens in NZB mice. Like other autoantigens, such as erythrocytes and DNA, they may play secondary roles, but they are not required primarily for autoimmunization. Whether an autoimmune reaction occurs against xenotropic viral antigens or other autoantigens depends on genes ("autoimmunity genes") that are distinct from viral genes.[9,13,21,22] This interpretation sets the NZB model apart from examples of organ-specific autoimmunity induced by *exogenous* viruses, in which case the infectious agent participates in both the etiology and pathogenesis of the immunological lesions.[24] The results obtained from the NZB × SWR cross brought a conceptual change in the direction of research in SLE because at that time retroviruses were thought to be the etiologic agents of this disease. The NZB × SWR crosses were next used as a genetic tool to analyze the role of various immunologic abnormalities in autoimmune disease.

Nonspecific Immunologic Abnormalities in SLE

An age-dependent deficiency of suppressor T cells was thought to be a primary defect causing a deregulation of the immune system that led to the development of autoimmune disease.[25,26] However, these T suppressor cells were not known to be specific for any particular autoantibody. A generalized deficiency of suppressor T cells could be secondary to the production of natural thymocytotoxic autoantibodies (NTA) by NZB mice.[27] However, the presence of NTA is not consistently associated with the production of anti-DNA and antierythrocyte antibodies in NZB crosses.[28,29] Furthermore, a decline of nonspecific T suppressor cells is not a predictable feature of human SLE,[30] nor is it always found in old NZB mice or the NZB × SWR crosses that develop lupus nephritis.[31,32] Moreover, selective depletion of nonspecific suppressor T cells can result in the development of organ-specific autoimmune diseases, but not SLE.[33] Finally, genetic studies with congeneic and mutant NZB mice showed that these nonspecific T-cell abnormalities can be dissociated from autoimmune manifestations.[34,35] Thus, a generalized deficiency of suppressor T cells, when present, may influence the severity of SLE, but it is not the fundamental etiologic mechanism.

Polyclonal hyperactivity of B lymphocytes with increased immunoglobulin production has been observed in all the murine models and also in human SLE.[3,23,30,32] This trait could be secondary to a decreased suppressor T-cell or an increased helper T-cell function, or it could be due to a primary B-cell defect. In NZB mice, these generalized B-cell abnormalities are complex and are influenced by unlinked sets of genes.[23] One of these B-cell hyperactivity traits is manifested by spontaneous hypersecretion of IgM.[36] This abnormality is expressed from fetal life, independent of any T-cell influence, and is determined by two sets of autosomal genes.[23,32] The NZB B cells that hypersecrete IgM have an unusual phenotype; they express Ly-1 antigen, which is a surface marker of T cells, especially those of the helper/inducer class.[37,38] Moreover, these spontaneously hyperactive B cells belong to the same B-cell subset that is affected by an X-linked recessive gene (*xid*) in the CBA/N mutant mice.[39,40] Introduction of the *xid* gene on the NZB background prevents the development of autoimmune disease.[34] Therefore, it has been widely postulated that intrinsic hyperactivity of this subpopulation of B cells in NZB mice results in the activation of autoreactive B cells, causing autoimmune disease.[3,32,34] The *xid* mutation, however, affects a relatively large subset of B cells (~60% of splenic B cells) that may also encompass autoantibody-producing clones of cells without a specific cause and effect relationship. Moreover, the Ly-1 positive B cells secrete only IgM, λ autoantibodies,[41] whereas, in SLE, pathogenic autoantibodies are IgG, κ in isotype.[42–44] Indeed, finer genetic segregation analysis in the NZB × SWR crosses and recombinant inbred lines showed that inheritance of the spontaneous B-cell hyperactivity trait that specifies increased secretion of IgM can be dissociated from development of autoantibodies and autoimmune disease.[10,23] Another B-cell abnormality of NZB mice manifests as a precocious hyperresponse to sheep red blood cell antigens. This trait is thought to be due to a primary B-cell defect in responsiveness to B-cell growth and differentiation factors.[3] This abnormality can also be genetically dissociated from autoantibody production in NZB-derived recombinant inbred lines.[23]

These results suggested that a generalized polyclonal B-cell abnormality is not the underlying cause of SLE and the spontaneously activated autoantibody-producing B cells constitute a far more restricted population than was previously considered. Supporting this interpretation are genetic studies that show that the inheritance and expression of each type of autoantibody, such as the anti-DNA, antierythrocyte, or anti-Sm antibody, can be independent of each other.[23,45,46] Thus, highly restricted abnormalities specific for the regulation of each family of autoreactive B cells have to be elucidated. Therefore, we focused our attention to the cells responsible specifically for anti-DNA autoantibody production.

ANTI-DNA AUTOANTIBODY IDIOTYPES IN NORMAL AND LUPUS MICE

The spontaneous production of anti-DNA autoantibodies is characteristic of human and murine SLE. These antibodies have been implicated in the pathogenesis of nephritis and other lesions of the disease.[47] However, very little is known about the specific regulation of anti-DNA antibody-producing B cells in human SLE. As a logical extension of findings in other antibody idiotype systems,[48,49] it was proposed that idiotype/anti-idiotype network regulation may also play a role in autoimmunity.[50] However, the role of spontaneously produced anti-idiotypic antibodies against autoantibodies in autoimmune disease remains confusing due to conflicting results. Circumstantial evidence suggested that they may have a favorable effect on the disease, as they were found during remission of SLE.[51] In other cases, however, anti-idiotypic antibodies were found to have a deleterious effect on disease.[52] In these examples, the autoantibody idiotypes were not defined. Deliberate manipulation with defined anti-idiotypic antibodies raised in the laboratory can either suppress or enhance the production of the corresponding anti-DNA idiotypes in murine models.[53,54] An explanation of these paradoxical results may be forthcoming as we begin to understand the origin of anti-DNA antibodies and learn more about the factors that regulate the production of nephritogenic anti-DNA antibodies in SLE.[55–58]

The ability to produce anti-DNA autoantibodies is not restricted to mice or humans that develop SLE. Normal individuals and also normal mice can spontaneously produce such antibodies with age or upon polyclonal stimulation of their B cells.[59–61] However, the latter situations do not usually lead to the development of SLE. These observations raise several questions: Are the antibodies produced by lupus mice qualitatively different and more pathogenic than their counterparts in normal mice? Do normal and autoimmune mice possess identical clones of anti-DNA antibody-producing cells whose regulation is impaired in the lupus strains? These questions were addressed by investigating if normal mice could produce antibodies with idiotypic markers of the anti-DNA antibodies of MRL-*lpr/lpr* mice, a strain that develops a lethal form of SLE. Spleen and fetal liver B cells of five different normal mouse strains could synthesize idiotypes shared by anti-DNA antibodies of the genetically autoimmune strain.[55] Although the antibodies produced by normal mice had idiotypes of lupus anti-DNA antibodies, the major proportion of those antibodies did not bind DNA. Analogous results have been recently found in humans.[62,63]

These findings have implications on the origin of anti-DNA antibodies; they indicate that the autoantibody idiotypes are related to a conserved family of antibody variable regions that are present in normal animals and they can be expressed very early in ontogeny.[55] These conserved antibody V regions are not primarily directed against DNA, but, like other inherited cross-reactive idiotypes, they are probably specific for common environmental pathogens.[55-57] This concept has been subsequently supported by immunochemical and sequencing studies of anti-DNA antibodies.[64-66] Spontaneously produced anti-DNA autoantibodies are polyspecific.[57] They bind to a wide variety of antigens, thus suggesting again that DNA may not be the primary antigen for these antibodies. Therefore, the binding to DNA of only a minority of antibodies in these "autoantibody" idiotype families represents cross-reactions and not unique antiself-reactions. The finding that the same idiotypic family encompassses both a minor DNA-binding and a major DNA-nonbinding population has many precedents in other idiotypic systems.[67] Such a situation can come about through recombination of V genes, presumably because the number of germlike V genes available for combinatorial association is limited.[68,69] If portions of a particular V-region gene (V-D-J) encoding a given idiotype is used by antibodies with two different specificities, they could share that idiotype.[69,70] Such antibodies become functionally connected as explained by Jerne's network hypothesis.[48,55,56] For instance, in the case of the anti-DNA idiotypes studied,[55] a bacterial antigen and not DNA may be the primary and natural target of the antibodies bearing those idiotypes (Ab1). These antibodies (Ab1) do not bind to DNA although they share idiotypes with anti-DNA antibodies. Ab1 induces the production of anti-idiotypic antibodies (Ab2) and is regulated by them. Certain members of this family of anti-idiotypic antibodies may bear the conformational determinants (internal image) of an autoantigen such as DNA. These anti-idiotypic antibodies (Ab2) in turn induce a population of antibodies (Ab3) that shares idiotypes with Ab1, but is now specific for nucleic acid antigens and not the primary (bacterial) antigen. According to Jerne, Ab3 constitutes a nonspecific parallel set of antibodies in the network.[48] The minor DNA-binding population in the autoantibody idiotypic families may belong to this parallel set of antibodies (Ab3). Although Ab1 and Ab3 have different antigenic specificities, by sharing the same idiotype they become connected as members of a regulatory idiotypic network.[56,71,72]

In human and mouse strains that are genetically prone to develop SLE, a spontaneous shift in the idiotype family occurs, leading not only to an expansion of the minor DNA-binding population, but also to a qualitative change in those antibodies as well.[58,62,63] The NZB × SWR cross system provides further clues regarding this immunoregulatory shift, as described below.

PATHOGENIC ANTI-DNA IDIOTYPES IN THE NZB × SWR CROSS

Autoimmune hemolytic anemia occurs in high frequency in NZB mice, whereas glomerulonephritis is infrequent, mild, and delayed in onset.[9,10] By contrast, most female F_1 hybrids derived from crossing NZB mice with the normal SWR stain develop severe glomerulonephritis between five and seven months. In fact, by one year of age, 100% of these animals die from renal lesions.[9,10] These results suggest that the normal SWR parent makes a genetic contribution to the development of lupus nephritis in (NZB × SWR)F_1 mice. The incidence and amount of circulating anti-DNA antibodies are similar in the NZB parents and the (NZB × SWR)F_1 hybrids,

TABLE 1. Antigen Binding Specificities of Anti-DNA Antibodies

Hybridoma	ssDNA	dsDNA	polyI	polydT	zDNA	Cardiolipin
Group I	+ + +[a]	−	+ + +	−	V	− (±)
Group II	+ + +	+ + +	V	V	V	− (±)
Group III	+ + +	− to ±	V	+ + +	V	− (±)
Group IV	+ + +	+ + +	+	+ +	V	− (±)

[a]Affinities: (+ + +) = strong, (+ +) = moderate, (+) = weak, (−) = none, and V = variable.[58]

but a qualitative difference in their antibodies may explain the difference in renal disease. Therefore, we analyzed a library of 65 monoclonal anti-DNA antibodies derived from the (NZB × SWR)F_1 mice and compared them with a collection obtained from the NZB parents.[56,58] The monoclonal autoantibodies were polyspecific and they could be classified broadly into four groups according to certain general similarities and differences in their avidities for nucleic acid antigens (TABLE 1).[58] Hybridoma antibodies derived from the NZB mouse resembled those from the F_1 hybrids in antigen specificity Groups II and III (TABLE 2). However, the antibodies in Groups I and IV were exclusively derived from the (NZB × SWR)F_1 hybrids (TABLE 2). The majority of anti-DNA antibodies derived from the (NZB × SWR)F_1 hybrids were IgG and were found to be cationic on isoelectric focusing.[58] By contrast, 77% of the NZB-derived antibodies were IgM and most of them were neutral or anionic in charge.[58] The cationic property of the F_1-derived IgG autoantibodies was not restricted to any particular antigen specificity group or IgG subclass, nor was there a preference for the allotype of either parent (FIGURE 1).[58] However, we identified a set of highly cationic IgG2b anti-DNA antibodies from the (NZB × SWR)F_1 hybrids that had the allotype of the normal SWR parent and it was found that these antibodies belonged to antigen specificity Groups I and IV (FIGURE 1; TABLES 1 and 2). Isoelectric focusing of intact antibodies and their heavy and light chains showed that the highly cationic charge of these antibodies was determined by their heavy-chain variable regions.[58] We have subsequently found that these highly cationic antibodies share a cross-reactive idiotype (CRI) called Id 564. Id 564 is found only among monoclonal antibodies derived from the F_1 hybrids and not in those derived from NZB mice. Moreover, Id 564 is present in the renal eluates of (NZB × SWR)F_1 hybrids suffering from nephritis. Hahn and Ebling have also identified a CRI among monoclonal cationic anti-DNA antibodies from other lupus strains of mice; however, if that idiotype is involved in the renal disease of those mice is not known.[73] In addition to Id 564, we have detected

TABLE 2. Isotypes and Allotypes of Monoclonal Anti-DNA Antibodies Derived from the (NZB × SWR)F_1 Hybrids and NZB Mice

Hybridomas	Group I	Group II	Group III	Group IV
Total number	6	9	44	6
NZB-derived	0	3	10	0
SNF$_1$-derived	6	6	34	6
Allotype-SNF$_1$[a]	SWR-5	SWR-1	SWR-6	SWR-4
	NZB-1	NZB-5	NZB-28	NZB-2
Isotype	γ2b-4	γ2a-7	γ-30	γ2b-6
	μ-2	γ3-1	γ2a-6	
		μ-1	γ2b-3	
			γ3-5	

[a]SNF$_1$ = (NZB × SWR)F_1 or (SWR × NZB)F_1.

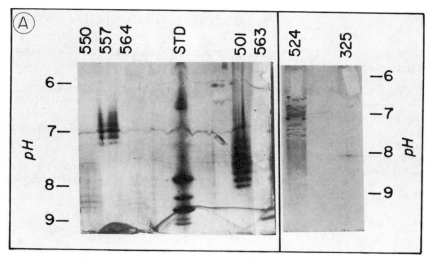

FIGURE 1A. Isoelectric focusing patterns (IEF) of monoclonal IgG anti-DNA antibodies. Antibodies 550, 564, and 563 are all F_1-derived IgG2b, κ monoclonals with SWR allotype and they belong to antigen specificity Group I (see TABLES 1 and 2). These antibodies have isoelectric points (pI) ranging between pH 8.28 and 8.80. Antibody 524 is also an F_1-derived IgG2b, κ monoclonal with SWR allotype, but it belongs to Group III and has a pI of pH 7.16. Antibody 325 is also from an F_1-derived IgG2b, κ hybridoma, but it has NZB allotype and belongs to antigen specificity Group III. Numbers 557 and 501 are F_1-derived IgG2a, κ antibodies with NZB allotype. They belong to Group III and have pI of pH 6.89 and 7.40, respectively. Antibodies 550, 564, and 563 of Group I share a CRI called Id 564. Id 564 is also shared by another highly cationic (pI, 8.06 pH), F_1-derived IgG2b, κ antibody with SWR allotype that belongs to Group IV. The latter antibody numbered 30 (not shown, see reference 58) has a very similar IEF pattern as antibody 13 in FIGURE 1B.

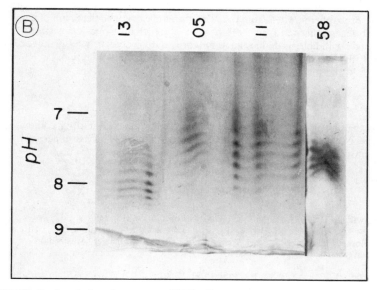

FIGURE 1B. Isoelectric focusing patterns (IEF) of monoclonal IgG anti-DNA antibodies. All monoclonal anti-DNA antibodies are F_1-derived IgG2b, κ and belong to antigen specificity Group IV. Antibodies 13 and 05 both have SWR allotype, whereas 11 and 58 have NZB allotype. (Reprinted from reference 58, with permission from *J. Immunol.*)

several other anti-DNA CRI families in the diseased F_1 kidneys. These latter idiotypes are not restricted to cationic anti-DNA antibodies or the allotype of either parent, but they are exclusively of F_1 origin.

IgG anti-DNA antibodies with cationic charge are especially pathogenic in SLE.[42] Moreover, since DNA, like the glomerulus, is negatively charged, the probability of its deposition and persistence in glomeruli will increase markedly if it is complexed with cationic anti-DNA antibodies.[74,75] Therefore, those highly cationic IgG2b antibodies bearing the allotype of the normal SWR parent probably contribute to the high incidence of severe nephritis in the F_1 hybrids. The results from the NZB × SWR cross indicate that a restricted family of pathogenic anti-DNA antibodies encoded by genes of normal, nonautoimmune mice can become expressed when they interact with genes of an abnormal autoimmune mouse.

SUMMARY

The investigations with the NZB × SWR model show that the development of systemic autoimmune disease is a multistep, multigene process. Severe lupus nephritis in the NZB × SWR hybrids results from the interaction of genes inherited from both the autoimmune NZB and the normal SWR parents. A similar genetic interaction occurs in the NZB × NZW hybrids,[76,77] but in this model, both the parental strains are abnormal[11] and the nature of the gene products or their mechanism of action is unknown. In the NZB × SWR model, we have been able to identify a restricted subpopulation of nephritogenic anti-DNA antibody idiotypes that are encoded by genes of the normal SWR parents. Thus, these are one set of genes that determine the development of severe lupus nephritis in the F_1 hybrids. In addition, another set of genes allows for the expansion of B cells that produce such pathogenic anti-DNA idiotypes in the F_1 hybrids since such B-cell clones remain dormant in the normal SWR parents. The latter category of genes, presumably specifying defects in immunoregulation, are probably inherited from the NZB parents or may be the result of complementation of genes inherited from both parents. Further investigations with the NZB × SWR model will help us define the immunoregulatory defects in SLE that are specific for the T and B cells involved in pathogenic autoantibody production.

ACKNOWLEDGMENTS

We thank Robert Schwartz and David Stollar for stimulating collaboration in different portions of the work summarized here. Thanks to Gary Brenner for preparing this manuscript.

REFERENCES

1. HOWIE, J. B. & B. J. HELYER. 1968. Adv. Immunol. 9: 215–268.
2. MURPHY, E. D. & J. B. ROTHS. 1978. In Genetic Control of Autoimmune Disease. N. E. Rose, P. E. Bigazzi & N. L. Warner, Eds.: 207–221. Elsevier. Amsterdam.
3. PRUD'HOMME, G. J., T. M. FIESER, F. J. DIXON & A. N. THEOFILOPOULOS. 1984. Immunol. Rev. 78: 160–183.
4. IZUI, S., V. E. KELLEY, M. KAZUSHIGE, H. YOSHIDA, J. B. ROTHS & E. D. MURPHY. 1984. J. Immunol. 133: 227–233.

5. HANG, L., M. T. AGUADO, F. J. DIXON & A. N. THEOFILOPOULOS. 1985. J. Exp. Med. 161: 423–428.
6. PISETSKY, D. S., S. A. CASTER, J. B. ROTHS & E. D. MURPHY. 1982. J. Immunol. 128: 2322–2325.
7. GIROIR, B. P., E. C. RAPS, R. M. LEWIS & Y. BOREL. 1983. Cell. Immunol. 75: 337–347.
8. STEINBERG, R. T., M. L. MILLER & A. D. STEINBERG. 1985. Clin. Immunol. Immunopathol. 35: 67–72.
9. DATTA, S. K., N. MANNY, C. ANDRZEJEWSKI, J. ANDRE-SCHWARTZ & R. S. SCHWARTZ. 1978. J. Exp. Med. 147: 854–871.
10. EASTCOTT, J. W., R. S. SCHWARTZ & S. K. DATTA. 1983. J. Immunol. 131: 2232–2239.
11. KELLEY, V. E. & A. WINKELSTEIN. 1980. Clin. Immunol. Immunopathol. 16: 142–150.
12. YOSHIKI, T., R. C. MELLORS, M. STRAND & J. T. AUGUST. 1974. J. Exp. Med. 140: 1011–1027.
13. DATTA, S. K., P. J. MCCONAHEY, N. MANNY, A. N. THEOFILOPOULOS, F. J. DIXON & R. S. SCHWARTZ. 1978. J. Exp. Med. 147: 872–881.
14. LEVY, J. A. 1976. Biomedicine 24: 84–93.
15. MELLORS, R. C. & J. W. MELLORS. 1976. Proc. Natl. Acad. Sci. USA 73: 233–237.
16. STRAND, M. & J. T. AUGUST. 1974. J. Virol. 14: 1584–1596.
17. PANEM, S., N. G. ORDONEZ, W. H. KIRSTEIN, A. I. KATZ & B. H. SPARGO. 1976. N. Engl. J. Med. 295: 470–475.
18. PHILIPS, P. E. 1978. Arthritis Rheum. 21 (suppl. 5): S76–81.
19. KIMURA, M., T. ANDOH & K. KAI. 1980. Arthritis Rheum. 23: 111–113.
20. EAST, J. 1970. Prog. Exp. Tumor Res 13: 84–134.
21. DATTA, S. K. & R. S. SCHWARTZ. 1976. Nature 263: 412–415.
22. DATTA, S. K. & R. S. SCHWARTZ. 1977. Virology 83: 449–452.
23. DATTA, S. K., F. L. OWEN, J. E. WOMACK & R. J. RIBLET. 1982. J. Immunol. 129: 1539–1544.
24. HASPEL, M. V., T. ONODERA, B. S. PRABHAKAR, P. R. MCCLINTOCK, K. ESSANI, U. R. ROY, S. YAGIHASHI & A. L. NOTKINS. 1983. Nature 304: 73–76.
25. BARTHOLD, D. R., S. J. KYSELA & A. D. STEINBERG. 1974. J. Immunol. 112: 9–16.
26. CANTOR, H., L. MCVAY-BOUDREAU, J. HUGENBERGER, K. NAIDORF, F. W. SHEN & R. K. GERSHON. 1978. J. Exp. Med. 147: 1116–1125.
27. SHIRAI, T., K. HAYAKAWA, K. O. OKUMURA & T. TADA 1978. J. Immunol. 120: 1924–1929.
28. RAVECHE, E. S., A. D. STEINBERG, L. W. KLASSEN & J. H. TJIO. 1978. J. Exp. Med. 147: 1487–1501.
29. MARUYAMA, N., K. OHTA, S. HIROSHA & T. SHIRAI. 1980. Immunol. Lett. 2: 1–6.
30. TSOKOS, G. C. & J. E. BALOW. 1984. Prog. Allergy 35: 93–161.
31. PRIMI, D., L. HAMMARSTROM & C. I. E. SMITH. 1978. J. Immunol. 121: 2241–2243.
32. MANNY, N., S. K. DATTA & R. S. SCHWARTZ. 1979. J. Immunol. 122: 1220–1227.
33. SAKAGUCHI, S., K. FUKUMA, K. KURIBAYASHI & T. MASUDA. 1985. J. Exp. Med. 161: 72–87.
34. TAUROG, J. D., E. S. RAVECHE, P. A. SMATHERS, L. H. GLIMCHER, D. P. HUSTON, C. T. HANSEN & A. D. STEINBERG. 1981. J. Exp. Med. 153: 221–234.
35. GERSHWIN, M. E., J. J. CASTLES, R. M. IKEDA, K. ERICKSON & J. MONTERO. 1979. J. Immunol. 122: 710–717.
36. MOUTSOPOULOS, H. M., M. BOEHM-TRUITT, S. S. KASSAN & T. M. CHUSED. 1977. J. Immunol. 119: 1639–1644.
37. MANOHOR, V., E. BROWN, W. M. LEISERSON & T. M. CHUSED. 1982. J. Immunol. 129: 532–538.
38. HAYAKAWA, K., R. R. HARDY, D. R. PARKS & L. A. HERZENBERG. 1983. J. Exp. Med. 157: 202–218.
39. NAKAJIMA, P. B., S. K. DATTA, R. S. SCHWARTZ & B. T. HUBER. 1979. Proc. Natl. Acad. Sci. USA 76: 4613–4616.
40. TAUROG, J. D., H. M. MONTSOPOULOS, Y. J. ROSENBERG, T. M. CHUSED & A. D. STEINBERG. 1979. J. Exp. Med. 150: 31–43.

41. HAYAKAWA, K., R. R. HARDY, M. HONDA, L. A. HERZENBERG, A. D. STEINBERG & L. A. HERZENBERG. 1984. Proc. Natl. Acad. Sci. USA 81: 2494–2498.
42. EBLING, F. & B. H. HAHN. 1980. Arthritis Rheum. 23: 392–403.
43. ROTHFIELD, N. F. & B. D. STOLLAR. 1967. J. Clin. Invest. 46: 1785–1794.
44. TALAL, N. 1976. Transplant. Rev. 31: 240–263.
45. RAVECHE, E. S., E. A. NOVOTNY, C. T. HANSEN, J. H. TJIO & A. D. STEINBERG. 1981. J. Exp. Med. 153: 1187–1197.
46. PISETSKY, D. S., G. A. MCCARTY & D. V. PETERS. 1980. J. Exp. Med. 152: 1302–1310.
47. KOFFLER, D., R. CARR, V. AGNELLO, R. THOBURN & H. G. KUNKEL. 1971. J. Exp. Med. 134: 294–312.
48. JERNE, N. K. 1974. Ann. Immunol. (Paris) 125: 373–389.
49. BONA, C. A. 1981. Idiotypes and Lymphocytes. Academic Press. New York.
50. WIGZELL, H., H. BINZ, H. FRISCHKNECHT, P. PETERSON & K. SEGE. 1978. In Genetic Control of Autoimmune Disease. N.E. Rose, P.E. Bigazzi & N. L. Warner, Eds.: 327–342. Elsevier. Amsterdam.
51. ABDOU, N. I., H. WALL, H. B. LINDSLEY, J. F. HALSEY & T. SUZUKI. 1981. J. Clin. Invest. 67: 1297–1304.
52. WASSERMAN, N. H., A. S. PENN, P. I. FREIMUTH, N. TREPTOW, S. WENTZERL, W. L. CLEVELAND & B. F. ERLANGER. 1982. Proc. Natl. Acad. Sci. USA 79: 4810–4814.
53. HAHN, B. H. & F. M. EBLING. 1983. J. Clin. Invest. 71: 1728–1736.
54. TITELBAUM, D., J. RAUCH, B. D. STOLLER & R. S. SCHWARTZ. 1984. J. Immunol. 132: 1282–1285.
55. DATTA, S. K., B. D. STOLLAR & R. S. SCHWARTZ. 1983. Proc. Natl. Acad. Sci. USA 80: 2723–2727.
56. DATTA, S. K. 1984. In Regulation of the Immune System, UCLA Symposia on Molecular and Cellular Biology, vol. 18. E. Sercarz, H. Cantor & L. Chess, Eds.: 877–886. Alan R. Liss. New York.
57. SCHWARTZ, R. S. & B. D. STOLLAR. 1985. J. Clin. Invest. 75: 321–327.
58. GAVALCHIN, J., J. A. NICKLAS, J. W. EASTCOTT, M. P. MADAIO, B. D. STOLLER, R. S. SCHWARTZ & S. K. DATTA. 1985. J. Immunol. 134: 885–894.
59. RUBIN, R. L. & R. I. CARR. 1972. J. Immunol. 122: 1604–1607.
60. FISH, F. & M. ZIFF. 1982. J. Immunol. 128: 409–414.
61. KOBAYAKAWA, T., J. LOUIS, S. IZUI & P. H. LAMBERT. 1979. J. Immunol. 122: 296–301.
62. DATTA, S. K., A. P. PISTORIO, B. D. STOLLAR & R. S. SCHWARTZ. 1984. Fed. Proc. Fed. Am. Soc. Exp. Biol. 43: 1860 (abstract).
63. DATTA, S. K., Y. NAPARSTEK & R. S. SCHWARTZ. 1986. Clin. Immunol. Immunopathol. 38: 302–318.
64. NAPARSTEK, Y., D. DUGGAN, A. SCHATTNER, M. MADAIO, F. GONI, B. FRANGIONE, B. D. STOLLAR, E. A. KABAT & R. S. SCHWARTZ. 1985. J. Exp. Med. 161: 1525–1538.
65. DIAMOND, B. & M. D. SCHARFF. 1984. Proc. Natl. Acad. Sci. USA 81: 5841–5844.
66. KOFLER, R., D. J. NOONAN, D. E. LEVY, M. C. WILSON, N. P. H. MOLLER, F. J. DIXON & A. N. THEOFILOPOULOS. 1985. J. Exp. Med. 161: 805–815.
67. MARION, T. N., E. A. DZIERZAK, H. S. LEE, R. L. ADAMS & C. A. JANEWAY. 1984. J. Exp. Med. 159: 221–233.
68. TONEGAWA, S. 1983. Nature 302: 575–581.
69. CAPRA, J. D. & M. FOUGEREAU. 1983. Immunol. Today 4: 177–179.
70. MARGOLIES, M. N., L. J. WYSOCKI & V. L. SATO. 1983. J. Immunol. 130: 515–517.
71. PAUL, W. E. & C. A. BONA. 1982. Immunol. Today 3: 230–234.
72. HORNBECK, P. V. & G. K. LEWIS. 1983. J. Exp. Med. 157: 1116–1136.
73. HAHN, B. H. & F. M. EBLING. 1984. J. Immunol. 133: 3015–3019.
74. LAWRENCE, Y., C. AGODOA, V. J. GAUTHIER & M. MANNIK. 1985. J. Immunol. 134: 880–884.
75. BARNES, J. L. & M. A. VENKATACHALAM. 1984. J. Exp. Med. 160: 286–293.
76. KNIGHT, J. G. & D. D. ADAMS. 1978. J. Exp. Med. 147: 1653–1660.
77. HIROSE, S., R. NAGASAWA, I. SAKIKAWA, M. HAMAOKI, Y. ISHIDA, H. SATO & T. SHIRAI. 1983. J. Exp. Med. 158: 228–233.

DISCUSSION OF THE PAPER

C. A. BONA (*Mount Sinai Medical Center, New York, NY*): Do you know the allotype of the idiotype positive antibody from the F_1?

S. K. DATTA (*Tufts University School of Medicine, Boston, MA*): Yes, that allotype is restricted to the SWR strain. However, there are also antibodies that have the allotype of the NZB parent and that have other idiotypes that are found in the F_1 kidney. Therefore, the gene families of both parents contribute to the disease. Nevertheless, there are families of antibodies that are restricted to the allotype of the normal SWR parent.

BONA: Does this mean that the V genes come from both parents, but the allotype of antibody only from one?

DATTA: No. There are multiple idiotypic families represented in the F_1 kidney. One of the idiotypes we have identified is restricted to the normal parent's allotype, but there are others derived from the NZB parent.

A. D. STEINBERG (*National Institutes of Health, Bethesda, MD*): Do you think it is likely that genes other than immunoglobulin genes are involved?

DATTA: The studies that you and us did on recombinant inbred mice show that at least some genetic factors are not linked to immunoglobulin genes. It seems important, however, that the V-gene families are very similar in both normal and autoimmune mice. That does not mean that there may be mutant genes that our linkage studies did not detect. It seems that production of the autoantibodies is a regulation problem rather than a problem in the immunoglobulin gene itself.

G. DIGHIERO (*Institut Pasteur, Paris, France*): We have studied a large collection of anti-DNA antibodies from BALB/c and NZB mice and we have found very frequently a cross-reaction between anti-DNA activity and cytoskeletal proteins. This has now been confirmed by Janine Andre Schwartz with lupus antibodies. Have you checked your F_1 mice for reactivity against cytoskeletal proteins?

DATTA: No, we have not yet done that.

DIGHIERO: Have you found cytoskeletal proteins complexed and deposited in the kidneys in lupus?

DATTA: I never looked for this.

Y. BOREL (*Harvard Medical School, Boston, MA*): Several mechanisms regulate the antibodies and, if so, how do you explain that there is still an increase of the expression of these antibodies?

DATTA: When we study the idiotypic markers with serologic reagents, we are trying to define relationships among members of families of antibodies. Now, within a given idiotypic family, the member antibodies may undergo changes in their quality and pathogenicity, yet still retain the idiotypic marker. Therefore, the idiotype is not itself pathogenic, but a marker of antibodies, some of which are pathogenic. I think that the change in quality of antibody comes from somatic mutation, which is in turn produced in an ongoing immune response, i.e., by the T cells that are triggering and driving B cells to mutate and to change the quality of the antibodies they produce.

Z. BENTWICH (*R. Ben Ari Institute of Clinical Immunology, Rehovot, Israel*): Is there a dominant idiotype in the group of nephritogenic antibodies? Have you carried out any experiments in which you have treated nephritic mice with an anti-idiotype?

DATTA: So far, the idiotypes we have defined have been present in all F_1 kidneys. This means that they are recurrent, but they are not necessarily dominant. As far as treatment, I think B. H. Hahn is going to talk about that and we have not approached it in that direction at all.

B. BLOMBERG (*University of Miami School of Medicine, Miami, FL*): I want to address the question that C. G. Fathman raised earlier about original "antigenic sin." That is, if you look early on, when the antibodies are being produced, can you detect one allotype or the other being triggered in an individual mouse?

DATTA: No, we have not done that.

BLOMBERG: Well, can you discuss the oligoclonality or monoclonality of the response? The question is whether at the initiation of the response it is monoclonal.

DATTA: I am not saying that the anti-DNA response is oligoclonal. What I am saying is that there is a set we can identify that is present in the kidney and that contains members of cross-reactive idiotypic families. Therefore, we are saying that there is preferential response of triggering of certain clones of B cells.

BLOMBERG: Within one F_1 mouse, are both allotypes produced?

DATTA: Yes.

G. WICK (*Institute of Innsbruck, Innsbruck, Austria*): Is the isoelectric focusing of the antibodies associated with a different affinity for glomerular basement membranes?

DATTA: We have not studied that question yet, but we are planning to inject these antibodies to see how they will deposit in the kidney.

Auto-Epitopes and Autoimmune Diseases

IAN R. MACKAY, IAN H. FRAZER, L. JANE McNEILAGE,
AND SENGA WHITTINGHAM

Clinical Research Unit
The Walter and Eliza Hall Institute
of Medical Research
and
The Royal Melbourne Hospital
Victoria 3050, Australia

INTRODUCTION

Central to studies on autoimmunity are autoantigens and autoantibodies. The term "autoantigen" has, in the past, been used very broadly to describe macromolecular structures in cell nuclei, cytoplasm, membranes, and secretory products. This broad usage of "autoantigen" is applicable to reactions with autoantibodies detected by immunofluorescence and, in the diagnostic laboratory, has helped define various diseases as belonging to the autoimmune category. This had led to the recognition of autoantibodies reactive with cellular organelles, with or without tissue specificity, and to the traditional classification of autoimmune diseases into organ-specific and non-organ-specific types. The polar organ-specific disorders include diseases in the thyrogastric group and the polar non-organ-specific or multisystem diseases include systemic lupus erythematosus (SLE) and related disorders; in between are a variety of autoimmune diseases not readily classifiable into either category.

With evolving knowledge, autoimmune diseases may be more appropriately considered according to the identity and distribution of the structure to which the autoantibody (or autoantibodies) is directed. Such structures are here referred to as auto-epitopes, accepting that the precise molecular characterization and configuration for most are still unknown. If autoimmune reactivity is to be pathogenic, the auto-epitope(s) should be accessible to antibodies or cells of the immune system and be vulnerable in the sense that reactivity with it is prejudicial to the structural or functional integrity of the cell or tissue. The identification, isolation, and purification of auto-epitopes should lead to a better understanding of autoimmune disease and it should provide for reagents for diagnostic immunoassays and even for new approaches to treatment (for example, by the raising of regulatory anti-idiotype antibodies).

AUTO-EPITOPES FOR "DISEASE-RELEVANT" AUTOANTIBODIES

The best example of an autoimmune disease for which auto-epitopes have been precisely identified is experimental autoimmune encephalomyelitis (EAE), which is induced in animals by injection with adjuvants of the basic protein of myelin (BPM). There are several amino-acid sequences in the BPM molecule that function as disease-inducing auto-epitopes in various mammalian species; however, there is no evident human counterpart of EAE.

For many human autoimmune diseases, some progress has been made towards identifying the macromolecule on which auto-epitopes might reside. For example, the auto-epitopes reactive with antinuclear antibodies present in sera from patients with the multisystem "lupus-related" autoimmune diseases reside on DNA, histones,and ribonucleoproteins (TABLE 1),[1-12] with the specificity of the autoantibodies depending on the particular autoimmune process. The multisystem autoimmune diseases, attributable to deposition of immune complexes in affected tissues, include systemic lupus erythematosus (SLE), its variants, and rheumatoid arthritis. There are two "sets" of autoantigens in SLE. One set is represented by native DNA containing a range of

TABLE 1. Macromolecules Bearing Antigenic Determinants and Presumably the Auto-Epitopes Reactive with Antinuclear Antibodies in the Multisystem Autoimmune Diseases

Disease	Autoantigen	Macromolecule(s) Bearing the Antigenic Determinant	Reference
Systemic lupus erythematosus (SLE)	DNA	Cross-reactivity with proteoglycans	1
	Sm	U1-U5 snRNPS 29 kd, 28 kd, 16 kd (13 kd)	2
	Ro(SS-A)	60 kd	3
	PCNA	Cyclin (35 kd)	4
Drug-induced SLE	Histones[a]	H1, H2A, H2B, H3, H4	5
Mixed connective tissue disease	(U1)RNP	U1 snRNP—68 kd, 33 kd, 22 kd	2
Primary Sjögren's syndrome	La(SS-B)	50 kd[b]	2
Scleroderma	Centromere	19.5 kd	6
	Scl-70	70 kd by biochemical purification, 86 kd by immunoblotting	7, 8
	Nucleolus	7-2 RNP, anti-To	9
	Periribosomal particles RNA polymerase 1	U3 RNP	9
Rheumatoid arthritis	IgG	Fc region Histones (cross-reaction)	10
Polymyositis	Jo-1	Histidyl-tRNA synthetase	11
	PL-7	Threonyl-tRNA synthetase	12
	PL-12	Alanyl-tRNA synthetase	

[a]Epitopes have been defined on the carboxy- and amino-termini (Fritzler, personal communication).
[b]An epitope has been defined on a cloned protein from a cDNA library.

auto-epitopes associated both with the backbone and the bases of the DNA molecule and with polynucleotides (see Stollar and Schwartz, this volume). The other set is associated with nucleic acid-binding proteins, including RNA-binding ribonucleoproteins (RNP), particularly Sm and Ro (SS-A), and a DNA-binding 70–80-kilodalton (kd) heterodimer.[13] The auto-epitopes on the two ribonucleoprotein antigens, Sm and Ro, are located on the protein rather than on the RNA. The Ro antigen contains a 60-kd antigenic polypeptide,[3] while several polypeptides bear antigenic determinants recognized by anti-Sm antibodies.[2] In rheumatoid arthritis, auto-epitopes are present on the Fc portion of the IgG (see NOTE ADDED IN PROOF), with some showing cross-reactivity with histones.[10]

Among the antireceptor diseases, auto-epitope(s) has been localized to what is described as the main immunogenic region of the alpha chain of the acetylcholine receptor.[14] Auto-epitopes reactive with autoantibodies present in Graves' disease (once known as long-acting-thyroid-stimulators) have been shown to be associated with glycoprotein and ganglioside components of the receptor for the thyroid-stimulating hormone (see Kohn, this volume), while in insulin-resistant diabetes mellitus, auto-epitopes are reported to be present on the α and β subunits of the insulin receptor.[15] Blood group antigens bear auto-epitopes that are recognized by autoantibodies present in hemocytolytic disease—for example, the auto-epitope in the "warm" type hemolytic anemia resides on the Rh antigen e in about 15% of cases and on the I-i blood group antigens in the "cold" antibody type; auto-epitopes in some cases of thrombocytopenic purpura have been identified with the IIIb-IIa glycoprotein complex of platelets.[16] Auto-epitopes for the bullous skin diseases, pemphigus vulgaris (PV) and pemphigus foliaceus (PF), have been identified as glycoproteins of MW (unreduced) of 210 kd (in PV) and 160 kd (in PF),[17] while for Goodpasture's disease, an auto-epitope has been identified as a polypeptide associated with a collagenase-resistant component of Type IV collagen of glomerular and pulmonary basement membranes.[18]

Auto-epitopes on microsomal antigens relevant to the thyroid-gastric-adrenal group of autoimmune diseases are mostly uncharacterized. For thyroiditis, auto-epitopes on the thyroid microsomal-microvillar antigen are reported to be present on a poorly glycosylated 105-kd peptide, which is probably stabilized by intrachain disulfide bonds.[19] For insulin-dependent diabetes mellitus, an auto-epitope may be associated with a 64-kd polypeptide expressed on the surface of the pancreatic beta-islet cell.[20]

There are several diseases, mostly organ or tissue specific, for which polypeptide autoantigens have been identified, but for which the relationship of the epitope to the disease is so far unexplained. These diseases and the antigens (in parentheses) include polymyositis (Jo-1, histidyl-RNA-synthetase), scleroderma, CREST variant (centromere, 19.5-kd polypeptide), systemic sclerosis (Scl-70, 70-kd polypeptide), primary Sjögren's syndrome (La, 50-kd polypeptide), and primary biliary cirrhosis (70-kd and 45-kd polypeptides, *vide infra*).

Primary biliary cirrhosis (PBC) is a presumed autoimmune disease of the liver that results from progressive destruction of intrahepatic cholangioles and has long been characterized by the presence of antibody to mitochondria detected by immunofluorescence. We have analyzed mitochondrial preparations from human placenta and other sources [including rodent liver and kidney, yeast, bacteria, and plants (bean shoots)] by SDS-PAGE and immunoblotting, using sera from 30 patients with PBC.[21] The PBC sera reacted with one or the other (or usually both) of two human mitochondrial polypeptides of apparent molecular weights of 70 kd and 45 kd, whereas 58 AMA-negative sera from other liver diseases did not react with the 70-kd polypeptide, but 4 reacted with the 45-kd polypeptide. Immunoblotting after two-dimensional separation by charge employing isoelectric focusing and by MW by SDS-PAGE identified two antigenic forms or isospecies of the 70-kd polypeptide and four antigenic forms of the 45-kd polypeptide. Reactivity to both the 70-kd and the 45-kd polypeptide was destroyed by brief exposure of the antigen preparation to trypsin. A counterpart of the 70-kd human mitochondrial polypeptide was detected as a 65–70-kd polypeptide in rat and mouse mitochondria and as a 55-kd polypeptide in yeast, bacteria, and bean shoots. The molecular weight of the 45-kd polypeptide was similar in most mitochondrial preparations tested, but no counterpart could be identified in bacteria or bean shoots. Beef heart mitochondria were used to show that, although the reactive polypeptides were present in a semipurified preparation of the F1 portion of mitochondrial H(+) ATPase, sera did not react with the beta subunit of ATPase, hitherto proposed as a candidate mitochondrial autoantigen. Absorption of a reactive serum with human placental mitochondria removed reactivity by immunoblotting against various preparations of mammalian, bacterial, and plant origin (FIGURE 1), suggesting that similar epitopes were present in all. Thus, the mitochondrial auto-epitopes, so far unidentified, with which PBC sera react are of wide provenance and are highly conserved molecules. Therefore, the proteins with which these are associated must either be of major importance in cellular metabolism or have an essential structural function.

A special interest of our group has been the La (SS-B) ribonucleoprotein that bears auto-epitopes reactive with the antinuclear antibody (ANA), anti-La. The La autoantigen is a cellular phosphoprotein that has a molecular weight of 50 kd. It binds to ribonucleic acids (RNAs) transcribed by RNA polymerase III, to viral RNAs transcribed by RNA polymerase III, particularly those encoded by Epstein-Barr virus and adenovirus,[22,23] and to U1 and U6, which are transcribed by polymerase II.[24] The binding is to the 3'-oligouridylate tail of the small RNAs,[25] with the efficiency of binding being determined by the number of uridylate residues at the RNA 3' terminus.

The auto-epitopes with which anti-La reacts are on the cellular protein that may also have auto-epitopes reactive with the ANA, anti-Ro. By immunoblotting, the La ribonucleoprotein has been shown to contain one antigenic polypeptide of MW 50 kd that could be further defined by two-dimensional gel electrophoresis as a heterogeneously charged acidic nuclear protein with 5–6 different isospecies.[26] A newly developed technique[27] has considerable potential for characterizing auto-epitopes relevant to autoimmune disease: recombinant cDNA clones derived from a gene expression library made from human liver were probed with anti-La sera to identify a protein reactive with anti-La, and the analysis of overlapping cDNA clones revealed one La auto-epitope on a strongly hydrophilic decapeptide in the C-terminal 12% of the La polypeptide.

Although anti-La has hitherto been specified as occurring in "lupus sera," work in our unit based on characteristics associated with the presence of anti-La in serum has revealed a remarkable degree of case homogeneity, along with a strong suggestion that anti-La (SS-B) is a predictor of primary Sjögren's syndrome;[26] thus, when 34 consecutive patients with anti-La were studied for disease markers, 31 (88%) had hypergammaglobulinemia, 33 (97%) had rheumatoid factor, and 27 (of 30 tested, 90%) had the HLA phenotype of B8, all characteristic of primary Sjögren's syndrome. In addition, labial biopsies in asymptomatic cases were positive for histologic sialadenitis.[26]

However, still unresolved is the pathogenetic relationship (if any) of anti-La to the histopathological changes of the associated exocrine adenitis characteristic of primary Sjögren's syndrome. It may be that a self-perpetuating inflammatory change in exocrine tissues is maintained by the formation *in situ* of tissue damaging immune complexes between La and anti-La. Another possibility, contingent on the participation of Epstein-Barr virus (EBV) in the pathogenesis of primary Sjögren's syndrome,[28] is that the La antigen becomes associated as hapten with EBV-encoded "carrier" molecules to create a self + x-determinant that is both the immunogen and target for the autoimmune response. A third explanation is that La is cross-reactive with an idiotype on antiviral antibodies and the sialadenitis that culminates in the sicca syndrome is due to chronic EBV infection, making anti-La an incidental finding.

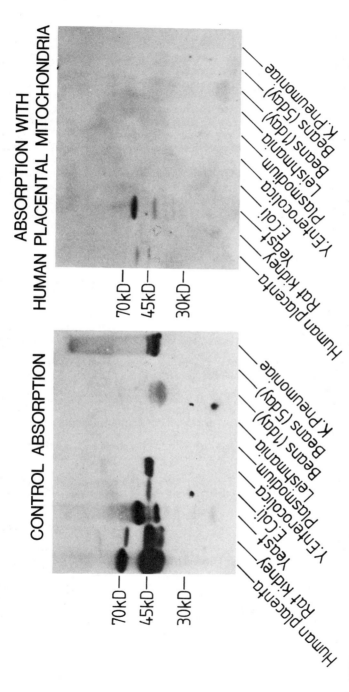

FIGURE 1. Reactivity of serum by immunoblotting with mitochondrial and other preparations after absorption with murine hepatocyte membranes (left) and absorption with human placental mitochondria (right). A serum from a patient with primary biliary cirrhosis, diluted 1/100, was exposed to 16 cycles of absorption with 1 mg of purified plasma membrane from mouse liver or 1 mg of a human placental mitochondria (HPM) preparation. The reactivities by immunoblotting with mitochondrial antigens from mammalian sources, yeast, and preparations from microorganisms and bean shoots were specifically removed by absorption with HPM.

CONCLUSIONS

The terms, "autoantigen" and "autoantibody," have now achieved a traditional status, but understanding of autoimmune disease in the future will require a more precise identification of the structures—auto-epitopes—to which autoantibodies are directed. This may reveal unexpected specificities among autoantibodies, provide important clues on the origin and activity of pathogenic as opposed to nonpathogenic autoantibodies, and lead towards targeted intervention in autoimmune disease.

[**Note added in proof:** Recently reported antigenic structures pertinent to auto-epitopes include the following: The DNA-binding protein designated as Ku,[29] or Ki[30] or p70/80,[31] on which there are at least three epitopes recognized by autoantibodies from patients with scleroderma-polymyositis; three highly conserved ribosomal proteins of 38 kd, 17 kd, and 19 kd recognized by 5–10% of patients with SLE;[32] and an epitope on the Fc region of the IgG molecule recognized by rheumatoid factor and staphlococcal protein A and involving the amino-acid side chains, His 435, Tyr 438, and one or both of His 433 and His 310.[33]]

REFERENCES

1. FABER, P., P. J. A. CAPEL, G. P. M. RIJKE, G. VIERWINDEN, L. B. A. VAN DE PUTTE & R. A. P. LOEW. 1984. Cross-reactivity of anti-DNA antibodies with proteoglycans. Clin. Exp. Immunol. **55:** 502–508.

2. PETTERSSON, I., M. HINTERBERGER, T. MIMORI, E. GOTTLIEB & J. A. STEITZ. 1984. The structure of mammalian small nuclear ribonucleoproteins. Identification of multiple components reactive with anti-(U1)RNP and anti-Sm autoantibodies. J. Biol. Chem. **259:** 5907–5914.

3. WOLIN, S. L. & J. A. STEITZ. 1984. The Ro small cytoplasmic ribonucleoproteins: identification of the antigenic protein and its binding site on the Ro RNAs. Proc. Natl. Acad. Sci. USA **81:** 1996–2000.

4. MATHEWS, M. B., R. M. BERNSTEIN, B. R. FRANZA & J. I. GARRELS. 1984. Identity of the proliferating cell nuclear antigen and cyclin. Nature **309:** 374–376.

5. FRITZLER, M. J. & E. M. TAN. 1978. Antibodies to histones in drug-induced and idiopathic lupus erythematosus. J. Clin. Invest. **62:** 560–567.

6. GULDNER, H. H., H-J. LAKOMEK & F. A. BAUTZ. 1984. Human-anticentromere sera recognise a 19.5 kD non-histone chromosomal protein from HeLa cells. Clin. Exp. Immunol. **58:** 13–20.

7. DOUVAS, A. S., M. ACHTEN & E. M. TAN. 1979. Identification of a nuclear protein (Scl-70) as a unique target of human antinuclear antibodies in scleroderma. J. Biol. Chem. **254:** 10,514–10,522.

8. VAN VENROOIJ, W. J., S. O. STAPEL, H. HOUBEN, W. J. HABETS, C. G. M. KALLENBERG, E. PENNER, & L. B. VAN DE PUTTE. 1985. Scl-86, a marker antigen for diffuse scleroderma. J. Clin. Invest. **75:** 1053–1060.

9. REDDY, R., E. M. TAN, D. HENNING, K. NOHGA & H. BUSCH. 1983. Detection of a nucleolar 7-2 ribonucleoprotein and a cytoplasmic 8-2 ribonucleoprotein with autoantibodies from patients with scleroderma. J. Biol. Chem. **258:** 1383–1386.

10. AGNELLO, V., A. ARBETTER, G. IBANEZ DE KASEP, R. POWELL, E. M. TAN & F. JOSLIN. 1980. Evidence for subset of rheumatoid factors that cross-react with DNA-histone and have a distinct cross-idiotype. J. Exp. Med. **151:** 1514–1527.

11. MATHEWS, M. B. & R. M. BERNSTEIN. 1983. Myositis autoantibody inhibits histidyl-tRNA synthetase: a model for autoimmunity. Nature **304:** 177–179.

12. MATHEWS, M. B., M. REICHLIN, G. R. HUGHES & R. M. BERNSTEIN. 1984. Anti-threonyl-tRNA synthetase, a second myositis-related autoantibody. J. Exp. Med. **160:** 420–434.

13. REEVES, W. H. 1985. Use of monoclonal antibodies for the characterization of novel

DNA-binding proteins recognized by human autoimmune sera. J. Exp. Med. **161:** 18–39.

14. TZARTOS, S. J. & J. M. LINDSTROM. 1980. Monoclonal antibodies used to probe acetyl choline receptor structure: Localization of the main immunogenic region and a detection of similarities between subunits. Proc. Natl. Acad. Sci. USA **77:** 755–759.

15. HARRISON, L. C. 1985. Anti-receptor antibodies. *In* The Autoimmune Diseases, chapter 23. N. R. Rose & I. R. Mackay, Eds. Academic Press. La Jolla, California.

16. WOODS, V. L., JR., E. H. OH, D. MASON & R. MCMILLAN. 1984. Autoantibodies against the platelet glycoprotein IIb/IIIa complex in patients with chronic ITP. Blood **63:** 635–375.

17. STANLEY, J. R., L. KOULU & C. THIVOLET. 1984. Distinction between epidermal antigens binding pemphigus vulgaris and pemphigus foliaceus autoantibodies. J. Clin. Invest. **74:** 313–320.

18. WIESLANDER, J., J. F. BARR, R. J. BUTKOWSKI, S. J. EDWARDS, P. BYGREN, D. HEINEGÅRD & B. G. HUDSON. 1984. Goodpasture antigen of the glomerular basement membrane: localization to non-collagenous regions of type IV collagen. Proc. Natl. Acad. Sci. USA **81:** 3838–3842.

19. BANGA, J. P., G. PRYCE, L. HAMMOND & I. M. ROITT. 1985. Structural features of the autoantigens involved in thyroid autoimmune disease: the thyroid microsomoal/microvillar antigen. Mol. Biol. **22:** 629–642.

20. BAEKKESKOV, S., T. DYRBERG & A. LERNMARK. 1984. Autoantibodies to a 64 kilodalton islet cell protein precede the onset of spontaneous diabetes in the BB rat. Science **224:** 1348–1350.

21. FRAZER, I. H., I. R. MACKAY, T. W. JORDAN, S. WHITTINGHAM & S. MARZUKI. 1985. Polypeptide antigens reactive with antimitochondrial autoantibodies. J. Immunol. **135:** 1739–1745.

22. LERNER, M. A., N. C. ANDREWS, G. MILLER & J. A. STEITZ. 1981. Two small RNAs encoded by Epstein-Barr virus and complexed with protein are precipitated by antibodies from patients with systemic lupus erythematosus. Proc. Natl. Acad. Sci. USA **78:** 805–809.

23. ROSA, M. A., E. GOTTLIEB, M. R. LERNER & J. A. STEITZ. 1981. Striking similarities are exhibited by two small Epstein-Barr virus-encoded ribonucleic acids and the adenovirus-associated ribonucleic acids VAI and VAII. Mol. Cell. Biol. **1:** 785–796.

24. MADORE, S. J., E. D. WIEBEN & T. PEDERSON. 1984. Eukaryotic small ribonucleoproteins. Anti-La human autoantibodies react with U1 RNA-protein complexes. J. Biol. Chem. **259:** 1929–1933.

25. MATHEWS, M. B. & A. M. FRANCOEUR. 1984. La antigen recognizes and binds to the 3'-oligouridylate tail of a small RNA. Mol. Cell. Biol. **4:** 1134–1140.

26. MCNEILAGE, L. J., S. WHITTINGHAM, I. JACK & I. R. MACKAY. 1985. Molecular analysis of the RNA and protein components recognized by anti-La (SS-B) autoantibodies. Clin. Exp. Immunol. **62:** 685–695.

27. CHAMBERS, J. C. & J. D. KEENE. 1985. Isolation and analysis of cDNA clones expressing human lupus antigen. Proc. Nat. Acad. Sci. USA **82:** 2115–2119.

28. WHITTINGHAM, S., L. S. MCNEILAGE & I. R. MACKAY. 1985. Primary Sjögren's syndrome following infectious mononucleosis. Ann. Intern. Med. **102:** 490–493.

29. MIMORI, T., J. A. HARDIN & J. A. STEITZ. 1986. Characterization of the DNA-binding protein antigen Ku recognized by autoantibodies from patients with rheumatic disorders. J. Biol. Chem. **261:** 2274–2278.

30. FRANCOEUR, A-M., C.L. PEEBLES, P.T. COMPPER & E.M. TAN. 1986. Identification of Ki (Ku, p70/p80) autoantigens and analysis of anti-Ki autoantibody reactivity. Immunology **136:** 1648–1653.

31. REEVES, W. H. 1985. Use of monoclonal antibodies for the characterization of novel DNA-binding proteins recognized by human autoimmune sera. J. Exp. Med. **161:** 18.

32. ELKON, K. B., A. P. PARNASSA & C. L. FOSTER. 1985. Lupus autoantibodies target ribosomal P proteins. J. Exp. Med. **162:** 459–471.

33. NARDELLA, F. A., D. C. TELLER, C. V. BARBER & M. MANNIK. 1985. IgG rheumatoid factors and staphylococcal protein A bind to a common molecular site on IgG. J. Exp. Med. **162:** 1811–1824.

Anti-Idiotypic Immunity in Autoimmunity[a]

PIERLUIGI E. BIGAZZI

Department of Pathology
University of Connecticut Health Center
Farmington, Connecticut 06032

INTRODUCTION

Carnegie and Mackay[1-3] have suggested that certain autoimmune diseases with fluctuating clinical symptoms, such as systemic lupus erythematosus and myasthenia gravis, could represent a failure of the normal function of antireceptor immunity to regulate unwanted responses against self-components. In those disorders, the temporary ascendency of a clone of "suppressor" lymphocytes resulting in the production of anti-idiotypic antibodies might reduce the pathogenic lymphocyte clones, with the consequent remission of the disease. In the same vein, Hans Wigzell[4-6] has proposed that auto-anti-idiotypic immunity might become useful in the treatment of individuals afflicted with autoimmune disease.

A network model such as the one postulated in Jerne's idiotype–anti-idiotype theory[7] may indeed best account for the frequent occurrence of autoimmune responses without autoimmune disease. In this case, the immunologic network would not be altered.[8] It would also account for the development of autoimmune disease as a consequence of a derangement of the immunologic network. However, there are still some serious reservations as to the role of anti-idiotypic immunity in autoimmunity. First, because autoimmune responses are usually polyclonal and heterogeneous, auto-anti-idiotypic immunity might be difficult if not impossible to generate. This might explain the relative scarcity of demonstrations of auto-anti-idiotypic antibodies in autoimmune disease and the doubts expressed by some immunologists, who have questioned "whether auto-anti-idiotypic antibodies have any relevance to the real world."[9] Second, assuming even very limited heterogeneity of autoantibodies, the geometric progression of anti-idiotypic antibodies to be generated might render any attempt at controlling autoimmune responses by treatment with anti-idiotypic antibodies quite difficult. In addition, it has been pointed out that suppression by anti-idiotype does not usually affect the overall level of antibodies, despite the fact that the idiotype itself is largely, if not completely inhibited.[10]

For these reasons, we have investigated the role of anti-idiotypic immunity in spontaneous and experimental models of autoimmune disease and concentrated our efforts toward answering the following questions:

(1) Are autoimmune responses idiotypically heterogeneous?
(2) Are auto-anti-idiotypic responses detectable in autoimmunity?
(3) Is it possible to demonstrate quantitative and/or qualitative changes in anti-idiotypic lymphocytes during the course of autoimmune disease?

---

[a]The experimental work reported was supported in part by grant no. CA-26053 from the National Cancer Institute, NIH, and by grant no. ESAI-3230 from the National Institute of Environmental Health Sciences, NIH.

TABLE 1. Study of Anti-Idiotypic Immunity in Autoimmune Disease

(1) Animal Models:
A. Spontaneous: Autoimmune thyroiditis of BUF rats.
B. Induced: Autoimmune glomerulonephritis of BN rats.
(2) Human:
A. Hashimoto's thyroiditis.

The present paper summarizes the results obtained thus far in our laboratory and discusses some of the possible answers to those questions above.

STUDIES OF ANTI-IDIOTYPIC IMMUNITY IN AUTOIMMUNE DISEASE

As shown in TABLE 1, we have performed studies of anti-idiotypic immunity in human autoimmunity as well as in animal models of autoimmune disease. The human autoimmune disease investigated in our laboratory is Hashimoto's thyroiditis.[11] The animal models chosen for our studies are the autoimmune thyroiditis that occurs spontaneously in inbred BUF rats[12,13] and the autoimmune glomerulonephritis induced experimentally in inbred BN rats by the chronic administration of mercuric chloride.[14-16]

We initiated our studies of these three autoimmune conditions by producing "conventional" anti-idiotypic antibodies, as outlined in TABLE 2. The rationale behind our approach is twofold. First, we preferred "conventional," i.e., polyclonal, to monoclonal anti-idiotypic antibodies because we wanted our antisera to react with several (and not just one or a few) idiotopes of autoantibodies. Second, we used purified idiotypes "pooled" from large numbers of individual rats or humans with the specific purpose of exposing the immunized rabbits to the largest possible numbers of idiotypic determinants of autoantibodies. In the following sections of this paper, we will show how the "conventional" anti-idiotypic antibodies obtained following this rationale have provided us with useful information on the cross-reactivity of idiotopes of autoantibodies. In ongoing experiments, we are now attempting to define the individual idiotypic determinants of autoantibodies by monoclonal anti-idiotypic antibodies.

TABLE 2. Protocol Followed for Production of Anti-Idiotypic Antibodies[a]

Purification of Autoantibodies
(ART or AGBM or AHT)
↓
Immunization of Rabbits
↓
Purification of Rabbit Immunoglobulins
↓
Repeated Absorption with "Normal" Immunoglobulins
(Lacking ART or AGBM or AHT)
↓
"Conventional" Anti-Idiotypic Antibodies

[a]Autoantibodies to rat thyroglobulin = ART; autoantibodies to glomerular basement membrane = AGBM; autoantibodies to human thyroglobulin = AHT.

ANIMAL MODELS OF AUTOIMMUNE DISEASE

For our investigation of idiotypic immunity in autoimmunity, we have chosen two animal models—one arising spontaneously and the other induced experimentally. One characteristic in common to the two models is that both occur in inbred strains of rats, which may have simplified our task by reducing the heterogeneity of the autoimmune responses observed. Another advantage of these models is that monoclonal antibodies to surface markers of rat lymphocytes (and subpopulations of T lymphocytes) are available,[17] thus allowing more precise investigations of the cell populations involved in autoimmune responses.

Spontaneous Autoimmune Thyroiditis of BUF Rats

The major characteristics of this animal model are outlined in TABLE 3. It should be noted that, while several animal models of autoimmune disease are available, very few of these disorders arise spontaneously in inbred animals. Besides this advantage, BUF rat thyroiditis is similar to the condition observed in humans because of its predilection for older females and the presence of circulating autoantibodies to thyroglobulin. The disorder develops spontaneously in up to 30% of animals[13] and thus it is possible to experimentally immunize "normal" rats with thyroglobulin and compare their autoimmune responses with those of animals affected by spontaneously occurring thyroiditis. The onset of the disease is accelerated and its incidence significantly increased in BUF rats that are chronically exposed to certain chemicals, such as methylcholanthrene, trypan blue, and 3-methyl-4-dimethylaminobenzene.[16,18] Autoimmune thyroiditis in BUF rats is also favored by neonatal thymectomy, which is a treatment that may accelerate the onset of this condition and increase its incidence to more than 80%. Thus, it has been hypothesized that both chronic exposure to certain drugs and early removal of the thymus may act in similar fashion, either preferentially eliminating T suppressor cells or otherwise altering the regulatory networks.[16,18]

Production of "Conventional" Anti-Idiotypic Antibodies

As shown in FIGURE 1, BUF rat IgG from approximately 100 sera containing autoantibodies to rat thyroglobulin (ART) and with a binding capacity higher than 30% by RIA was chromatographed through an immunoabsorbent column (activated Sepharose coated with rat thyroglobulin).[19] The material eluted from this column was rat IgG, as shown by immunoelectrophoresis, and more precisely, rat IgG1 and IgG2a, as demonstrated by precipitation in agar gel with specific antisera. The eluted IgG was tested by the RIA used to detect ART and it was found that 20 μg of eluted IgG bound 35–40% of radiolabeled rat thyroglobulin. Two rabbits (no. 275 and no. 276), immunized with purified ART, produced anti-idiotypic antibodies to ART. Sera from these rabbits contained antibodies to rat immunoglobulins, as determined by passive

TABLE 3. Spontaneous Autoimmune Thyroiditis of BUF Rats

---

1. Occurs in an inbred strain.
2. Has higher incidence in older female rats.
3. Is characterized by circulating autoantibodies to rat thyroglobulin (ART).
4. Purification of ART by affinity chromatography is relatively easy.

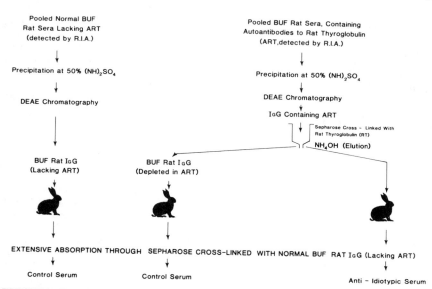

FIGURE 1. Experimental protocol for the production of "conventional" anti-idiotypic antibodies to ART.

hemagglutination and immunodiffusion in agar gel. After repeated immunoabsorptions through a Sepharose 4B column coated with "normal" BUF rat IgG (i.e., lacking ART), no antibodies to rat immunoglobulins could be detected by immunodiffusion or passive hemagglutination. However, immunoabsorbed sera from rabbits no. 275 and no. 276 still reacted by immunodiffusion in agar against purified ART. Using a radioassay with radioiodinated idiotype, it was found that both sera were specifically bound to ART and that after immunoabsorption with cold idiotype, there was little or no binding to radiolabeled ART. We also noted that the two antisera reacted with both spontaneous and experimentally induced ART, but not with radiolabeled normal BUF rat IgG. Preimmune sera from the two rabbits and immunoabsorbed sera from control animals immunized with normal BUF rat IgG did not react with radiolabeled ART. On the basis of these results, we concluded that sera from rabbits no. 275 and no. 276 contained anti-idiotypic antibodies to ART. Interestingly, both antisera bound less than half the radiolabeled idiotype, which suggests that they recognized some, but not all of the idiotypic determinants of ART.

The results described above demonstrated that we had obtained anti-idiotypic antibodies capable of binding to ART and precipitating with it as well. However, they gave no information on the functional ability of such antibodies to recognize the antigen-combining sites of ART. Therefore, the various antisera were examined to detect possible *in vitro* inhibitory effects on the reaction between idiotype (ART) and radiolabeled antigen (rat thyroglobulin, RT). We observed that antiserum no. 276 inhibited the binding of radiolabeled RT to ART, but not the binding of radiolabeled BSA to rat antibodies to BSA. The degree of inhibition was dependent on the amount of antiserum used. The preimmune serum of rabbit no. 276, the antiserum from rabbit no. 275, and the control sera did not inhibit the binding of ART to RT. In summary, our *in vitro* experiments indicated that one of the two anti-idiotypic antisera not only specifically bound to the idiotype, but was also functionally capable of inhibiting the binding of the idiotype to its antigen, thyroglobulin. This suggested that anti-idiotypic antibodies in serum no. 276 were directed against antigenic determinants of the idiotype closely associated with its antigen-binding site. The partial inhibition of ART-RT binding by anti-idiotypic antibodies was an interesting, but not unexpected finding and it indicated that such antibodies recognized some, but not all of the idiotopes of ART. These might be the cross-reactive (or public) and not the individual (or private) idiotypes of ART. Also of interest is the fact that antiserum no. 275 had no *in vitro* effects on the binding of RT or ART. This may be due to anti-idiotypic antibodies directed to determinants outside the antigen-binding site of ART.

Idiotypic Cross-Reactivity of Autoantibodies

These experiments were performed to determine whether rabbit anti-idiotypic antibodies to ART reacted with ART from individual BUF rats whose sera had not been included in the initial pool from which we purified the idiotypes used to obtain anti-idiotypic antibodies. To this purpose, we examined sera from 18 BUF rats with persistent levels of circulating ART. When we determined the inhibition of the binding between radiolabeled RT and ART (obtained when each of these sera was preincubated with anti-idiotypic antiserum no. 276), we found that 12/18 (67%) were inhibited, with a mean inhibition of 23%. No significant inhibition was found in the remaining 6 rat sera. The results indicate that ART from individual BUF rats can react with anti-idiotypic antibodies to ART and bring suggestive evidence in favor of the presence of cross-reactive idiotopes on autoantibodies from animals of the same inbred strain.

Anti-idiotypic antibodies also inhibited the binding of experimentally induced ART to radiolabeled RT in six of seven sera from inbred Fischer rats. Similarly, ART from outbred rabbits and guinea pigs, experimentally immunized with RT, were inhibited by antiserum no. 276. The same antiserum was also capable of inhibiting the binding of RT by human autoantibodies to thyroglobulin, cross-reacting with rat thyroglobulin. The two human sera tested were consistently inhibited. These experiments provide suggestive evidence in favor of cross-reacting idiotypes on autoantibodies (occurring spontaneously or experimentally induced by active immunization) in different strains of the same species or across species barriers.

Analysis of Lymphocytes

Using indirect immunofluorescence in noncapping conditions, we found that anti-idiotypic antibodies revealed significant numbers of idiotype-bearing (Id$^+$) cells (0.75% and 0.70%) in unfractionated spleen cells from BUF rats with spontaneous or experimentally induced ART.[20] By the same technique, we compared the numbers of Id$^+$ cells with those of cells reacting with RT (RT$^+$) in the same spleen cell populations and found that the percentages of such cells were quite close, with a mean of 0.64% for Id$^+$ and 0.74% for RT$^+$ cells. We also noticed that soluble RT competed with anti-idiotypic antibodies for cell-surface-associated antibody molecules, causing a significant inhibition in the numbers of cells stained by anti-idiotypic antibodies. Finally, we tested the ability of anti-idiotypic serum no. 276 to inhibit the binding of radiolabeled RT to spleen cells from BUF rats with autoimmune thyroiditis and a significant inhibition was observed. These results suggest that idiotopes similar to those of circulating ART are present on significant numbers of spleen lymphocytes from

BUF rats with autoimmune thyroiditis. Currently, two-color FACS analysis is being used in our laboratory to repeat these experiments.

Circulating Auto-Anti-Idiotypic Antibodies

Over the years, we have performed various experiments employing precipitation in agar, passive hemagglutination, RIA, and ELISA to demonstrate the presence of auto-anti-idiotypic antibodies in the circulation of BUF rats, either normal or with autoimmune thyroiditis. Thus far, all these experiments have failed to show detectable levels of auto-anti-idiotypic antibodies.

Autoimmune Glomerulonephritis of BN Rats

The major characteristics of this model of autoimmune disease are outlined in TABLE 4. One of the advantages of the model is that no injections of autoantigens and adjuvants are required for the induction of autoimmune responses. Inbred rats of the BN strain produce autoantibodies to the glomerular basement membrane of the kidney (AGBM) after chronic administration of mercuric chloride.[14–16] The disorder is characterized by a two-stage membranous nephropathy. During the first 15 days of mercuric chloride treatment, the examination of kidney biopsies shows linear binding of AGBM to the glomerular basement membrane, while the second stage is characterized by the deposition of granules of immunoglobulins and complement at the same

TABLE 4. Experimentally Induced Autoimmune Glomerulonephritis of BN Rats

1. Is caused in an inbred strain by the administration of mercuric chloride.
2. Is characterized by circulating autoantibodies to rat glomerular basement membrane (AGBM).
3. Is characterized by a two-stage membranous nephropathy—first with linear binding of AGBM to the glomerular basement membrane (GBM), then with granular deposits of immunoglobulins.
4. The kidney GBM functions as a natural immunoabsorbent for idiotype (AGBM).

level. We have investigated the kinetics of AGBM production in BN rats and found that AGBM are detectable in the serum 8–9 days after the initial injection of mercuric chloride, reach their peak titer by day 12–15, and then fall rapidly, returning to baseline values in the following two weeks.

We have hypothesized that one of the possible mechanisms to explain the transient appearance of AGBM may be due to self-regulation of autoantibody production that is perhaps mediated by auto-anti-idiotypic immunity.[21,22] In this view, the switch from linear to granular deposits of immunoglobulins in the kidneys might be caused by the formation of idiotype–anti-idiotype (AGBM–anti-AGBM) immune complexes.

Production of "Conventional" Anti-Idiotypic Antibodies

Anti-idiotypic antibodies were induced in rabbits following a procedure similar to that outlined in FIGURE 1. However, it should be noted that the idiotypes, i.e., AGBM,

TABLE 5. FACS Analysis of Spleen Lymphocytes from BN Rats Treated with Mercuric Chloride

Antibody	Marker of	Percentage of Positive Cells
W3/13	T cells	55–68
W3/25	T helper	35–47
OX 8	T supp./cytotox.	7–9
OX 6	Ia (B cells)	32–40
Anti-rat IgG	B cells	21–23
Anti-Id (anti-AGBM)	Id$^+$ cells	0.7–1.1

were not purified from various sera by affinity chromatography, but were obtained by low pH elution of kidney homogenates prepared from animals with AGBM spontaneously bound to the glomerular basement membrane (GBM) of their kidneys. In this case, the kidney GBM itself functioned as a natural immunoabsorbent for idiotype (AGBM), thus avoiding the possibility of alterations of the autoantigen that might occur during conventional immunoabsorption, either at the time of purification of the GBM or during its subsequent cross-linking to the chromatography gel.

After repeated immunizations, the serum of one rabbit reacted by ELISA with both AGBM and "normal" BN IgG (lacking AGBM), with a titer of 10^{-5} and a maximum OD$_{405}$ of 0.300. After purification by affinity chromatography on a column of "normal" BN IgG, the rabbit antiserum retained a high specificity for AGBM, with a titer of 10^{-5} and a maximum OD$_{405}$ of 0.200. However, it did not react any longer with "normal" BN immunoglobulins. The immunoglobulin fraction of this antiserum was also capable of inhibiting the reaction between AGBM and GBM, which was detectable by ELISA.

Idiotypic Cross-Reactivity of Autoantibodies

In these experiments, we have examined whether rabbit anti-idiotypic antibodies to AGBM react with AGBM from the sera of individual BN rats whose idiotypes were not used to immunize the rabbits against AGBM. AGBM-containing immunoglobulins from nine out of ten BN rats reacted by ELISA with rabbit anti-idiotypic antibodies, thus suggesting that cross-reactive idiotopes are present on autoantibodies from animals of the same inbred strain. Similarly, AGBM from rats of the MAXX strain (an inbred strain initially developed from a cross between BN and LEW rats) reacted with the same rabbit anti-idiotypic antibodies, suggesting once more that autoantibodies from different strains of the same species share idiotypic determinants.

TABLE 6. Human Autoimmune Thyroiditis

1. Has higher incidence in older females.
2. Is characterized by circulating autoantibodies to human thyroglobulin (AHT).
3. Its course is relatively mild; thus, it is possible to perform long-term idiotype studies on autoantibodies and lymphocytes from patients that are not treated with immunosuppressive drugs.
4. Purification of AHT by affinity chromatography is relatively easy.

Analysis of Lymphocytes

Recently, we have initiated a FACS analysis of lymphocytes from BN rats with mercuric-chloride-induced autoimmune glomerulonephritis (TABLE 5). As previously observed in BUF rats, the number of Id$^+$ lymphocytes in these animals ranges between 0.7% and 1.1%.

In addition, preliminary experiments performed by lymphocyte stimulation indicate that lymphocytes from BN rats with autoimmune glomerulonephritis react with purified AGBM and suggest that cells with surface anti-idiotypic receptors may be present during autoimmune responses.

Circulating Auto-Anti-Idiotypic Antibodies

Numerous experiments by various serological procedures (precipitation in agar, passive hemagglutination, ELISA) have failed to demonstrate the presence of auto-anti-idiotypic antibodies in the sera of BN rats. Particularly intriguing has been the absence of such antibodies in sera obtained during the second–third week of mercuric chloride treatment, when AGBM levels start declining and auto-anti-idiotypic antibodies might be operative in the down-regulation of autoantibody responses.

HUMAN AUTOIMMUNE DISEASE

For the study of anti-idiotypic immunity in human autoimmune disease, we have chosen to investigate Hashimoto's thyroiditis, whose major characteristics are outlined in TABLE 6. As compared to other autoimmune disorders, the advantages of the thyroiditis model are numerous.[11,23,24] First, the disease expresses itself as an inflammatory process with humoral and cellular autoimmune responses that are easily quantitated. Second, only a limited variety of autoantibodies is produced in autoimmune thyroiditis (in contrast with the more complex situation occurring in SLE) and autoantibodies to thyroglobulin seem to be the most relevant from a pathogenetic point of view. Third, the purification of autoantibodies to thyroglobulin by affinity chromatography is relatively easy. Finally, since patients with autoimmune thyroiditis run a relatively mild course, it is possible to perform idiotype studies on their autoantibodies and lymphocytes for longer periods than in other life-threatening conditions. At the same time, since the disease does not require immunosuppressive treatment, one can study anti-idiotypic immunity in these patients without the problem of therapeutically induced alterations of the immune response.

Production of "Conventional" Anti-Idiotypic Antibodies

The protocol employed for the production of anti-idiotypic antibodies is basically the same as outlined in TABLE 2 and FIGURE 1. A total of 138 sera containing autoantibodies to human thyroglobulin (AHT) were pooled and their immunoglobulin fraction was isolated by ammonium sulfate precipitation.[24] Then AHTs were purified on an immunosorbent column containing human thyroglobulin (HT). The column was prepared coupling HT to cyanogen-bromide-activated Sepharose 4B by mixing for 2 hours at room temperature and 16 hours at +4°C, followed by repeated washes in acetate and borate buffers. AHT were absorbed on the HT-immunosorbent column and then eluted using a sequence of high and low pH buffers. The eluate was tested for AHT by radioimmunoassay and ELISA. The idiotype (1 mg AHT in 1 ml PBS) was emulsified in complete Freund's adjuvant (CFA) and injected into the backs of New Zealand White rabbits. Injections were given weekly for four weeks and monthly thereafter, substituting incomplete Freund's adjuvant for the CFA after the fourth week. Rabbits were bled 5–6 days after each injection, beginning with the fourth injection. Control rabbits were injected with normal human immunoglobulins. Antisera were tested by immunodiffusion, immunoelectrophoresis, ELISA, and, in some instances, RIA for activity against both the idiotype and normal immunoglobulins. Anti-idiotypic antisera were repeatedly absorbed with "normal" human immunoglobulins (not containing AHT) linked to CNBr-activated Sepharose until no activity remained against normal immunoglobulins in any of the immunoassays.

Rabbit antisera to affinity-purified AHT reacted strongly with both normal human immunoglobulins and AHT (FIGURE 2). After repeated absorptions with "normal" human immunoglobulins (not containing AHT), their reactivity with normal immunoglobulins dropped to negligible levels, while reactivity with the idiotype remained (FIGURE 2). It should be noted that rabbit antisera to AHT required extensive absorptions in order to remove all reactivity against normal human immunoglobulins.

These results demonstrated that we had obtained anti-idiotypic antibodies capable of binding to purified AHT. However, they give no information on the functional ability of such antibodies to recognize the antigen-combining sites of AHT. Experiments addressing this issue are currently ongoing in our laboratory, following similar protocols to those described for anti-idiotypic antibodies to ART. Also in progress are studies of the idiotypic cross-reactivity of autoantibodies and lymphocytes from several patients with autoimmune thyroiditis, as well as an investigation of circulating auto-anti-idiotypic antibodies in the same patients.

INDUCTION OF ANTI-IDIOTYPIC IMMUNITY IN ANIMALS WITH AUTOIMMUNE DISEASE

In preliminary experiments, we attempted to suppress preexisting autoimmune responses (and disease) by *passive* transfer of anti-idiotypic antibodies. BUF rats with autoimmune thyroiditis were treated following the protocol outlined in FIGURE 3, which basically consists of a sequential combination of immunosuppression and anti-idiotypic treatment. The rationale for such combination was based on evidence previously published by other investigators (reviewed in reference 19) showing that in order to obtain an effective inhibition of antibody formation, anti-idiotypic antibodies must be administered at the time of immunization. This is obviously impossible in BUF rats with established thyroiditis or humans with autoimmune disease. To circumvent this difficulty, we suppressed, by sublethal x-irradiation, the immune responses of BUF rats with thyroiditis, thus eliminating most or all lymphocytes already sensitized by thyroglobulin. Immunosuppressive treatment was followed by the injection of anti-idiotypic antibodies, with the aim to specifically inactivate or eliminate the newly emerging lymphocytes carrying idiotypes specific for thyroglobulin. A decrease in circulating ART was observed in all rats passively immunized with anti-idiotypic antibodies. In most of these animals, serum ART levels were found to be lower than the initial values starting from the second week of treatment and, in all of them, the decrease continued to the end of the experiment. As expected from the *in vitro* studies, none of the anti-idiotypic-treated rats showed a dramatic drop in ART, but a significant negative change was observed when autoantibody levels at seven weeks were compared to pretreatment values. On the other hand, serum ART levels in rats

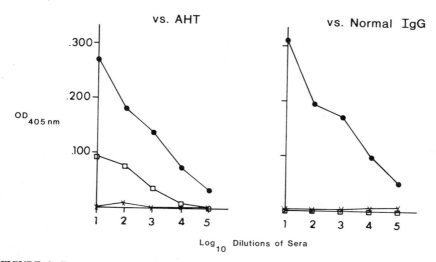

FIGURE 2. Demonstration of anti-idiotypic antibodies to AHT. The symbol ● is R 302 unabsorbed, □ is R 302 absorbed with normal IgG, and × is R 302 prebled. (Reprinted with permission from *Life Sciences,* vol. 32, p. 113, McCoy *et al.,* 1983, Pergamon Press, Ltd.)[24]

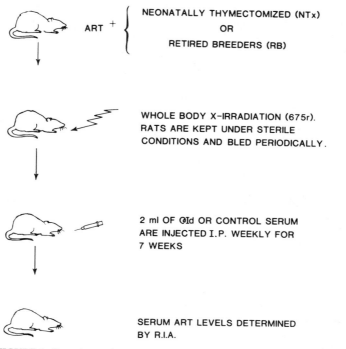

FIGURE 3. Experimental protocol for the suppression of ART production.

given control antiserum showed a modest, but continuous increase over the initial values. We also observed that anti-idiotypic-treated rats with lower levels of serum ART experienced a decrease of Id$^+$ cells, while anti-idiotypic-treated rats whose serum ART levels did not change had similar numbers of Id$^+$ cells as rats treated with control sera.

More recently, we have investigated the effects of *active* anti-idiotypic immunity in BN rats with mercuric-chloride-induced autoimmune glomerulonephritis. Untreated animals were immunized with idiotype in CFA and then injected with mercuric chloride. One group of control animals was immunized with "normal" BN immunoglobulins (not containing idiotype) and similarly injected with the chemical. A second group of controls was not immunized and similarly injected with mercuric chloride. When sera from all these animals were tested by ELISA for circulating AGBM, it was found that the group immunized with idiotype had developed a very strong AGBM response that was accelerated in its initiation and protracted in time. Serum levels of AGBM were elevated after ten days from the first immunization, peaked on day 24, and remained high until day 55, when the experiment was terminated. On the other hand, control animals produced much lower levels of AGBM, which decreased to baseline values by day 55. Thus, in this animal model of autoimmunity, the induction of active anti-idiotypic immunity apparently resulted in a more vigorous autoimmune response.

DISCUSSION

During the last seven years, we have investigated the role of anti-idiotypic immunity in two different animal models of autoimmune disease and in human autoimmune thyroiditis.[19–22,24] Both animal models share certain characteristics, i.e., they arise in inbred strains of rats, are organ-specific autoimmune disorders (with lesions that seem to correlate with the production of autoantibodies), and have a relatively mild course with very low mortality rates. The two models differ in that the autoimmune thyroiditis of BUF rats arises spontaneously in certain animals, while autoimmune glomerulonephritis is induced in most, if not all BN rats by the chronic administration of mercuric chloride. They also differ in the lesions observed in the target organs since the thyroid is heavily infiltrated by a chronic inflammatory process in BUF rats with autoimmune responses to thyroglobulin, while the kidneys of BN rats with circulating AGBM do not show much evidence of inflammation. On the other hand, overt clinical signs of thyroid dysfunction are usually lacking in BUF rats (except for the occasional elevation of serum CK levels), while proteinuria is present in BN rats with autoimmune glomerulonephritis. Finally, BUF rats are excellent immune responders to thyroglobulin, but not other autoantigens, which is in contrast to BN rats, who produce excellent responses to GBM, tubular basement membrane, and spermatozoal autoantigens.[25]

Human autoimmune thyroiditis is characterized by humoral and cell-mediated immune responses to thyroid-specific autoantigens (most notably thyroglobulin) and by inflammatory infiltration and tissue damage localized in the thyroid gland.[11,23] As compared to other autoimmune disorders, it has the advantage of having a mild course. Therefore, it is possible to perform long-term idiotype studies on autoantibodies and lymphocytes from patients that are not treated with immunosuppressive drugs.

The results obtained in our studies of human and animal autoimmune disease may be summarized as follows:

(1) In spite of the fact that many autoimmune responses are polyclonal,[19,26] we

have obtained "conventional" anti-idiotypic antibodies against human and animal autoantibodies.

(2) Using these anti-idiotypic antibodies, we have demonstrated the presence of cross-reacting idiotopes on human and animal autoantibodies as well as lymphocytes from animals with autoimmune disease. This finding is in agreement with the observations by other investigators, who have reported the presence of shared idiotypic determinants on rheumatoid factors, autoantibodies to acetylcholine receptors, and autoantibodies to DNA, as well as lymphocytes from patients with rheumatoid arthritis.[27-33]

(3) Thus far, we have failed to detect circulating auto-anti-idiotypic antibodies in any of the three models investigated. This contrasts with the numerous examples of auto-anti-idiotypic antibody formation observed by other investigators in the course of immunization. However, most of those studies utilized extremely intense immunization protocols that resulted in hyperimmune levels of antibody production. Only recently, Rodkey and Adler[34] have shown that "natural" immune responses can elicit immunoregulatory auto-anti-idiotypic antibodies. As far as autoimmune disease is concerned, the evidence is still very sparse. Factors that possibly are auto-anti-idiotypic antibodies have been detected in the sera of SLE patients in remission[35] and in the circulation of F_1 hybrids of NZB mice that produce less antierythrocyte autoantibodies and develop a milder hemolytic anemia than their NZB parents.[36] Perhaps the difficulties in detecting "natural" auto-anti-idiotypic antibodies are mostly technical, as Rodkey and Adler[34] have suggested. However, it is also possible that the idiotype–anti-idiotype network is operative at the cellular rather than the humoral level.

(4) Finally, our preliminary experiments on the induction of anti-idiotypic immunity in animals with autoimmune disease have provided intriguing results. Studies in BUF rats with autoimmune thyroiditis have shown that established autoimmune responses may be inhibited, albeit partially, by passive anti-idiotypic immunity. This observation is in agreement with the reports of the inhibition of interstitial nephritis by passive or active anti-idiotypic immunity. Brown et al.[36] have shown that severe tubulointerstitial nephritis of inbred guinea pigs was inhibited by passive transfer of heterologous anti-idiotypic antibodies at the same time of immunization with tubular basement membrane antigens. Similarly, Neilson and Phillips[37] have demonstrated that interstitial nephritis of BN rats can be suppressed by auto-anti-idiotypic immunity induced by active immunization with antigen-reactive T lymphoblasts prior to experimental autoimmunization with tubular basement membrane antigens. As previously pointed out,[19] the difference between these experiments and our own consists in the use of experimental animals with an already established autoimmune disease, a situation that is closer to that occurring in man. On the other hand, the induction of active anti-idiotypic immunity in BN rats with autoimmune glomerulonephritis has resulted in more vigorous and protracted autoimmune responses, possibly caused by an "internal image" phenomenon or the production of Ab1-like anti-anti-idiotypic antibodies (Ab3), as previously obtained by Couraud et al.[39] using antihormone antibodies.

In conclusion, the anti-idiotypic approach to the treatment of autoimmune disease may be more complex than was originally anticipated.[6] A more precise analysis of the idiotopes involved in the pathogenesis of autoimmune disease seems absolutely necessary at this point. In addition, quantitative and qualitative investigations of idiotypic and anti-idiotypic lymphocytes are required to delineate the cellular interactions occurring in autoimmune disease.

SUMMARY

It has been hypothesized that autoimmune disease may result from a derangement of the idiotype–anti-idiotype network. However, the evidence in favor of a role of anti-idiotypic immunity in autoimmunity is still scarce. For this reason, we have investigated animal models of autoimmune thyroiditis and glomerulonephritis, addressing the following questions: Are autoimmune responses idiotypically heterogeneous? Are auto-anti-idiotypic antibodies detectable in autoimmunity? Is it possible to demonstrate quantitative or qualitative changes in idiotypic and anti-idiotypic lymphocytes during the course of autoimmune disease?

To date, results obtained in our laboratory may be summarized as follows:

(1) Cross-reacting idiotypes were present on human and animal autoantibodies;
(2) Circulating auto-anti-idiotypic antibodies were not detected in any of the models studied;
(3) Changes in idiotypic and anti-idiotypic lymphocytes were observed in animals with autoimmune disease.

ACKNOWLEDGMENTS

The author thanks M. Zanetti, J. P. McCoy, Jr., and J. H. Michaelson for their expert collaboration and Ruth Conrod for excellent secretarial assistance.

REFERENCES

1. CARNEGIE, P. R. & I. R. MACKAY. 1975. Lancet 2: 684–687.
2. MACKAY, I. R. & P. R. CARNEGIE. 1977. *In* Autoimmunity. N. Talal, Ed.: 597–620. Academic Press. New York.
3. CARNEGIE, P. R. & I. R. MACKAY. 1982. Springer Semin. Immunopathol. 5: 379–388.
4. WIGZELL, H. 1977. *In* Autoimmunity. N. Talal, Ed. Academic Press. New York.
5. BINZ, H. & H. WIGZELL. 1978. Fed. Proc. Fed. Am. Soc. Exp. Biol. 37: 2365–2369.
6. WIGZELL, H., H. BINZ, H. FRISCHKNECHT, P. PETERSON & K. SEGE. 1978. *In* Genetic Control of Autoimmune Disease. N. R. Rose, P. E. Bigazzi & N. L. Warner, Eds.: 327–338. Elsevier. Amsterdam.
7. JERNE, N. K. 1974. Ann. Immunol. (Inst. Pasteur) 125C: 373–389.
8. TALAL, N. 1978. Arthritis Rheum. 21: 853–861.
9. GODING, J. W. 1982. Springer Semin. Immunopathol. 5: 463–475.
10. ROITT, I. M., D. K. MALE, G. GUARNOTTA, L. P. DeCARVALHO, A. COOKE, F. C. HAY, P. M. LYDYARD & Y. THANAVALA. 1981. Lancet 1: 1041–1045.
11. BIGAZZI, P. E. 1979. *In* Mechanisms of Immunopathology. S. Cohen, P. A. Ward & R. T. McCluskey, Eds.: 157–180. Wiley. New York.
12. BIGAZZI, P. E. & N. R. ROSE. 1975. Prog. Allergy 19: 245–274.
13. NOBLE, B., T. YOSHIDA, N. R. ROSE & P. E. BIGAZZI. 1976. J. Immunol. 117: 1447–1455.
14. DRUET, P., E. DRUET, P. POTDEVIN & C. SAPIN. 1978. Ann. Immunol. (Inst. Pasteur) 129C: 777–792.
15. MICHAELSON, J. H., J. P. McCOY, JR. & P. E. BIGAZZI. 1981. Kidney Int. 20: 285–288.
16. BIGAZZI, P. E. 1985. *In* Toxicology of the Immune System. J. H. Dean, Ed.: 277–290. Raven Press. New York.

17. BRIDEAU, R. J., P. B. CARTER, W. R. MCMASTER, D. W. MASON & A. F. WILLIAMS. 1980. Eur. J. Immunol. **10:** 609–615.
18. ROSE, N. R., P. E. BIGAZZI, B. NOBLE & D. SILVERMAN. 1982. PAR. Pseudo-Allergic Reactions **3:** 48–61.
19. ZANETTI, M. & P. E. BIGAZZI. 1981. Eur. J. Immunol. **11:** 187–195.
20. ZANETTI, M., R. W. BARTON & P. E. BIGAZZI. 1983. Cell Immunol. **75:** 292–299.
21. MICHAELSON, J. H. & P. E. BIGAZZI. 1982. Fed. Proc. Fed. Am. Soc. Exp. Biol. **41:** 550.
22. MICHAELSON, J. H. & P. E. BIGAZZI. 1983. Fed. Proc. Fed. Am. Soc. Exp. Biol. **42:** 1213.
23. BIGAZZI, P. E. 1983. In Principles and Practice of Surgical Pathology. S. G. Silverberg, Ed.: 57–75. Wiley. New York.
24. MCCOY, J. P., JR., J. H. MICHAELSON & P. E. BIGAZZI. 1983. Life Sci. **32:** 109–118.
25. TAKAMI, T., H. W. KUNZ, T. J. GILL III & P. E. BIGAZZI. 1982. Am. J. Reprod. Immunol. **2:** 5–7.
26. NYE, L., L. P. DECARVALHO & I. M. ROITT. 1981. Clin. Exp. Immunol. **46:** 161–170.
27. DOBLOUG, J. H., O. FORRE, J. B. NATVIG & T. E. MICHAELSEN. 1979. Scand. J. Immunol. **9:** 273–279.
28. FORRE, O., J. H. DOBLOUG, T. E. MICHAELSEN & J. B. NATVIG. 1979. Scand. J. Immunol. **9:** 281–289.
29. LEFVERT, A. K. 1981. Scand. J. Immunol. **13:** 493–497.
30. LENNON, V. A. & E. H. LAMBERT. 1981. Ann. N.Y. Acad. Sci. **377:** 77–98.
31. RAUCH, J., E. MURPHY, J. B. ROTHS, B. D. STOLLAR & R. S. SCHWARTZ. 1982. J. Immunol. **129:** 236–241.
32. SCHWARTZ, M., D. NOVICK, D. GIVOL & S. FUCHS. 1978. Nature **273:** 543–545.
33. SOLOMON, G., J. SCHIFFENBAUER, H. D. KEISER & B. DIAMOND. 1983. Proc. Natl. Acad. Sci. USA **80:** 850–854.
34. RODKEY, L. S. & F. L. ADLER. 1983. J. Exp. Med. **157:** 1920–1931.
35. ABDOU, N. I., H. WALL, H. B. LINDSLEY, J. F. HALSEY & T. SUZUKI. 1981. J. Clin. Invest. **67:** 1297–1304.
36. COHEN, P. L. & R. A. EISENBERG. 1982. J. Exp. Med. **156:** 173–180.
37. BROWN, C. A., K. CAREY & R. B. COLVIN. 1979. J. Immunol. **123:** 2102–2107.
38. NEILSON, E. G. & S. M. PHILLIPS. 1982. J. Exp. Med. **155:** 179–189.
39. COURAUD, P. O., B-Z. LU & A. D. STROSBERG. 1983. J. Exp. Med. **157:** 1369–1378.

DISCUSSION OF THE PAPER

B. BLOMBERG (*University of Miami School of Medicine, Miami, FL*): How do you define your idiotype? Do you have a monoclonal antibody? How do you know you are dealing with one antibody?

P. E. BIGAZZI (*University of Connecticut Health Center, Farmington, CT*): As I mentioned, we have used conventional polyclonal anti-idiotypic antibodies. My personal bias is that a polyclonal anti-idiotype would more closely approximate the polyclonal auto-anti-idiotypic response in the animal than a monoclonal anti-idiotype would.

BLOMBERG: Wait, I am not asking about the anti-idiotype. Instead, I am asking about the idiotype.

BIGAZZI: The idiotype in the human case is polyclonal and actually is a pool of autoantibodies derived from several people. That was done to expose the immunized animal to a large number of epitopes; the same strategy was used for the autoantibodies in the Buffalo rat.

C. A. BONA (*Mount Sinai Medical Center, New York, NY*): Do you know if there are idiotype–specific T cells that expand during this response to anti-idiotype?

BIGAZZI: I do not have data on that point.

Y. NAPARSTEK (*Tufts New England Center, Boston, MA*): Your reagent for the study of idiotypes was a polyclonal antibody that was not affinity-purified, but absorbed on a human Ig column. Was that the case?

BIGAZZI: Yes.

NAPARSTEK: Then you envision a situation in which your reagents also contain anti-anti-idiotypic antibodies?

BIGAZZI: Yes, that is a very good point. I agree. We should try to affinity-purify the way you are suggesting.

G. WICK (*Institute of Innsbruck, Innsbruck, Austria*): In your basement membrane system, what was the antigen?

BIGAZZI: These experiments are done with GBM, which, as you know, is a term that covers a lot of substances. I have found that laminin is one of the components, but I have not done any investigation of any others.

Idiotypes and Anti-Idiotypes in Experimental Autoimmune Myasthenia Gravis[a]

MIRIAM C. SOUROUJON AND SARA FUCHS

Department of Chemical Immunology
The Weizmann Institute of Science
Rehovot 76100, Israel

INTRODUCTION

Acetylcholine receptor (AChR) is the main autoantigen in the autoimmune disease, myasthenia gravis (MG), and its animal model, experimental autoimmune myasthenia gravis (EAMG).[1] Ideally, one would like to specifically eliminate the anti-AChR autoimmune response in MG, while not affecting the host's general immune status. One of the proposed therapeutic approaches for MG is to specifically suppress or turn off the immune response to AChR by the use of specific anti-idiotypic antibodies.

One of the problems of the anti-idiotype approach is posed by the heterogeneity of anti-AChR antibodies in EAMG and in MG.[2] It is therefore necessary to first identify the anti-AChR subpopulations that are involved in the immunopathogenic process in terms of their antigenic specificity and idiotypic specificity. Once these antigenic and idiotypic specificities are known, the appropriate anti-idiotypes can be prepared and employed for the specific immunotherapy of myasthenia.

Some studies on the idiotypic specificity of anti-AChR antibodies and the attempts to regulate EAMG by anti-idiotypes have been reported: By analyzing anti-AChR sera from myasthenic patients, Lefvert[3] has demonstrated a shared idiotype between anti-AChR antibodies from different patients. We have previously analyzed the idiotypes of polyclonal anti-AChR antibodies by using anti-idiotypes raised in mice against syngeneic spleen cells educated *in vitro* with AChR. These studies have demonstrated a broad cross-reactivity between idiotypes of anti-AChR antibodies from different mouse strains, as well as with anti-AChR antibodies from other species.[4] We also showed that anti-idiotypes raised against polyclonal anti-AChR antibodies isolated from a rabbit with EAMG were successful in preventing the initial development of EAMG and possibly in modifying existing EAMG.[5]

A useful way to analyze the idiotypes that comprise the polyclonal anti-AChR response is to study the idiotypic specificities of monoclonal anti-AChR antibodies. By using anti-idiotypes against anti-AChR monoclonal antibodies (mcAbs), Lennon and Lambert[2] have demonstrated a dominant idiotype, common to four anti-AChR mcAbs, in the sera of rats immunized with AChR. However, anti-idiotypes directed against this common idiotype did not protect rats against EAMG.

In the following, we will report on studies from our laboratory employing

[a]This research was supported in part by the Muscular Dystrophy Association of America, the Los Angeles Chapter of the Myasthenia Gravis Foundation, and the United-States–Israel Binational Science Foundation (BSF).

81

monoclonal anti-AChR antibodies and their respective anti-idiotypes for evaluation of their role in the maintenance and regulation of EAMG.

EXPRESSION OF ANTI-AChR ANTIBODY SPECIFICITIES IN EAMG

Previous studies from our laboratory[6] have demonstrated a correlation between the clinical state of AChR-injected rabbits and the antigenic specificity of their antibodies. For those studies, we have employed a denatured AChR preparation (RCM-AChR[6,7]) that by itself did not induce EAMG in rabbits. Nevertheless, RCM-AChR was shown to have an immunosuppressive effect on EAMG, either by preventing the onset of the disease or by reversing the clinical symptoms in myasthenic rabbits.[6]

We chose to employ our library of anti-AChR mcAbs as probes for following the expression of various antibody specificities in the sera of rabbits at different clinical stages of EAMG. This expression was monitored by measuring the ability of mcAbs directed against well-defined determinants on the AChR molecule to inhibit the binding of the polyclonal rabbit antibodies to the receptor.

The assay conditions for this study were as follows: radiolabeled Torpedo AChR was preincubated with a large excess of the tested mcAb, after which a limited amount of rabbit anti-AChR serum was added. Only rabbit antibodies to antigenic determinants on the AChR, different from the antigenic determinant recognized by the mcAb, would be expected to bind. Subsequently, goat anti-rabbit IgG (preadsorbed on a Sepharose-NMIg column) was added to precipitate the rabbit antibodies along with any ^{125}I-AChR to which they were bound. This procedure enabled us to measure the fraction of antibodies in a given rabbit serum that are directed to the region to which a certain mcAb binds.

The results of this study are essentially in agreement with those obtained earlier by using polyclonal anti-AChR antibodies;[6] however, they provide a more detailed analysis due to the employment of mcAbs (TABLE 1). In all cases, the expression of antibody specificities against antigenic determinants that are denaturation-sensitive ("anti-native" or antibodies directed against conformation-dependent antigenic determinants) is elevated when AChR-injected animals develop the disease and is diminished when the disease is reversed by RCM-AChR. The level of antibody specificities directed to denaturation-resistant determinants ("anti-denatured") seems not to change significantly at the different stages of our trial.

TABLE 1 describes the analysis of the antigenic specificity in several bleedings of two representative rabbits: a myasthenic rabbit (no. 1) and a second rabbit (no. 2), which was treated with RCM-AChR when EAMG was observed. The immunization course, bleedings, and development of EAMG are described schematically at the bottom of this table. As can be seen in TABLE 1, after one injection with AChR, rabbit no. 1 produced antibodies to both conformation-dependent antigenic determinants ("native" or denaturation-sensitive) and to nonconformation-dependent determinants ("denatured" or denaturation-resistant) of AChR. However, at the onset of disease, the fraction of anti-AChR antibody specificities raised against "native" determinants was increased, while the expression of almost all "anti-denatured" antibodies was either decreased or unchanged (TABLE 1). Similarly, in rabbits protected from EAMG by preimmunization with RCM-AChR, there was a lower expression of "anti-native" antibody specificities than in rabbits that received a similar preimmunization, but were not protected (data not shown). On the other hand, reversal of clinical signs of EAMG by RCM-AChR was accompanied by a decrease in the expression of "anti-native" specificities (TABLE 1, rabbit no. 2). However, in this rabbit (no. 2), there seemed to be

TABLE 1. Expression of Anti-AChR Antibody Specificities in EAMG

		Expression of Antibody Specificity (% inhibition)[a]				
		Myasthenic Rabbit (no. 1)[b]		Treated Rabbit (no. 2)		
mcAb	Specificity[c]	Before EAMG(A)[d]	During EAMG(B)	Before EAMG(A)	During EAMG(B)	After Reversal of EAMG(C)
5.5	"anti-native"	0	1	8	0	0
5.34	"anti-native"	19	27	17	23	14
5.39	"anti-native"	9	23	9	17	9
5.46	"anti-native"	29	44	20	36	23
1.24	"anti-native"	14	28	9	21	9
5.14	"anti-denatured"	22	19	10	4	7
1.22	"anti-denatured"	18	10	4	5	6
1.34	"anti-denatured"	24	11	7	0	5
1.39	"anti-denatured"	10	12	`0	0	2
1.17	"anti-denatured"	6	20	3	5	5

[a]Radiolabeled Torpedo AChR (50 μl) was preincubated overnight with a large excess of the tested mcAb (50 μl) before the addition of 100 μl of rabbit anti-AChR serum at a dilution that binds 20% of total ^{125}I-AChR. After a 30-min incubation at 30°, goat anti-rabbit was added to precipitate the rabbit antibodies. After an overnight incubation, the precipitate was washed and counted in a γ counter. Percent inhibition was calculated according to:

$$\left(1 - \frac{\text{cpm in the presence of the tested mcAb}}{\text{cpm in the presence of a control nonrelated mcAb}}\right) \times 100.$$

[b]The immunization course, bleeding, and development of EAMG are as follows:

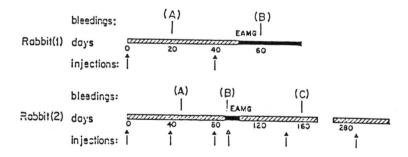

Open arrows, injection with RCM-AChR; solid arrows, AChR (from Bartfeld and Fuchs, 1978).

[c]"Anti-native" defines an mcAb that is directed against an antigenic determinant that is present only in native, intact, or proteolyzed AChR (a denaturation-sensitive antigenic determinant). "Anti-denatured" defines an mcAb that is directed against an antigenic determinant that does not change following denaturation (a denaturation-resistant or sequential antigenic determinant).

[d]Bleeding.

no dramatic change in the expression of "anti-denatured" specificities during the course of disease and remission.

It should be noted that only a minor fraction of the anti-AChR response is directed to the cholinergic site, which is demonstrated by the poor inhibition exerted by mcAb 5.5. Hence, the expression of the antisite mcAb (5.5), which represents an antibody specificity that may be very important in the immunopathogenesis of myasthenia, could not be followed by this method.

SPECIFICITY ANALYSIS OF RABBIT AND MOUSE ANTI-IDIOTYPES

In this study, we attempted to test the feasibility of the anti-idiotype approach for the specific regulation of myasthenia. For that, anti-idiotypes were prepared in rabbits and mice by repeated immunizations with monoclonal and polyclonal anti-AChR antibodies.[8,9] The anti-Torpedo AChR mcAbs to which the anti-idiotypes were prepared (mcAbs 5.5, 5.14, and 5.34) represent three distinct antigenic specificities that might play a role in the pathogenesis of EAMG. All three mcAbs cross-react with muscle AChR and two of them (mcAb 5.5 and 5.34) were shown to affect muscle AChR turnover. The mcAb 5.5 is directed to the cholinergic binding site and acts as an antagonist of Torpedo and muscle AChR. A detailed description of the mcAbs is given elsewhere.[10,11]

Anti-Idiotypes in Rabbits

Rabbits developed anti-idiotypic antibodies to the monoclonal idiotypes after two immunizations with the idiotype (100 μg of immunoglobulins precipitated from the respective ascitic fluid). All sera were exhaustively adsorbed on a Sepharose-normal mouse immunoglobulin (NMIg) column until no significant binding to NMIg was observed. The binding of the various anti-idiotypes prepared against the monoclonal idiotypes was shown to be restricted to each immunizing idiotype (FIGURE 1). There

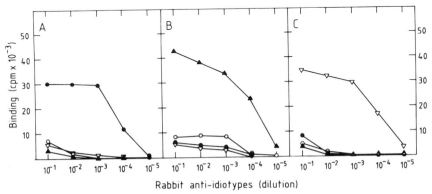

FIGURE 1. Binding specificity of rabbit anti-idiotypes to anti-AChR mcAbs. Binding of (A) rabbit anti-mcAb 5.5, (B) rabbit anti-mcAb 5.14, and (C) rabbit anti-mcAb 5.34 to mcAb 5.5 (●——●), mcAb 5.14 (▲——▲), mcAb 5.34 (▽——▽), and anti-(T, G)-A—L mcAb as control (○——○).

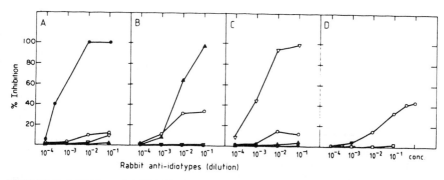

FIGURE 2. Inhibition of AChR binding to different mouse idiotypes by the following anti-idiotypes: (A) rabbit anti-mcAb 5.5; (B) rabbit anti-mcAb 5.14; (C) rabbit anti-mcAb 5.34; (D) rabbit anti-polyclonal mouse anti-AChR antibodies. Inhibition of AChR binding to: mcAb 5.5 (●—●); mcAb 5.14 (▲—▲); mcAb 5.34 (▽—▽); polyclonal mouse anti-AChR antibodies (O---O); and polyclonal mouse anti-BSA antibodies (□—□).

was no significant binding to other anti-AChR idiotypes or to nonrelated mcAbs. Similar results were obtained when binding was measured in a solid-phase radioimmunoassay (SPhRIA) where the $(Fab')_2$ fragments of the different mcAbs were used for coating the plates.

In order to find out whether the idiotypes recognized by the anti-idiotypic antibodies are associated with the binding site of the idiotypes, we have tested their ability to inhibit the binding of AChR to the idiotypes (FIGURE 2). These experiments also demonstrate restricted specificity of the anti-idiotypes. Each of the three anti-idiotypes, as well as the monomeric Fab' fragments derived from them, completely inhibited AChR binding to the homologous idiotype, whereas no significant inhibition to other anti-AChR mcAbs was observed.

Each of the anti-idiotypes was tested also for their ability to inhibit the binding of AChR to polyclonal mouse anti-AChR serum. It was found that anti-idiotypes raised against mcAbs 5.5, 5.14, and 5.34 inhibit this binding to the extent of 12%, 32%, and 14%, respectively (FIGURE 2). Since these values were deduced from the inhibition exerted by a high excess of each of the anti-idiotypes (and are plateau values), they represent the expression of the idiotypes borne by the different mcAbs in the polyclonal anti-AChR response.

We also produced in rabbits anti-idiotypes against affinity-purified polyclonal anti-AChR antibodies from C57BL/6 mice. In order to minimize the production of rabbit antibodies to NMIg, we induced tolerance towards this antigen by injecting the rabbits with a high amount of NMIg prior to the immunization with the polyclonal idiotypes. The rabbit anti-idiotypes elicited against polyclonal mouse anti-AChR antibodies inhibited the binding of AChR to C57BL/6 anti-AChR serum up to 42%, while no inhibition of an irrelevant antigen-antibody reaction by these anti-idiotypes was observed at all (FIGURE 2D). The binding of AChR to anti-AChR antibodies from other strains of mice bearing different Ig-1 alleles was inhibited to the same extent as well (TABLE 2). Thus, although each of the anti-idiotypes reacted exclusively with the homologous idiotype, there exists an interstrain and also an interspecies cross-reactivity of idiotypes, as reported earlier by us.[4] Such a cross-reactivity probably reflects the expression of parallel idiotypes for similar antibody specificities in different mouse strains and various species.

TABLE 2. Idiotypic Cross-Reactivity of Anti-AChR Antibodies in Different Mouse Strains

Anti-AChR Serum[a] (mouse strain)	H-2 Haplotype	Ig-1 Allotype	Inhibition[b] (%)
C57BL/6	b	b	33
AKR/J	k	d	24
DBA/2	d	c	20
A/J	a	e	30
BALB/c	d	a	36

[a]The amount of anti-AChR serum used in each case was that which binds 20% of the ^{125}I-AChR added.

[b]Inhibition achieved in the presence of a 1/10 dilution of the anti-idiotypic serum raised in rabbits against C57BL/6 anti-AChR purified antibodies. The percentage of inhibition was calculated according to:

$$\left(1 - \frac{\text{cpm in the presence of anti-idiotype}}{\text{cpm in the presence of normal rabbit serum}}\right) \times 100.$$

Anti-Idiotypes in Mice

Anti-idiotypic antibodies were elicited in AKR/J mice. Four immunizations were required before anti-idiotypes could be detected in the sera of the injected allogeneic mice. Mouse anti-idiotypes produced against purified polyclonal C57BL/6 anti-AChR antibodies inhibited AChR binding to the preparation of polyclonal anti-AChR antibodies used for immunization by 16% (data not shown). These anti-idiotypes did not inhibit the binding of a nonrelated antigen to its specific antibodies prepared in C57BL/6 mice. As can be seen in FIGURE 3, each anti-idiotypic serum produced against the mcAbs inhibited the binding of AChR to the immunizing idiotype, as was similarly demonstrated for rabbit anti-idiotypes (FIGURE 2). This specificity was also confirmed by the binding in SPhRIA of the anti-idiotypes to the (Fab')$_2$ fragment of the immunizing idiotype.

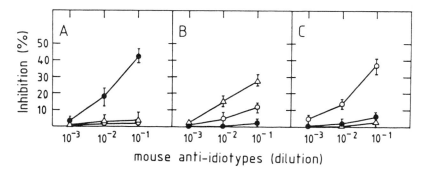

mouse anti-idiotypes (dilution)

FIGURE 3. Inhibition of ^{125}I-AChR binding to monoclonal anti-AChR antibodies by mouse anti-idiotypes. Inhibition by: (A) mouse anti-mcAb 5.5; (B) mouse anti-mcAb 5.14; (C) mouse anti-mcAb 5.34. Antibody inhibited: mcAb 5.5 (●—●); mcAb 5.14 (△—△); mcAb 5.34 (○—○). Anti-idiotypic sera were drawn from individual mice 12 weeks following the first immunization with the respective idiotype. The amount of mcAb used was that which binds 20% of the ^{125}I-AChR added. Vertical bars represent SE.

TABLE 3. Effect of Preimmunization of Mice with Anti-AChR mcAbs on Idiotypic Expression[a]

| Preimmunization with | Idiotype Expression (%)[b] | | |
	5.5 idiotype	5.14 idiotype	5.34 idiotype
NMIg	12.0 ± 0.8	32.4 ± 1.5	14.0 ± 2.0
5.5	8.1 ± 0.4[d]	23.4 ± 2.1[d]	27.1 ± 2.1[c]
5.14	13.4 ± 0.2	9.3 ± 0.4[c]	8.5 ± 1.9[d]
5.34	14.3 ± 0.3	17.1 ± 0.9[d]	1.4 ± 0.9[c]

[a]For this experiment, rabbit anti-idiotypes elicited against mcAbs 5.5, 5.14, and 5.34 were used as inhibitors of AChR binding to mouse anti-AChR sera of the different groups.

[b]The numbers represent the % inhibition of AChR binding to mouse anti-AChR antibodies by a high excess of each of the respective rabbit anti-idiotypes. The % inhibition was calculated as follows:

$$\left(1 - \frac{\text{cpm in the presence of anti-idiotype}}{\text{cpm in the presence of normal rabbit serum}}\right) \times 100.$$

The results are the mean value of ten mice ± SD.
[c]Significantly different from the control group: $p < 0.001$.
[d]Significantly different from the control group: $p < 0.05$.

MODULATION OF THE ANTI-AChR RESPONSE IN MICE BY PREIMMUNIZATION WITH IDIOTYPES

Currently, the treatment of MG and other autoimmune diseases is limited to broad-spectrum immunosuppressive measures that interfere with the patient's ability to mount immune responses against unrelated antigens. Ideally, one would like to specifically eliminate the anti-AChR autoimmune response in MG, while not affecting the host's general immune status. Because the AChR has been purified and well characterized, EAMG serves as an ideal system to assess autoantigen-specific means of immunotherapy.

Our aim was to study the effect of autologous anti-idiotypes on the anti-AChR response. To do this, groups of mice producing anti-idiotypes against mcAbs (5.5, 5.14,

TABLE 4. Anti-AChR Titer in Mice Preimmunized with Idiotypes

| Idiotype Injected | Anti-Torpedo AChR | | Anti-Muscle AChR | |
	Antibody Titer × 10^{-7}[a]	Suppression of Titer (%)	Antibody Titer × 10^{-9}	Suppression of Titer (%)
Normal mouse Ig	100.0 ± 18.0	0	8.6 ± 0.4	0
Mouse anti-AChR antibodies	1.8 ± 0.5[b]	98	0.2 ± 0.1[b]	99
mcAb 5.5 Ig	30.0 ± 4.8[c]	70	2.3 ± 0.2[c]	74
mcAb 5.14 Ig	40.0 ± 6.1[c]	60	2.0 ± 0.4[c]	77
mcAb 5.34 Ig	4.6 ± 0.6[b]	95	0.5 ± 0.2[b]	94

[a]Titer is given in moles AChR precipitated by 1 liter serum. The results are the mean values of ten mice ± SD. Statistical analysis of the difference in antibody activity between control and idiotype injected groups was performed by Student's t test.
[b]Significantly lower than the control group: $p < 0.001$.
[c]Significantly lower than the control group: $p < 0.05$.

and 5.34) and polyclonal mouse anti-AChR antibodies, as well as an NMIg injected group, were challenged with 10 μg of Torpedo AChR twelve weeks after the first immunization with the idiotypes. At the time of challenge with Torpedo AChR (40 days after the last immunization with idiotype), all mice had comparable anti-idiotypic titers (FIGURE 3) and they showed no detectable anti-AChR activity. The mice were bled individually 32 days after the challenge and the expression of the different idiotypes and total anti-AChR titers were evaluated (TABLES 3 and 4).

It was of interest to test first whether preimmunization of mice with a certain idiotype leads to a preferential suppression of this particular idiotype. In order to follow the expression of the different idiotypes in the anti-AChR response, we employed the rabbit anti-idiotypic antibodies described above. The idiotypic expression was deduced from the inhibition of AChR binding to the tested mouse anti-AChR sera by a large excess of rabbit anti-idiotypes specific for the idiotypes borne by mcAbs 5.5, 5.14, and 5.34. It was found that preimmunization with a certain idiotype led to a significant suppression of the immunizing idiotype as compared with the expression of that particular idiotype in control mice (TABLE 3). In some cases, other idiotypes also seemed to be affected to some extent (TABLE 3). Thus, preimmunization with mcAbs 5.14 and 5.34 mutually suppressed the idiotypes of each other to a certain extent. The idiotype borne by mcAb 5.14 was partially suppressed by preimmunization with all three idiotypes tested. Mice preimmunized with mcAb 5.5 had elevated levels of the 5.34 idiotype. A possible explanation for this latter result may be that the suppression of some idiotypes is compensated by the elevation of other idiotypes in the polyclonal response to AChR. It should be noted that in the sera of mice preimmunized with NMIg (control group), the representation of each of the idiotypes was similar to that found in the pooled sera of nonimmunized mice (FIGURE 2).

We then tested the effect of preimmunization with distinct idiotypes on the overall humoral response to AChR. To do this, the individual sera of mice preimmunized with the different idiotypes and later challenged with AChR were scored for titer towards Torpedo AChR. The mean titers are given in TABLE 4. As can be seen, preimmunization of mice with polyclonal anti-AChR antibodies resulted in essentially an abolishment (98% reduction) of the anti-AChR humoral response as compared to mice preimmunized with NMIgs. Interestingly, pretreatment with either mcAbs 5.5, 5.14, or 5.34 resulted in a higher reduction of the anti-AChR titer than would be expected from the representation of each of the respective idiotypes in mouse anti-AChR sera (TABLE 3, FIGURE 2). Thus, a decrease of 95%, 70%, and 60% in the anti-AChR titer was obtained following immunization with mcAb 5.34, 5.5, and 5.14, respectively (see TABLE 4). It therefore seems that a narrower idiotypic specificity is observed in experiments performed in vitro than in the in vivo regulation of the anti-AChR response. For example, the idiotype of mcAb 5.34 is expressed in about 14% of the anti-AChR antibodies (TABLE 3), but leads to a 95% decrease in the total anti-AChR response (TABLE 4).

It is of course important to find out whether "vaccination" with idiotypes can protect mice from experimental myasthenia induced by active immunization with AChR. Since clinical signs of EAMG are rather inconsistent in mice, we measured the anti-"self" AChR titer as a parameter of an autoimmune response. It was found that the antibody titers towards AChR from mouse muscle were also decreased and that there was a good correlation between the reduction of anti-Torpedo and anti-"self" AChR titers (TABLE 4).

It appears that not all anti-idiotypes have a similar regulating capacity and that there is no correlation between the representation of a certain idiotype and the suppressive effect of its respective anti-idiotypes. For instance, preimmunization with mcAb 5.34 was more effective in reducing the anti-AChR titer than was preimmunization with mcAb 5.14, although mcAb 5.14 is more widely represented in the polyclonal anti-AChR serum. In this line, Lennon and Lambert[2] have reported that preimmunization of rats with a common anti-AChR idiotype did not affect the overall titer towards AChR.

Two possible mechanisms for the suppressive effect by anti-idiotypes could be clonal deletion of B cells and T-cell regulation. We have demonstrated here that preimmunization with idiotypes affects not only the expression of the immunizing idiotype, but suppresses the overall anti-AChR response. We, therefore, favor the explanation of the regulation via T cells because T-cell receptor idiotypes are known to be less heterogenous than B-cell receptor idiotypes.[12-16] The manipulation by anti-idiotypes on the level of T cells could thus affect the overall response to the antigen and not just the expression of the specific idiotype. Simple neutralization of idiotype by anti-idiotypic antibody is probably inadequate to explain the mechanism of suppression. It appears that the small amount of anti-idiotype present in the sera of the mice is greatly exceeded by the amount of idiotype produced by the immunized control animals.

Our results provide evidence that the humoral response to AChR can be manipulated by the anti-idiotypic approach, in spite of the complexity and heterogeneity of this immune response. Moreover, the use of the appropriate anti-idiotypes may have a potential in the regulation of the autoimmune response directed against the receptor in myasthenia.

PASSIVE TRANSFER OF EAMG AND ITS REVERSAL BY ANTI-IDIOTYPES

An important requirement for the application of a treatment modality in an experimental model to the human disease is that it be successful in treating the ongoing disease process. Except for our previous observation that anti-idiotypic antibodies are successful in suppressing EAMG in rabbits induced by immunization with AChR,[5] there has been no antigen-specific treatment modality shown to be effective in suppressing ongoing clinical weakness in EAMG.

The possible treatment of MG by anti-idiotypes would probably require the passive transfer of heterologous anti-idiotypes to myasthenic patients. We therefore attempted to test the feasibility of passively transferred rabbit anti-idiotypes to prevent and reverse myasthenic symptoms in an experimental model. For such experiments, we wanted to have a visible, easily diagnosed EAMG. Since EAMG in mice is rather inconsistent and sometimes transient, we chose to examine the regulatory effect of anti-idiotypes on EAMG in chickens, in which the disease has been induced by transfer of mcAb.

For the transfer of monoclonal anti-AChR antibodies into chickens, we have employed conditions similar to those reported by Gomez and Richman.[17] Passive transfer into chicken hatchings of mcAbs 5.5, 5.14, and 5.34, as well as polyclonal mouse anti-AChR antibodies, was performed by an i.p. injection of 20–100 mg of immunoglobulin per kg body weight. Although all three mcAbs bind to chick muscle AChR,[11] only mcAb 5.5, which is directed to the cholinergic binding site, affected neuromuscular transmission to a clinically detectable degree under our experimental conditions. When injected into chicken hatchings, it produced acute paralysis (FIGURE 4). Weakness appeared 8–10 hours after i.p. administration of mcAb 5.5 (FIGURE 4b). Chickens that were injected with a high dose of mcAb 5.5 (100 mg Igs per kg body weight) died within 20 hours. Lower doses of mcAb 5.5 (20–50 mg Igs/kg) resulted in severe breathing problems and complete paralysis. Occasionally, spontaneous recovery was observed in the low-dose-transferred chickens, starting 96 hours after mcAb 5.5 transfer. It should be noted that no spontaneous recovery was noticed in α-

bungarotoxin (α-Bgt) injected chickens. Animals injected with 0.16 mg α-Bgt per kg body weight (or higher) died within 5 hours. Lower doses of α-Bgt had no effect at all.

Similar to our results, Gomez and Richman[17] have reported earlier on the induction of an acute form of EAMG in chickens by other site-directed anti-AChR mcAbs. As reported by them,[17] we also did not succeed in inducing a neuromuscular block in rats and mice by passive transfer of our anticholinergic-site mcAb (5.5), although this mcAb was shown to cross-react with AChR from rat, mouse, and chicken muscle.[10] We have no conclusive explanation for the inability of the anticholinergic-site mcAb (5.5) to transfer a neuromuscular block to mice and rats. It is possible that the architecture of the neuromuscular junction of mice and rats is different from that of chickens, thus resulting in a different binding of antibody to AChRs *in vivo*.

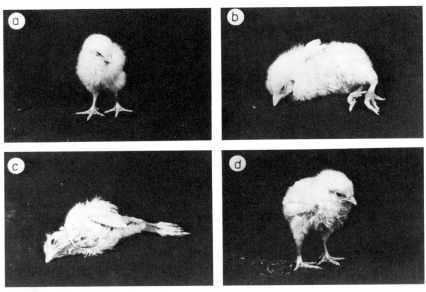

FIGURE 4. Induction of a neuromuscular block by transfer of mcAb 5.5 and its reversal by anti-idiotypes. One mg of mcAb 5.5 immunoglobulin was transferred to chickens b, c, and d. (a) Control chicken, (b) 24 hours after transfer of mcAb 5.5, (c) 48 hours after transfer of mcAb 5.5, and (d) 48 hours after transfer of mcAb 5.5 and treatment twice with anti-5.5 anti-idiotypic antibodies 12 and 18 hours after transfer of mcAb 5.5.

The observation that an antisite mcAb is capable of inducing an acute neuromuscular disease resembling myasthenia provides strong evidence that the mechanism of immunopharmacological blockade of AChR plays a significant role in the pathogenesis of myasthenia. It should be noted that EAMG has been successfully transferred into mice, rats, and guinea pigs by *rat* mcAbs that are not directed to the receptor binding site.[18,19] We did not succeed in inducing clinical symptoms of EAMG in mice and rats by the transfer of any of our *mouse* anti-AChR mcAbs. However, in a sensitive electromyography (EMG) measurement, it was possible to demonstrate a decremental EMG response in mice passively transferred with mcAb 5.34.[20]

In an attempt to regulate EAMG, anti-idiotypes against mcAbs 5.5, 5.14, and 5.34

TABLE 5. Effect of Pretreatment with Anti-Idiotypes on a Passively Transferred Neuromuscular Block in Chickens

Pretreatment[a]	Neuromuscular Block after mcAb 5.5 Transfer (% incidence)[b]
—	100 (6/6)[c]
anti-mcAb 5.5	0 (0/4)
anti-NMIg	75 (3/4)
anti-mcAb 5.14	100 (3/3)
anti-mcAb 5.34	100 (4/4)

[a]Chickens received two 1-ml injections of anti-idiotypes 12 and 6 hours before transfer of 1 mg mcAb 5.5 immunoglobulins.
[b]Paralysis of chickens was monitored 20 hours after transfer of mcAb 5.5.
[c]The numbers in parentheses represent the number of animals.

(and for control, rabbit anti-NMIg) were injected i.p. into chickens 12 and 6 hours before the administration of mcAb 5.5.[9,21] As demonstrated in TABLE 5, anti-idiotypes elicited against mcAb 5.5 protected the chickens against the paralyzing effect induced by transfer of mcAb 5.5. The other anti-idiotypes and rabbit anti-NMIg had no protecting ability.

In order to test whether passively transferred anti-idiotypes can affect an already existing neuromuscular block, we tried to reverse the neuromuscular block induced in chickens by various anti-idiotypic antibodies. Two injections, at 6-hour intervals, of anti-idiotypic antibody against mcAb 5.5 were given 12 and 18 hours after transfer of mcAb 5.5. This treatment resulted in a recovery from the neuromuscular block that started as early as 48 hours after idiotype (mcAb 5.5) transfer (TABLE 6, FIGURE 4d). A similar therapeutic effect by the specific anti-idiotypes against mcAb 5.5 was also observed when the treatment with anti-idiotypes was started earlier (6 hours after transfer) or later (18 hours after transfer). In untreated and control chickens treated with rabbit anti-NMIg, as well as in chickens treated with anti-idiotypes against mcAbs 5.14 or 5.34, or anti-idiotypes against polyclonal anti-AChR antibodies, there was no recovery 48 hours after the transfer or earlier. Occasional spontaneous recovery was sometimes observed later (TABLE 6).[9,21]

In conclusion, anti-idiotypes against mcAb 5.5 could prevent the onset and reverse the neuromuscular block induced by mcAb 5.5. The mechanism of the *in vivo* action of the anti-idiotypes is not known. It seems that it is not the mere antigen-antibody complexes formed between idiotypes and anti-idiotypes because hyperimmune rabbit anti-NMIg, which also binds to mcAb 5.5, did not have the same effect as specific

TABLE 6. Recovery from an Induced Neuromuscular Block by Specific Anti-Idiotypes

Treatment[a]	Percent Recovery Hours after Transfer of mcAb 5.5[b]		
	48	60	72
Rabbit anti-5.5 (anti-idiotypes)	25 (3/12)[c]	50 (6/12)	80 (10/12)
Rabbit anti-NMIg (control)	0 (0/6)	16 (1/6)	50 (3/6)
Untreated	0 (0/6)	0 (0/6)	16 (1/6)

[a]Two injections of the respective anti-idiotypes were given i.p. 12 and 18 hours after transfer of mcAb 5.5.
[b]All chickens were given 1 mg of the immunoglobulin fraction of mcAb 5.5 (i.p.).
[c]The numbers in parentheses represent the number of animals.

anti-idiotypes. Since anti-idiotypes and AChR compete for the same binding site in mcAb 5.5, it is possible that the anti-idiotypes bind to 5.5 molecules that are in circulation, resulting in an equilibrium shift and a dissociation of antibody from the AChR in the synapse.

It was reported that sera of myasthenic patients contain auto-anti-idiotypes,[22] thus suggesting that anti-idiotypes may have a regulatory role in MG. In this study, we demonstrate that passive transfer of anti-idiotypes of the right specificity can reverse the pathogenic effect of anti-AChR antibodies and that the application of anti-idiotypes in the treatment of myasthenia may be feasible. However, as the anti-AChR response in myasthenia is heterogeneous, the question still remains as to which idiotype(s) should be used for elicitation of the appropriate anti-idiotypes, which might in turn be used for clinical application. It has been suggested that the anti-AChR response in human myasthenia is oligoclonal[23] and idiotype-restricted.[3] It is also possible that only a limited number of these idiotypes are pathogenic. Therefore, the application of a general anti-idiotypic reagent for specific immunotherapy of myasthenia may be feasible. In any event, the demonstration that appropriate anti-idiotypic antibodies can "cure" animals with EAMG is an important step towards the treatment of human myasthenics with anti-idiotypic antibodies.

ACKNOWLEDGMENTS

We wish to thank Dora Barchan and Irit Weiss for excellent technical assistance.

REFERENCES

1. FUCHS, S. 1979. Curr. Top. Microbiol. Immunol. **85**: 1–29.
2. LENNON, V. A. & E. H. LAMBERT. 1981. Ann. N.Y. Acad. Sci. **377**: 77–96.
3. LEFVERT, A. K. 1981. Scand. J. Immunol. **13**: 493–497.
4. SCHWARTZ, M., D. NOVICK, D. GIVOL & S. FUCHS. 1979. Nature **273**: 543–545.
5. FUCHS, S., D. BARTFELD, D. MOCHLY-ROSEN, M. SOUROUJON & C. FEINGOLD. 1981. Ann. N.Y. Acad. Sci. **377**: 110–124.
6. BARTFELD, D. & S. FUCHS. 1978. Proc. Natl. Acad. Sci. USA **75**: 4006–4010.
7. BARTFELD, D. & S. FUCHS. 1977. FEBS Lett. **77**: 214–218.
8. SOUROUJON, M. C., D. BARCHAN & S. FUCHS. 1985. Immunol. Lett. **9**: 331–336.
9. FUCHS, S., M. SOUROUJON & S. BOGEN. 1985. *In* Molecular Basis of Nerve Activity. Proceedings of the International Symposium in Memory of David Nachmanson. J-P. Changeux, F. Hucho, A. Maelicke & E. Neumann, Eds.: 493–504. de Gruyter. Berlin.
10. MOCHLY-ROSEN, D. & S. FUCHS. 1981. Biochemistry **20**: 5920–5924.
11. SOUROUJON, M. C., D. MOCHLY-ROSEN, A. S. GORDON & S. FUCHS. 1983. Muscle and Nerve **6**: 303–311.
12. NISSONOF, A., S. T. JU & F. L. OWEN. 1977. Immunol. Rev. **34**: 89–118.
13. EICHMAN, K. 1978. Adv. Immunol. **26**: 195–254.
14. BINZ, H. & H. WIGZELL. 1977. Contemp. Top. Immunobiol. **7**: 113–121.
15. KRAWINKEL, U., M. CRAMER, I. MELCHERS, T. IMANISHI-KARI & K. J. RAJEWSKY. 1978. J. Exp. Med. **147**: 1341–1347.
16. MOZES, E. & J. HAIMOVICH. 1979. Nature (London) **276**: 56–57.
17. GOMEZ, C. M. & D. P. RICHMAN. 1983. Proc. Natl. Acad. Sci. USA **80**: 4089–4093.
18. LENNON, V. A. & E. H. LAMBERT. 1980. Nature (London) **285**: 238–240.
19. RICHMAN, D. P., C. M. GOMEZ, P. W. BERMAN, S. A. BURRES, F. W. FITCH & B. G. W. ARNASON. 1980. Nature (London) **286**: 738–739.
20. PACHNER, A. R., F. KANTOR & S. FUCHS. 1981. Ann. Neurol. **10**: 83.
21. SOUROUJON, M. C., A. R. PACHNER & S. FUCHS. 1986. Neurology. In press.

22. DWYER, D. S., R. J. BRADLEY, C. KENRICH-URQUHAR & J. F. KEARNY. 1983. Nature **301**: 611–614.
23. TZARTOS, S. J., M. E. SEYBOLD & J. M. LINDSTROM. 1982. Proc. Natl. Acad. Sci. USA **79**: 188–192.

DISCUSSION OF THE PAPER

UNIDENTIFIED DISCUSSANT: You reminded us that the acetylcholine receptor with its molecular weight of 250,000 is something that is hard to consider as an antigen. If it is an antigen, it has a lot of determinants. Do you feel there are determinants on multideterminant antigens that we can call autoepitopes? Could a structure on the alpha chain of the receptor be the autoepitope for myasthenia gravis?

S. FUCHS (*Weizmann Institute of Science, Rehovot, Israel*): That is what I am after. The fact that the receptor has a molecular weight of 250 kd means that the number of potential antigenic determinants is huge. However, we know from analysis of antigenic determinants of other proteins that they do not express many of their potential epitopes. The idea is that the binding site of the receptor may be an important antigenic determinant; however, this has been questioned by various people working in myasthenia. Nevertheless, I do believe in the importance of the binding site of the receptor and I would like to produce antibodies against this site.

I. MACKAY (*Hall Institute for Medical Research, Melbourne, Australia*): Yes, that idea was a little heterodox, but it has always appealed to me that the site should actually bind to the autoantibody.

FUCHS: I have a feeling that this idea is coming back a little bit.

C. G. FATHMAN (*Stanford University School of Medicine, Stanford, CA*): I have been working with synthetic peptides also and have found that generally the denatured antigens elicit T-cell responsiveness. However, they do not generate antibodies that recognize the native configuration, as you showed with your RCM model. Therefore, do you think the synthetic peptides really would have efficacy, say, as vaccines, if you knew someone that was genetically susceptible to development of myasthenia? One of them, in theory, should be myasthenigenic, but others may not be.

FUCHS: Actually, I am not so sure that I understood all your statements, but I'll say what I have in mind concerning what I did understand. The idea of the synthetic peptide actually came from our earlier experiments, in which we succeeded in reversing clinical signs in rabbits by treatment with denatured receptor. Therefore, maybe antibodies to synthetic peptides that recognize sequential determinants are not so bad. Interestingly, however, some of our antibodies against synthetic peptides do react with the native receptor.

UNIDENTIFIED DISCUSSANT: Have you used any of those peptides to try and induce tolerance in myasthenia? If you have peptides that generate antibodies that see the native molecule, would they serve as vaccines to block the induction of myasthenia?

FUCHS: That is one of the main directions of our work, but I have no results to present now.

J. F. BACH (*Hospital Necker, Paris, France*): Have you had the opportunity to look for the presence of anti-idiotypic antibodies in serum of myasthenic patients, particularly those improving after some time, by looking at the possible anti-idiotypic activity against antibodies collected at the acute phase of the disease?

FUCHS: We did not do this. However, I want to mention a study by Dan Drachman, who is here in the audience, who has reported a correlation between blocking antibodies and severity of the disease.

D. DRACHMAN (*John Hopkins School of Medicine, Baltimore, MD*): Yes, about 90% of the patients were found to have blocking antibody.

T and B Cell Connections in Experimentally Induced Autoimmunity

D. K. MALE, G. PRYCE, A. COOKE, P. HUTCHINGS,
S. MARSHALL-CLARKE, AND I. M. ROITT

Department of Immunology
Middlesex Hospital Medical School
London W1P 9PG, England

In addition to the well-established effects of T-helper and T-suppressor cells on B cells, there is increasing recognition that B cells and their products can influence the expression of the T-cell repertoire. For example, B-cell derived mice produced by neonatal administration of anti-μ show normal antigen-specific T-cell help in the spleen, but diminished antigen-specific T-cell proliferation in the lymph nodes. This is apparently so because B cells play a role in antigen presentation in the lymph node, but not in the spleen.[1,2] Further, anti-idiotypic T cells that help Id-bearing B cells are not demonstrable in such μ-suppressed animals.[3,4] Similarly, anti-T15 Id T-helpers do not appear to be demonstrable in mice that are not expressing the T15 idiotype.[5,6]

B cells or their products may also drive T-cell regulatory circuits[7–9] and it is noteworthy that μ-suppressed mice are resistant to leishmania infection because they do not develop suppressor cells.[10]

In the present study, we describe such mutual T-B interactions in two experimentally induced autoimmune responses involving thyroid and erythrocyte.

RECURRENT IDIOTYPES (IDs) ON MURINE THYROGLOBULIN AUTOANTIBODIES

We have used monoclonal mouse thyroglobulin (Tg) autoantibodies to raise anti-Ids in rabbits. These are designated P4, P11, D8, G4, and G12, of which the first three are IgG1, while G4 is IgG2a and G12 is IgM. The occurrence of these idiotypes in experimental autoallergic thyroiditis (EAT) and normal sera was measured by a solid-phase radioimmunoassay, in which Id in the test sera inhibited the binding of purified Id to anti-Id. Each of the idiotypes was associated with autoanti-Tg in that the levels in EAT sera were significantly greater than in normal sera. The amounts present in EAT sera ranged from 0–20 μg/ml (FIGURE 1), whereas the various Ids were only detected in occasional normal sera, with the amounts being less than 5 μg/ml. Since the total amount of anti-Tg in EAT sera ranges upwards from 100 μg/ml, this means that the Ids investigated are recurrent in EAT sera, but they cannot be considered dominant.

The presence of the Ids on other monoclonal anti-Tg antibodies was estimated similarly by inhibition of Id/anti-Id binding. In this case, it was noted that D8 inhibited binding of G12 to its anti-Id and vice versa, but not as effectively as the homologous Id blocking. Because the anti-Ids used are polyvalent, this result can be interpreted as saying that D8 and G12 share an idiotope, but are not idiotypically completely identical. G12 also appeared to share idiotopes with four other autoanti-Tg antibodies, but since G12 lost its Id activity on labeling, further investigations on this antibody were curtailed. D8, G4, P4, and P11 were used in subsequent investigations.

It was not possible to block the binding of anti-G4.Id or anti-D8.Id to their respective Ids by Tg, but the binding of anti-P4.Id was totally inhibited and that of anti-P11.Id was substantially reduced in this system.[11] This indicates that the D8 and G4 Ids are not site-associated, whereas P4 and P11 Ids are. The failure to inhibit the binding of D8 and G4 Ids with Tg was not due to a higher affinity of the Id for anti-Id than for Tg because anti-Id could not block Id/Tg binding either.

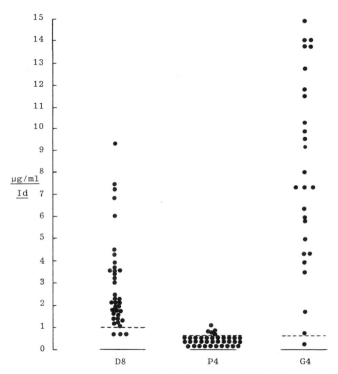

FIGURE 1. Sera of EAT mice were assayed for the presence of the idiotypes indicated in an inhibition radioimmunoassay. The amounts of each idiotype present, expressed in μg/ml, are indicated. This indicates that the Ids are recurrent in EAT sera, but not dominant. The dotted line indicates the limit of detection for the assay.

THE INDUCTION OF IDs BY ANTI-ID

It was possible to modulate the anti-Tg response of EAT mice by prior injection of anti-Id. By giving 20 μg of anti-D8.Id in complete Freund's adjuvant (CFA) seven days before a marginally immunogenic dose of Tg, the subsequent response showed an increase in the levels of Id and a considerable enhancement of the anti-Tg response. Similar effects could be produced with anti-G4 and anti-P11, but not with anti-P4, which is a less common Id. The increase in anti-Tg could be explained either on the basis of the priming of Id$^+$ B cells or could be due to stimulation of anti-Tg specific T cells. To discriminate between these possibilities, we measured the levels of Id in the sera before and after absorption on a Tg affinity column and simultaneously measured the amount of anti-Tg bound to the affinity column. This provides a way of assaying the levels of anti-Tg$^+$, D8$^+$, anti-Tg$^+$, D8$^-$, and anti-Tg$^-$, D8$^+$ antibodies.

This study showed that the levels of both D8$^+$ and D8$^-$ anti-Tg were increased by anti-D8.Id priming (FIGURE 2). The increase in the levels of anti-Tg$^+$, D8$^+$ in CBA can be explained by the priming of Id$^+$ B cells, some of which might be identical to the original D8 clonotype used to raise the anti-D8.Id. Another explanation is required to explain the increase in D8$^-$ anti-Tg: one possibility is that the anti-D8 primes Tg-specific T cells. If this occurs through direct interaction with the T-cell receptors, it would imply that the D8 idiotype (or something cross-reacting with it) is a feature of both the B- and T-cell receptors; furthermore, it is likely to be a structure that contributes to the formation of a Tg binding site, or is associated with it, rather than being an integral part of the binding site itself, since anti-D8 does not block combination of Tg with D8 and vice versa. Another way in which Tg-specific T cells

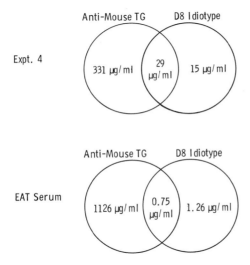

FIGURE 2. The Venn diagrams express the overlap of anti-Tg activity and D8.Id antibody in CBA/Ca mice where the antibody has been induced either by Tg/CFA alone (lower) or by priming with anti-D8.Id/CFA followed by challenge with Tg (upper). The idiotype levels were estimated before and after absorption of the serum pools on a Tg column and the anti-Tg was assayed by measuring the amount of antibody adsorbed to these columns (from reference 11).

could be primed would be through effective presentation of Tg to autoreactive T cells by the stimulated and expanded population of Id-positive B cells.

TRANSFER OF Tg-SPECIFIC ANTI-ID PRIMED CELLS

To confirm that anti-D8.Id was indeed able to induce anti-Tg T cells, animals were first primed with anti-D8.Id as before and spleen cells were taken at day 7. These were fractionated into T-cell and B-cell enriched populations by passage through nylon wool columns. The cells were then injected i.v. into normal recipient isogeneic mice that were challenged with Tg as above. The anti-Tg responses in these animals showed that both T cells and B cells can transfer responsiveness to Tg, although neither population is as effective as the unfractionated spleen cells (FIGURE 3). Furthermore, the T cells are slightly, but significantly, more effective at transferring anti-Tg reactivity than the B cells, thus indicating that anti-D8.Id does induce T cells.

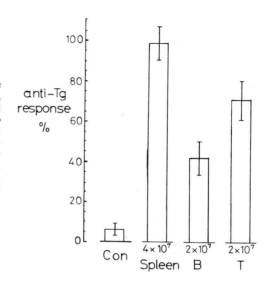

FIGURE 3. CBA/Ca animals were primed with anti-D8.Id. At day 7, spleen cells were taken, fractionated into T and B cells, and injected into recipients, which were then challenged with soluble Tg. Animals with no transferred cells (Con) produced relatively little anti-Tg at day 7 after transfer, while unfractionated cells (spleen), B cells, or T cells were able to transfer anti-Tg responsiveness.

INDUCED D8$^+$ ANTI-Tg

We also undertook an examination of the type of antibody response induced in animals primed with anti-D8.Id. In addition to induction of D8 and anti-Tg in the CBA strain (above), D8$^+$ molecules and anti-Tg can be induced in other strains by the same immunization schedule. It is noticeable, though, that the proportion of antibodies that are both D8$^+$ and anti-Tg in these other strains are relatively low by comparison with CBA, where 67% of the induced D8$^+$ antibodies are anti-Tg (FIGURE 4). CBA is the strain from which the original D8 clone was derived.[12]

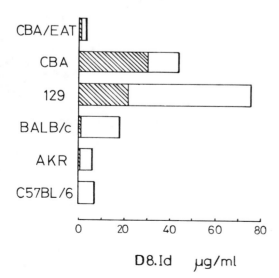

FIGURE 4. The levels of D8.Id in mice of different strains primed with anti-Id and challenged with Tg are compared with the level present in conventionally immunized CBA/Ca EAT mice (top). The hatched regions indicate the proportion of the induced D8.Id that is anti-Tg. This proportion is highest in the CBA/Ca strain, from which the D8 clonotype was originally generated. (Adapted from reference 12.)

Because CBA mice have a propensity to make D8$^+$ anti-Tg, this suggested that they already have a pool of B cells available for expansion. If this is so, one might expect the induced D8.Id in CBA mice to be identical to the D8 clonotype even though they have never come directly into contact with exogenous D8. To test this idea, the antibodies from animals with induced D8.Id were resolved by isoelectric focusing and blotted onto nitrocellulose membranes. Then the D8$^+$ antibodies were visualized by staining with pure anti-D8.Id and labeled goat anti-rabbit Ig. An autoradiograph of such an analysis is shown in FIGURE 5. In all the CBA animals, a spectrotype corresponding to the D8 hybridoma antibody was discernible, although there were several other D8$^+$ clones as might be anticipated from the finding of anti-Tg$^-$,D8$^+$ antibodies. The D8 clonotype was absent from the sera of non-CBA mice with induced D8$^+$ antibodies and anti-Tg. Furthermore, if the same experiment was carried out in CBA mice using sera containing induced G4.Id (by anti-G4 Id priming), G4$^+$ antibodies corresponding to the original G4 clonotype could not be detected. This suggests that the D8$^+$, anti-Tg clone is unusual since there is a pool of B cells available in the CBA mouse capable of producing this antibody, which in turn implies either that the D8$^+$, anti-Tg is germline encoded or is structurally similar to a germline gene—possibly for another antigen; possibly for Tg itself.

We speculated whether there might be some role for a germline anti-Tg antibody in the B-cell repertoire. In view of the previous evidence for a connection between the B-cell repertoire and the T-cell repertoire in this system, one possibility is that the D8.Id is involved in an immunoregulatory circuit to control autoanti-Tg reactivity. To test this theory, we injected CBA mice with small doses of D8 (up to 10 μg) or G4 as a

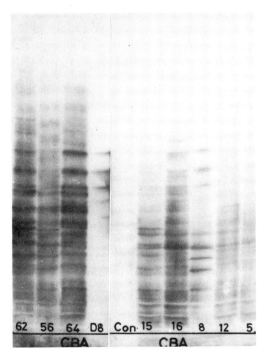

FIGURE 5. The autoradiograph shows the spectrotype of D8.Id antibodies from CBA mice induced with anti-Id and Tg. This was obtained by absorbing the sera with cross-linked rabbit Ig, focusing them in a flatbed gel, blotting the gel, and staining the bands with pure anti-Id and labeled goat anti-rabbit Ig. Figures indicate the amount of D8.Id detected in each serum by competition radioimmunoassay. A spectrotype corresponding to the original D8 clonotype is present in all the sera in variable amounts. In a separate control experiment, anti-G4.Id priming did not induce the G4 clonotypic antibody (from reference 12).

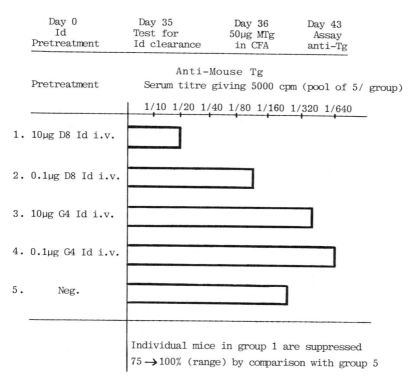

FIGURE 6. D8.Id induced suppression of the anti-Tg response. CBA/Ca mice were injected with 0.1 or 10 µg of pure D8 or G4 (Con) on day 0. Then, after all of the antibody had disappeared from the serum (day 36), they were challenged with MTg in CFA. Sera tested for anti-Tg activity by RIA on day 43 showed that the animals injected with 10 µg D8 were significantly suppressed ($p < 0.01$) by comparison with G4-pretreated controls or normal animals (neg).

control, on day 0, i.v. in saline. The animals were then left for 35 days, until there was no Id detectable in their serum (detection limit of 200 ng/ml). They were then challenged with an immunogenic dose of mouse Tg (50 µg) i.p. in CFA. Finally, the sera were tested for anti-Tg activity and for the presence of Id on days 42 and 49. In some experiments, there was a very large reduction (75–100%) in the amount of anti-Tg present in the D8-treated animals by comparison with the G4-treated animals or the untreated controls (FIGURE 6). This was assayed as the serum dilution producing cpm equivalent to 20% of the positive control EAT serum in a solid-phase RIA. The levels of D8.Id and G4.Id in each case were close to the limits of detection, so it was not possible to determine whether the Id treatment had also altered the subsequent expression of Id. It must be emphasized, however, that in several experiments D8 failed to produce significant suppression of anti-Tg. Thus, we have been unable to determine the cause of this variability, although it does suggest that while a series of factors may be involved in setting the immune system at activation or suppression, once set in a given mode, this represents a relatively stable state.

EXAMINATION OF OTHER IDs

While we have studied the D8.Id most extensively (because of its apparent relation to the idiotype network in autoimmune thyroiditis), initial studies on the P11.Id have also proved interesting. In particular, we have found that anti-P11.Id by itself induces a small amount of anti-Tg antibody in all of the 13 immunized animals and that anti-P11.Id is effective at priming animals to produce a strong anti-Tg response when challenged with a weakly immunogenic dose of Tg. Since P11, unlike D8, is site-associated and consistently induces some anti-Tg when injected by itself, we consider it as a candidate for the internal image of one of the epitopes on Tg itself.[13] In

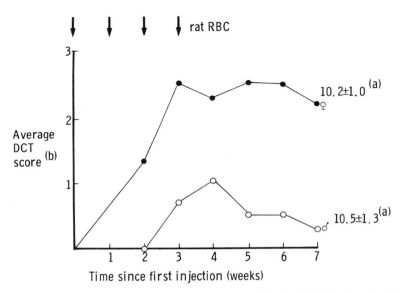

FIGURE 7. Defective autoantibody production in CBA/N mice. Male (O) or female (●) (CBA/N × BALB/c)F$_1$ mice were injected i.p. weekly for four weeks with 2 × 10^8 rat RBC. Erythrocyte autoantibodies were measured by a direct Coombs' test (DCT) and serum antibodies were measured against rat RBC by an agglutination test.[14] (Adapted from reference 16.) Notation: (1) Rat agglutination titer; (b) Direct Coomb's Score: Agglutination was scored microscopically on a scale ranging from positive, visible only under the microscope (1), to a massive agglutination involving all the cells (4).

view of the evidence for connections between the T cells and B cells in EAT, it is of interest to examine similar interactions in another autoimmune system involving induced red cell autoantibodies.

INDUCTION OF RED CELL AUTOANTIBODIES IN CBA/N MICE

When normal mice are immunized with rat red blood cells (RBC), they produce autoantibodies to their own intact red cells, which can be detected by a direct Coombs' test (DCT).[14] CBA/N mice carry an X-linked B-cell defect. (CBA/N × BALB/c)F$_1$

TABLE 1. Restoration of Autoantibody and Rat Agglutinin Responses in CBA nu/nu Mice Reconstituted with CBA (Ca) or CBA in Spleen Cells or T Cells

Transferred Cells	No. of Mice Positive Week 5	Average Rat Agglutinin Titer[a]
None	0/10	0
CBA (Ca) spleen	8/10	6.8 ± 1.5
CBA/N spleen	5/5	7.25 ± 0.95
CBA (Ca) 'T'	7/12	7.75 ± 2.5
CBA/N 'T'	7/12	6.5 ± 1.5

[a]Agglutination titer is expressed as the last well giving agglutination, using doubling dilutions of the test sera and starting the dilution at 1.2.

female mice are therefore normal, while their male littermates have defective B-cell responses.[15] When (CBA/N × BALB/c)F$_1$ females are immunized with rat RBC, they produce antibodies against their own red blood cells, whereas their defective male littermates produce significantly less autoantibody (FIGURE 7).[16] This is despite the fact that both sexes produce similar amounts of antibody to noncross-reacting (foreign) determinants on the rat RBC. Furthermore, while stimulation of (CBA/N × BALB/c)F$_1$ females or (CBA/Ca × BALB/c)F$_1$ mice with lipopolysaccharide (LPS) leads to an increase in the number of plaque-forming cells against enzyme-treated

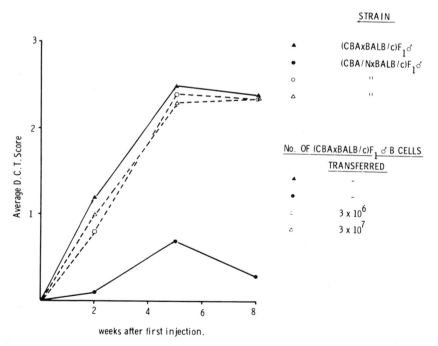

FIGURE 8. Restoration of autoantibody production in CBA/N mice by normal B cells. (CBA/N × BALB/c)F$_1$ male mice were given 3 × 10^6 (O) or 3 × 10^7 (Δ) (CBA/Ca × BALB/c)F$_1$ mice B cells (anti-thy-1.2 treated spleen cells) i.v. one day before the first injection of rat RBC.

autologous RBC, this fails to occur in defective males, despite the fact that they respond normally to LPS as judged by the increase in total IgM and anti-TNP. These mice with an X-linked B-cell defect are therefore deficient in the production of two different red cell autoantibodies.

The inability of mice manifesting the CBA/N B-cell defect to make erythrocyte autoantibodies in response to rat RBC is related to the B-cell defect in these animals. This can be shown in two ways: (a) restoration of autoantibody and rat agglutinin responses in CBA nu/nu mice reconstituted with CBA/Ca or CBA/N T cells (TABLE 1); (b) increased autoantibody response in defective male (CBA/N × BALB/c)F$_1$ mice reconstituted with normal histocompatible splenic B cells (anti-thy-1.2 treated spleen cells) (FIGURE 8).

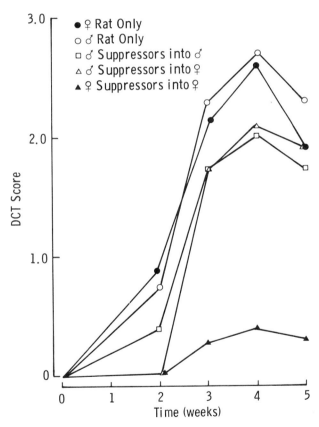

FIGURE 9. Lack of autoantigen-specific suppressor cells in CBA/N mice. Autoantigen-specific suppressor activity of male and female (CBA/N × BALB/c)F$_1$ mice. ●, female (CBA/Ca × BALB/c)F$_1$ rat RBC only; O, male (CBA/Ca × BALB/c)F$_1$ rat RBC only; △, male (CBA/N × BALB/c)F$_1$ suppressor cells into female (CBA/Ca × BALB/c)F$_1$; □, male (CBA/N × BALB/c)F$_1$ suppressor cells into male (CBA/Ca × BALB/c)F$_1$. Fifty million suppressor cells were injected i.v. 24 hours before the first i.p. injection of rat RBC. All mice received 2 × 10^8 rat RBC i.p. at weekly intervals for four weeks. (Adapted from reference 21.)

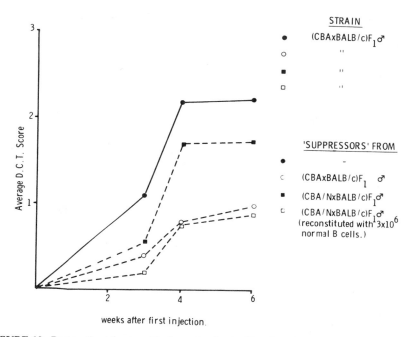

STRAIN

● (CBAxBALB/c)F₁♂

○ "

■ "

□ "

'SUPPRESSORS' FROM

● –

○ (CBAxBALB/c)F₁ ♂

■ (CBA/NxBALB/c)F₁♂

□ (CBA/NxBALB/c)F₁♂
(reconstituted with 3x10⁶
normal B cells.)

weeks after first injection.

FIGURE 10. Restoration of autoantibody production in CBA/N mice leads to the development of antigen-specific suppressor cells. □, (CBA/N × BALB/c)F₁ male mice reconstituted with 3 × 10⁶ (CBA/Ca × BALB/c)F₁ male splenic B cells develop suppressor cells in response to rat RBC.

When normal mice are immunized with rat RBC, they not only develop autoantibodies, but they also develop suppressor cells that can specifically suppress the induction of erythrocyte autoantibodies.[17,18] This suppression is only demonstrable in transfer experiments and is specific for the autoantibody response; the response to noncross-reacting determinants on rat RBC (serum agglutinin or splenic plaque-forming cells to rat RBC) is not suppressed. The 50 × 10⁶ rat RBC primed spleen cells or the 25 × 10⁶ rat RBC primed splenic T cells will suppress autoantibody induction by inducing suppressor effectors in recipient animals.[19] The suppressor inducer cell present in the spleens of rat RBC primed animals appears to be an Ly1⁺ T cell.[20]

When spleen cells are transferred from rat RBC primed (CBA/N × BALB/c)F₁ female mice into (CBA/Ca × BALB/c)F₁ females, suppression can be observed of the induced erythrocyte autoantibody response. On the other hand, spleen cells from rat RBC primed (CBA/N × BALB/c)F₁ male mice do not mediate suppression (FIGURE 9).[21] Defective male (CBA/N × BALB/c)F₁ mice make a poor autoantibody response following rat RBC immunization and they do not develop suppressor cells. Defective (CBA/N × BALB/c)F₁ male mice can make a good autoantibody response if given normal (CBA/Ca × BALB/c)F₁ male splenic B cells (α-thy-1.2 treated spleen cells) (FIGURE 8). When spleen cells are transferred from such reconstituted and rat RBC primed (CBA/N × BALB/c)F₁ male mice, suppression of induced erythrocyte autoantibodies in the recipient (CBA/Ca × BALB/c)F₁ male mice can be observed (FIGURE 10).

The inference is that the development of the Ly1$^+$ T inducers of suppression in this system is dependent on the presence of B cells or their product. Whether the connection between B and T cells is mediated through antigen or idiotype remains to be resolved.

REFERENCES

1. RON, Y., P. DE BAETSELIER, J. GORDON, M. FELDMANN & S. SEGAL. 1981. Eur. J. Immunol. **12:** 964.
2. TZEHOVAL, E., P. DE BAETSELIER, Y. RON, B. TARTAKOVSKY, M. FELDMANN & S. SEGAL. 1983. Eur. J. Immunol. **13:** 89.
3. JANEWAY, C. A., JR., B. BROUGHTON, E. DZIERZAK, B. JONES, D. EARDLEY, S. D. DURUM, K. YAMAUCHI, D. R. GREEN & R. K. GERSHON. 1981. *In* Immunoglobulin Idiotypes. C. A. Janeway, Jr., E. Sercarz & H. Wigzell, Eds.: 661. Academic Press. New York.
4. JANEWAY, C. A., R. A. MURGITA, F. I. WEINBAUM, R. ASOFSKY & H. WIGZELL. 1977. Proc. Natl. Acad. Sci. USA **74:** 4582.
5. BOTTOMLEY, K., C. A. JANEWAY, JR., B. J. MATHIESON & D. E. MOSIER. 1980. Eur. J. Immunol. **10:** 159.
6. BOTTOMLEY, K. & E. DUNN. 1983. Ann. N.Y. Acad. Sci. **418:** 230.
7. L'AGE-STEHR, J., H. TUCHMAN, R. K. GERSON & H. CANTOR. 1980. Eur. J. Immunol. **10:** 21.
8. GERSHON, R. K., S. ORBACH-ARBOUYS & S. CALKINS. 1974. Prog. Immunol. **2:** 123.
9. SHIMAMURA, T. K., K. HASHIMOTO & S. SASAKI. 1982. Cell Immunol. **68:** 104.
10. SACKS, D. L., P. A. SCOTT, R. ASOFSKY & F. A. SHER. 1984. J. Immunol. **132:** 2072.
11. MALE, D. K., G. PRYCE, R. QUARTEY-PAPAFIO & I. M. ROITT. 1983. Eur. J. Immunol. **13:** 942.
12. MALE, D. K., G. PRYCE & I. M. ROITT. 1985. Mol. Immunol. **22:** 255.
13. ROITT, I. M., A. COOKE, D. K. MALE, F. C. HAY, G. GUARNOTTA, P. M. LYDYARD, L. CARVALHO, Y. THANAVALA & L. IVANYI. 1981. Lancet **i:** 1041.
14. PLAYFAIR, J. H. L. & S. MARSHALL-CLARKE. 1973. Nature (New Biol.) **243:** 213.
15. SCHER, I., A. D. STEINBERG, A. K. BERNING & W. E. PAUL. 1975. J. Exp. Med. **142:** 637.
16. MARSHALL-CLARKE, S., A. COOKE & P. HUTCHINGS. 1979. Eur. J. Immunol. **9:** 820.
17. NAYSMITH, J. D. & C. J. ELSON. 1977. Abstr. Allergologia Immunopathol. **5:** 480.
18. COOKE, A., P. R. HUTCHINGS & J. H. L. PLAYFAIR. 1978. Nature (London) **273:** 154.
19. HUTCHINGS, P. R. & A. COOKE. 1981. Cell. Immunol. **63:** 221.
20. HUTCHINGS, P. R., S. MARSHALL-CLARKE & A. COOKE. 1985. Immunology. In press.
21. COOKE, A., P. R. HUTCHINGS & S. MARSHALL-CLARKE. 1980. Immunology **41:** 815.

DISCUSSION OF THE PAPER

UNIDENTIFIED DISCUSSANT: In any of the experiments involving anti-idiotype manipulations, was there any thyroiditis?

I. M. ROITT (*Middlesex Hospital Medical School, London, England*): In those experiments, although CBA mice do not usually get thyroiditis, we did not look.

UNIDENTIFIED DISCUSSANT: Have you ever noticed any intensification of the anti-thyroglobulin response when you gave the idiotype to suppress this response?

ROITT: No.

UNIDENTIFIED DISCUSSANT: Is it possible that the anti-Id injection induced high-affinity idiotypes to the anti-Id, and by this mechanism, induced mutations that deviated the antibodies from recognition of thyroglobulin?

ROITT: Yes, that is perfectly possible because we were using a solid-phase assay, which is notoriously sensitive to affinity changes. However, what is really important is that even if we are overestimating, we are still left with a tremendous amount of ID-negative anti-thyroglobulin.

E. A. CLARK (*University of Washington, Seattle, WA*): I wonder if your experimental protocol increases the proportion of Ly1 B cells in the peritoneum. Also, does Freund's adjuvant have an effect on levels of anti-thyroglobulin in subsequent challenges?

ROITT: Well, it certainly did have an effect, but even in the absence of Freund's adjuvant, the problem was still there. However, everything was scaled up when we used the Freund. The Ly1 B cell is an interesting point and at the stage of those experiments we were not so aware of how important the Ly1 B cells might be; however, my prejudice in many ways is that they are more related to autoimmunity and to polymeric antigens, but perhaps this is not the place for prejudice.

Rheumatoid Factors

Immunochemical, Molecular, and Regulatory Properties[a]

MARC MONESTIER, BLANCHE BELLON, AUDREY J.
MANHEIMER, AND CONSTANTIN A. BONA

Department of Microbiology
Mount Sinai School of Medicine
New York, New York 10029

Rheumatoid factors (RF) are autoantibodies specific for antigenic determinants of autologous IgG. They were discovered in patients with rheumatoid arthritis and later were found associated with various autoimmune diseases, chronic inflammations, hypergammaglobulinemia, and acute phases of viral, bacterial, and parasitic diseases. The majority of RFs are IgM, but they also can be IgG, IgA, or IgE.

Human RFs react with antigenic determinants located on the Fc portion of IgG molecules, particularly on CH_2 and CH_3 domains. They include Gm allotypic determinants,[1] along with antigenic determinants shared by various IgG subclasses[2] or by IgG from various species.[3] RFs obtained from the 129/Sv mouse strain recognize antigenic determinants located on the CH_3 domain of IgG_1, and in the case of IgG_{2a}, it is the C-terminal eight residues of the CH_2 domain and the complete CH_3 domain.[4]

The precursors of RF-producing B cells are present in human cord blood, in normal adult bone marrow, and in peripheral blood, [5–7] and their frequency increases several-fold after birth.[7]

Several mechanisms have been incriminated in the expression and maturation of precursors into RF-producing cells, such as stimulation by bacterial polyclonal mitogens, xenogenous antigen cross-reacting with immunoglobulins, and immune complexes.

One of the most important questions with respect to the nature of RFs is whether or not they can be antibodies primarily specific for Fc fragments or if they are multispecific antibodies.

ARE RFs MULTISPECIFIC ANTIBODIES? EPIBODY CONCEPT

The affinity of RFs for antigenic determinants of the Fc fragment is very low (10^5liter/mole)[8] and can be artificially increased by alteration of the Fc fragment's tridimensional structure subsequent to mild heating or binding of IgG to antigen. The low affinity of RFs for the Fc fragment of various IgG subclasses suggests that perhaps there may exist another epitope to which RFs bind with high affinity. Thus, RFs can be multispecific antibodies like heteroclitic anti-NP antibodies, which bind better to NIP, a related hapten.[9] Actually, there are several examples indicating that autoantibodies bind to various antigens and therefore exhibit multispecific binding activities for

[a]This study was supported by grant no. AB/AM02716-01 from the National Institute of Aging, NIH, Bethesda, Maryland. Marc Monestier is supported by a fellowship from the Fondation pour la Recherche Medicale (Paris). Blanche Bellon is a visiting scientist from CNRS ERA 48, INSERM U28, France.

various antigens such as nuclear antigens,[10] LE factors,[11] or DNA-histones.[12] The concept of multispecificity of RFs is strongly supported by the discovery of epibodies.

The study of the binding specificity of mouse anti-Id antibodies produced in various mouse strains against IdX Wa of a human paraprotein with RF activity (Glow) demonstrated that:

(a) anti-IdX antibodies prepared in A/J mice bind to various myeloma proteins sharing the IdX Wa, as well as to human IgG;
(b) the binding to IdX Wa$^+$ proteins was inhibited by Fc fragments, whereas the binding to IgG was inhibited by Fab fragments of IdX Wa$^+$ IgM.[13]

These data showed that the antibodies produced in A/J mice against IdX Wa, a major idiotype shared by about 60% of human paraproteins exhibiting RF activity, were also bound to human IgG and therefore displayed rheumatoid factor activity. Chen *et al.*[14] recently elucidated the molecular basis of binding activity of epibodies. Antibodies were raised in rabbits against a synthetic peptide corresponding to the CDRI of the light chain of the Glow paraprotein used in our study. It was shown, by using a panel of IdX Wa$^+$ paraprotein with known sequences, that the antibodies against the synthetic peptide recognize the val-ser-ser-ser sequence. These antibodies also were bound to human IgG. The authors pointed out that a ser-ser-ser sequence is found at position 195–197 on human Fcγ.

We also found that rabbit anti-Id antibodies against anti-a or b series allotype antibodies bind to human Fcγ and therefore display rheumatoid factor binding activity (FIGURE 1).[15] Taken collectively, these results strongly support the concept that RFs, like other autoantibodies, are multispecific antibodies, namely, primarily specific for idiotopes and secondarily bound to human Fc fragment.

The epibody concept provides a working hypothesis for the studying of the mechanism(s) of the activation of precursors of RFs and perhaps of cells producing autoantibodies.

IMMUNOCHEMICAL AND MOLECULAR PROPERTIES OF MURINE RFs

A panel of RF monoclonal antibodies of various origins has been prepared in our laboratory from:

(a) 5-month-old MRL/lpr mice displaying lymphoproliferative syndrome;
(b) aged 129/Sv mice with high titers of RF activity;
(c) spleen cells from normal BALB/c mice stimulated *in vitro* with LPS;
(d) spleen cells from BALB/c mice previously injected with Yersinia enterocolitica.

The binding specificity to various IgG subclasses, the idiotypes expressed on their variable regions, and the V_H gene used in hybridomas producing RF monoclonal antibodies have all been studied in order to characterize their immunochemical and molecular properties.

The binding specificity was studied in a RIA using heat-aggregated monoclonal IgGλ for coating and a monoclonal rat ^{125}I anti-kappa antibody as the developing reagent. All our RF monoclonal antibodies used the kappa light chain and the vast majority were of μ isotype (one α and two γ3). Idiotypy was studied using a sensitive RIA technique in which the microtiter plates coated with RFs had been incubated with affinity-purified rabbit and anti-Id antibodies. The binding of anti-Id antibody was measured by using donkey ^{125}I F(ab')2 anti-rabbit Ig. In pilot experiments, it was established that murine RF monoclonal antibodies did not bind to rabbit normal Ig nor to donkey F(ab′)2 anti-rabbit Ig.

The V_H family of active V_H genes expressed in the hybridomas producing RF monoclonal antibodies was studied via slot blot analysis of cytoplasmic lysates and ^{32}P-nick-translated probes of V_H441-4, V_HJ606, V_H36-30, V_HJ558, V_HS107, $V_HQPCN52$, and V_H81X, which are the prototypes of seven murine V_H families.[16]

The methodology used is illustrated in FIGURE 2. The results are summarized in TABLE 1. They show that 4 monoclonal antibodies bind with high affinity to only IgG_{2a} and 10 of 20 bind with low affinity to one or several IgG subclasses. The remaining 6 bind with high affinity to some IgG subclasses and with low affinity to others.

Based on their binding activity, murine RF monoclonal antibodies can be divided into two major categories: one specific for only IgG_{2a} and another for various IgG subclasses. It should be pointed out that we did not find an allotype specificity as it was previously reported[17] for RFs specific for IgG_{2a} a or b.[18] The idiotypy of RFs was

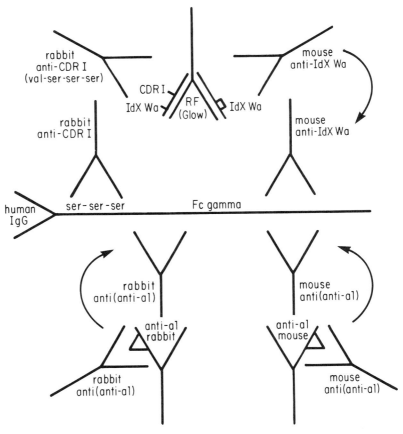

FIGURE 1. Binding properties of epibodies. Rabbit antibodies specific for the CDRI synthetic peptide of $V_{KIII}b$ used in Glow protein, mouse antibodies specific for IdX Wa of Glow protein, and rabbit or mouse anti-Id (anti-al allotype) antibodies display binding activity to human Fcγ.

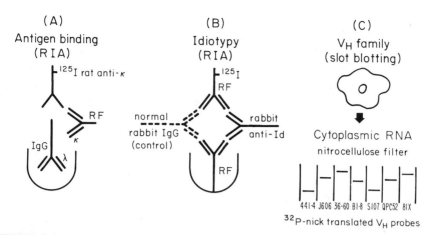

FIGURE 2. Schematic illustrations of the methods used to study the specificity, idiotypy, and V_H genes of monoclonal rheumatoid factors.

studied by employing rabbit anti-Id antibodies prepared against one RF obtained from 129/Sv mice (i.e., 129–48) and against two RFs obtained from BALB/c mice, either from *in vitro* LPS stimulated lymphocytes (i.e., LPS10-1) or from spleen cells obtained from mice immunized with Y. enterocolitica (Y19-10). These anti-Id antibodies recognized cross-reactive idiotypes that were shared by several RFs independently of their origin. Whereas 129-48 and LPS10-1 idiotypes were identified on 14 of 20, the Y19-10-Id was identified on 7 of 20 monoclonal RF antibodies.

The study of VH genes encoding these RFs indicate that they originate from only three families: 5 of 14 from V_HJ558 family, 7 of 14 from V_H7183, and 2 of 14 from V_HQPCN52 family.

It is important to note that there is no correlation between expressed idiotypes and V_H family. A similar situation was observed in influenza virus hemagglutinin specific monoclonal antibodies in which syngeneic monoclonal anti-Id antibodies produced against an X-31 HA specific monoclonal antibody using a gene from V_HJ558 family were bound to a monoclonal antibody using a gene from V_H7183 family.[19] Three alternative hypotheses can be entertained to explain these results:

(a) anti-Id antibodies recognize a V_L idiotype;
(b) anti-Id antibodies contain a subset of molecules carrying internal image of Fc and therefore can bind to RF independently of V_H genes encoding their specificity;
(c) conserved DNA segments are shared among autoantibodies encoded by V_H genes belonging to different families.

cDNA sequencing in progress will enable us to understand better the molecular basis of these shared idiotopes of RFs.

REGULATORY FUNCTION OF RFs

There is a large body of evidence demonstrating that the binding of antibodies specific for the antigenic determinants of immunoglobulin (i.e., idiotype, allotype, and

TABLE 1. Summary of Immunochemical and Molecular Properties of Rheumatoid Factors

Monoclonal Antibodies	Specificity[a]			Idiotypes[b]			V_H Family[c]
	Isotypes	High Affinity	Low Affinity	129-48 Id	LPS10-1 Id	Y19-10 Id	
129/48	μk		γ1,γ2b	+++	+++	++	7183
129/78	μk	γ2b	γ3	−	−	−	7183
129/76	μk		γ2b	−	−	−	ND
129/101	μk		γ3,γ2a,γ2b	++	++	±	ND
129/61	μk	γ1,γ2b		+++	+++	++	ND
129/74	γ3k	γ2a		−	−	−	7183
129/102	αk	γ2a		−	−	−	7183
129/77	γ3k	γ2a		−	−	−	7183
Y19-10	μk		γ1,γ2b	+++	+++	+++	J558
Y19-16	μk		γ2b	++	++	+	J558
Y43-5	μk	γ1,γ2b,γ2a		+	+	−	ND
LPS-10-1	μk	γ1,γ2b,γ2a	δ	+++	+++	+	7183
LPS-5-4	μk	γ2a	γ3,γ1	+	++	+	J558
LPS-5-7	μk	γ1,γ2b,γ3	γ2a	+++	+++	+	ND
LPS-7-3	μk		γ1,δ	+++	+++	+	QPCN52
MRL-5-51	μk		γ3,γ2b	++	++	−	QPCN52
MRL-22-46	μk		γ3,γ2b,γ2a,α	++	++	±	7183
MRL-50-8	μk		γ2b,γ2a	++	+	−	J558
MRL-55-18	μk	γ2a		−	−	−	J558
MRL-55-23	μk		γ1,γ2b	+	+	−	ND

[a]Specificity to Fcγ was determined in RIA using microtiter plates coated with γ proteins of various subclasses.
[b]Presence of idiotypes was determined in a sandwich assay using rabbit anti-129-48, LPS10-1, and Y19-10 Id antibodies.
[c]Results of slot blotting using V_H441-4, V_HJ606, V_H36-60, V_HJ558, V_HS107, V_HQPCN52, and V_H81X germline gene probes.

isotype) can affect the proliferation of resting B lymphocytes, their maturation into plasma cells, and Ig secretion (see data reviewed in reference 20). Following the rationale that RFs recognize antigenic determinants of CH_2 and CH_3 domains of the Fc fragment of IgG and that they can bind to B cells, studies were undertaken in our laboratory to investigate the effects of RFs on antibody-forming cells. These studies were aimed to explore:

(a) whether or not spontaneously occurring RFs affect the isotypes of anti-TNP antibodies produced during a secondary immune response;
(b) if *in vivo* expansion of RF-producing cells subsequent to parenteral injection of LPS has an effect on *in vitro* IgG and IgM PFC response specific for SRBC;
(c) what the effect is of RFs on the PFC response induced by TI_1 and TI_2 antigens.

The study of the occurrence of RFs during the TNP-KLH secondary response in 129/J and MRL+/+ and their congeneic RF-producing counterparts, 129/Sv and MRL/lpr, have shown high serum titers of RFs in (1–6)-month-old mice. The RFs exhibited a binding specificity for various IgG subclasses.[18] However, when we studied the concentration of various isotypes of anti-TNP antibodies produced during this response, there was only a depression of IgG_{2a} anti-TNP antibodies in 6-month-old 129/Sv mice[21] and an almost lack of IgG (γ3, γ1, γ2b, γ2a) anti-TNP antibodies in 6-month-old MRL/lpr mice.[22]

At first glance, one might relate this observation to a clearance of antibodies by RFs that have spontaneously occurred in (3–6)-month-old 129/Sv and MRL/lpr mice, especially since Edleman *et al.*[23] have shown that RFs can bind to immune complexes. Several findings suggest different interpretation. First, in 129/Sv mice, only the IgG_{2a} anti-TNP antibody response was depressed, while RFs specific for various IgG subclasses were found in their blood. Secondly, high titers of RFs were observed in 129/J and MRL+/+ (as well as in 1-month-old 129/Sv and MRL/lpr) without any significant effect on the level of IgG anti-TNP antibodies. Finally, *in vitro* studies showed that both T and B cells from old 129/Sv and MRL/lpr mice were unable to collaborate for an IgG anti-TNP PFC response elicited by TNP-KLH.[21,22]

These findings led us to propose that there are two major categories of RFs:

(i) those occurring during conventional antibody responses elicited by T-independent, TI_1[24] or TI_2,[18] and T-dependent antigens,[21,22] and having no inhibitory effect and perhaps being beneficial for the host;
(ii) a second group that includes RFs that occur in animals that are disease-prone and exhibit an inhibitory effect particularly on the IgG response. This effect can be related to the high affinity of RF for a certain IgG subclass. Thus, in 6-month-old 129/Sv mice, only a depressed IgG_{2a} anti-TNP antibody response was observed, despite the fact that the presence of high levels of RFs specific for γ3, γ1, γ2b, and γ2a were noted.

In our panel of RFs obtained from 129/Sv mice, it was observed that all RFs exhibit a high binding affinity for IgG_{2a}, whereas those obtained from MRL/lpr mice exhibit high affinity for various IgG subclasses. It therefore appears that only high affinity RFs exhibit a regulatory role on lymphocytes and the activation of clones producing such RFs is genetically determined.

In other sets of experiments, Bellon *et al.*[24] showed that the coculture of lymphocytes from LPS primed 129/Sv mice with SRBC primed 129/J spleen has a significant inhibitory effect on the *in vitro* secondary IgG anti-SRBC response. No inhibitory effect, though, was observed on the IgM anti-SRBC response.

These results also indicated that the expansion of 129/Sv RF-producing cells by

LPS, a potent stimulus of these cells,[15] had affected the IgG secondary response of lymphocytes in a subline (i.e., 129/J) that is not prone to produce RFs.

Finally, *in vitro* studies on the effect of monoclonal antibodies on PRF responses induced by TNP-NWSM (TI$_1$) or bacterial levan (TI$_2$) showed that RFs exhibiting reactivity for IgD had a significant effect on the magnitude of the responses.[25]

Taken together, these results suggest that RFs may promote the clearance of antigen-antibody complexes as well as exerting a regulatory role on antibody-producing cells.

REFERENCES

1. NATVIG, J. B. & H. G. KUNKEL. 1967. Detection of genetic antigens utilizing gammaglobulins coupled to red blood cells. Nature **215**: 68.
2. ALLEN, J. C. & H. G. KUNKEL. 1966. Hidden rheumatoid factors with specificity for native γ globulins. Arthritis Rheum. **9**: 758.
3. WILLIAMS, R. C. & H. G. KUNKEL. 1963. Separation of rheumatoid factors of different specificities using columns conjugated with gammaglobulins. Arthritis Rheum. **6**: 665.
4. STASSIN, V., P. G. COULIE, B. K. BIRSCHTEIN, D. S. SCHER & J. L. VAN SNICK. 1983. Determinants recognized by murine rheumatoid factors: molecular localization using a panel of mouse myeloma variant immunoglobulins. J. Exp. Med. **158**: 1763.
5. FONG, S., J. J. MILLER, T. L. MOORE, C. D. TSOUKAS, J. H. VAUGHAN & D. A. CARSON. 1982. Frequency of Epstein-Barr virus inducible IgM anti-IgG B lymphocytes in normal children and in children with juvenile rheumatoid arthritis. Arthritis Rheum. **25**: 953.
6. FONG, S., J. H. VAUGHAN, C. D. TSOUKAS & D. A. CARSON. 1982. Selective induction of autoantibody secretion in human bone marrow by Epstein-Barr virus. J. Immunol. **129**: 1941.
7. FONG, S., C. D. TSOUKAS, L. A. FRINCKE, S. K. LAWRENCE, T. L. HOLBROOK, J. H. VAUGHAN & D. A. CARSON. 1981. Age associated changes in Epstein-Barr virus-induced human lymphocyte autoantibody responses. J. Immunol. **126**: 910.
8. MANNICK, M. 1974. Rheumatoid Factors in Arthritis and Allied Conditions. J. C. Hollander & D. S. McCarthy, Jr., Eds.: 504. Lea & Febiger. Philadelphia.
9. MÄKELÄ, O. & T. IMANISHI. 1975. Expression of an immunoglobulin V$_H$ gene in natural anti-hapten antibodies. Eur. J. Immunol. **5**: 202–205.
10. HANNESTAD, K. & A. JOHANNESSEN. 1976. Polyclonal human antibodies to IgG which cross-react with cell nuclei. Scand. J. Immunol. **5**: 544.
11. HANNESTAD, K., D. P. RECKVIG & A. HUSBEAK. 1981. Cross-reacting rheumatoid factors and lupus erythematosus (LE) factors. Springer Semin. Immunopathol. **4**: 133.
12. AGNELLO, V., A. ARBELTER, G. I. DEKESEF, R. POWELL, E. M. TAN & F. JOSLIN. 1980. Evidence for a subset of rheumatoid factors that cross-react with DNA-histone and have a distinct cross-idiotype. J. Exp. Med. **151**: 1514.
13. BONA, C. A., S. FINLEY, S. WATERS & H. G. KUNKEL. 1982. Anti-immunoglobulin antibodies. III. Properties of sequential anti-idiotypic antibodies to heterologous anti-γ-globulins. Detection and reactivity of anti-idiotype antibodies with epitopes of Fc fragment (homobodies) and with epitopes and idiotopes (epibodies). J. Exp. Med. **156**: 986.
14. CHEN, P. P., S. FONG, R. A. HOUGHTEN & D. A. CARSON. 1985. Characterization of an epibody. An anti-idiotype that reacts with both idiotype of rheumatoid factors (RF) and the antigen recognized by RF. J. Exp. Med. **161**: 323.
15. BONA, C. A., B. GOLDBERG, D. METZGER, J. URBAIN & H. G. KUNKEL. 1984. Anti-immunoglobulin antibodies. IV. Cross-reaction of anti-idiotypic antibodies specific for rabbit and murine anti-a-allotype antibodies with Fc fragment of human immunoglobulins. Eur. J. Immunol. **14**: 548.
16. BRODEUR, P. H. & R. RIBLET. 1984. The immunoglobulin heavy chain variable region (IghV) locus in mouse. I. 100 Igh V gene comprise 7 families of homologous genes. Eur. J. Immunol. **14**: 932.
17. VAN SNICK, J. L. & P. L. MASSON. 1979. Age dependent production of IgA and IgM autoantibodies against IgG$_{2a}$ in a colony of 129/Sv mice. J. Exp. Med. **149**: 1519.

18. MANHEIMER, A. J., C. VICTOR-KOBRIN, K. E. STEIN & C. A. BONA. 1984. Anti-immunoglobulin antibodies. V. Age-dependent variation of clones stimulated by polysaccharide T1-2 antigens in 129 and MRL mice spontaneously producing anti-γ-globulin antibodies. J. Immunol. **138:** 562.

19. MORAN, T., M. A. THOMPSON, M. MONESTIER, M. A. REALE, J. L. SCHULMAN, R. RIBLET & C. A. BONA. Characterization of variable region genes of antibodies specific for PR8 and X31 influenza virus hemagglutinins sharing cross-reactive idiotopes. Submitted.

20. BONA, C. & P. A. CAZENAVE, Eds. 1981. Lymphocyte regulation by antibodies. Wiley. New York.

21. MANHEIMER, A. & C. BONA. 1985. Anti-immunoglobulin antibodies. VI. Age-dependent isotype and autoanti-immunoglobulin variation during secondary immune response in 129 mice. Mech. Ageing Dev. **30:** 187.

22. MANHEIMER, A. & C. BONA. 1985. Age-dependent isotype variation during secondary immune response in MRL/lpr mice producing auto-anti-γ-globulin antibodies. Eur. J. Immunol. **15:** 722.

23. EDELMAN, G. M., H. G. KUNKEL & E. C. FRANKLIN. 1958. Interaction of the rheumatoid factor with antigen-antibody complexes and aggregated gammaglobulin. J. Exp. Med. **103:** 105.

24. BELLON, B., A. J. MANHEIMER & C. A. BONA. 1985. Anti-idiotype and antigammaglobulin antibodies. *In* Two Regulatory Forces within Immune Network in Antibodies: Protective, Destructive, and Regulatory Role. F. Milgram, Ed.: 213. Karger. Basel.

25. MANHEIMER, A. J., B. BELLON & C. BONA. 1985. Rheumatoid factors and aging. *In* Functional and Molecular Aspects in Aging and Immune Responses. E. Goidl, Ed. M. Dekker. New York. In press.

DISCUSSION OF THE PAPER

K. J. BARRETT (*Tufts University School of Medicine, Boston, MA*): I have been studying anti-DNA antibodies obtained from R. Schwartz's lab and among MRL/lpr hybridomas that produce anti-DNA antibodies, 30% belong to the 71-83 V gene family. Including the J558 family, which occurs in about half of the mouse B-cell repertoire, there are only four families.

B. H. HAHN (*University of California, Los Angeles, CA*): F. Dixon stated that lupus mice use the entire repertoire of the V and J gene regions. However, the data of others suggest a restriction in the number of V_H gene families that encode autoantibodies. What I am going to show later is that there is a tremendous restriction of idiotype expression by the time the NZB/NZW mouse has full-blown lupus disease. However, there is much more idiotypic diversity earlier in the disease. I wonder if the discrepancy in data relates to the time in the life span of the mouse. If we looked early, I think we would come to the conclusion that there is wide use of V_H genes, and if we look late, it is possible that the expressed V_H genes encompass only a narrow range.

C. A. BONA (*Mount Sinai School of Medicine, New York, NY*): I think your comment is a very important idea.

UNIDENTIFIED DISCUSSANT: Everybody talked about rheumatoid factor as if there is only one rheumatoid factor. Is there a difference between the rheumatoid factors in rheumatoid arthritis and the rheumatoid factors that are found in a disease like bacterial endocarditis?

BONA: Perhaps there are two categories of rheumatoid factor—those that have a pathological role and those that have a physiological role. This second category can be envisioned in two ways: One, just a scavenger effect, like macrophages, cleaning immune complexes from the blood; two, other rheumatoid factors might have a regulatory role on B cells, perhaps in the process of Ig switching.

A Novel Chimeric Antibody with Circular Network Characteristics: Autobody[a]

CHANG-YUIL KANG AND HEINZ KOHLER

Department of Molecular Immunology
Roswell Park Memorial Institute
(a unit of the New York State Department of Health)
Buffalo, New York 14263
and
Department of Microbiology
State University of New York at Buffalo
Buffalo, New York 14214

INTRODUCTION

According to the network theory,[1] we must conceive the coexistence of one paratope and one or more idiotope sites on each antibody molecule. We have recently[2,3] analyzed the topographical distribution of idiotope determining regions (IDR) within the three-dimensional structure of the Ig molecule. From these studies, it becomes evident that idiotopic determinants are located in minidomains. The relationship of IDR domains with respect to CDR (paratope) shows independent expression of IDR specificities. Some of the IDR domains overlap with CDR structures, while other IDRs are separated from the paratope.

IDRs express idiotypic determinants that are recognized by anti-idiotypic antibodies. However, IDRs also can mimic structures of nominal antigen. These antigen-mimicking IDRs are called the internal images of antigen.

The topographical separation and the functional independence of paratope and IDRs permit the coexpression of a given paratope and its complementary internal image structure, the internal antigen. For example, Bona and colleagues[4] described a peculiar anti-idiotypic antibody that reacts not only with the corresponding idiotope, but also with the epitope of the original antigen. They reported this antibody as "epibody," so as to indicate the presence of an idiotypic determinant that mimics the epitope structure of the antigen for the idiotype (Ab1).

From these considerations, it should be possible that one antibody molecule carries the internal antigen image and at the same time has a binding site for the antigen, internal or nominal. The coexpression of paratope and internal antigen image on the same Ig molecule has important implications for the network theory, as well as for the rational design of so-called idiotope vaccines.[3,5]

While working on idiotype vaccines, we discovered a monoclonal anti-idiotypic antibody that exhibits the so-called epibody characteristics. More importantly, we found that this particular anti-idiotypic antibody forms complexes with itself. This self-binding is completely inhibited by the original epitope. Because this antibody is syngeneic in origin, one must envision the possibility that such epibodies can occur

[a]This work was supported in part by grant no. C000533 from the AIDS Institute, New York State Department of Health, grant no. IM-405 from the American Cancer Society, and grant no. AG04180 from the National Institute on Aging, DHEW.

during the course of a normal immune response. Ig molecules of a dual network specificity are self-recognizing and will lead to self-complexing. This property obviously addresses the question of autoimmune complexes. Accordingly, we propose the term "autobody" to signify the potential role of such antibodies in the regulation of the network and in the etiology of autoimmune diseases.

MATERIALS AND METHODS

Mice

Athymic BALB/c nu/nu mice, six weeks old, were obtained from my own breeding colony. Originally, these mice were obtained from the National Institutes of Health, Bethesda, Maryland.

Myeloma and Hybridoma Proteins

Myeloma cell lines TEPC15 (T15), MOPC167 (M167), MOPC603 (M603), and MOPC (M511) were obtained from Bionetics, Kensington, Maryland, and were purified from ascitic fluid by affinity column purification. Hybridoma cell lines HPCM2, HPCG11, and HPCG12 were gifts from P. Gearhart, Baltimore, Maryland, and were purified from ascitic fluid on affinity columns. HPCG13 and HPCG14 hybridoma proteins were also gifts from P. Gearhart. The anti-T15 hybridoma F6.3 was prepared in our laboratory[6] and was purified on T15-Sepharose column. The anti-TNP myeloma proteins, MOPC315 (M315) and MOPC460 (M460), were purified on TNP columns. Monoclonal antibody 11E7 was purified from ascites by affinity chromatography on T15-Sepharose column or PC-Sepharose column.

Immunization and Fusion

Athymic BALB/c nude mice were intraperitoneally primed with 100 μg of T15 in Freund's incomplete adjuvant three times at three-week intervals. Three days after the last immunization, splenic lymphocytes were fused with P3-X63Ag8.653 myeloma cells and hybrids were selected in the Hypoxanthine-Aminopterin-Thymidine medium. Culture supernatants were tested by ELISA. One clone, 11E7, an IgM kappa producing hybridoma, was selected, subcloned twice by limiting dilutions, expanded in tissue culture, and then carried as an ascites tumor in BALB/c mice.

ELISA

For hybridoma screening, 96 well microtiter plates (Becton-Dickinson, Oxnard, California) were coated for 18 hours with 0.1 ml of purified T15 (2 μg/ml) in PBS, washed three times, and incubated for 1 hour with 1% BSA in PBS. After washing, alkaline-phosphatase-coupled goat-antimouse IgG and IgM (Southern Biotechnology Associates, Birmingham, Alabama) were used to detect antibodies binding to T15-coated plates. Substrate was added and O.D. at 405 nm was measured. For further details on other assays, see the captions of the figures in this paper.

RESULTS

Binding of 11E7 to T15 and PC-BSA

11E7 was isolated from fusion of anti-T15 immune nude BALB/c mice with P3-X63Ag8.653 myeloma cells. Only one out of a thousand primary clones was bound to T15-coated plates. This clone was cloned twice. The 11E7 subclone also was bound to plates coated with PC-BSA (see FIGURE 1). Ascites was raised in BALB/c mice and purified by affinity chromatography using PC-Sepharose column or T15-Sepharose column. Antibodies purified from either PC-Sepharose or T15-Sepharose have identical specificities in ELISA (data not shown); that is, they bind to PC and T15.

Serial dilutions of culture supernatant were added to T15- or PC-BSA-coated plates. As shown in FIGURE 1, the PC binding declines with increasing dilutions. However, binding to T15-coated plates was low at initial dilutions of supernatant; with further dilutions of 11E7 supernatant, binding to T15-coated plates increased and then decreased.

Anti-Idiotypic Specificity of 11E7

In BALB/c mice, PC-binding antibodies use one heavy-chain germline gene and three different light-chain germline genes.[7] According to the light-chain sequence and fine specificity, PC-binding antibodies are divided into three idiotype families: T15 idiotype, M603 idiotype, and M167/M511 idiotype family.[8] To establish the fine specificity of 11E7 as anti-idiotype antibody, binding of 11E7 to several representative idiotypes was analyzed. This was done in the range of exponential binding of 11E7 concentration. The data are shown in FIGURE 2. Strong binding was observed to insolubilized T15, M603, and HPCG14. Low binding was observed to HPCG12 and HPCG11, which are both T15-positive.

The binding of 11E7 to T15, M603, and HPCG14, as well as the binding to HPCG12 and HPCG11, can be completely inhibited by free PC and PC analogues (see FIGURE 3; data not shown for inhibition of 11E7 binding to M603, HPCG14, HPCG11, and HPCG12). Furthermore, neither the light or heavy chain of T15 inhibited the 11E7 binding to T15 (data not shown). 11E7 did not bind to M167, M511, HPCG13, and M460. In summary, the binding of 11E7 to anti-PC antibodies of two different idiotypes is hapten inhibitable and thus involves the paratope site of anti-PC antibodies.

Self-Binding of 11E7

The data so far discussed suggest that 11E7 might express the internal PC image. It also suggests that 11E7 has a PC paratope site at the same time. If so, one should detect self-binding or self-aggregation of 11E7 molecules. To confirm this, purified 11E7 coupled with alkaline phosphatase was added to plates coated with 11E7, T15, and M167 and the ELISA was performed. The results shown in FIGURE 4 demonstrate that the enzyme-coupled 11E7 binds to insolubilzed T15 and 11E7, but not to insolubilized M167. Furthermore, self-binding of 11E7 was completely inhibited by PC and analogues, as shown in FIGURE 5. These results indicate that in the self-binding of 11E7, the PC binding site of one molecule and the Ab2-beta idiotope[9,10] of another 11E7 molecule are interacting.

Idiotope Expression of 11E7

The idiotype family relationship of 11E7 was investigated in order to describe the genetic origin of the 11E7 antibody. A monoclonal anti-T15 antibody, F6-3, was insolubilized and serial dilutions of 11E7 or HPCM2 (a T15-positive IgM anti-PC hybridoma) were added. After washing, enzyme-labeled goat-antimouse IgM antibody was added. The results from this ELISA are shown in FIGURE 6 and demonstrate that 11E7 expresses the T15 idiotope. These results suggest that 11E7 possibly

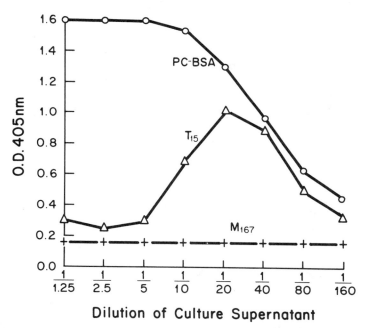

Dilution of Culture Supernatant

FIGURE 1. Binding profile of 11E7 to PC-BSA and T15 using culture supernatant. The microtiter plates were coated for 18 h with 100 μl/well of T15 (2 μg/ml) or 100 μl/well of PC$_7$-BSA (2 μg/ml) in PBS, washed three times, and incubated for 1 h with 1% BSA in PBS. After washing three times, culture supernatant in 1% BSA - 0.05% Tween 20-BBS solution was added. Enzyme-coupled goat-antimouse IgM was used for detecting antibody binding to microtiter plates. After washing three times, color was developed with substrate and the O.D. at 405 nm was measured.

originated from the T15 germline gene and that it had undergone somatic mutation or gene recombination to create an internal image idiotope site.

DISCUSSION

The data described in this report show the existence of a peculiar type of antibody having two functional sites that are complementary. This type of molecule has been described recently by Bona and colleagues[4] and by Carson and colleagues.[11] Their

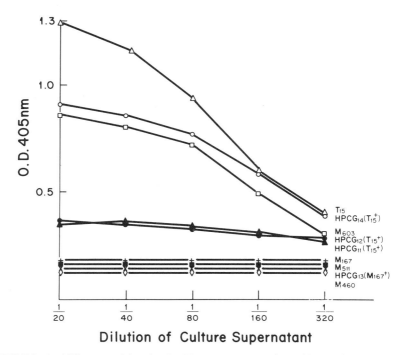

FIGURE 2. Anti-idiotype activity of 11E7. The assays were performed in a similar manner as in FIGURE 1, except the plates were coated with T15, HPCG14, M603, M511, M167, M460, HPCG12, HPCG13, and HPCG11.

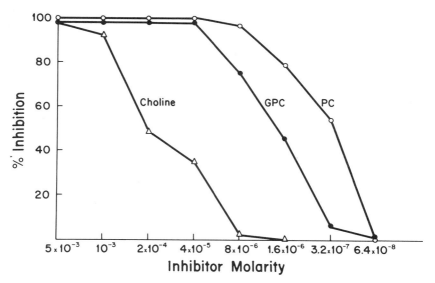

FIGURE 3. PC and PC analogues inhibit 11E7 binding to T15. The assays were performed in a similar manner as in FIGURE 1, except 25 ng of enzyme-coupled 11E7 was coincubated with different concentrations of PC and PC analogues and the percent inhibitions were calculated.

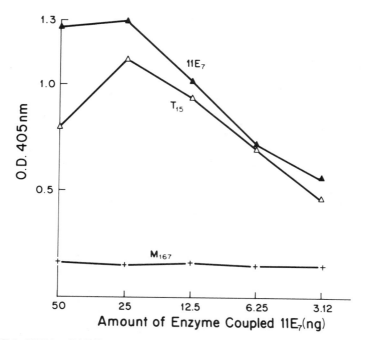

FIGURE 4. 11E7 is self-binding. Microtiter plates were coated for 18 h with 100 μl/well of 11E7 or T15 (2 μg/ml) in PBS, washed three times, and incubated for 1 h with 1% BSA in PBS. After washing three times, enzyme-coupled 11E7 in 1% BSA - 0.05% Tween 20-BBS solution was added. After washing three times, color was developed with substrate and the O.D. at 405 nm was measured.

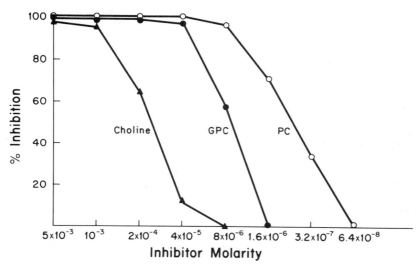

FIGURE 5. PC and PC analogues inhibit 11E7 self-binding. The assays were performed in a similar manner as in FIGURE 4, except 25 ng of enzyme-coupled 11E7 was coincubated with different concentrations of inhibitors and the percent inhibitions were calculated.

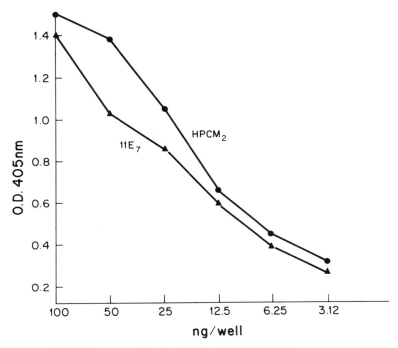

FIGURE 6. 11E7 binds to a monoclonal anti-T15 antibody (F6.3). The assay was performed in a similar manner as in FIGURE 1, except F(ab)$'_2$ of F6.3 was used to coat the plate. HPCM2 was used as a positive control.

antibodies have dual properties of a Fc specific idiotypic determinant and an anti-Fc specific paratope. They proposed the term "epibody" to describe the presence of the internal image of the original epitope on an anti-idiotypic antibody.

In order to exclude the possibility that the 11E7 hybridoma preparation consists of a mixture of two different molecules (one being a PC-binding antibody and the other an anti-idiotype antibody), we will consider the following data. First, we cloned the 11E7 cell line twice using a limiting dilution at 0.5 cells per well. The culture supernatant of the recloned cells binds to T15 and PC-BSA in ELISA as shown in FIGURE 1. Second, we purified ascites using two different immunoabsorbent columns, PC-Sepharose and T15-Sepharose. It was found that purified antibodies from either column have binding activities identical to the original culture supernatant.

There are two ways by which 11E7 could be self-binding. In model A (see FIGURE 7), each 11E7 molecule uses only one of its two sites to interact with another 11E7 molecule. Either, one 11E7 binds to another 11E7 via the PC paratope or it binds via the PC image. According to this model, it is possible to form large complexes without steric restrictions. Thus, we call this model the "open-ended complex" model.

In the second model B (see FIGURE 7), each 11E7 molecule can bind by using simultaneously both sites, the PC paratope and the PC image. The result of this "closed loop" binding would be the formation of dimers. Larger complexing is also possible in this model, but there would be more steric restriction because of the interdigitating nature of the self-binding.

In our study on 11E7, we could demonstrate that the 11E7 can bind to itself and that this self-binding is completely inhibited by free hapten PC. We propose here that this self-binding plays an important biological role in the regulation of the immune response. From a conceptual view, 11E7 represents the key elements of the immune network in as much as it is idiotype, AB1, and anti-idiotype, Ab2-beta. Thus, the regulatory functions of the idiotype network should be, at least in part, carried out by this type of antibody that in essence could function as a "mini-network." The most important property of the 11E7 antibody appears to be its self-complexing capacity. In contrast to epibodies with Fc specificity, the complexes of 11E7 are specific for a external antigen (PC); that is, free PC dissociates the 11E7 complex. By this virtue, 11E7 could act like a buffer during an anti-PC response. At initial high concentration of PC antigen, the 11E7 complex would dissociate and neutralize the PC antigen. As the PC antigen is cleared from the circulation, 11E7 returns to a complex state. As complex, 11E7 would be removed faster from circulation than noncomplexed antibody. By this model, autobody would provide a very efficient way of adjusting to antigen loads and prevent prolonged persistence of free and unnecessary antibody.

Besides the role of autobody in the normal regulatory mechanism of the immune response, pathological conditions may develop in which such self-complexing antibodies could be produced in large excess. In such a situation, large complexes could form, leading to depositions in critical tissues and inducing damage associated with autoimmune diseases. Complex depositions of this type would not include antigen material. It is of interest to note here that in several instances it is difficult to demonstrate antigen material in autoimmune complex deposits.

The utility of the described antibody having complementary binding sites and idiotopes for the design of the so-called idiotope vaccines should be considered. Idiotope vaccines modeled according to the autobody concept would be able to deliver both passive and active immunity. Via the specific paratope site, autobody vaccines could provide immediate protection and at the same time immunize actively through its internal antigen. Of course, it remains to be seen how frequent these autobodies are

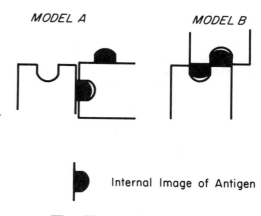

FIGURE 7. Self-binding models of 11E7.

Internal Image of Antigen

Binding Site of Antibody

and how difficult it will be to isolate hybridoma antibodies exhibiting these properties.

REFERENCES

1. JERNE, N. K. 1974. Ann. Immunol. Inst. Pasteur (Paris) **125C:** 373.
2. KOHLER, H., R. REIN & T. KIEBER-EMMONS. 1986. Immunol. Rev. In press.
3. KIEBER-EMMONS, T., R. E. WARD, S. RAYCHAUDHURI, R. REIN & H. KOHLER. 1986. Int. Rev. Immunol. **1:** 1.
4. BONA, C. A., S. FINLEY, S. WATERS & H. G. KUNKEL. 1982. J. Exp. Med. **156:** 986.
5. MCNAMARA, M. K., R. WARD & H. KOHLER. 1984. Science **226:** 1325.
6. WITTNER, M. K., M. A. BACH & H. KOHLER. 1982. J. Immunol. **128:** 595.
7. GEARHART, P. J., N. D. JOHNSON, R. DOUGLAS & L. HOOD. 1981. Nature (London) **291:** 29.
8. CLAFLIN, J. L., S. HUDAK & A. MADDALENA. 1981. J. Exp. Med. **153:** 352.
9. BONA, C. & H. KOHLER. 1984. *In* Receptor Biochemistry and Methodology, vol. IV. J. C. Venter, C. M. Fraser & J. Lindstrom, Eds: 141. Alan R. Liss. New York.
10. KOHLER, H., S. MULLER & C. BONA. 1985. Proc. Soc. Exp. Biol. Med. **178:** 189.
11. CHEN, P. P., S. FONG, R. A. HOUGHTEN & D. A. CARSON. 1985. J. Exp. Med. **161:** 323.

DISCUSSION OF THE PAPER

Y. NAPARSTEK (*Tufts New England Medical Center, Boston, MA*): We have a very similar observation. We found, in serum from a rabbit that was immunized with a monoclonal human anti-DNA antibody, a subpopulation of antibodies that bound both the idiotype and an anti-idiotype. They showed exactly the same characteristics as your monoclonal antibody.

H. KOHLER (*Roswell Park Memorial Institute, Buffalo, NY*): Do you have any idea of what percentage this antibody was represented at in your antiserum?

NAPARSTEK: I think it was not in a minor percentage, but it is very difficult to say exactly how much.

KOHLER: Did the rabbit have any pathology?

NAPARSTEK: We do not know.

B. F. ERLANGER (*Columbia University, New York, NY*): One of my students, Harry Koo, has made a monoclonal antibody to the adenosine receptor through the auto-anti-idiotypic route. It binds both the anti-adenosine antibody and the adenosine conjugates in a very similar situation to yours. On the other hand, we did not see this by radioimmunoassay and we do not know what that means. Radioimmunoassay is much more sensitive to the binding constant than ELISA is, so perhaps we ought to be a little careful at the moment.

Z. BENTWICH (*R. Ben Ari Institute of Clinical Immunology, Rehovot, Israel*): I would like to add one more thing. I think that a big problem with the T-cell antigen-specific factor is that it contains MHC components and yet it recognizes MHC. Now, however, your results provide a very nice possibility to account for such a combination on a relatively small molecule.

Monoclonal Autoantibodies That React with Multiple Organs

Basis for Reactivity

ABNER LOUIS NOTKINS AND BELLUR S. PRABHAKAR

Laboratory of Oral Medicine
National Institutes of Dental Research
National Institutes of Health
Bethesda, Maryland 20205

Serum from patients with certain autoimmune disorders such as systemic lupus erythematosus and polyendocrine disease reacts with antigens in a number of different organs. The nature of this multiple-organ autoreactivity of serum has never been fully explained. There are at least two possibilities, which are not mutually exclusive. The first is that the serum contains a number of different organ-specific antibodies. The second is that the serum contains antibodies that recognize common proteins or epitopes in different organs. Using hybridoma technology and transformation of B lymphocytes by Epstein-Barr Virus (EBV), it is now becoming possible to address this question by studying the reactivity of monoclonal autoantibodies. In this report, we briefly summarize some of our studies on preparing and characterizing monoclonal autoantibodies. In addition, we show that many monoclonal autoantibodies are of the multiple-organ reactive (MOR) type and that lymphocytes that make MOR autoantibodies are common and are part of the host's normal B-cell repertoire.

MONOCLONAL MOR AUTOANTIBODIES FROM MICE WITH AUTOIMMUNE POLYENDOCRINE DISEASE

Several years ago, we showed that mice infected with reovirus type-1 developed an autoimmune polyendocrine disease. Autoantibodies that reacted with anterior pituitary, pancreas, thyroid, and gastric mucosa were more commonly found in the sera of reovirus-infected than uninfected mice.[1,2] By using hybridoma technology, we succeeded in preparing a large number of monoclonal autoantibodies.[3] In brief, we fused spleen cells from mice with reovirus-induced autoimmunity with myeloma cells. The resulting hybridomas were screened for autoantibodies with a panel of six or more normal host tissues using indirect immunofluorescence or immunoperoxidase staining. By this method, more than 35 hybridomas synthesizing IgM monoclonal autoantibodies were prepared.

During the course of this work, we observed that many of the monoclonal autoantibodies reacted with antigens in more than one organ. We refer to these multiple-organ-reactive antibodies as MOR antibodies. FIGURE 1 shows the reactivity of one of these autoantibodies designated MOR-1. This antibody reacted with cells in the gastric mucosa, anterior pituitary, small intestine, and pancreatic islet of Langerhans. The reactivity pattern of MOR-1 and six other monoclonal MOR antibodies are summarized in TABLE 1. All the antibodies reacted with cells in the anterior pituitary and gastric mucosa. Also one reacted with cells in the small intestine and pancreatic

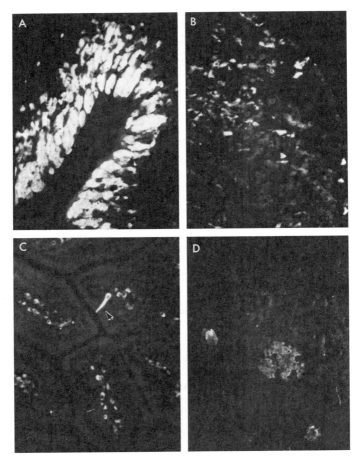

FIGURE 1. Reactivity of MOR-1 isolated from a mouse[3] with reovirus type-1 induced autoimmune polyendocrine disease with cells in (A) gastric mucosa, (B) anterior pituitary, (C) small intestine, and (D) pancreatic islets of Langerhans.

TABLE 1. Reactivity Pattern of Monoclonal Autoantibodies Generated from Mice with Autoimmune Polyendocrine Diseases[a]

Monoclonal Autoantibody	Fluorescent Antibody Titer			
	Gastric Mucosa	Anterior Pituitary	Small Intestine	Pancreatic Islets
MOR-1	800	800	400	40
MOR-2	100	50	<2	10
MOR-3	400	50	<2	<2
MOR-4	100	100	<2	<2
MOR-5	100	10	<2	10
MOR-6	400	400	<2	20
MOR-7	100	400	<2	10

[a]See reference 3.

islets. Five out of seven of these antibodies showed moderate to weak reactivity with pancreatic islet cells. None of the antibodies reacted with mouse kidney, spleen, liver, muscle, or lung.

MONOCLONAL MOR AUTOANTIBODIES FROM NORMAL MICE

Generation of MOR autoantibody-producing hybridomas from mice with autoimmune disease raised the possibility that the B lymphocytes capable of making autoantibodies are normally present in the animal and are triggered by the viral infection to synthesize and secrete autoantibodies to a level that is detectable in the serum. To test this possibility, we fused splenic lymphocytes from normal SJL/J and BALB/c mice with myeloma cells.[4] Supernatants from the hybrid cultures were screened by the indirect immunofluorescence on autologous pituitary, pancreas, stomach, and salivary glands. Twenty hybrids producing autoantibodies were cloned and eight stable hybridomas that synthesized IgM monoclonal autoantibodies were established. Five of the monoclones were of the MOR type, two reacted with stomach, and one with nuclei. FIGURE 2 shows the reactivity of one of these antibodies (MOR-N1) with cells in the anterior pituitary, gastric mucosa, interstitium of testis, and corpus luteum of ovary. The reactivity pattern of five of these antibodies is summarized in TABLE 2. All autoantibodies reacted with anterior pituitary and stomach and four out of the five reacted with cells in the salivary glands. MOR-N1 also reacted with cells in the testes and ovaries and MOR-N5 reacted with cells in the pancreatic islets.

HUMAN MONOCLONAL MOR AUTOANTIBODIES PREPARED BY HYBRIDOMA TECHNIQUES

The experiments in mice were extended to humans.[5] Peripheral blood leukocytes from patients with insulin-dependent diabetes or Hashimoto's thyroiditis, or both, were fused with either mouse myeloma or human myeloma cells. Immunoglobulin-secreting hybridomas were screened with a panel of normal tissues by indirect immunofluorescence or immunoperoxidase. Out of a total of 150 Ig-secreting cultures from 20 different patients, 9 secreted autoantibodies. Seven of these produced MOR autoantibodies. MOR-h1 and MOR-h2 were human-mouse heterohybridomas, whereas the other 5 were human-human hybridomas. TABLE 3 summarizes the partial reactivity of these antibodies with normal human tissues. All 7 MOR antibodies reacted with anterior pituitary, gastric mucosa, thyroid follicle, and ducts or islets in the pancreas. MOR-h5 and MOR-h7 also reacted with smooth muscle and MOR-h4, MOR-h5, MOR-h6, and MOR-h7 reacted with cultured cells.

HUMAN MONOCLONAL MOR AUTOANTIBODIES PREPARED BY EPSTEIN-BARR VIRUS TRANSFORMATION OF LYMPHOCYTES

The demonstration that many monoclonal autoantibodies are of the MOR type initially came from the preparation of hybridomas using tumor cells (myelomas) as fusion partners. Recently, we showed that human B lymphocytes transformed by EBV could also make monoclonal autoantibodies and that many of these antibodies were of the MOR type. In these experiments, peripheral blood leukocytes from patients with

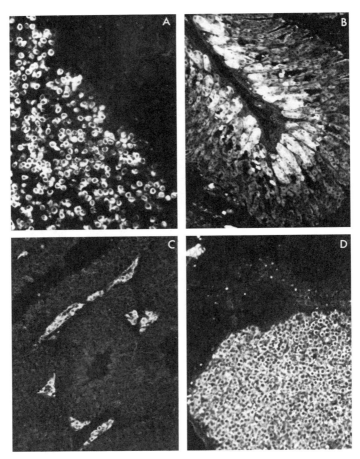

FIGURE 2. Reactivity of MOR-N1 isolated from a normal BALB/c mouse[4] with cells in the (A) anterior pituitary, (B) gastric mucosa, (C) interstitium of the testis, and (D) corpus luteum of the ovary.

TABLE 2. Reactivity Pattern of Monoclonal Autoantibodies Generated from Normal Mice[a]

	Tissues Showing Reactivity						
Monoclonal Antibodies	Anterior Pituitary	Stomach (chief cells)	Salivary Gland (ducts)	Pancreas (periphery of islet)	Ovary (corpus luteum)	Testis (interstitial)	Nuclei
MOR-N1	+	+	+	−	+	+	−
MOR-N2	+	+	+	−	−	−	−
MOR-N3	+	+	+	−	−	−	−
MOR-N4	+	+	+	−	−	−	−
MOR-N5	+	+	−	+	−	−	−

[a]See reference 4.

insulin-dependent diabetes and thyroiditis were transformed with EBV.[6] In some experiments, lymphocytes from normal individuals without any evidence of autoimmune disease also were used. The supernatants from each of the wells containing EBV-transformed cells were tested for reactivity with normal human or monkey tissues by the avidin-biotin immunoperoxidase method. A number of the EBV-transformed cell cultures from both normal individuals and patients with autoimmune disease were cloned by the limiting dilution method and about a dozen cell lines making monoclonal autoantibodies were established.[6] These cell lines secreted 0.5 to 2.0 μg/ml of IgM. All the antibodies were of the MOR type. FIGURE 3 shows the reactivity of one of these monoclonal antibodies, designated H10-3-5, with basement membrane of the esophagus, axons of the nerve, parathyroid, smooth muscle of the stomach, ductal cells of the salivary gland, and transitional epithelium of the bladder. TABLE 4 summarizes the partial tissue reactivity of four of these monoclonal autoantibodies.

TABLE 3. Reactivity Pattern of Human Monoclonal Autoantibodies Prepared by Hybridoma Technology[a]

Monoclonal Antibodies	Myeloma Cell	Tissues Showing Reactivity					
		Anterior Pituitary	Thyroid	Gastric Mucosa	Pancreas	Smooth Muscle	Cultured Cells
MOR-h1	Mouse	+ +	+ +	+ +	+	−	−
MOR-h2	Mouse	+	+ +	+ +	+	−	−
MOR-h3	Human	+	+	+	+	−	−
MOR-h4	Human	+	+	+ +	+	−	+
MOR-h5	Human	+	+ +	+ +	+	+ +	+ +
MOR-h6	Human	+	+	+	+	−	+
MOR-h7	Human	+	+	+ +	+	+ +	+ +

[a]See reference 5.

COMPARISON OF METHODS FOR GENERATING HUMAN MONOCLONAL AUTOANTIBODIES

A general comparison of the various methods used for preparing human monoclonal autoantibodies,[7] based on a still limited number of experiments, is given in TABLE 5. The frequency of establishing immortalized cell lines was higher with EBV. The cloning efficiency, however, of EBV-transformed cells was low as compared to hybridomas. It also should be noted that the avidin-biotin immunoperoxidase method, which is perhaps more sensitive than immunofluorescence, was used to detect autoantibodies in the culture supernatants of EBV-transformed cells.[7] Irrespective of the method, it is now clear that human cell lines producing monoclonal MOR autoantibodies can be readily established.

BASIS FOR MULTIPLE-ORGAN REACTIVITY

What is the nature of the antigen(s) with which these autoantibodies react? Each antibody, of course, will have to be analyzed separately. We have concentrated our efforts on one of the human monoclonals, MOR-h1. By double immunofluorescence

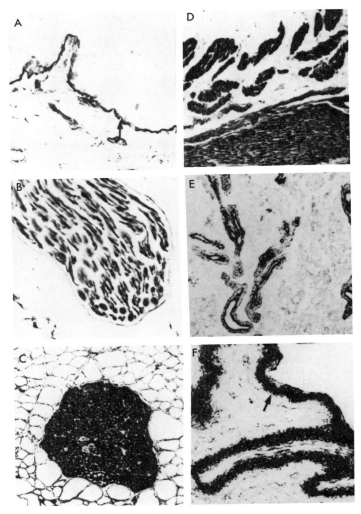

FIGURE 3. Reactivity of a human MOR antibody (H10-3-5) prepared by EBV transformation of human peripheral blood leukocytes[6] with (A) basement membrane of esophagus, (B) axons of the peripheral nerve, (C) parathyroid, (D) smooth muscle of stomach, (E) ductal cells of the salivary gland, and (F) transitional epithelium of the bladder.

techniques, using antibodies to a variety of known pituitary hormones, we showed that MOR-h1 reacts specifically with growth-hormone-containing cells.[8] Then, by ELISA, we demonstrated that MOR-h1 reacts specifically with growth hormone.[8] However, MOR-h1 also reacts with the stomach, pancreas, and thyroid, which do not contain growth hormone. The absence of growth hormone in these tissues was confirmed by the ability of a hyperimmune sera to growth hormone to react with pituitary, but not with thyroid, pancreas, or stomach. The reactivity of MOR-h1 with tissues after adsorption

TABLE 4. Reactivity Pattern of Human Monoclonal Autoantibodies Prepared by Transformation of Human Peripheral Leukocytes by EBV[a]

Monoclonal Autoantibody	Tissues Showing Reactivity				
	Thyroid	Pancreas	Stomach	Stratified Squamous Epithelium	Nerve
D5-2-19	Acinar	Islets, ductules	Smooth muscle	Perinuclear region	Axons
E10-1-19	Colloid	Basement membrane of ducts	None	None	None
H10-3-5	Acinar	Acinar, ducts	Smooth muscle	Basement membrane	Axons
D1-2	Acinar	None	None	Reserve cells	None

[a]See reference 6.

with human growth hormone is illustrated in FIGURE 4. Not only was the reactivity of MOR-h1 with the anterior pituitary eliminated, but its reactivity was eliminated also with thyroid, stomach, and pancreas. This suggested that MOR-h1 was reacting with growth hormone in the anterior pituitary, but with another molecule in the thyroid, stomach, and pancreas.

Proof for this came from isolating the antigens with which MOR-h1 reacted. An immunoaffinity column with MOR-h1 was prepared and extracts of pituitary, thyroid, and stomach were passed through the column. The antigens that bound to the column were eluted and electrophoresed on a polyacrylamide gel. As seen in FIGURE 5, a 21.5-kD band was isolated from the pituitary extract, but not from the thyroid or stomach extracts. This band comigrates with purified natural human growth hormone obtained from the National Pituitary Agency and DNA-derived biosynthetic human growth hormone obtained from Genentech. In addition to the 21.5-kD protein, another polypeptide with a molecular weight of approximately 35 kD was isolated from the pituitary. This polypeptide was also found in the thyroid and stomach. Thus it appears

TABLE 5. General Comparison of Methods for Generating Human Monoclonal Autoantibodies[a]

Properties of Cell Lines	Human-Mouse Hybridoma	Human-Human Hybridoma	EBV Virus Transformation
Frequency of establishing immortalized cell lines	3.3×10^{-6} [b]	3.4×10^{-7} [b]	$>1 \times 10^{-4}$ [c]
Percent of cell lines producing Ig[d]	18%	75%	73%
Ig-producing cell lines making autoantibodies[e]	23%	13%	69%
Cloning efficiency[f]	28%	18%	3%

[a]See reference 7.

[b]A total of 26 human-mouse and 53 human-human fusion experiments using total peripheral blood leukocytes were performed.

[c]EBV transformation was produced in 100% of the wells seeded with 1×10^4 nylon-wool-adherent cells.

[d]Cell lines making at least 1 μg/well antibody as detected in an ELISA.

[e]Screened by either indirect immunofluorescence (hybridomas) or avidin-biotin immunoperoxidase (EBV-transformed cells) method.

[f]Cells were plated at 1 cell/well.

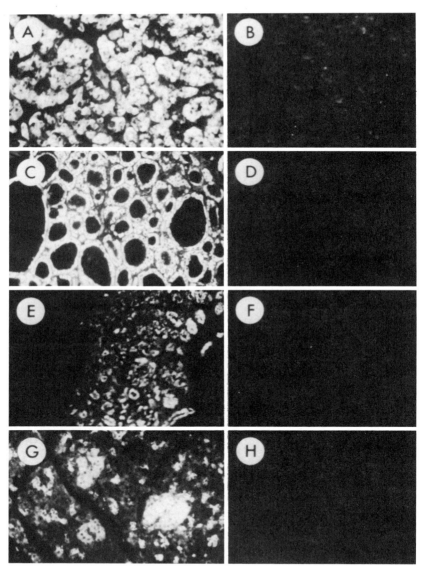

FIGURE 4. Reactivity of MOR-h1 with pituitary (A, B), thyroid (C, D), stomach (E, F), and pancreas (G, H) before (A, C, E, G) and after (B, D, F, H) adsorption with human growth hormone.[8]

that MOR-h1 reacts with two different proteins: one is the 21.5-kD growth hormone and the other is a 35-kD protein that presumably shares a common epitope with growth hormone.[8]

When we began these studies on autoimmunity, we thought that MOR antibodies were unusual and rare. As a result of more extensive screening procedures with a large panel of normal tissues that contain perhaps thousands of antigenic determinants, we are now finding many MOR antibodies. In fact, MOR antibodies are turning out to be the rule rather than the exception. Even monoclonal antibodies that we initially thought reacted only with a single protein show MOR activity.[9] For example, PI-6, a

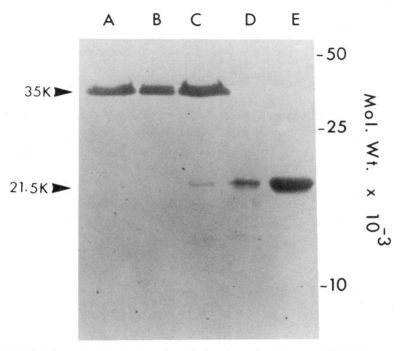

FIGURE 5. Polyacrylamide gel electrophoresis of antigens eluted from an MOR-h1 immunoaffinity column. Lanes: (A) thyroid, (B) stomach, (C) pituitary, (D) purified natural human growth hormone, and (E) DNA-derived biosynthetic human growth hormone.[8]

mouse monoclonal antibody, reacts with beta cells in the pancreas. By several methods, we have shown that this antibody reacts with insulin. Nonetheless, this anti-insulin monoclonal antibody also reacts with cells in several other organs that do not contain insulin. For example, PI-6 reacts with acinar cells in the salivary gland, interstitial cells of testis, the corpus luteum of ovary, and the ductus deferens.[9] Adsorption of PI-6 with insulin not only eliminates its capacity to react with beta cells, but also its capacity to react with all the other cell types (TABLE 6). Similarly, mouse monoclonal antibody AP-2 reacts with growth hormone and yet stains a number of tissues that do not contain growth hormone. The most likely explanation is that PI-6 and AP-2 are reacting with a specific epitope present on insulin and growth hormone, respectively, and still another protein in other organs.

Several explanations for multiple-organ reactivity are illustrated in FIGURE 6. The first (FIGURE 6A) is that the same protein is present in two different organs and the monoclonal antibody recognizes that protein (e.g., reactivity of MOR-h1 with the 35-kD protein in pituitary, thyroid, and stomach). The second (FIGURE 6B) is that the same epitope is present on different proteins and the monoclonal antibody reacts with that epitope (e.g., perhaps reactivity of MOR-h1 with growth hormone and the 35-kD protein). However, the third alternative is more complex. Here, the monoclonal antibody may recognize different epitopes on different proteins (FIGURE 6C). For example, a monoclonal antibody may be directed against a complex epitope on the protein in organ B. However, this monoclonal antibody might be able to react, albeit with a different affinity, with the epitope on the protein in organ A and also with the epitope on the protein in organ C. This would be an example of molecular mimicry. It is fairly easy to distinguish between examples depicted in FIGURES 6A and 6B, but it is difficult to distinguish between examples depicted in FIGURES 6B and 6C. What this says is that the simple interaction of a monoclonal antibody with an unknown protein does not prove or establish molecular identity. Biochemical confirmation is required to establish the identity of the molecule.

Perhaps one reason that we have been successful in recognizing the multiple-organ reactivity or polyreactivity of monoclonal antibodies is because we have screened each antibody against a panel of many normal tissues that contain a substantial part of the host's "antigenic repertoire." Whether any of these antibodies are actually the ones expressed in autoimmune disease is still not clear. Many of these antibodies probably represent products of germline genes that are ordinarily silent and not expressed (i.e., not secreting antibodies) in normal individuals. Immortalization of cells carrying these genes by fusion with myeloma cells or transformation by EBV is allowing us, at the least, to investigate the host's potential autoantibody repertoire.

SUMMARY

We have been able to make monoclonal MOR antibodies in several different ways. First, we have been able to prepare MOR antibodies from mice with autoimmune

TABLE 6. Tissue Reactivity of Absorbed and Unabsorbed Monoclonal Anti-Hormone Antibodies[a]

Antibody	Absorbed with	Reactivity of Antibodies by Indirect Immunofluorescence with			
		Pancreatic Islets	Anterior Pituitary	Salivary Glands	Stomach
PI-6	PBS	+	+	+	−
	Insulin	−	−	−	−
	Growth hormone	+	+	+	−
AP-2	PBS	+	+	−	+
	Insulin	+	+	−	+
	Growth hormone	−	−	−	−
Anti-insulin		+	−	−	−
Anti-growth hormone		−	+	−	−

[a]See reference 9.

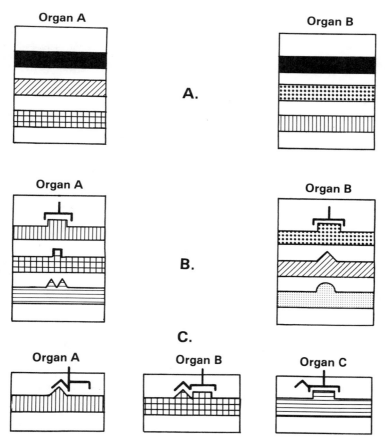

FIGURE 6. Basis for multiple-organ reactivity. (A) Recognition of the same protein; (B) Recognition of the same epitope on different proteins; (C) Recognition of different epitopes on different proteins. The dark lines above the rectangle in FIGURES 6B and 6C represent antibodies. Rectangles within each organ represent different proteins.

disease and from humans with autoimmune disease. Second, we have prepared MOR antibodies from normal mice without autoimmune disease and from healthy humans without evidence of autoimmune disease. Third, we have prepared MOR antibodies by hybridoma technology and by transformation of lymphocytes with EBV. We have shown that MOR antibodies are common and are part of the host's normal B-cell repertoire. Our studies raise the possibility that most monoclonal autoantibodies, when extensively screened, will to a greater or lesser degree be of the MOR type.

ACKNOWLEDGMENT

The authors wish to acknowledge the excellent editorial assistance of Nancy O. Walsh.

REFERENCES

1. ONODERA, T., A. TONIOLO, U. R. RAY, A. B. JENSON, R. A. KNAZEK & A. L. NOTKINS. 1981. J. Exp. Med. **153:** 1457–1473.
2. ONODERA, T., U. R. RAY, K. A. MELEZ, H. SUZUKI, A. TONIOLO & A. L. NOTKINS. 1982. Nature **297:** 66–68.
3. HASPEL, M. V., T. ONODERA, B. S. PRABHAKAR, P. R. MCCLINTOCK, K. ESSANI, U. R. RAY, S. YAGIHASHI & A. L. NOTKINS. 1983. Nature **303:** 73–76.
4. PRABHAKAR, B. S., J. SAEGUSA, T. ONODERA & A. L. NOTKINS. 1984. J. Immunol. **133:** 2815–2817.
5. SATOH, J., B. S. PRABHAKAR, M. V. HASPEL, F. GINSBERG-FELLNER & A. L. NOTKINS. 1983. N. Engl. J. Med. **309:** 217–220.
6. GARZELLI, C., F. E. TAUB, J. E. SCHARFF, B. S. PRABHAKAR, F. GINSBERG-FELLNER & A. L. NOTKINS. 1984. J. Virol. **52:** 722–725.
7. TAUB, F., J. SATOH, C. GARZELLI, K. ESSANI & A. L. NOTKINS. 1985. Human monoclonal autoantibodies reactive with multiple organs. *In* Human Hybridomas and Monoclonal Antibodies. E. G. Engleman, S. K. H. Foung, J. Larrick & A. Reubitschek, Eds.: 263–275. Plenum. New York.
8. SATOH, J., K. ESSANI, P. R. MCCLINTOCK & A. L. NOTKINS. 1984. J. Clin. Invest. **74:** 1526–1531.
9. SAEGUSA, J., T. ONODERA, U. R. RAY, B. S. PRABHAKAR & A. L. NOTKINS. 1985. Endocrinology **116:** 761–764.

DISCUSSION OF THE PAPER

UNIDENTIFIED DISCUSSANT: Is the phenomenon you are observing random or not? This question has to do with Frank Dixon's comment, that in the MRL mouse, the entire V_H gene repertoire is being used, and then with the later comment stating that there appears to be some restriction in the genes encoding autoantibodies. Also, suppose you examined all these hybridomas for reactivity against a battery of what we as immunologists would arbitrarily consider as a foreign antigen, such as a chemical hapten. What do you think the result would be? Do you think you would find a similar distribution of apparently spontaneously occurring anti-hapten antibodies or do you think that the population is switched in strong bias toward autoantigens?

A. L. NOTKINS (*National Institutes of Health, Bethesda, MD*): My prejudice is that when you test any antibody and you screen it against enough antigens, you are going to find multiple-organ reactivity or polyreactivity. I think the reason we are finding this is simply because of the way that we are screening. In the past, most people immunized animals. They knew what the antigen that they were after was and they tested against just that antigen. However, we are screening against a dozen different normal tissues, with each tissue containing many different cell types and thousands of antigens. I think if you took enough chemicals off the shelf randomly and screened them, you would find polyreactivity.

UNIDENTIFIED DISCUSSANT: What you are saying, then, is that there is no bias for autoantibody reactivity in the population that you are studying.

NOTKINS: No, I would not go that far.

Natural Autoantibodies Constitute a Substantial Part of Normal Circulating Immunoglobulins

G. DIGHIERO,[a] P. LYMBERI,[b] B. GUILBERT,[b]
T. TERNYNCK,[b] AND S. AVRAMEAS[b]

[a]Service d'Immunohématologie et d'Immunopathologie
[b]Unité d'Immunocytochimie
Institut Pasteur
75724 Paris Cedex 15, France

According to Burnet's clonal selection theory,[1] in the early 1960s, explanations for tolerance and autoimmunity were attractively simple. Autoreactive lymphocytes were deleted during embryonic life to provide self-tolerance, and autoantibodies, always noxious, were the products of mutant forbidden clones that were able to circumvent this process of immunological homeostasis. However, during the last two decades, several groups succeeded in challenging clonal deletion as a general explanation for tolerance to self[2] by: (a) Inducing autoimmune diseases by injecting organ extracts; (b) Demonstrating the presence of numerous autoantibodies in normal serum coming from a normal population;[3] (c) Demonstrating the presence of normal autoreactive B cells;[4] (d) Inducing in an animal numerous autoantibodies after challenging with mitogens.

The existence of natural antibodies in normal human serum was first reported by Landsteiner in 1900, when he discovered the presence of natural hemagglutinins in serum directed against blood group determinants of the A-B-O system. Accordingly, Boyden[5] defined natural antibodies as a family of molecules present in the body fluids of normal animals that is able to specifically combine with antigens, but not with the immunologically acceptable molecules normally present in the body fluids. Nevertheless, natural antibodies directed against various antigens have been reported in different animal species and are often directed against various autoantigens. Obviously, a clear distinction between autoantibodies and natural antibodies is difficult to establish. During preparation of specific antisera against cytoskeletal proteins, we also detected the presence of natural antitubulin antibodies in the sera of normal humans and several species of normal nonimmunized animals.[6] We subsequently isolated and characterized these antibodies, which were able to interact with autologous tubulin.

For several years, we have been working on natural autoantibodies at the Unité d'Immunocytochimie of Pasteur Institute. The results of these studies are reported in the present work.

EVIDENCES THAT NATURAL AUTOANTIBODIES CONSTITUTE A SUBSTANTIAL PART OF NORMAL CIRCULATING Ig

In order to demonstrate in normal human serum the presence of natural autoantibodies, we immobilized nine different antigens (actin, tubulin, thyroglobulin, fetuin, myoglobin, albumin, transferrin, collagen, and cytochrome C) on "Ultrogel" beads.

Sera from normal donors were successively run through the nine immunoadsorbents and the proteins retained on the beads were eluted with glycine buffer, pH 2.8.[7] The affinity chromatography isolated proteins, and on analysis, they were found to be composed mainly of IgG (about 70%), IgA (about 15%), and IgM (about 15%). They were always accompanied by significant, but variable amounts of albumin. Eluted immunoglobulins were bound strongly to the corresponding antigens used for their isolation, whereas the immunoglobulins present in the elution from other columns reacted in most cases with several other antigens in varying degrees that never exceeded 50% of that of the homologous antibody. The competitive enzyme immunoassays enabled the isolated antibodies to be classified into three groups. The first was composed of antitubulin and antithyroglobulin, which were only inhibited by the homologous antigen. The second consisted of antiactin, antimyoglobin, and antifetuin. These antibodies were mainly inhibited by their homologous antigens, but they were also inhibited by two or three additional antigens to a significant degree. Thus, the reaction between antiactin antibodies and immobilized actin was inhibited mainly by actin; however, tubulin and thyroglobulin also inhibited the reaction to a certain extent. The third group comprised antialbumin, antitransferrin, anticollagen, and anticytochrome C antibodies, which were inhibited only slightly (30%) or not at all by their homologous antigen. Additional proofs concerning the specificity of the binding of such natural antibodies were afforded by immunocytochemical staining of human cultured hepatocytes and the fact that the reactivity was mediated by the F(ab) fragment of immunoglobulin.

MIg FREQUENTLY CORRESPOND TO THE EXPANSION OF A CLONE NORMALLY PRODUCING A NATURAL ANTIBODY

Monoclonal immunoglobulins (MIg) were for a long time considered "abnormal" immunoglobulins (Ig) without known functional antibody activity. Studies carried out during the last two decades have indicated that MIg correspond to normal synthetic products whose counterparts can be found in the heterogenous normal Ig population. Although some human MIg are known to possess antibody activity directed against autoantigens, like the Fc fragment of IgG and the Ii blood group, the incidence of other auto- and hetero-antigens is almost negligible.[8]

The results obtained with normal human serum prompted us to examine whether some MIg possessed antibody activities directed against actin, tubulin, myosin, thyroglobulin, double-stranded DNA (dsDNA), myoglobin, fetuin, albumin, and transferrin.[9,10]

Serum samples containing a total of 612 different MIg (273 IgG, 158 IgM, 136 IgA, 30 Bence-Jones proteins, 31 IgD, and 13 double MIg) were tested by enzyme immunoassay. Of the 612 sera examined, 576 did not exhibit binding in excess of normal values. The remaining 36 sera contained antibody activity against one or more antigens. One MIg (IgAK) was found to bind exclusively to tubulin, one (IgMλ) was bound to dsDNA only, one (IgGλ) was bound to thyroglobulin only, and one (IgGK) was bound chiefly to myosin and, to a lesser extent, to actin and tubulin. The 32 remaining sera (10 IgMK, 5 IgMλ, 7 IgGK, 6 IgGλ, 1 IgAλ) reacted mainly with actin, but they also reacted constantly and significantly with tubulin and thyroglobulin. Five of these 32 sera were also bound significantly to myosin.

The interaction of the MIg with the respective antigen was demonstrated by immunoenzymatic methods with monospecific antisera and by blotting experiments. Furthermore, this interaction in the 12 cases studied was mediated by the dimeric fragment F(ab')2 of the MIg. The MIg with antitubulin, antithyroglobulin, and anti-dsDNA activities were exclusively inhibited by their homologous antigens. Those with antiactin activity were predominantly inhibited by actin and also by tubulin and thyroglobulin. The one binding to myosin was, for the most part, inhibited by myosin and also significantly by actin and tubulin.

Retrospective clinical analysis was possible for 31 out of the 36 patients. Twenty-six of 31 patients had malignant lymphoplasmocytic disorders. The 5 others were followed for miscellaneous disorders without overt signs of multiple or Waldenström's macroglobulinemia. The data for the 31 patients were surveyed in order to determine whether the particular antibody activity of the MIg contributed to the symptomatology of the corresponding disease. No such indication was found. In particular, the patient with a monoclonal anti-dsDNA did not exhibit clinical features related to systemic lupus erythematosus and the 30 patients exhibiting anticytoskeletal activity did not show any special or common features either.[10]

PRODUCTION OF HYBRIDOMA CELL LINES SECRETING NATURAL MONOCLONAL AUTOANTIBODIES

In order to examine whether autoreactive B-cell clones are present under normal physiological conditions, we fused nonimmunized BALB/c splenocytes with nonsecreting myeloma lines. Hybrids were selected in HAT medium screened for Ig production and for antibody activity against the aforesaid panel of antigens.

To begin with, we fused spleen cells from 12-week-old nonimmunized BALB/c mice, resulting in 161 Ig-secreting hybrids of which 3 were found to react with dsDNA, 1 with thyroglobulin only, and 1 was found to react mainly with myosin, but also significantly with actin, tubulin, spectrin, and dsDNA.[11]

Three of these five potentially positive clones were lost during the first week of culture. The two remaining clones were successively subcloned and then injected into BALB/c mice in order to induce ascites and to produce MIg. The first clone corresponded to an IgM (D23) that reacted mainly with dsDNA and that exhibited reactivity with cytoskeletal proteins in direct binding experiments. However, only significant inhibition was obtained with dsDNA. The second clone (E7) was also an IgM, which reacted mainly with myosin, but also reacted significantly with actin, tubulin, myosin, spectrin, TNP, and dsDNA. Its binding was specifically inhibited by mouse myosin, but also (to a lesser, but significant extent) by actin, tubulin, spectrin, TNP, and dsDNA. Blotting experiments enabled us to confirm that this antibody bound to myosin, actin, tubulin, and spectrin. Furthermore, E7 was found to react with rat, rabbit, mouse, and chicken myosin. Although, it was found to bind with light meromyosin, heavy meromyosin, S2, S1, and rod fragments, no reaction has been found yet with the light chain of myosin. The binding to dsDNA could be clearly established by the fact that E7 was found to react with purified dsDNA obtained from PBR 322 plasmid.

More recently, in collaboration with A. Couthinho (Institut Pasteur), we obtained a large collection of Ig-secreting natural hybridomas with spleen cells from 6-day-old BALB/c and BALB.B10 nonimmunized mice.[12] Twenty-four (6.25%) out of the 384 hybrids were shown to react with at least one antigen of the panel. Ten of these hybrids were cloned and propagated, and the corresponding monoclonal IgM protein was isolated from ascitic fluids and further characterized. At least four groups of antibody specificities were identified: (1) One clone reacting with TNP only; (2) One clone reacting with both actin and tubulin; (3) Two clones that bound both to actin and TNP; (4) A fourth group, comprising the six other clones, that exhibited all widespread reactivity and bound to actin, tubulin, myosin, and TNP. The latter clones were isolated by affinity chromatography on a DNP immunoadsorbent and these isolated MIg were found to conserve their widespread reactivity.

HIGH INCIDENCE OF CROSS-REACTIVE IDIOTYPES AMONG MURINE NATURAL AUTOANTIBODIES

Almost all the idiotypic (Id) studies have been carried out with anti-Id antisera raised against induced antibodies that possess a sharp specificity, in contrast to natural antibodies that exhibit broad reactivities involving self- and nonself-antigens. Since natural antibodies are present in high amounts in the sera of normal patients, we felt it was of interest to analyze the idiotypy of these antibodies.

We induced anti-idiotypic (anti-Id) antibodies in rabbits against two natural monoclonal IgM autoantibodies, D23 and E7,[11] which both exhibited a broad reactivity. These anti-Id were used to test the reactivities of 12 natural monoclonal autoantibodies corresponding to the above-mentioned fusions obtained from adult and newborn nonimmunized mice. Both anti-Id (anti-D23 and anti-E7) recognized cross-reactive idiotopes frequently shared by natural monoclonal autoantibodies. All of the Id-bearing antibodies possessed widespread reactivity with structurally dissimilar self- and nonself-antigens. In most cases, their cross-reactive Id determinants seemed to be located outside of their antigen-binding sites. Furthermore, the presence in normal mouse sera of significant levels of D23 and E7 idiotopes correlated with the presence of natural antibody activity and was mainly associated with IgM and IgG2b fractions. Finally, D23 idiotopes were also found in induced murine antimyosin antibodies.[13]

CONCLUSIONS

Our results unequivocally demonstrate the existence in human serum of natural antibodies against the nine antigens examined. Therefore, it seems logical to extrapolate them in order to formulate the hypothesis that natural autoantibodies reacting with a wide variety of autoantigens will be found in normal human serum and will constitute a substantial part of normal circulating Ig. Our results should be associated with those reported from other groups, demonstrating the presence in normal serum of natural antibodies directed against a wide variety of autoantigens.[7,14,15] In our opinion, the existence of natural antibodies directed against autoantigens raises doubt concerning the distinction between a self- and nonself-antigen. It has been postulated that B cells bearing highly specific receptors for a given foreign structure are responsible for the accelerated synthesis of specific antibodies directed against this structure, which occurs after specific stimulation. In our opinion, it is improbable that an identical structure is not present in the host. It has been argued that such host structures are incapable of inducing an immune response since they correspond to hidden antigens that are not present at the cell surface and therefore never challenge the immune system. However, this view does not seem justified since some of these autoantibodies are directed against circulating proteins, like Fc fragment of IgG, albumin, and transferrin. Moreover, cells and tissues are continuously undergoing destruction and regeneration in all individuals. These results challenge the clonal deletion theory as a general and unique explanation for self-tolerance. However, autoantibodies directed against very specific antigens (e.g., the A antigen in the case of a subject belonging to the A group) or against polymorphic antigens of the major histocompatibility system have not been described until now to our knowledge. Therefore, clonal deletion mechanisms cannot, at the present time, be completely excluded for such particular cases.

The presence of natural autoantibodies in normal serum implies essentially the existence of autoreactive clones under normal physiological conditions. Our results obtained by fusing nonimmunized 12-week-old BALB/c, 6-day-old BALB/c, and BALB.B10 mice with a nonsecreting myeloma line indicated the existence of B-cell clones that were reactive against self-antigens and carried antibody specificities similar to those of natural antibodies found in normal human serum. In these studies, the frequencies of B cells binding to cytoskeletal proteins, TNP, and DNA are very high, and should be compared to those observed among clonal precursor cells after stimulation with LPS. Frequencies of 1/10 for NIP12-sheep red cells, 1/50 for TNP30-sheep red cells, 1/100 for NIP1-sheep red cells, 1/160 for TNP3-sheep red cells, 1/500 for horse red cells, and 1/1000 for sheep red cells have been reported previously.[16] More recently, frequencies of 1/50 to 1/500 for phosphorylcholine have also been found.[17] In view of our results showing that an important percentage of the clones reacting with TNP also bind to cytoskeletal proteins, it may be assumed that among the clones reacting with TNP, phosphorylcholine, and other haptens, an important number may also react with cytoskeletal proteins, as revealed in our preliminary results (Lymberi *et al.*, unpublished results).

The overall frequency of clones obtained after fusions of 6-day-old splenocytes is clearly higher than that observed with 12-week-old cells. Even though we cannot exclude that the 6-day-old "immature" lmphocytes are possibly more suitable for fusions, if such a tendency is confirmed by fusing 6-month-old BALB/c mice, it may be assumed that a part of this specificity repertoire is deleted during postnatal development. Although it is probable that the frequency of these clones decreases with age, the results with adult mice have shown that this group of antibody specificities constitutes at least 2% of the natural antibody repertoire. Alternatively, these clones could be present at the same frequencies in adults, but a strict control is exerted on them, precluding their activation.

In view of these observations, it is not surprising to find that these natural monoclonal antibodies exhibit a high incidence of cross-reactive idiotypes. The two anti-Id antibodies raised against the two polyspecific D23 and E7 natural monoclonal autoantibodies appeared to bind to structures within or near the antigen-combining site since the homologous Id–anti-Id interactions were inhibited by ds-DNA and myosin, respectively. Furthermore, it is quite probable that these anti-Id recognize Id determinants located outside the antigen-combining site of the autoantibodies. This conclusion is supported by the finding that cross-reaction between anti-Id antibodies and a significant number of natural monoclonal antibodies possessing similar, but not identical antibody specificities was not inhibited by those common antigens that they recognized.

The pressure of D23 and E7 Id in normal mouse sera indicates that the clones producing these natural monoclonal antibodies that arise from fusion experiments truly correspond to autoreactive B clones that secrete these products. A new and intriguing fact raised by these studies concerns the finding that these Id are mainly located in the IgG2B and IgM fractions. These results also seem to indicate that antibody exhibiting "D23- and E7-like" activities correspond to recurrent and frequent Id. Taken together, these observations suggest that restricted families of germline genes encode for at least some of these natural autoantibodies, either in the same individual or among different individuals.

Although some human MIg are known to possess antibody activity directed against autoantigens, bacterial antigens, and haptens, the high incidence of autoantigen activity found in our study with 672 MIg (36/612; 5.75%) and the autoantigen activity especially found against actin (32/612; 5.22%) varies from previous reports.[8] So far, an incidence of this order has only been found for the Fc fragment of IgG and the Ii blood group. Moreover, the high incidence has until now been confined to monoclonal IgM. In this study, we found 15 IgM, 6 IgA, and 15 IgG among the 36 positive sera.

This study also has defined new antibody activities for MIg and reported the first cases of MIg directed against tubulin and dsDNA. Until now, only a few cases of MIg directed against thyroglobulin, myosin, actin, and intermediate filaments[18-20] have been reported. The frequency of MIg binding mainly to actin is impressive, whereas the frequencies found to react with tubulin, thyroglobulin, and myosin are lower.

In many cases of monoclonal gammopathies, the clinical symptoms led to the discovery of several autoantibody activities of MIg: anti-Ii (chronic cold agglutinin disease), antilipoproteins (xanthomas), anticitroflavin (cutaneous pigmentation), and the recently reported cases of Waldenström's macroglobulinemia associated with polyneuropathy, which displayed anti-intermediate-filament activity.[21] As opposed to these reports, no clinical symptoms related to the presence of the MIg could be found among the 31 patients where a follow-up could be established. However, the absence of any underlying immunological disease in most patients is not surprising in view of our previous results with normal serum in which we consistently found natural autoantibodies. Normal natural antitubulin and antithyroglobulin appeared to be specific and were only inhibited by their homologous antigens. On the other hand, normal natural antiactin antibodies reacted strongly with actin and were specifically inhibited by actin and also significantly by tubulin and thyroglobulin. These binding specificities appear to be closely related to those found for MIg. This would imply that, at least for some patients, the MIg produced might reflect the expansion of a clone normally producing a natural autoantibody. Assuming that certain malignant monoclonal gammopathies arise from the proliferation of a clone normally producing a natural antibody, it may be postulated that this might be caused by the dysfunction of the system that normally regulates such antibody production.

Another important point raised by our results is the widespread reactivity observed for both natural antibodies and monoclonal natural antibodies. The simultaneous binding of antibodies (to several cytoskeletal proteins) to cytoskeletal proteins and thyroglobulin, to cytoskeletal proteins and TNP, and to cytoskeletal proteins and DNA, has been clearly demonstrated by our work. The results obtained in competitive binding experiments and by using affinity-purified antibodies on a TNP immunoadsorbent indicate that whatever arguments might be raised concerning the affinity of these interactions, the overall binding affinity is substantial and these reactions are definitely specific. This broad specificity raises the question of the epitope on these antigens recognized by the antibodies. No evident homologies exist between actin, tubulin, myosin, TNP, and DNA, and, therefore, the cross-reactive structures between these antigens are unknown. Recently, André-Schwartz et al.[22] confirmed our finding by demonstrating, among anti-DNA monoclonal antibodies, the presence of frequent cross-reactions with cytoskeletal proteins. Similar unexpected cross-reactions with other monoclonal antibodies have now been widely observed and studied, and in most cases no satisfactory explanation for these cross-reactions is currently available.[23-29] Therefore, the physicochemical basis of such cross-reactions needs to be delineated and the identification of an autoantibody as "antiactin" may only partially describe the range of its immunological capabilities. Alternative explanations for the molecular basis underlying multireactive antibodies have been proposed,[30] based on the notion that antibody combining sites are considerably larger than that needed to be complementary to a single epitope. A relatively large binding site may consist of separate subregions having the capacity to react with different epitopes. Thus, antigens may display coinhibition because of overlapping spatial requirements rather than because of the same amino-acid contacts within the antibody combining site.[26]

This widespread reactivity contrasts with the high specificity found for induced antibodies. It is possible that these polyspecific natural antibodies are able to recognize similar structures present on many antigens. If found to be correct, this hypothesis would imply that B cells carry a polyspecific, though monoclonal, receptor capable of fixing many different antigens. Varga *et al.*[29] postulated that when such a clone exhibiting a multispecific cell surface receptor is induced by one of the binding antigens, the antibody produced by this clone would keep its capacity to bind several different antigens. Alternatively, we have already postulated that upon active immunization, the corresponding B cells are stimulated on binding to a given antigen to the receptor into a series of divisions and mutations, which under the selective pressure of the antigen would induce the production of highly specific antibodies for a given epitope of that antigen.[11-31] Recent data on the high frequency of mutations observed in rearranged V-genes[32] would be compatible with the rapid generation of a large number of variants and intraclonal heterogeneity.

It has been assumed that natural antibodies arise as a consequence to continuous polyclonal stimulation induced by intestinal flora, food, external aggression, etc. Even though hybridoma collections derived from germ and antigen-free animals are required to prove this hypothesis, our results showing significantly higher frequencies of clones producing natural autoantibodies at six days as compared to two months of age may indicate that these clones are indeed a result of internal stimulation and are actually "diluted out" in adult mice as a result of responses to environmental antigens. Furthermore, their presence at early times could be compatible with a germline origin.

Although the origin of autoantibodies remains a subject of controversy, two different approaches have been carried out during the last years in order to define the subpopulation involved in their production. Hayakawa *et al.*[33] defined a small subpopulation of normal B cells characterized by the simultaneous presence of both B- and T-cell markers, which they called Ly-1B cells. This subpopulation constitutes about 1–2% of BALB/c spleen and 5–10% of NZB spleen cells. Interestingly, this subpopulation, which appears to be strongly represented among peritoneal B cells, contains, in the opinion of the authors, virtually all of the spleen cells that secrete IgM autoantibodies reactive with bromelin-treated mouse erythrocytes and DNA. An alternative approach to this problem emerges from the studies performed on CBA/N mice. This mouse strain has a sex-linked immunodeficiency characterized by the presence of a gene or a closely linked group of genes (named Xid). It results in several changes characterized by the lack of a subset of B lymphocytes defined by the presence of the Lyb-5 surface marker and the failure to respond to TI-2 antigens.[34] When challenged with LPS or poly-(IC), CBA/N mice secrete little or no anti-DNA and antialtered mouse erythrocyte autoantibodies, whereas normal strains produce large amounts of these autoantibodies. The latter results associated with those obtained with (CBA/N × NZB)F$_1$ mice and especially with congeneic NZB-Xid led some authors to propose that the Lyb-5$^+$ cells lacking in Xid mice may be important for autoantibody production and that in their absence autoantibody production is markedly reduced.[35]

To gain insight into this problem, we recently fused spleen cells from 6-day-old (CBA/N × BALB/c)F$_1$ male and female mice to the SP2/0 line. As the Xid gene is inherited as an X-linked recessive trait, the mating of a CBA/N female with a male from a normal strain yields male offsprings that express this defect, whereas the female offsprings are heterozygous and phenotypically normal.[36] Thus, the MIg secreted by the males were compared to those secreted by the females for their ability to bind with DNA, cytoskeletal proteins, and TNP. The results indicate that CBA/N mice do carry the genetic information for the production of natural autoantibodies against these antigens. Hence, we postulated that the Lyb-5$^-$ population that largely predominates in Xid is involved in the production of natural autoantibodies against the above-mentioned specificities, and that the Xid gene might be a regulatory gene because Xid mice in contrast to normal ones are unable to secrete anti-DNA autoantibodies upon mitogenic stimulation, despite carrying the genetic information. This regulatory mechanism could also explain the failure of NZB Xid mice to fully manifest the autoimmune syndrome characteristic of NZB mice.

The presence of antibodies exhibiting a widespread reactivity may be advantageous to the animal. These antibodies may constitute a first barrier of defense against external aggression while more specific antibodies are in the process of being produced. They may also play a dominant role in the elimination of dead tissues, as suggested by Grabar.[37] Moreover, we cannot exclude the possibility that these antibodies binding to self-determinants do not play a major role in "self-tolerance," either by binding to self-antigens and thus precluding the activation of other self-reactive B cells or through interactions within the idiotypic network.

The widespread presence of these autoantibodies and the ease with which they have been obtained suggest that they are a major component of the B-cell repertoire and that this repertoire is actually expressed at low amounts in normal human and mouse serum. Since these normal autoantibodies appear to share antibody specificities with those obtained from lupus patients and autoimmune mice,[11-22] it has been postulated that these diseases may arise as a consequence of the immunoregulatory system by environmental factors, which can induce lymphocytes to secrete autoantibodies.[25-38] However, on 31 patients with monoclonal gammopathies exhibiting high levels of MIg with autoantibody specificities, we failed to show clinical symptoms that could be related to the presence of these autoantibodies. Interestingly, the patient whose M-component showed antinative DNA activity did not present clinical or biological features suggestive of systemic lupus erythematosus.[10] It appears, then, that this problem may be rather more complex, and that inside these autoantibodies, there might be a subpopulation accounting, in our opinion, for most of those with a physiological role and another subpopulation for those with a noxious role. A large collection of monoclonal autoantibodies obtained from normal and autoimmune mouse and human lymphocytes are available now for studies on the molecular level, which will further elucidate and give interesting insight into this problem.

ACKNOWLEDGMENTS

We wish to acknowledge Azad Kaushik for reviewing the English version of this paper and Francine Auzeloux for typing the manuscript.

REFERENCES

1. BURNET, F. M. 1959. The Clonal Selection Theory of Acquired Immunity. Cambridge University Press. London/New York.
2. MACKAY, I. R. 1983. Natural autoantibodies to the fore-forbidden clones to the rear? Immunol. Today 4: 340–342.
3. HOOPER, B., S. WHITTINGHAM, J. D. MATHEWS et al. 1972. Auto-immunity in a rural community. Clin. Exp. Immunol. 12: 79–87.
4. ROBERTS, I. M., S. WHITTINGHAM & I. R. MACKAY. 1973. Tolerance to an autoantigen-thyroglobulin. Antigen-binding lymphocytes in thymus and blood in health and auto-immune disease. Lancet ii: 936–940.
5. BOYDEN, S. V. 1964. Autoimmunity and inflammation. Nature (London) 201: 200–201.

6. KARSENTI, E., B. GUILBERT, M. BORNENS & S. AVRAMEAS. 1977. Antibodies to tubulin in normal nonimmunized animals. Proc. Natl. Acad. Sci. USA **74:** 3997–4004.

7. GUILBERT, B., G. DIGHIERO & S. AVRAMEAS. 1982. Naturally occurring antibodies against nine common antigens in normal humans. I. Detection, isolation, and characterization. J. Immunol. **128:** 2779–2787.

8. SELIGMANN, M. & J. C. BROUET. 1973. Antibody activity of human myeloma globulins. Semin. Hematol. **10:** 163–177.

9. DIGHIERO, G., B. GUILBERT & S. AVRAMEAS. 1982. Naturally occurring antibodies against nine common antigens in human sera. II. High incidence of monoclonal Ig exhibiting antibody activity against actin and tubulin and sharing antibody specificities with natural antibodies. J. Immunol. **128:** 2788–2792.

10. DIGHIERO, G., B. GUILBERT, J. P. FERMANT, P. LYMBERI, F. DANON & S. AVRAMEAS. 1983. Thirty-six human monoclonal immunoglobulins (MIg) with antibody activity against cytoskeleton proteins, thyroglobulin, and native DNA. Immunological studies and clinical correlations. Blood **62:** 264–270.

11. DIGHIERO, G., P. LYMBERI, J. C. MAZIÉ, S. ROUYRE, G. S. BUTLER-BROWNE, R. G. WHALEN & S. AVRAMEAS. 1983. Murine hybridomas secreting natural monoclonal antibodies reacting with self-antigens. J. Immunol. **131:** 2267–2272.

12. DIGHIERO, G., P. LYMBERI, D. HOLMBERG, I. LUNDQUIST, A. COUTINHO & S. AVRAMEAS. 1985. High frequency of natural autoantibodies in normal newborn mice. J. Immunol. **134:** 765–771.

13. LYMBERI, P., G. DIGHIERO, T. TERNYNCK & S. AVRAMEAS. 1985. A high incidence of cross-reactive idiotypes among murine natural autoantibodies. Eur. J. Immunol. **15:** 702–707.

14. WALFORD, R.L. 1969. The Immunologic Theory of Aging. Munksgaard. Copenhagen.

15. LUTZ, H. U. & G. WIPF. 1982. Naturally occurring auto-antibodies to skeletal proteins from human red blood cells. J. Immunol. **128:** 1695–1699.

16. ANDERSON, J., A. COUTINHO & F. MELCHERS. 1977. Frequencies of mitogen reactive B cells in the mouse. II. Frequencies of B cells producing antibodies which lyse sheep or horse erythrocytes and trinitrophenylated or nitroiodophenylated sheep erythrocytes. J. Exp. Med. **145:** 1520–1529.

17. LEVY, M. 1984. Frequencies of phosphorylcholine-specific and T15-associated 10/13 idiotope-positive B cells within lipopolysaccharide-reactive B cells of adult BALB/c mice. Eur. J. Immunol. **14:** 864–868.

18. WAGER, O., J. A. RÄSÄNEN, K. HALTIA & C. WASASTJERNA. 1971. M components with antibody activity. Anti-smooth muscle, anti-thyroglobulin and anti-streptolysin O activity in five M component sera. Ann. Clin. Res. **3:** 86–95.

19. TOH, B. H., R. CEREDIG, F. N. CORNELL & F. M. CLARKE. 1977. Multiple myeloma and monoclonal IgA with anti-actin reactivity. Clin. Exp. Immunol. **30:** 379–385.

20. DELLAGGI, K., J. C. BROUET, J. PERREAU & D. PAULIN. 1982. Human monoclonal IgM with autoantibody activity against intermediate filaments. Proc. Natl. Acad. Sci. USA **79:** 446–450.

21. DELLAGI, K., P. DUPOUEY, J. C. BROUET, A. BILLECOCQ, D. GOMEZ, J. P. CLAUVEL & M. SELIGMANN. 1984. Waldenström's macroglobulinemia and peripheral neuropathy: A clinical and immunologic study of 25 patients. Blood **62:** 280–285.

22. ANDRÉ-SCHWARTZ, J., S. K. DATTA, Y. SHOENFELD, D. A. ISENBERG, B. D. STOLLAR & R. S. SCHWARTZ. 1984. Binding of cytoskeletal proteins by monoclonal anti-DNA lupus autoantibodies. Clin. Immunol. Immunopathol. **31:** 261–271.

23. HANNESTAD, K. & B. D. STOLLAR. 1978. Certain rheumatoid factors react with nucleosomes. Nature **275:** 671–672.

24. LANE, D. & H. KOPROWSKI. 1982. Molecular recognition and the future of monoclonal antibodies. Nature **296:** 200–202.

25. PRABHAKAR, B. S., J. SAEGUSA, T. ONODERA & A. L. NOTKINS. 1984. Lymphocytes capable of making monoclonal autoantibodies that react with multiple organs are a common feature of the normal B cell repertoire. J. Immunol. **133:** 2815–2817.

26. RUBIN, R. L., R. S. BALDERAS, E. M. TAN, F. J. DIXON & A. N. THEOFILOPOULOS. 1984. Multiple autoantigen binding capabilities of mouse monoclonal antibodies selected for rheumatoid factor activity. J. Exp. Med. **159:** 1429–1440.

27. RAUCH, J., H. MASSICOTTE & H. TANNENBAUM. 1985. Hybridoma anti-DNA auto-antibodies from patients with rheumatoid arthritis and systemic lupus erythematosus demonstrate similar nucleic acid binding characteristics. J. Immunol. **134:** 180–186.
28. SCHWARTZ, R. S. & B. D. STOLLAR. 1985. Origins of anti-DNA autoantibodies. J. Clin. Invest. **75:** 321–327.
29. SHOENFELD, Y., J. RAUCH, H. MASSICOTTE, S. K. DATTA, J. ANDRÉ-SCHWARTZ, B. D. STOLLAR & R. S. SCHWARTZ. 1983. Polyspecificity of monoclonal lupus autoantibodies produced by human-human hybridomas. N. Engl. J. Med. **308:** 414–420.
30. VARGA, J. M., W. H. KONIGSBERG & F. F. RICHARDS. 1973. Immunoglobulin with multiple binding functions. Induction of single immunoglobulin species with structurally dissimilar haptens. Proc. Natl. Acad. Sci. USA **70:** 3268–3274.
31. AVRAMEAS, S., G. DIGHIERO, P. LYMBERI & B. GUILBERT. 1983. Studies on natural antibodies and autoantibodies. Ann. Immunol. (Paris) **134D:** 103–113.
32. GEARHART, P. J. & D. F. BOGENHAGEN. 1983. Clusters of point mutations are found exclusively around rearranged antibody variable genes. Proc. Natl. Acad. Sci. USA **80:** 3439–3445.
33. HAYAKAWA, K., R. R. HARDY, M. HONDA, L. A. HERZENBERG, A. D. STEINBERG & L. A. HERZENBERG. 1984. Ly-1 B cells: Functionally distinct lymphocytes that secrete IgM autoantibodies. Proc. Natl. Acad. Sci. USA **81:** 2494–2498.
34. SCHER, I. 1982. The CBA/N mouse strain: An experimental model illustrating the influence of the X-chromosome on immunity. Adv. Immunol. **33:** 2–69.
35. SMITH, H. R. & A. D. STEINBERG. 1983. Autoimmunity, a perspective. Ann. Rev. Immunol. **1:** 175–210.
36. DIGHIERO, G., P. PONCET, S. ROUYRE & J. C. MAZIÉ. Newborn Xid mice carry the genetic information for the production of natural autoantibodies against DNA, cytoskeletal proteins, and TNP. J. Immunol. In press.
37. GRABAR, P. 1975. Autoantibodies and immunological theories: an analytical review. Clin. Immunol. Immunopathol. **4:** 453–466.
38. HANG, L., J. H. SLACK, C. AMUNOLSON, S. IZUI, A. N. THEOFILOPOULOS & F. J. DIXON. 1983. Induction of murine auto-immune disease by chronic polyclonal B cell activation. J. Exp. Med. **157:** 974–886.

DISCUSSION OF THE PAPER

C. A. BONA (*Mount Sinai Medical Center, New York, NY*): The problem I have in interpreting your results is in defining the criteria for a true antigen-antibody interaction.

G. DIGHIERO (*Institut Pasteur, Paris, France*): We can call the reactions "antigen-antibody" because IgG fractions of the serum are inhibited by the antigen and because they are mediated by the Fab fractions of the Ig. We know now the affinity of the first two antibodies, D-23 and E-7, against TNP and found that it was at least 10^{-6}.

A. D. STEINBERG (*National Institutes of Health, Bethesda, MD*): Others have found Lyb-5-positive cells in the Peyer's patches of XID mice. Howard Smith in my lab has found Lyb-5-positive cells in the spleens of XID mice. It seems that after eliminating the Lyb-5-positive cells, the spleens of XID mice no longer make autoantibodies in culture. I agree with your conclusion that there is a maturational defect in mice with the XID gene defect, but I think that until we know more about the gene, a discussion of the cellular immunology of Xid mice will not be productive.

DIGHIERO: All I tried to say is that Xid mice have the genetic information for the production of autoantibodies. I cannot answer the question if Lyb-5-positive cells carry genetic information for autoantibodies.

Y. NAPARSTEK (*Tufts New England Medical Center, Boston, MA*): We tried to study the same question on a molecular level, together with Malcolm Geffer of MIT. We studied a set of antibodies that uses one V_H gene, namely, the $V_H Id^{CR}$ gene that is used for the antiarsonate system. In short, what we found is that the germline gene-encoded antibodies of this system do not bind arsonate, but are actually autoantibodies of the type that you described. They bind DNA and cytoskeletal structures. After immunization with arsonate, the $V_H Id^{CR}$ gene undergoes mutations and the corresponding antibodies become high-affinity antiarsonate antibodies and lose their autoantibody activity. Therefore, I think our results fit your theory. I also think that the preimmune repertoire is actually composed of germline-encoded autoantibodies.

Postinfectious Autoimmunity: Two Distinct Phases of Coxsackievirus B3-Induced Myocarditis[a]

NOEL R. ROSE, LUANNE J. WOLFGRAM,
AHVIE HERSKOWITZ, AND KIRK W. BEISEL

*Departments of Immunology and Infectious Diseases
and of Medicine
The Johns Hopkins Medical Institutions
Baltimore, Maryland 21205*

An encounter between an infectious agent and a host involves a complex of interactions that may or may not lead to disease. The genetic composition of both the host and the infectious agent will determine the extent of the initial infection and the severity of the resulting pathology. The immune response toward the invading pathogen is the major host mechanism affecting the severity both of the infection and of the resultant disease and in limiting subsequent infections. The immune response, however, can play a paradoxical role by leading to exacerbation of disease rather than promoting recovery.

A wide variety of viruses has been shown to produce myocarditis in man.[1] The most common are the RNA viruses of the Picornavirus,[2-4] Orthomyxovirus,[5] Paramyxovirus,[6] Togavirus,[7] Rhabdovirus,[8] and Arenavirus[9] families. The most common of these viruses, the Coxsackievirus B group, is associated with about half of the clinical cases of infectious myocarditis.[10,11] Of this group, Coxsackievirus B_3 (CB_3) induces the highest incidence of myocardial disease.[12] Usually, the association of this virus with cardiac disease is inferred from serological studies since isolation and identification of the virus itself has been difficult. The diagnosis of myocardiopathy often requires endomyocardial biopsy.[13] The principal drawbacks of this diagnostic method are the focal nature of the inflammatory cellular infiltrate and the lack of universally accepted guidelines for histologic assessment.[14,15]

Several pathogenetic mechanisms have been proposed to account for virus-induced myocardiopathy.[1,16-18] Since CB_3 is a lytic virus, one plausible mechanism is direct injury to the myofibers. In addition, myocardial tissue injury can be correlated with the severity of the inflammatory lesions, suggesting that inflammation itself may be responsible for the injury. On the other hand, a protective effect has been associated with the inflammatory response.[19,20] Treatment of mice with corticosteroids[19] and cyclophosphamide[20] to reduce inflammation caused more severe disease. During the last decade, several lines of evidence have pointed to autoimmunity as a cause of myocarditis. Maisch and his colleagues[18] have described heart-specific autoantibodies in patients with infectious myocarditis. These antibodies were found to mediate myocyte lysis by complement,[21] as well as cell-mediated antibody-dependent cytotoxicity.[22] In a murine model using BALB/c mice, Woodruff and his colleagues[1,23] and

[a]This work was supported by U. S. Public Health Service grant nos. HL-27932, HL-30144, and CA-34202 from the National Heart, Lung, and Blood Institute and from the National Cancer Institute.

subsequently Huber *et al.*[24,25] demonstrated the presence in the spleens of CB_3-infected animals of cytolytic T cells capable of damaging myocytes.

HISTOPATHOLOGY

We have undertaken an investigation designed to dissect the immunopathological mechanisms responsible for postinfectious myocarditis. We have concluded that Coxsackievirus-induced myocarditis is a complex polygenic disease, but with distinguishable stages. Based on the pioneering reports of Woodruff[17] and of Lerner,[26] we constructed a murine model that allowed us to study the progression of disease in a variety of strains. For these studies, we infected two-week-old animals with 0.1 ml of 10^5 $TCID_{50}$ of CB_3 (Nancy) obtained from a Vero cell lysate. Tissue samples were

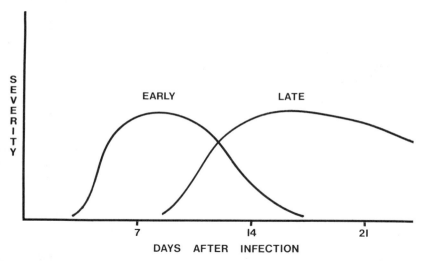

FIGURE 1. Schema of the time course of the early virus-induced and the late immunopathic Coxsackievirus B_3-induced myocarditis.

removed from infected and noninfected animals at various times after infection. We have been able to take advantage of the large number of genetically defined mouse strains to highlight the diversity in the progression of CB_3-induced myocardial disease. This approach was used to great advantage by Yoon *et al.*[27] to determine susceptibility to CB_4-induced diabetes.

A time-course experiment was set up to delineate the progression of myocardial disease, as represented in FIGURE 1. This idealized concept is based mainly on a study using six different inbred strains (A.BY, A.SW, A.CA, C3H.NB, B10.PL, and B10.S), which varied greatly in the tempo and severity of myocarditis. Histological examination of the hearts from these animals showed two distinct patterns.[28,29] The first histological evidence of myofibril injury was observed at the third day after infection. In general, the histopathology[29] was similar in all strains , with no gross abnormalities being observed in the hearts. Myocardial lesions were focal and were associated with contraction band necrosis. The injured myocytes could be identified by dense eosinophilic changes, loss of myofibrillar definition, and disruption of the cell membranes. These histological changes were associated with small cellular infiltrates predominantly of polymorphonuclear leukocytes (PMN) and occasional macrophages. By day 7, the focal lesions had become less cellular and more fibrotic. Still, the lesions contained cellular infiltrates, consisting primarily of PMNs, and some mononuclear cells.

Later, the histopathological picture changed considerably. Some mouse strains (B10.S and B10.PL) were characterized by the absence of new focal lesions and by the replacement of the older lesions with dense linear bands of connective tissue that divided the muscle bundles. There was no evidence of active inflammation after day 9 in these strains. In general, the myocardial injury continued to resolve, as indicated by a gradual decrease in the total proportion of the myocardium affected. In contrast, a pattern of ongoing increasing inflammation was found in the A.BY, A.SW, A.CA, and C3H.NB strains. At day 9, the focal lesions were heavily calcified and quite discrete. Inflammatory cells within the lesions were prominent and they were principally macrophages and lymphocytes. A diffuse interstitial infiltrate characterized this later stage of myocarditis. This interstitial infiltrate, composed of both large and small mononuclear cells, peaked 15 to 21 days after infection. Contraction band necrosis was rarely observed after day 9, except in the most severely affected cases. Some focal lesions containing PMNs reflected ongoing acute necrosis. Even 45 days after infection, evidence of continued inflammation with persistent interstitial mononuclear cellular infiltration was present, thus indicating a more chronic disease. Heart-specific autoantibodies were also present in mouse strains with the continuing disease. We therefore refer to the second phase of disease as "immunopathic."

Several other investigators[1,31,32] have examined the histopathology of the heart after infection with CB_3. Reexamination of their data has indicated that their strains developed varying degrees of continuing myocarditis. However, they did not separate and distinguish the initial virus-induced myocardial damage and the accompanying inflammation from the ensuing immunopathic disease.

CHARACTERISTICS OF EARLY DISEASE

During the time-course study, several characteristics of the early disease were noted.[33] There were differences in the level and duration of viremia, in the content and persistence of virus in the heart, spleen, thymus, and pancreas, in the onset of the neutralizing antibody response, and in the severity of myocarditis. As demonstrated in FIGURE 2, the six strains could be separated into two significantly different categories. The more susceptible strains, A.BY and A.SW, had virus levels in the serum greater than 10^4/ml two and three days after infection. In contrast, the more resistant strains, A.CA, B10.S, B10.PL, and C3H.NB, had significantly lower CB_3 virus levels. Day 3 appeared to be a critical point for the appearance of neutralizing antibodies in the serum of the resistant strains since the two most susceptible strains (A.BY and A.SW) had no detectable antibodies to CB_3 on day 3. Yet no significant differences were observed in the final neutralizing antibody titers among the six strains. In general, the virus content of the spleen, thymus, and pancreas was greater in the susceptible strains. However, the amounts of CB_3 recovered from the heart did not show any statistical difference (FIGURE 3). The virus content of the heart peaked in all strains at day 5, paralleling the time of the initial peak of myocardial injury. No infectious virus was detected in the heart after day 15. In contrast, the pancreas has been found to contain infectious CB_3 as long as 21 days after infection. Recently, other investigators, using the technique of *in situ* hybridization, have been able to identify CB_3 RNA in the hearts of infected mice 35 days after infection (Tracy and Gauntt, personal communication). Thus, these animals have a persistent viral infection.

As judged by histological appearance, the peak of myocardial injury was greatest at 5 to 7 days after infection in all strains examined.[29,30] There were differences among the six strains in both the prevalence and severity of disease. Three categories of myocarditis were distinguished, namely, susceptible, intermediate, and resistant (TABLE 1). Some pathological changes were observed even in the most resistant strains, but disease was confined to several small focal lesions.

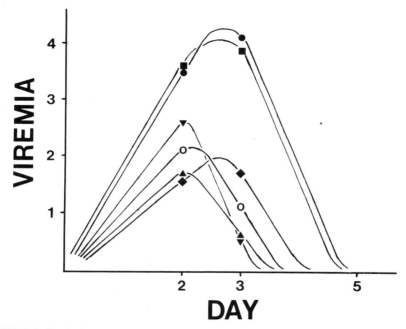

FIGURE 2. Strain differences in viremia. The titer of infectious CB_3 was determined for each strain at day 2, 3, and 5 after infection and was expressed as the $\log_{10}$ mean CB_3 titer/0.1 ml of serum. The strains examined were A.BY (■), A.SW (●), A.CA (▲), B10.S (▼), B10.PL (♦), and C3H.NB (O) (from Wolfgram *et al.*[30]).

Genetic analysis suggests that susceptibility to infection by CB_3 is under polygenic control.[30] The A.SW (H-2^s) mice were highly susceptible to the CB_3 infection and the resulting myocarditis, whereas the B10.S (H-2^s) animals were resistant to CB_3 infection and developed moderate to mild myocardial lesions (see TABLE 1). The B10.S strain carries the H-2^s haplotype derived from the A.SW congenic line. From this comparison, we conclude that the non-H-2 background gene(s) determines susceptibility or resistance of mice to the CB_3 infection and the ensuing myocarditis. A major histocompatibility complex (MHC) influence was discerned by comparing various H-2 congenics on the A strain background (i.e., A.BY and A.SW versus A.CA). Thus, both MHC and non-MHC genes influence the degree of susceptibility to CB_3 infection and the resulting virus-induced myocarditis. In a subsequent study,[34] we have examined a

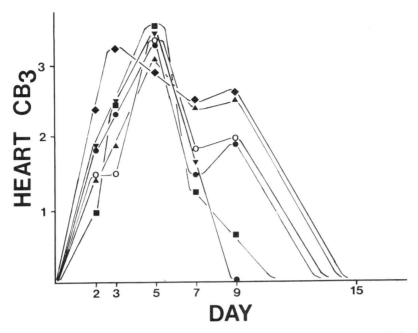

FIGURE 3. Strain differences in heart CB_3 content. The content of infectious CB_3 in the heart from various strains was determined at days 2, 3, 5, 7, 9, and 15 after infection. The titer of CB_3 was expressed as the $\log_{10}$ mean CB_3 titer/0.1 g of heart tissue. The strains examined were A.BY (■), A.SW (●), A.CA (▲), B10.S (▼), B10.PL (♦), and C3H.NB (○) (from Wolfgram et al.[30]).

larger panel of B10 *H-2* congenic strains carrying independent haplotypes for their susceptibility to myocardial injury (TABLE 2). Three different phenotypes of disease were observed: the susceptible stains were B10.Q (*H-2^q*), B10.BR (*H-2^k*), and B10.D2 (*H-2^d*); the intermediate strains were B10.PL (*H-2^u*), B10.M (*H-2^f*), B10.WB (*H-2^j*), B10.SM (*H-2^v*), and B10.S (*H-2^s*); and the resistants were B10 (*H-2^b*),

TABLE 1. Strain Variations in Early Myocarditis[a]

Strain	*H-2* Haplotype	Phenotype[b]
A.BY	b	susceptible
A.SW	s	susceptible
B10.S	s	intermediate
B10.PL	u	intermediate
C3H.NB	p	intermediate
A.CA	f	resistant

[a]Adapted from Wolfgram et al.[30]

[b]The phenotype of myocarditis was determined by the prevalence and severity of the myocardial lesions observed in animals at days 5 and 7 after infection.

B10.RIII (*H-2ʳ*), and B10.A (*H-2ᵃ*). These studies support the finding that the MHC influences the severity of myocarditis.

The interrelationship between the non-*H-2* and *H-2* genes may be a complex one.[30] Mouse strains that carry the A background genome have been reported to carry several genetic traits that lead to increased susceptibility to various infectious diseases.[35] First, a macrophage defect has been identified.[36] Also, the A strains are low producers of α/β interferon.[37] There may be many other heritable properties that are responsible for the general susceptibility of this strain to viral infection.[38] Our current working hypothesis is that the non-MHC gene(s) determines mainly the extent of virus infectivity and the amount of virus replication in the tissue. If left unchecked by neutralizing antibody, severe disease ensues. However, if the MHC gene(s) directs a more vigorous immunological response, then moderate to little disease results.

TABLE 2. Influence of the MHC on Early Myocarditis[a]

Strain	*H-2* Haplotype	Phenotype of Early Myocarditis
B10.Q	q	susceptible
B10.BR	k	susceptible
B10.D2	d	susceptible
B10.PL	u	intermediate
B10.M	f	intermediate
B10.WB	j	intermediate
B10.SM	v	intermediate
B10.S	s	intermediate
B10	b	resistant
B10.RIII	r	resistant
B10.A	a	resistant

[a]Adapted from Beisel *et al.*[34]

CHARACTERISTICS OF LATER DISEASE

There are two markers of late disease: diffuse mononuclear infiltration and heart-specific autoantibodies.[29,30,39] Transition from the early to late myocarditis began at day 9, when an interstitial mononuclear cell infiltrate was first noted. In strains that did not develop late disease, no new lesions appeared and the older focal lesions were replaced by dense linear bands of fibrous scar tissue. These healing lesions contained few infiltrating cells. In strains that developed late disease, myocarditis was most severe 15 to 21 days after infection.[29,39]

Several different autoantibodies were found in the postinfection sera. These sera were tested, using indirect immunofluorescence, with normal uninfected heart, liver, pancreas, salivary gland, skeletal muscle, kidney, and stomach. Reactions were observed in a majority of postinfection sera from all six mouse strains (both with and without the later myocarditis) and they were most often directed to smooth and skeletal muscle and to nuclei. Such autoantibodies are commonly found in association with many viral infections.[40] However, only in animals with the late disease were there detectable heart-specific antibodies.[30] Two fluorescent patterns were recognized, one characterized by localization at the sacrolemma/myolemma and the other by reaction with contractile proteins of both heart and skeletal muscles. Because the antisera reacted with both skeletal and heart tissues, absorption analyses were done.[39] Exhaustive absorptions with lyophilized whole skeletal muscle homogenates[39] removed the reactions with skeletal muscle, but left autoantibodies to the sarcolemma/subsarcolemma and to the contractile proteins of heart (TABLE 3). These heart-specific autoantibodies were not species-specific because they reacted with rat and baboon hearts[39] and have now been found to react with cardiac myosin.[33]

The presence of sarcolemmal/subsarcolemmal antibodies could be used as an indicator of autoimmune disease since almost all of the animals with these antibodies had the characteristic histopathology of late disease. Similar heart-specific autoantibodies have been described in patients with poststreptococcal rheumatic fever,[41] Chagas' disease,[42,43] postpericardiotomy syndrome,[44,45] and postmyocardial infarction syndrome.[44,45]

Detailed comparisons were made between animals with and without heart autoantibodies using mouse strains that had been classified by pathological criteria as having the late disease. These findings showed that the late disease was more severe in animals with heart-specific autoantibodies. This observation was well borne out in the A.CA strain, which has a high prevalence of the late disease and a high titer of heart-specific autoantibodies.[39] Both the characteristic mononuclear cellular infiltrate and the

TABLE 3. Absorption of Autoantibodies with Tissue Homogenates[a]

	Reaction with[b]		
Treatment	Liver	Skeletal Muscle	Heart
Unabsorbed	0	3	4
Absorbed with:			
liver	0	3	4
skeletal muscle	0	0	2
heart	0	0	0

[a]Adapted from Wolfgram et al.[39]
[b]Tissue reaction was determined by indirect immunofluorescence. The intensity of fluorescence observed was graded on a 0–4 scale.

presence of heart-specific autoantibodies support the concept that the late disease is immunopathic with an autoimmune origin. Recent studies in our laboratory suggest that the presence of IgG autoantibodies specific for cardiac myosin is a serological marker of immunopathic myocarditis.[46]

Strain differences were noted in the prevalence and in the severity of the late disease (TABLE 4). Examination of the genetics suggested that the non-MHC gene(s) led to a predisposition to the autoimmune myocarditis.[39] This conclusion was derived from observations that all the A strain congenics produced immunopathic disease, whereas the B10 congenics did not. No differences were seen in the severity of immunopathic disease among the three A congenic strains studied. Recent data from our laboratory have suggested that the MHC may also play some role in determining predisposition because three of eleven B10 congenic lines (B10.D2, B10.BR, and B10.Q) with differing independent haplotypes developed immunopathic myocarditis.[33] These three B10 *H-2* congenics were the ones with the most severe forms of early disease. At present, we suggest that heart-specific autoimmunity may also be produced in non-predisposed strains of mice as a result of unusually extensive myocardial injury caused by the earlier viral infection.

The MHC does play a role in regulating the heart-specific humoral response.[39] A/J

TABLE 4. Strain Variations in Late Myocarditis[a]

Strain	H-2 Haplotype	Phenotype[b]
A.BY	b	susceptible
A.CA	f	susceptible
A.SW	s	susceptible
C3H.NB	p	susceptible
B10.S	s	resistant
B10.PL	u	resistant

[a]Adapted from Wolfgram *et al.*[30]

[b]The phenotype of myocarditis was determined by the presence of heart-specific autoantibodies and an interstitial mononuclear cell infiltrate at days 15 and 21 after infection.

($H-2^a$), A.BY ($H-2^b$), A.CA ($H-2^f$), and A.SW ($H-2^s$) strains were examined for the prevalence and titer of heart-specific autoantibody (TABLE 5). We found that the A.SW and A.CA strains are high responders, the A/J animals are intermediate, and the A.BY animals are low responders. Thus, late myocarditis is an immunopathic disease under polygenic regulation. Predisposition to heart autoimmunity is determined by non-MHC gene(s), whereas the strength of the heart-specific antibody response is influenced by the MHC.

VALUE OF THE MURINE MODEL

There has been much speculation about chronic myocarditis and the development of cardiac immunity. Clinical studies have described the presence of heart-specific autoantibodies in patients with suspected viral myocarditis,[18,21] Adriamycin cardiomyopathy,[47] *Trypanosoma cruzi* myocarditis,[42,43] postpericardiotomy,[44,45] and postinfarction syndromes.[44,45] The diagnosis of immunopathic myocarditis has been difficult because of the requirement for needle biopsies for their detection. The presence of heart-specific autoantibodies in serum may be a useful marker of ongoing myocardial disease.

Our model emphasizes the wide diversity of patterns of myocardial disease, depending upon the genetic predisposition of the individual to virus-induced myocardial injury and to the subsequent development of autoimmune myocarditis. With further genetic analyses, a number of genes may be identified that can determine an individual's susceptibility to heart disease and provide a means of risk assessment, as well as suggest the most appropriate treatment. Use of selected mouse strains will also provide excellent tools to explore the mechanism of autoimmune tissue damage. Mouse sera containing heart-specific autoantibodies can identify the pertinent myocardial

TABLE 5. MHC Influence on Heart-Specific Autoantibody Response

Strain	H-2 Haplotype	Percent Positive for Autoantibodies
A.BY	b	14
A/J	a	50
A.CA	f	100
A.SW	s	100

autoantigen(s). It is possible that the spectrum of expressions of myocardial disease observed in our mouse strains can serve to provide insight into the question of why viral myocarditis resolves in some patients, while it progresses to chronic cardiomyopathies in others.

REFERENCES

1. WOODRUFF, J. F. 1980. Viral myocarditis: A review. Am. J. Pathol. **101**: 426–479.
2. SAPHIR, O. & S. A. WILE. 1942. Myocarditis in poliomyelitis. Am. J. Med. Sci. **203**: 781–788.
3. HIRSCHMAN, S. Z. & G. S. HAMMER. 1974. Coxsackie virus myopericarditis: A microbiological and clinical review. Am. J. Cardiol. **34**: 224–232.
4. RUSSELL, S. J. M. & E. J. BELL. 1970. Echovirus and carditis. Lancet **1**: 784–785.
5. FINLAND, M., F. PARKER, JR., M. W. BARNES & L. S. JOLIFFE. 1945. Acute myocarditis in influenza infections: Two cases of non-bacterial myocarditis with isolation of virus from the lungs. Am. J. Med. Sci. **209**: 455–468.
6. GIUSTRA, F. X. & D. C. NILSSON. 1950. Myocarditis following measles. Am. J. Dis. Child. **79**: 487–490.
7. OBEYESEKERE, I. & Y. HERMON. 1972. Myocarditis and cardiomyopathy after arbovirus infections (dengue and chikungunya fever). Br. Heart J. **34**: 821–827.
8. ROSS, E. & S. A. ARMENTROUT. 1962. Myocarditis associated with rabies: Report of a case. N. Engl. J. Med. **266**: 1087–1089.
9. THIEDE, W. H. 1962. Cardiac involvement in lymphocytic choriomeningitis. Arch. Intern. Med. **109**: 50–54.
10. SMITH, W. G. 1970. Coxsackie B myopericarditis in adults. Am. Heart J. **80**: 34–46.
11. GRIST, N. R. & E. J. BELL. 1974. A six-year study of Coxsackievirus B infections in heart disease. J. Hyg. (London) **73**: 165–172.
12. LERNER, A. M. & F. M. WILSON. 1973. Viral myocardiopathy. Prog. Med. Virol. **15**: 63–91.
13. OLSEN, E. G. J. 1978. Endomyocardial biopsy. Br. Heart J. **40**: 95–98.
14. FRENCH, W. J. & J. M. CRILEY. 1984. Caution in the diagnosis and treatment of myocarditis. Am. J. Cardiol. **54**: 445–446.
15. JAMES, T. N. 1983. Myocarditis and cardiomyopathy. N. Engl. J. Med. **308**(1): 39–41.
16. MELNICK, J. L. & G. C. GOODMAN. 1951. Pathogenesis of Coxsackie virus infection. Multiplication of virus and evolution of the muscle lesion in mice. J. Exp. Med. **93**: 247–266.
17. WOODRUFF, J. F. & J. J. WOODRUFF. 1974. Involvement of T lymphocytes in the pathogenesis of Coxsackie virus B3 heart disease. J. Immunol. **113**: 1726–1734.
18. MAISCH, B., P. A. BERG & K. KOCHSIEK. 1980. Autoantibodies and serum inhibition factors (SIF) in patients with myocarditis. Klin. Wochenschr. **58**: 219–225.
19. WOODRUFF, J. F. 1979. Lack of correlation between neutralizing antibody protection and suppression of Coxsackie virus B-3 replication in target organs: Evidence for involvement of mononuclear inflammatory cells in host defense. J. Immunol. **123**: 31–36.
20. RAGER-ZISMAN, B. & A. C. ALLISON. 1973. Effects of immunosuppression on Coxsackie B-3 virus infection and passive protection by circulating antibodies. J. Gen. Virol. **19**: 339–351.
21. MAISCH, B., R. TROSTEL-SOEDER, E. STECHEMESSER, P. A. BERG & K. KOCHSIEK. 1982. Diagnostic relevance of humoral and cell-mediated immune reactions in patients with acute viral myocarditis. Clin. Exp. Immunol. **48**: 533–545.
22. MAISCH, B., E. MAYER, U. SCHUBERT, P. A. BERG & K. KOCHSIEK. 1983. Immune reactions in infective endocarditis. II. Relevance of circulating immune complexes, serum inhibition factors, lymphocytotoxic reactions, and antibody-dependent cellular cytotoxicity against cardiac target cells. Am. Heart J. **106**: 338–344.
23. HUBER, S. A., L. P. JOB, K. R. AULD & J. F. WOODRUFF. 1981. Sex-related differences in the rapid production of cytotoxic spleen cells active against uninfected myofibers during Coxsackie virus B-3 infection. J. Immunol. **126**: 1336–1340.
24. HUBER, S. A. & P. A. LODGE. 1984. Coxsackievirus B-3 myocarditis in BALB/c mice: evidence for autoimmunity to myocyte antigens. Am. J. Pathol. **116**: 21–29.

25. GUTHRIE, M., P. A. LODGE & S. A. HUBER. 1984. Cardiac injury in myocarditis induced by Coxsackievirus Group B, Type 3 in BALB/c mice is mediated by Lyt 2+ cytolytic lymphocytes. Cell. Immunol. **88**: 558–567.

26. WILSON, F. M., Q. R. MIRANDA, J. L. CHASON & A. M. LERNER. 1969. Residual pathologic changes following Coxsackie A and B myocarditis. Am. J. Pathol. **55**: 253–265.

27. YOON, J. W., M. A. LESNIAK, R. FUSSGANGER & A. L. NOTKINS. 1976. Genetic differences in susceptibility to pancreatic beta cells to virus-induced diabetes mellitus. Nature **264**: 178–190.

28. HERSKOWITZ, A., K. W. BEISEL, L. J. WOLFGRAM & N. R. ROSE. 1985. Coxsackievirus B₃ murine myocarditis: wide pathologic spectrum in genetically defined inbred strains. Hum. Pathol. **16**: 671–673.

29. HERSKOWITZ, A., L. J. WOLFGRAM, N. R. ROSE & K. W. BEISEL. 1986. The pathology of Coxsackievirus murine myocarditis: A quantitative study in multiple genetically defined inbred strains. Submitted.

30. WOLFGRAM, L. J., K. W. BEISEL, A. HERSKOWITZ & N. R. ROSE. 1986. Variations in the susceptibility to Coxsackievirus B₃-induced myocarditis among different strains of mice. J. Immunol. **136**: 1846–1852.

31. KHATIB, R., J. L. CHASON, B. K. SILBERBERG & A. M. LERNER. 1980. Age-dependent myocardial pathogenesis of group B coxsackievirus in Swiss-Webster mice: comparisons to the pancreas. J. Infect. Dis. **141**: 394–403.

32. HASHIMOTO, I., T. KOMATSU & T. KOHARA. 1983. Variation in virulence of Coxsackie virus B3 in the heart of mice. II. Pathological comparisons. Microbiol. Immunol. **27**: 291–345.

33. ALVAREZ, F., N. NEU, S. CRAIG & K. BEISEL. 1986. Immunochemical characterization of heart-specific autoantibodies induced by Coxsackievirus B₃ infection. Fed. Proc. **45**: 3238 (abs.).

34. BEISEL, K., L. WOLFGRAM, A. HERSKOWITZ & N. ROSE. 1985. Differences in severity of Coxsackievirus B₃-induced myocarditis among *H-2* congenic mouse strains. *In* Genetic Control of Host Resistance to Infection and Malignancy, vol. 3. E. Skameme, Ed.: 195–205. Alan R. Liss. New York.

35. NESBITT, M. N. & E. SKAMENE. 1984. Recombinant inbred strains derived from A/J and C57BL/6: a tool for the study of genetic mechanisms in host resistance to infection and malignancy. J. Leukocyte Biol. **36**: 357–364.

36. SKAMENE, E., S. L. JAMES, M. J. MELTZER & M. N. NESBITT. 1984. Genetic control of macrophage activation for killing of extracellular targets. J. Leukocyte Biol. **35**: 65–72.

37. DEMAEYER, E. & J. DEMAEYER-GUIGNARD. 1979. Consideration on mouse genes influencing interferon production and action. Interferon **1**: 75–101.

38. BRINTON, M. A., K. J. BLANK & N. NATHANSON. 1984. Host genes that influence susceptibility to viral disease. *In* Concepts in Viral Pathogenesis. A. L. Notkins & M. B. A. Oldstone, Eds.: 71–78. Springer-Verlag, New York/Berlin.

39. WOLFGRAM, L. J., K. W. BEISEL & N. R. ROSE. 1985. Heart-specific autoantibodies following murine Coxsackievirus B3 myocarditis. J. Exp. Med. **161**: 1112–1121.

40. NOTKINS, A. L., T. ONODERA & B. PRABHAKAR. Virus-induced autoantibody. *In* Concepts in Viral Pathogenesis. A. L. Notkins & M. B. A. Oldstone, Eds.: 210–215. Springer-Verlag. New York/Berlin.

41. KAPLAN, M. H. 1972. Nature of the streptococcal and myocardial antigens involved in the immunologic cross-reaction between Group A *Streptococcus* and heart. *In* Cellular Antigens. A. Nowotny, Ed.: 77–86.

42. SZARFMAN, A., V. P. TERRANOVA, S. I. RENNARD, J-M. FOIDART, M. DE FATIMA LIMA, J. I. SCHEINMAN & G. R. MARTIN. 1982. Antibodies to laminin in Chagas' disease. J. Exp. Med. **155**: 1161–1171.

43. ACOSTA, A. M., M. SADIGURSKY & C. A. SANTOS-BUSH. 1983. Anti-striated muscle antibody activity produced by *Trypanosoma cruzi*. Proc. Soc. Exp. Biol. Med. **172**: 364–369.

44. VAN DER GELD, H. 1964. Anti-heart antibodies in the postpericardiotomy and the postmyocardial-infarction syndromes. Lancet **2**: 617–621.

45. KAPLAN, M. H. & J. D. FRENGLEY. 1969. Autoimmunity to the heart in cardiac disease:

current concepts of the relation to autoimmunity, to rheumatic fever, postcardiotomy, and postinfarction syndromes. Am. J. Cardiol. **24:** 459–473.

46. NEU, N., K. BEISEL, M. TRAYSTMAN, N. ROSE & S. CRAIG. 1986. Myosin specific autoantibodies following Coxsackie B_3 infection in mice. Fed. Proc. **45:** 1970 (abs.).

47. MAISCH, B., H. WILKE, S. MARCIN, C. WERNER & W. GEBHARDT. 1984. Adriamycin cardiotoxicity: an echocardiographic and immunologic follow-up study. Circulation **70**(suppl. II): 149–157.

DISCUSSION OF THE PAPER

P. CHRISTADOSS (*University of Vermont, Burlington, VT*): Have you tested F_1 mice? Is there dominant gene control of susceptibility or is there codominant control?

N. R. ROSE (*Johns Hopkins Medical Institutions, Baltimore, MD*): F_1 experiments have been carried out and the answer depends on what trait you are looking for. Are you considering, for example, early disease or late disease? Those are two different phenomena. In addition, autoantibody production is under separate genetic control. My colleague, K. W. Beisel, is studying genetic regulation of CB_3-induced myocarditis.

K. W. BEISEL (*Johns Hopkins Medical Institutions, Baltimore, MD*): In the F_1 mice, resistance to both the early and late myocardial disease is under dominant genetic control. Most likely, these two disease processes are under separate regulation. Preliminary data from our laboratory suggest that the quantitative differences in heart-specific autoantibody production is under dominant control by the MHC.

S. A. HUBER (*University of Vermont, Burlington, VT*) Is there any influence of the Ig-1 locus?

ROSE: We do not have any data concerning the Ig-1 as yet. That might be one of the non-*H-2* traits.

H. WEINER (*Harvard University, Boston, MA*): In the late disease, have you been able to alter the course with immunosuppression? Have you looked for any T-cell reactivity to the myocardial antigens?

ROSE: Immunosuppression experiments trying to alter the second part of this disease have been carried out with cyclosporine. The critical event is when one gives the drug. If one gives it a little too early, then one can make the viral disease worse; if one gives it too late, it may not have a therapeutic effect on the immunopathy. The therapeutic window may be very narrow. Thus, it is going to be extremely important to decide when the process has become primarily autoimmune rather than a virus-induced process. We have not examined cellular immunity in autoimmune myocarditis.

G. WICK (*Institute of Innsbruck, Innsbruck, Austria*): I want to raise a general question about molecular mimicry in the context of your work. The origins of that term had to do with the evolution of parasite-host relationships. I think it is especially interesting in relation to your model because we are dealing with an abnormal host for a particular virus. An example of the consequences of molecular mimicry is rheumatic fever, which occurs only in a few individuals after infection with *Streptococci*.

ROSE: I agree with what you are suggesting. It looks as if, at least in some cases, an autoimmune response may be the price that some individuals have to pay to develop an immune response to certain infectious agents. Nevertheless, thus far, we have been unable to demonstrate any cross-reaction of the autoantibodies we have described and CB_3 viral proteins.

Monoclonal Antibody Studies Defining the Origin and Properties of Autoantibodies in Graves' Disease

LEONARD D. KOHN, FRANCISCO ALVAREZ, CLAUDIO
MARCOCCI, ANDREA D. KOHN, DANIELA CORDA,
WILLIAM E. HOFFMAN, DONATELLA TOMBACCINI,
WILLIAM A. VALENTE, MICHELE DE LUCA, PILAR
SANTISTEBAN, AND EVELYN F. GROLLMAN

Section on Cell Regulation
Laboratory of Biochemistry and Metabolism
National Institute of Arthritis, Diabetes,
and Digestive and Kidney Diseases
National Institutes of Health
Bethesda, Maryland 20205

INTRODUCTION

Graves' disease is an autoimmune disorder of the thyroid characterized by (a) a diffusely enlarged thyroid gland (goiter), (b) symptoms of hyperthyroidism, and (c) episodically associated connective tissue complications (for example, exophthalmos and pretibial myxedema). The weight of evidence suggests that Graves' disease is a disturbance of the immune system that results in the entrance, into the sera, of thyroid-stimulating autoantibodies (TSAbs) that stimulate the thyroid and induce the hyperthyroid state.[1-4] The idea evolved that TSAbs were related to the thyrotropin (TSH) receptor since IgG preparations from the sera of many Graves' patients could inhibit TSH binding.[5-7]

The concept that all the signs and symptoms of Graves' disease reflected the action of autoantibodies to the TSH receptor developed, however, several problems.[4,8-13] First, when numerous laboratories evaluated Graves' IgG preparations for their thyroid-stimulatory and TSH-inhibition activities, at least one-third of the preparations existed with only one activity and no correlation existed between the levels of activity when both were present simultaneously. Second, it was recognized that there might be a distinct class of antibodies in Graves' sera that did not cause hyperfunction, but instead stimulated thyroid cell growth to cause goiter formation.[14-17] There was no evidence this group of autoantibodies were directed against the TSH receptor. Third, evidence in experimental models that suggested that the TSH receptor might be involved in the connective tissue complications of Graves' disease, such as exophthalmos,[18,19] were argued to be nonapplicable to the human situation.

In sum, clinical data led to a belief that antibodies to thyroid membranes existed in the sera of Graves' patients and were important in the pathogenesis of the disease. It was, however, less clear that these antibodies were directed against the TSH receptor as opposed to other membrane determinants or if there were multiple antibodies to the TSH receptor structure [for example, one involved in binding, one for adenylate-cyclase activation, one for goiter production (growth), etc.]. Resolution of the discrepancies in the clinical studies required a greater understanding of the characteristics of individual antibodies within the spectra present in a single patient's serum. Resolution also required knowledge of the potential role of different determinants on the TSH receptor for TSH binding, thyroid cell growth, adenylate-cyclase stimulation, pretibial myxedema, and exophthalmos.

THE THYROTROPIN RECEPTOR: A COMPLEX STRUCTURE OF MORE THAN ONE MEMBRANE COMPONENT

Perhaps the problem of the relationship of the autoantibodies to the TSH receptor might have been resolved more rapidly if there had been a clear idea of the structure of the TSH receptor. Unfortunately, when binding studies did define membrane components able to interact with TSH, TSAbs, or TBIAbs, a controversial model of the receptor evolved.[21–27]

Two membrane components were identified that bound TSH with specificity (FIGURE 1).[21–27] The first, a membrane glycoprotein, was generally agreed to be that component of the TSH receptor that bound TSH to the cell with high affinity; its loss, for example, when cells were exposed to trypsin, resulted in a loss in both TSH-binding and TSH-stimulated functions. The role of the second component, a membrane ganglioside, was more controversial. The evidence for its physiologic importance derived mainly from the observations that (i) higher order gangliosides, with the ability to interact with TSH, were absent in a thyroid tumor that had lost its functional TSH receptor; (ii) resynthesis or reconstitution of gangliosides in membranes from this tumor could cause both a return of TSH binding and the ability of TSH to stimulate adenylate-cyclase activity;[21–28] (iii) this reconstitution was effected by a thyroid-specific ganglioside. The ganglioside was suggested to modulate the apparent specificity, affinity, and capacity of the glycoprotein receptor component and induce a conformational change in the hormone believed to be necessary for subsequent message transmission. It coupled the high affinity binding site to the adenylate-cyclase signal system by acting as an emulsifying agent to allow the hormone to interact with other membrane components within the hydrophobic environment of the lipid bilayer.

MONOCLONAL ANTIBODIES CONFIRM THE TWO COMPONENT TSH RECEPTOR MODEL AND RELATE THE MULTICOMPONENT RECEPTOR STRUCTURE TO AUTOANTIBODIES IN THE SERA OF GRAVES' PATIENTS

The monoclonal antibody approach involved the merging of two separate sets of studies.[26–34] The initial approach involved: the injection of crude solubilized thyroid membrane preparations into mice followed by spleen cell fusion with non-IgG-producing mouse myeloma cells; production of hybridomas secreting antibodies capable of binding to the intact thyroid membrane preparation; functional identification of antibodies related to the TSH receptor structure; and, finally, characterization of the antigenic determinants of the antibodies with respect to the already identified TSH-binding components.

Because each Graves' autoantibody could be presumed to be the product of a clonal line of B cells present in these patients, the second approach involved the following: Fusion of lymphocytes from patients with active Graves' disease with a non-IgG-secreting mouse myeloma cell line; identification of heterohybridomas that secreted antibodies capable of stimulating thyroid function or blocking TSH binding; and characterization of the antigenic determinants of these antibodies with respect to the structural or functional components of the TSH receptor identified by the monoclonal antibodies derived from the first approach.

In both cases, anti-TSH receptor producing clones were identified by the following criteria: (i) The antibody had to inhibit TSH binding to thyroid membranes or, conversely, be itself prevented from binding to thyroid membranes by TSH; (ii) Binding inhibition had to be specific and had to be competitive as opposed to

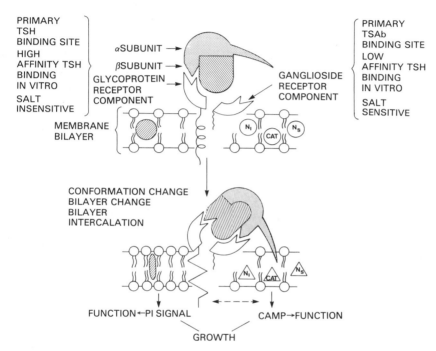

FIGURE 1. Model of TSH receptor based on binding studies with ^{125}I-TSH and on studies involving monoclonal antibodies to the TSH receptor. The evidence indicates that the glycoprotein receptor component is linked to phosphoinositol (PI) signal systems, whereas the ganglioside is linked to cAMP signaling. The PI function identified is iodide transport into the follicular lumen and iodination of thyroglobulin. A cAMP function is iodide uptake into the cell from the bloodstream. It is presumed that the beta subunit of TSH has the primary recognition determinants based on reconstitution experiments; the alpha subunit may contribute more than a conformational constraint on the beta subunit. The alpha-subunit portion that intercalates within the bilayer is presumed to include that region with nonapeptide hormone sequence analogies.

noncompetitive or uncompetitive; (iii) The antibody had to competitively inhibit TSH-stimulated thyroid functions (i.e., adenylate-cyclase activity, iodide uptake, or thyroid hormone release) or, conversely, had to mimic TSH activity and exhibit properties of competitive agonism.

With the identification of over 30 antibodies satisfying the above criteria,[26-34] the antibodies could be broadly grouped into three classes: inhibitors, stimulators, and mixed antibodies (TABLE 1). The term of "inhibitor" antibody was used because the antibodies inhibited TSH binding like the thyrotropin-binding inhibiting antibodies (TBIAbs) of Graves' sera. These antibodies competitively inhibited ^{125}I-TSH binding; they were also competitive inhibitors of binding and TSH-stimulated adenylate-cyclase activity, iodide uptake, and thyroidal iodine release. They had no direct stimulatory action as measured by thyroid adenylate-cyclase activity, T_3/T_4 release, and iodide uptake and they were not reactive with TSH (i.e., they were not simply anti-TSH antibodies). The term of "inhibitor" antibody is a misnomer, though, because they can be active as growth-promoting antibodies or as exophthalmogenic autoantibodies (TABLE 1).

The antibodies in the "inhibitory" group were shown to interact with the glycoprotein component of the TSH receptor in studies using liposomes embedded with this component and in purification studies summarized below. Inhibition of TSH binding by the antibodies could be detected under all *in vitro* conditions used to measure TSH binding, i.e., low or high salts and low or high pH; it was thus evident

TABLE 1. Representative Monoclonal Antibodies to the TSH Receptor

Clone No.	TSH Receptor Source	Primary Classification[c]	Growth Activity (degree)	Exophthalmogenic Activity	Pretibial Myxedema Activity
13D11	bovine	inhibitor	no	yes	no
11E8	bovine	inhibitor	no	yes	no
59C9	human	inhibitor	no	no	no
60F5	human	inhibitor	yes (++)	no	—
129H8[a]	human	inhibitor	yes (+)	weak	no
122G3[a]	human	inhibitor	no	weak	no
22A6	bovine	stimulator	yes (+)	no	no
206H3[a]	human	stimulator	yes (++)	no	—
307H6[a,b]	human	stimulator	yes (++)	yes	weak
304D3[a,b]	human	stimulator	yes (+)	no	no
308L2[a,b]	human	stimulator	yes (+)	no	no
410F9[a]	human	stimulator	yes (+)	no	no
52A8	human	mixed	yes (++++)	no	yes
208F7[a]	human	mixed	yes (+++)	no	yes

[a]Heterohybridomas.
[b]From the same patient.
[c]Inhibitor = TBIAb; stimulator = TSAb.

that arguments concerning the condition-dependent measurement of this receptor component were, in retrospect, wrong. Inhibition was evident whether the glycoprotein component was derived from human, bovine, or rat thyroid membranes. This suggested that the primary TSH binding site in these different species was similar in structure and accounted for the observation that bovine TSH was highly active independent of the species of thyroid studied.

Stimulating antibodies were those that mimicked the activity of thyroid-stimulating antibodies (TSAbs) from Graves' patients in all respects. They thus exhibited direct, TSH-like, stimulatory action of adenylate-cyclase activity, iodide uptake, and T_3/T_4 release by the thyroid. They were also competitive agonists with respect to TSH when they were included with different concentrations of TSH in assays measuring adenylate-cyclase activity. In contrast to the "inhibitor" group, they were weak inhibitors of ^{125}I-TSH binding, despite equally potent competitive inhibition of

TSH-stimulated adenylate-cyclase activity. In short, these are the TSAbs in the sera of patients with no or with weak TBIAb activity. In solid-phase assays, all the stimulating antibodies interacted with ganglioside preparations from thyroid membranes,[24-34] but only minimally with ganglioside preparations from bovine brain.

The monoclonal TSAbs exhibited species specificity. Thus, 22A6, an antibody made using thyroid membranes as the antigen, was a stimulator of both bovine and human thyroid adenylate-cyclase activity and reactive with both bovine and human thyroid gangliosides. In contrast, 307H6, a human heterohybridoma TSAb, exhibited human specificity in both reactions. This suggested that the phenomenon of TSAb species specificity, defined in the concept of LATS versus LATS protector,[1-4] rests in structural differences in the ganglioside rather than in the glycoprotein component of the TSH receptor. More specifically, it rests in the carbohydrate structure of the ganglioside.

The third or "mixed" group had all of the stimulatory properties of a stimulating antibody (TSAb), but the group also had the ability to inhibit ^{125}I-TSH binding to a significant degree, like a TBIAb. Their importance as a distinct group of autoantibodies was established in mixing experiments and in studies of their effects on thyroid cell growth (see below).

The conclusive evidence that inhibitor and stimulator monoclonal antibodies were directed at distinct biochemical determinants of the membrane (which, nevertheless, functionally acted together) was derived from mixing experiments.[35,36] Thus, 11E8 could inhibit TSH stimulation, but it was ineffective in inhibiting the stimulating activity of 22A6, 307H6, or any Graves' TSAb, even at 10,000-fold higher concentrations than used to completely inhibit TSH. An important clinical implication of the data was as follows: If a Graves' patient has both an "inhibiting" and "stimulating" antibody present in his or her serum, the phenotypic expression will be a hyperthyroid state. This is evident because the TBIAb will not inhibit a TSAb, despite its capacity to inhibit TSH.[35,36]

The inability of 11E8 to block 22A6 or 307H6 activity in mixing experiments clearly indicated that these monoclonals were antibodies to different determinants on the TSH receptor. Because *in vitro* experiments described above indicated that the 11E8 monoclonal antibody interacted predominantly with the membrane glycoprotein, whereas the 22A6 and 307H6 monoclonal antibodies interacted predominantly with the ganglioside, the simplest way of reconciling the observations was to apply the two component receptor model suggested in receptor binding studies (FIGURE 1). Thus, TSH could be envisaged to interact first with the glycoprotein component of the TSH receptor that exhibits high affinity binding properties. Its biological action, however, required an additional or subsequent interaction with the ganglioside. In contrast, TSAbs represented by 307H6 and 22A6 could be envisaged to bypass the glycoprotein receptor component and interact with the ganglioside to initiate the hormonelike signal.

The mixing experiments also established that "mixed" antibodies (for example, 208F7 and 52A8) were directed against a unique set of receptor determinants different from 11E8 or 307H6, yet common to both. Thus, unlike the TSAbs, 22A6 or 307H6, 208F7 was partially inhibited by 11E8[35,36] at higher concentrations than necessary to inhibit TSH. One explanation for this result was that the mixed antibodies were directed at determinants on a "physiologic TSH receptor," which was a functional complex of ganglioside and glycoprotein; this explanation was confirmed in purification studies.

In sum, the monoclonal data confirmed the two component receptor model proposed from *in vitro* binding experiments. The data also showed that the autoantibodies in Graves' sera that related to hyperfunction of the thyroid are those related to inhibition of TSH binding that were directed at different components of this receptor, the ganglioside and glycoprotein, respectively.

THE TSH RECEPTOR IS A COMPLEX OF GLYCOPROTEIN AND GANGLIOSIDE

Immunoprecipitation of detergent solubilized thyroid membrane preparations by monoclonal TBIAb antibodies 11E8 or 13D11 indicates that the glycoprotein component of the TSH receptor is an approximately 280-kilobase (K) protein (FIGURE 2A), which, when stored in the absence of protease inhibitors, forms a 70-K derivative (FIGURE 2B) that not only still interacts with TSH and TBIAbs, but is readily cross-linked with TSH.[26] TSH causes the thyroid cell to increase both the synthesis and degradation of the glycoprotein receptor component (FIGURE 3). This apparently results in further fragmentation of the 70-K receptor derivative to 40–50-K and 25–35-K fragments (FIGURE 3), which have also been seen in cross-linking studies and in immunoprecipitation studies using solubilized membranes from thyroid tissues removed from different animal species.[26–29] The 280-K protein reacts with the autoimmune TBIAbs such as 122G3 or 129H8 (FIGURE 2C). Surprisingly, it also reacts with the TSAbs whose predominant *in vitro* reaction was with the ganglioside (FIGURE 2C).

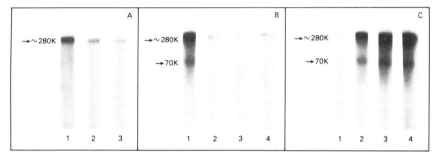

FIGURE 2. (A) Autoradiograph of analytic slab gels containing a ^{35}S-methionine-labeled ~280-K TSH receptor from FRTL-5 rat thyroid cells after sequential purification (12,000-fold) by TSH affinity chromatography and 11E8 monoclonal anti-TSH receptor immunopurification. Gel 1: Purified receptor eluted from 11E8 antibody bound to Sepharose. Gel 2: Decreased amount of receptor is bound to 11E8-Sepharose-coupled antibody when coincubated with 1×10^{-10} M TSH, washed, and then eluted. Gel 3: No significant 280-K receptor is bound to normal mouse IgG coupled to Sepharose when eluted as per Gel 1. Gels are 5% acrylamide and are run using a sodium dodecyl sulfate - 0.1 M mercaptoethanol buffer system. (B) Autoradiograph of a ^{35}S-methionine-labeled TSH receptor purified from FRTL-5 thyroid cells (as noted in FIGURE 2A) and then incubated 24 hours in buffers wherein the aprotinin protease inhibitor used in purification buffers was removed. Gel 1: Material from Gel 1, FIGURE 2A incubated without aprotinin, then reimmunoprecipitated with 11E8-Sepharose antibody to TSH receptor and eluted with glycine buffer, pH 2.5. Gel 2: The same material as used in the Gel 1 experiment, but incubated with 1×10^{-10} M TSH during the second immunoprecipitation. Neither the ~280-K receptor glycoprotein nor the 70-K fragment now bind to 11E8. Gel 3 and 4, respectively: no receptor binds or elutes if 11E8-Sepharose is replaced with normal mouse IgG-Sepharose or with Sepharose coupled to a "normal" mouse monoclonal that binds to thyroid membranes, but is not directed against the TSH receptor. (C) Immunoprecipitation of TSH receptor by normal human IgG coupled to Sepharose (Gel 1) by human IgG monoclonal TBIAbs, 129H8 (Gel 2) or 122G3 (Gel 3), or by a human monoclonal TSAb, 307H6 (Gel 4). Elution is with glycine HCl.

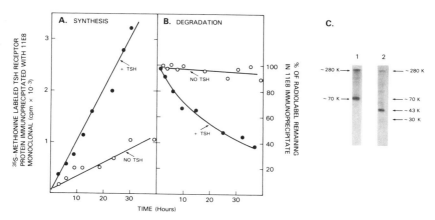

FIGURE 3. TSH regulation of the synthesis (A) and degradation (B) of the TSH receptor glycoprotein in FRTL-5 cells as measured by ^{35}S-methionine incorporation into 11E8 monoclonal (TBIAb) immunoprecipitable receptor material after pulsing cells with ^{35}S-methionine (A) or after an equilibrium labeling period followed by a "chase" with medium without radiolabeled methionine (B). In (A), FRTL-5 cells were grown in the presence of TSH to near confluency. At zero time, ^{35}S-methionine was added and the cells maintained in the presence or absence of TSH. At the times noted, cells were washed, solubilized with a triton/deoxycholate/sodium-dodecyl-sulfate mixture, immunoprecipitated with 11E8 coupled to Sepharose or normal IgG coupled to Sepharose, and the 11E8-specific, immunoprecipitable radiolabel was plotted as a function of time. In (B), the cells were equilibrium labeled by incubating them in ^{35}S-methionine for four days, at which time fresh media with unlabeled methionine and with (+) TSH or without (NO) TSH was added. The cells were solubilized at the times noted and the 11E8-bound radiolabel was measured. In (C), the autoradiograph of 11E8 immunoprecipitable material from a ^{35}S-methionine equilibrium labeled FRTL-5 cell not exposed to TSH for five days is compared with that from a comparably labeled FRTL-5 cell exposed to TSH for the same period. The TSH causes a dramatic decrease in the 70-K 11E8 binding component and an increase in the components having molecular weights of approximately 45 K and 30–35 K.

This last observation is explained by the fact that the ganglioside is tightly bound to the glycoprotein. Thus, if the immunoprecipitates of the glycoprotein receptor component obtained with either a TSAb or a TBIAb are Folch extracted, then thin-layer chromatography of the aqueous soluble lipid extract will show that the glycoprotein contains a specific ganglioside distinct from the total ganglioside pool (FIGURE 4). In bovine thyroid glycoprotein receptor component preparations, this ganglioside is the same as a thyroid-specific ganglioside identified in earlier experiments[37] to have the highest ability to inhibit TSH binding to thyroid membranes.

Little is know about the ganglioside. It fractionates on DEAE as a disialoglyco-lipid; it probably has a G_{DIb} rather than a G_{DIa} configuration; it is sensitive to neuraminidase treatment, which destroys its reactivity with the TSAbs; and it may contain a fucose residue.[24–34]

GROWTH AUTOANTIBODIES IN GRAVES' DISEASE

As noted in the INTRODUCTION, recent studies indicated that Graves' patients had antibodies in their sera that could promote growth, but that did not bear a simple relationship to autoantibodies related to thyroid hyperfunction.[14–17] The existence of a

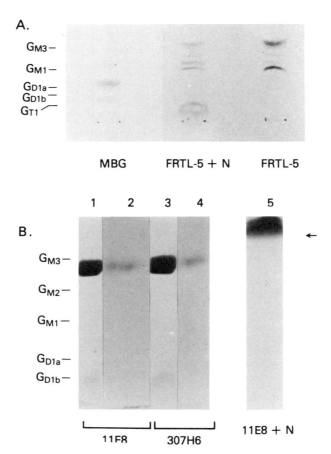

FIGURE 4. Thin-layer chromatography of the gangliosides extracted from FRTL-5 cells (A) or from the 12,000-fold purified ~280-K TSH receptor glycoprotein (FIGURE 2A, Gel 1) from FRTL-5 cells (B) after it was immunopurified by 11E8 (B, lanes 1, 2, and 5) or after it was immunopurified by 307H6 (B, Gels 3 and 4). In (B), the 280-K protein was from FRTL-5 cells labeled with $[^3H]$-N-acetyl glucosamine. The thin-layer plates in (B) were cut in strips and they either were resorcinol stained (lanes 2 and 4) or subjected to autoradiography (lanes 1 and 3). In (A), the gangliosides from the FRTL-5 extract were stained with resorcinol. A thin-layer chromatogram of a mixed brain ganglioside (MBG) preparation is presented for comparison to the FRTL-5 gangliosides. Gangliosides were extracted and purified after the FRTL-5 cell membrane preparation or the 280-K receptor glycoprotein preparation was sonicated (Ultrasonics Inc. Model W185 D cell disrupter; 3 min; output 3) under a stream of nitrogen. The final fraction was obtained using a Sep Pak™ cartridge. The purified fractions, dried under a stream of nitrogen and dissolved in methanol, were chromatographed on silica gel 60 HP-TLC plates (E. Merck, Darmstadt, Germany). The running buffer was chloroform:methanol:KCl 2.5 mg/ml (120:70:16 by vol). Neuraminidase treatment (+N) of a ganglioside preparation was for 24 hours with a cholera vibrio enzyme; reactions were terminated by 10-fold dilution with methanol; the gangliosides were reconstituted in buffer after drying with a stream of nitrogen. Gangliosides were chromatographed with authentic standards, each of whose migration is noted.

panel of monoclonal antibodies to the TSH receptor allowed the asking of a simple question: What was the activity of the TSH receptor monoclonals on growth?

The answer to this question depended on an assay that used a continuous line of functioning rat thyroid cells whose growth had been shown to be dependent on the presence of TSH and on measurements of cell number or radiolabeled thymidine incorporation.[17,38] When the monoclonal TSH receptor antibodies were tested, it was found that all TSAbs stimulated the growth activity of FRTL-5 rat thyroid cells, whether measured as cell number or as [³H]-thymidine uptake (TABLE 1). All "mixed" antibodies also stimulated growth activity, but they had threefold or higher ratios of growth to adenylate-cyclase stimulatory activity than the TSAbs when normalized to equivalence with respect to adenylate-cyclase activity. "Inhibitor" antibodies could, surprisingly, be either inhibitors of TSH-stimulated growth and adenylate-cyclase activity (122G3, 59C9) or stimulators of growth, but inhibitors of TSH binding and

TABLE 2. Effect of Monoclonal Antibodies to the TSH Receptor on the Growth of FRTL-5 Thyroid Cells as Measured by Radiolabeled Thymidine Uptake into DNA

| | [³H]-Thymidine Uptake^a (cpm/μg DNA) | |
Monoclonal Antibody	Alone	+Indomethacin
None	1600	1400
N1 IgG	1450	1510
TSH $1 \times 10^{-10} M$	6800	3500
$1 \times 10^{-9} M$	31,000	14,800
"Stimulating" TSABs		
22A6	6800	6900
307H6	8700	9200
"Mixed" Antibodies^b		
52A8	28,600	7400
208F7	24,700	6500
"Inhibiting" TBIAbs		
122G3	9350	1460
129H8	5600	1480

^{a}Seventy-two-hour thymidine uptake, measured as detailed in references 17 and 38.
^{b}Tested at concentrations of IgG that increased cAMP levels in FRTL-5 thyroid cells to exactly the same extent.

TSH-stimulated adenylate-cyclase activity (129H8, 60F5). Though these data clearly state that the same structural TSH receptor is used to signal growth as well as adenylate-cyclase activity, differences in signal coupling and differences in the linkage of the receptor components to the signals seemed likely.

That this was true was suggested by the following observations: TSH growth activity could be partially inhibited by indomethacin (TABLE 2); indomethacin is a cyclooxygenase inhibitor that limits arachidonic acid processing to derivatives such as prostaglandins. Indomethacin partially inhibited the growth activity of the mixed antibodies, 208F7 and 52A8 (TABLE 2), and it had no affect on the growth action of TSAbs such as 307H6; however, it completely inhibited the growth activity of the 129H8 and 60F5 TBIAbs. In short, it appeared that the TSH-modulated growth activity of the thyroid cell involved both adenylate-cyclase and Ca^{++}/phospholipid modulation signals. Furthermore, phospholipid signaling seemed to be linked more to the glycoprotein receptor component and adenylate-cyclase action seemed linked more to the ganglioside component.

Several clinical implications emerge from this data. First, distinct growth-promoting TSAbs and cyclase stimulatory TSAbs can exist in patients and can be present at different levels. Second, it seemed possible, based on the monoclonal antibody studies, that thyroid stimulation in Graves' disease might result from a small goiter potently stimulated by a 307H6-type antibody to actively release thyroid hormones. Alternatively, Graves' disease might be associated with a large goiter, caused by a 129H8 antibody, whose release of excess thyroid hormone reflects the existence of an excess of responsive tissue. It is also possible that the presence of (i) a mixed antibody or (ii) a mixture of a TBIAb antibody, which is a growth stimulator, and a TSAb, such as 307H6, would result in two independent and potent stimulators being present simultaneously, thus causing, most likely, the most severe cases of thyroid stimulation. In the last mixture, it must be remembered (see above) that the 129H8 TBIAb would not inhibit the TSAb; the presence of the two autoantibodies would thus be complementary in their pathogenic action.

MONOCLONAL ANTIBODIES TO THE TSH RECEPTOR, NONTHYROIDAL TSH RECEPTORS, AND THE CONNECTIVE TISSUE COMPLICATIONS OF GRAVES' DISEASE

Exophthalmos

Nonthyroidal TSH "receptors" have been argued to be important in the pathogenesis of exophthalmos and the connective tissue complications of Graves' disease.[19,20]

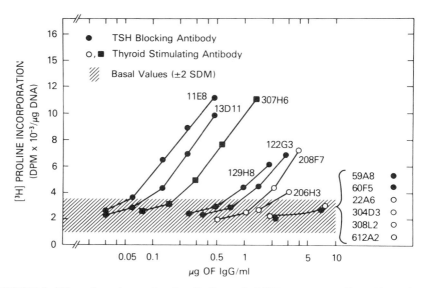

FIGURE 5. Effect of noted monoclonal antibodies to the TSH receptor on collagen biosynthesis in human fibroblasts. Collagen biosynthesis is measured as [3H]-proline incorporation into pepsin-insensitive, salt-precipitated collagen.

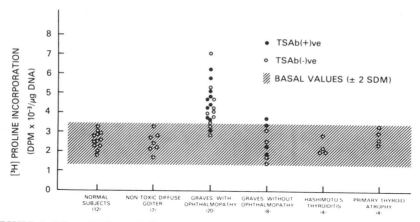

FIGURE 6. Effect of different IgG preparations from patients with or without thyroid opthalmopathy on collagen biosynthesis in human fibroblasts. Collagen biosynthesis is measured as [^{3}H]-proline incorporation into pepsin-insensitive, salt-precipitated collagen.

Thus, in the 1970s, studies of exophthalmos in experimental animal models suggested that there was a TSH receptor in retroorbital tissues and that exophthalmos involved expression of the TSH receptor in the presence of an abnormal serum gamma globulin found in exophthalmos patients.[19,20] Until the monoclonal antibody approach cited above, there was no simple approach that could be reasonably anticipated to prove this point.

The application of a monoclonal approach to the mechanism of exophthalmos involved an extension of the monoclonal approach to define the TSH receptor in the thyroid and related it to autoantibodies causative of thyroid hyperfunction.[20,39] Monoclonal antibodies derived from the lymphocytes of patients with Graves' disease without exophthalmos were compared with those of patients with Graves' disease plus exophthalmos. One stimulating antibody (307H6), derived from the exophthalmos group, was found to stimulate collagen biosynthesis in human skin fibroblasts (FIGURE 5);[39] this antibody had all the characteristics of a stimulator antibody to the TSH receptor defined above. It was only one of over a dozen TSAb monoclonals that were active in the fibroblast assays and that originated from a patient with exophthalmos who also had TSAbs fibroblast activity. The 307H6 data clearly established that a unique stimulator TSAb could exist that also stimulated fibroblasts; separate studies using patient IgGs established that the fibroblast assay was a good measure of exophthalmos (FIGURE 6). Thus, approximately 90% of Graves' patients with exophthalmos are positive in this assay, whereas patients with thyroid disease, but no exophthalmos, were uniformly negative in the assay (FIGURE 6).

A second important observation evolved during the testing of a range of monoclonal antibodies to the TSH receptor that were in the "inhibitory" group. Surprisingly, several had potent activities as stimulators of collagen biosynthesis in fibroblasts (FIGURE 5).

The activity of the "exophthalmogenic" IgGs were comparable to the positive monoclonals. Thus, in the same assay, 11E8 and 13D11 (the two mouse monoclonal antibodies to the bovine TSH receptor) and 307H6 (the human monoclonal to the TSH receptor from a Graves' patient with exophthalmos) were as active in stimulating collagen incorporation of [^{3}H]-proline as the most potent IgG preparations from exophthalmos patients, but they were active at ∼1000- to 10,000-fold lower IgG concentrations. In conclusion, it seemed possible (i) that the fibroblast collagen biosynthesis assay was a valid means of measuring exophthalmogenic autoantibodies whether it was TSAb positive or not and (ii) that selected populations of autoantibodies to the TSH receptor could duplicate this *in vitro* activity.

The antibodies clearly reflect a common thyroidal and connective tissue antigen. Thus, preadsorption of the 11E8 antibody on thyroid membranes resulted in the loss of fibroblast activity, whereas preadsorption on liver or kidney membranes had no such effect. TSH did not inhibit the activity of the monoclonal in the fibroblast assay. This was of interest in several respects. First, it fit with data in experimental exophthalmos studies wherein TSH and the antibody were additive activators, not antagonists.[19,20] Second, it indicated that more than the TSH receptor determinant was necessary for the fibroblast activity. Since exophthalmos has been linked to cellular rather than humoral immunity,[19,20] it is possible a T-cell-like recognition phenomenon exists wherein tissue-specific or histocompatibility antigen determinants are also involved in recognition. This is particularly of interest given data below concerning cross-reactivity of the 11E8 monoclonal and concerning anti-idiotypes.

Pretibial Myxedema

Recent studies indicate that antibody stimulation of glycosaminoglycan synthesis in FRTL-5 thyroid cells may be used as a measure of the patient's IgG associated with pretibial myxedema. When the panel of TSH receptor monoclonals was evaluated in the same assay, it was evident that a TSH receptor monoclonal could elicit this activity (TABLE 1) and that this was a unique property not common to all or even most monoclonals. The nature of the common antigen remains to be elicited; however, it is evident that the monoclonal approach can address this issue.

IDIOTYPES AND ANTI-IDIOTYPES

In Anti-TSH Preparations

A polyclonal antibody population made against TSH should have individual antibodies that are directed at that determinant on the TSH molecule important for receptor recognition (binding site) or adenylate-cyclase stimulation (effector site). If, in turn, antibodies were made to these idiotypes, one could have anti-idiotypes, one of which would be equal to a TSAb (i) in its interaction with a thyroid ganglioside, (ii) in its ability to increase FRTL-5 cAMP levels, and (iii) in its inability to be inhibited by a TBIAb.

Using a random human anti-TSH preparation from the National Pituitary Agency, we examined the possibility of the anti-binding-site idiotype by taking advantage of the fact that cholera toxin can bind to the glycoprotein component of the TSH receptor. The anti-binding-site idiotype can thus be detected by the ability of the polyclonal preparation to inhibit cholera-toxin action. To examine for the existence of the anti-stimulatory-site idiotype, inhibition of TSAb action was measured. As noted in TABLE 3, both types of idiotypes exist. To complete the search, at low dilutions of the anti-TSH preparation, an effector anti-idiotype was found that stimulated like a TSAb and was, like a TSAb,[36,37] not 11E8 inhibited (TABLE 3).

In Patients with Graves' Disease

A Graves' patient should make antibodies against the TSAb. In this case, the anti-idiotype antibodies should include an inhibitor of TSAb stimulatory action and this could play a role in disease expression or remission. A patient presumed to have Hashimoto's disease, but who had three Graves' children, has been described.[40,41] The presumption existed that this patient had lymphocytes capable of producing stimulator antibodies (TSAbs), but who also had lymphocytes producing inhibitors of TSAbs. That one of these inhibitors might be an anti-idiotype inhibitor was suggested when the patient's IgG preparation was found to be a better inhibitor of a TSAb when the two

TABLE 3. Ability of an Antihuman TSH Preparation to Increase cAMP Levels in FRTL-5 Thyroid Cells as well as to Inhibit Cholera Toxin or TSAb-Stimulated Activity in FRTL-5 Cells

Ligands Added	cAMP Level (pmol/μg of DNA)[a]	Inhibition (%)
None	0.5	—
Anti-TSH IgG[b]	0.4	—
Anti-TSH IgG 1/10[b]	2.4	—
Anti-TSH IgG 1/100[b]	7.2	—
Anti-TSH IgG 1/1000[b]	7.2	—
Anti-TSH IgG 1/1000[b] + 11E8	7.8	—
TSH (1×10^{-11} M)	24	0
+Anti-TSH IgG[b]	0.4	100
+Anti-IgG	25	0
+11E8	23	0
Graves' Serum TSAb IgG	8.2	0
+Anti-TSH IgG[b]	3.8	54
+N1 IgG	8.1	0
+11E8	8.4	0
307H6 TSAb	5.2	0
+Anti-TSH IgG[b]	1.7	77
+N1 IgG	5.1	0
+11E8	5.3	0
Cholera Toxin	17	0
+Anti-TSH IgG[b]	4	76
+N1 IgG	18	0

[a]Values are the means of triplicate assays; error values were in all cases less than 4.5%.
[b]Undiluted at 2 mg/ml and then diluted 1/10, 1/100, and 1/1000.

IgGs were premixed rather than if the inhibitor IgG was first incubated with the thyroid cells (TABLE 4).

The patient's lymphocytes were fused and clones reactive as TSAbs were screened (i.e., clones able to increase cAMP levels in FRTL-5 cells). Of 2500 separate fusion products, ~150 reactive with thryoid membranes were found and about 12 acted as TSAbs. Also identified were clones reactive with TSH and a mouse monoclonal TSAb, 22A6. Six TSH and 22A6 positive clones were identified; three of these clones were able to inhibit the activity of a monoclonal TSAb from the same or a different patient.

In sum, it is evident that this patient has both stimulator TSAbs and anti-idiotype inhibitors of the stimulator TSAbs. In fact, the latter, at least in part, may account for the lack of hyperfunction in the patient.

Anti-Idiotypes and TSH Receptor Structure

The anti-idiotype approach has yielded valuable information with respect to the structure of the TSH receptor. The 11E8 mouse monoclonal TBIAb was used in an *in vitro* fusion to make mouse IgM anti-idiotypes. The product clones were screened for reactivity with a human TSAb (307H6), a human TBIAb (122G3), and a human mixed autoimmune Graves' stimulator (208F7), as well as for reactivity with TSH. It was initially anticipated that the anti-idiotypes might only react with the 122G3 antibody. Six clones that reacted only with 122G3 were indeed found. Surprisingly, however, three that reacted only with a TSAb were also found and two were found that reacted with both (12263 and a TSAb) and with 208F7.

TABLE 4. The Ability of an IgG from a Patient with Autoimmune Thyroid Disease to Inhibit TSAb Activity

Sequence of Incubation Components or Events			cAMP Level in FRTL-5 Cells (pmol/µg DNA)
1	2	3	
FRTL-5 Cells[a]	TSAb 307H6	N1 IgG	8.4
FRTL-5 Cells[a]	TSAb 307H6	Patient IgG	7.2
FRTL-5 Cells[a]	Patient IgG	TSAb 307H6	
	(1/10)		1.4
	(1/100)		7.2
Patient[b] IgG	TSAb 307H6	FRTL-5 cells	
(1/10)			0.5
(1/100)			0.5

[a]FRTL-5 cells were incubated with the first antibody for three hours, then incubated an additional three hours with the second IgG or a normal IgG.

[b]Antibodies were preincubated for 30 minutes, then simultaneously added to the FRTL-5 cells and assayed $5\frac{1}{2}$ hours later.

This result has several implications. First, it is clear that the TSH receptor "active site" on the complex of glycoprotein and ganglioside is geometrically or spatially accommodated in the dimensions of an antibody combining site. Second, it is evident that monoclonal TBIAbs or TSAbs may be unique in their actions not because they are antibodies made against one or the other TSH receptor determinant in an isolated state, but because they are antibodies that are viewing the receptor from different sides. Third, the anti-idiotype monoclonals can be used clinically to measure Graves' autoantibodies in patients. Thus, one such anti-idiotype detected Graves' autoantibody in IgG preparations from the sera of 12 Graves' patients and 3 Hashimoto's, but not in the sera from 16 normals, 8 nontoxic goiters, 4 toxic goiters, 3 toxic adenomas, and 1 nontoxic adenoma. These data raise the hope that a simple radioimmunoassay will replace current bioassays used to measure TSAbs, TBIAbs, etc.

SUMMARY

The present report summarizes experiments with monoclonal antibodies to the TSH receptor. The data provide further insight into the TSH receptor structure and into the basis of autoimmune antibodies implicated in the pathogenesis of Graves' disease. They resolve many clinical questions and provide new approaches to enhance our understanding of autoimmune disease.

In one new approach, it has been noted that the 11E8 TBIAb can precipitate the phosphorylated β subunit of the insulin and IGF_1 receptor. This cross-reactivity or recognition of determinants adjacent to the TSH receptor may not be random. Insulin, IGF_1, α_1 adrenergic, and TSH receptors have been linked to a synergistic cascade response system of the thyroid involving growth, thyroglobulin biosynthesis, iodination of thyroglobulin, and thyroid hormone formation. Future studies with the monoclonals may help unravel this cascade system and its regulatory relationships, along with the relationships between autoimmune thyroid disease and autoimmune diseases of other organs.

REFERENCES

1. DONIACH, D. 1975. Clin. Endocrinol. Metab. **4:** 267–285.
2. ZAKARIJA, M. & J. M. MCKENZIE. 1980. *In* Autoimmune Aspects of Endocrine Disorders. A. Pinchera, D. Doniach, G. F. Fenzi & L. Baschieri, Eds.: 83–90. Academic Press. New York.
3. ADAMS, D. D. 1981. *In* Vitamins and Hormones, vol. 38. E. Diczfalusy & R. E. Olson, Eds.: 119–161. Academic Press. New York.
4. PINCHERA, A., G. F. FENZI, E. MACCHIA, P. VITTI, F. MONZANI & L. D. KOHN. 1982. Ann. Endocrinol. (Paris) **43:** 520–533.
5. SMITH, B. R. & R. HALL. 1974. Lancet **2:** 427–430.
6. MANLEY, S. W., J. R. ROURKE & R. J. HAWKER. 1974. Endocrinology **63:** 437–448.
7. MEHDI, S. W. & S. S. NUSSEY. 1975. Biochem. J. **145:** 105–111.
8. ORGIAZZI, J., D. E. WILLIAMS, I. J. CHOPRA & D. H. SOLOMON. 1976. J. Clin. Endocrinol. Metab. **42:** 341–354.
9. SCHLEUSENER, H., P. KOTULLA, R. FINKE, H. SORVE, H. MEINHOLD, E. ADLKOFER & K. W. WENZEL. 1978. J. Clin. Endocrinol. Metab. **47:** 379–388.
10. SUGENOYA, A., A. KIDD, V. V. ROW & R. VOLPE. 1979. J. Clin. Endocrinol. Metab. **48:** 398–402.
11. PINCHERA, A., G. FENZI, L. BARTALENA, L. CHIOVATO, C. MARCOCCI, R. TOCCAFONDI, C. ROTELLA, S. ATERINI & R. ZONEFRATI. 1980. *In* Thyroid Research, VIII. J. R. Stockigt & S. Nagataki, Eds.: 707–716. Australian Academy of Science. Canberra, Australia.
12. ZAKARIJA, M. & J. M. MCKENZIE. 1980. Ann. Intern. Med. **93:** 28–34.
13. MACCHIA, E., G. F. FENZI, F. MONZANI, F. LIPPI, P. VITTI, L. GRASSO, L. BARTALENA, L. BASCHIERI & A. PINCHERA. 1981. Clin. Endocrinol. (Oxford) **15:** 175–183.
14. DONIACH, D., G. F. BOTTAZZO & E. L. KHOURY. 1980. *In* Autoimmune Aspects of Endocrine Disorders, pp. 25–38. Academic Press. London.
15. DREXHAGE, H. A., G. F. BOTTAZZO & D. DONIACH. 1980. Lancet **2:** 287–291.
16. DREXHAGE, H. A., G. F. BOTTAZZO, L. BITENSKY, J. CHAYEN & D. DONIACH. 1981. Nature **289:** 594–596.
17. VALENTE, W. A., P. VITTI, C. M. ROTELLA, S. M. ALOJ, F. S. AMBESI-IMPIOMBATO & L. D. KOHN. 1983. N. Engl. J. Med. **309:** 1028–1034.
18. WINAND, R. J. & L. D. KOHN. 1977. *In* Rational Diagnosis of Thyroid Disease. R. Hofer, Ed.: 93–120. Verlag H. Egermann. Vienna.

19. KOHN, L. D. 1985. *In* The Thyroid: A Fundamental and Clinical Text, 5th edition. S. Ingbar, L. Braverman & S. Werner, Eds. Harper and Row. Hagerstown, Maryland. In press.

20. WALL, J. R. 1984. *In* The Eye and Orbit in Thyroid Disease. G. Gorman, J. Dyer & R. Waller, Eds.: 103–145. Raven Press. New York.

21. KOHN, L. D. 1978. *In* Receptors and Recognition, series A, vol. 5. P. Cuatrecasas & M. F. Greaves, Eds.: 133–212. Chapman and Hall. London.

22. KOHN, L. D. & S. SHIFRIN. 1982. *In* Hormone Receptors, Horizons in Biochemistry and Biophysics, vol. 6. L. D. Kohn, Ed.: 1–42. John Wiley and Sons. New York.

23. KOHN, L. D., S. M. ALOJ, F. BEGUINOT, P. VITTI, E. YAVIN, Z. YAVIN, P. LACCETTI, E. F. GROLLMAN & W. A. VALENTE. 1982. *In* Membrane and Genetic Diseases. J. Shepard, Ed.: 55–83. Alan R. Liss. New York.

24. KOHN, L. D., W. A. VALENTE, P. LACCETTI, J. L. COHEN, S. M. ALOJ & E. F. GROLLMAN. 1983. Life Sci. **32:** 15–30.

25. LACCETTI, P., D. TOMBACCINI, S. M. ALOJ, E. F. GROLLMAN & L. D. KOHN. 1984. *In* Ganglioside Structure Function and Biomedical Potential. R. Ledeen, R. Yu, M. Rapport & K. Suzuki, Eds.: 355–367. Plenum. New York.

26. KOHN, L. D., S. M. ALOJ, S. SHIFRIN, W. A. VALENTE, S. J. WEISS, P. VITTI, P. LACCETTI, J. L. COHEN, C. M. ROTELLA & E. F. GROLLMAN. 1985. *In* Receptors for Polypeptide Hormones. B. T. Posner, Ed.: 299–344. Dekker. New York.

27. KOHN, L. D., S. M. ALOJ, D. TOMBACCINI, C. M. ROTELLA, R. TOCCAFONDI, C. MARCOCCI, D. CORDA & E. F. GROLLMAN. 1985. *In* Biochemical Actions of Hormones. G. Litwak, Ed.: 457–512. Dekker. New York.

28. YAVIN, E., Z. YAVIN, M. D. SCHNEIDER & L. D. KOHN. 1981. Proc. Natl. Acad. Sci. USA **78:** 3180–3184.

29. YAVIN, E., Z. YAVIN, M. D. SCHNEIDER & L. D. KOHN. 1981. *In* Monoclonal Antibodies in Endocrine Research. R. E. Fellows & G. Eisenbarth, Eds.: 53–67. Raven Press. New York.

30. YAVIN, E., Z. YAVIN, M. D. SCHNEIDER & L. D. KOHN. 1981. *In* Monoclonal Antibodies to Neural Antigens. R. McKay, M. Rass & L. Reichardt, Eds.: 141–152. Cold Springs Harbor Laboratories. Cold Spring Harbor, New York.

31. VALENTE, W. A., Z. YAVIN, E. YAVIN, E. F. GROLLMAN, M. D. SCHNEIDER, C. M. ROTELLA, R. ZONEFRATI, R. S. TOCCAFONDI & L. D. KOHN. 1982. J. Endocrinol. Invest. **5:** 293–301.

32. VALENTE, W. A., P. VITTI, Z. YAVIN, E. YAVIN, C. M. ROTELLA, E. F. GROLLMAN, R. S. TOCCAFONDI & L. D. KOHN. 1982. Proc. Natl. Acad. Sci. USA **79:** 6680–6684.

33. KOHN, L. D., E. YAVIN, Z. YAVIN, P. LACCETTI, P. VITTI, E. F. GROLLMAN & W. A. VALENTE. 1983. *In* Monoclonal Antibodies: Probes for Study of Autoimmunity and Immunodeficiency. G. Eisenbarth & R. Haynes, Eds.: 221–258. Academic Press. New York.

34. KOHN, L. D., D. TOMBACCINI, M. L. DE LUCA, M. BIFULCO, E. F. GROLLMAN & W. A. VALENTE. 1984. *In* Receptors and Recognition: Antibodies to Receptors. M. F. Greaves, Ed.: 201–234. Chapman and Hall. London.

35. EALEY, P. A., L. D. KOHN, R. P. EKINS & N. J. MARSHALL. 1984. J. Clin. Endocrinol. Metab. **58:** 909–914.

36. EALEY, P. A., W. A. VALENTE, R. P. EKINS, L. D. KOHN & N. J. MARSHALL. 1985. Endocrinology **116:** 124–131.

37. MULLIN, B. R., T. PACUSZKA, G. LEE, L. D. KOHN, R. O. BRADY & P. H. FISHMAN. 1978. Science **119:** 77–79.

38. VALENTE, W. A., P. VITTI, L. D. KOHN, M. L. BRANDI, C. M. ROTELLA, R. TOCCAFONDI, D. TRAMONTANO, S. M. ALOJ & F. S. AMBESI-IMPIOMBATO. 1982. Endocrinology **112:** 71–79.

39. ROTELLA, C. M., R. ZONEFRATI, R. TOCCAFONDI, W. A. VALENTE & L. D. KOHN. 1986. J. Clin. Endocrinol. Metab. **62:** 357–367.

40. HOFFMAN, W. H., P. SAHASRANANAN, S. S. FERANDOS, C. L. BUREK & N. R. ROSE. 1982. J. Clin. Endocrinol. Metab. **54:** 354–356.

41. Zakarija, M., J. M. McKenzie & W. E. Hoffman. 1984. 7th Int. Cong. Endocrinology, p. 1553. Excerpta Medica. Amsterdam

DISCUSSION OF THE PAPER

G. Wick (*Institute of Innsbruck, Innsbruck, Austria*): May I ask about the fibrotic activity that you have mentioned? The TSH receptors were present in the retroorbital tissue, but they were also in other tissues. Why, then, is the retroorbital tissue such a prime target for the activity that you mentioned?

L. D. Kohn (*National Institutes of Health, Bethesda, MD*): The question comes up as to whether the retroorbital tissue is in some way primed in terms of the structure of the receptor or in the cross-reactivity with IGF-I and insulin receptors. In tentative experiments, that appears to be true.

E. A. Clark (*University of Washington, Seattle, WA*): Have you noted anything about your inhibitory versus stimulatory monoclonal antibodies; whether they differ or are similar in their effect in, say, very early events of the membrane, such as calcium flux, depolarization, etc.?

Kohn: Yes, they are. The antibodies that relate to the glycoprotein component are those that would stimulate the calcium flux. The stimulating antibodies do not.

Speculation on the Role of Somatic Mutation in the Generation of Anti-DNA Antibodies[a]

ANNE DAVIDSON,[b] ROBERTA HALPERN,
AND BETTY DIAMOND[c]

Department of Microbiology and Immunology
Albert Einstein College of Medicine
Bronx, New York 10461

Systemic lupus erythematosus (SLE) is a disease characterized by the production of multiple autoantibodies, including antibodies to double-stranded DNA. Recently, studies using human and mouse monoclonal anti-DNA antibodies have demonstrated that a restricted population of antibodies may account for a broad range of antigenic specificities found in SLE autoantibodies (reviewed in reference 1). Furthermore, demonstration of cross-reactive idiotypes on anti-DNA antibodies suggests that the same germline genes or gene families are used to encode anti-DNA antibodies in unrelated patients with SLE.[2-4]

While much has been learned in recent years about the nature of autoimmune anti-DNA antibodies both in human lupus and in murine models of lupus, several important questions remain unanswered. We do not know the molecular basis for the genetically determined predisposition to systemic lupus that has been abundantly demonstrated in epidemiologic studies. We do not know the molecular mechanisms responsible for generating anti-DNA antibodies or whether these are either encoded by particular autoimmune germline immunoglobulin genes or constructed from genes used in the course of the normal antibody response to foreign antigen. In this paper, we report some experiments that suggest a mechanism for the generation of anti-DNA antibodies and for the genetic predisposition to make such antibodies.

We have previously described the production of a monoclonal anti-idiotype, 3I, that recognizes a cross-reactive idiotype on anti-DNA antibodies in approximately 85% of over 150 patients with SLE.[2] This anti-idiotype was generated by obtaining from one patient with SLE an enriched fraction of anti-DNA antibodies. This fraction was then used to immunize a BALB/c mouse and conventional hybridoma technology was employed to fuse spleen cells from the immunized mouse with a drug-marked, nonproducing myeloma cell line. Two of approximately 100 hybridomas showed high-titered idiotypic activity. We have studied one of these, 3I.

The 3I anti-idiotype does not react with autoantibodies, in general, as it does not show high-titered reactivity with serum from patients with rheumatoid arthritis (who have rheumatoid factor in their serum) or with serum from patients with drug-induced lupus (who have antihistone antibodies).[5] We have examined over 300 clinically

[a]This work was supported by NIH grant nos. AM-32371 and AI-10702, NCI grant no. 3P0CA1330, and the SLE Foundation.

[b]A.D. is the recipient of a Damon Runyon Walter Winchell Cancer Fund fellowship, no. DR9038.

[c]B.D. is an Established Investigator of the American Heart Association.

unaffected individuals and only one shows high-titered 3I reactivity. The 3I anti-idiotype therefore selectively shows strong reactivity with serum of lupus patients.

3I does not react with the DNA binding site on anti-DNA antibodies and it can therefore recognize both monomeric anti-DNA antibodies and anti-DNA antibodies present in immune complexes. High-titered 3I reactivity is found both with serum in which anti-DNA antibodies are detectable in conventional DNA binding assays and with serum in which no anti-DNA activity is detectable by such assays and in which anti-DNA antibodies are presumably bound in immune complexes. These anti-DNA antibodies can be unmasked when serum is analyzed under dissociating conditions by isoelectric focusing and Western blotting.[6]

To demonstrate that the 3I anti-idiotype reacts with a significant portion of anti-DNA antibodies, anti-DNA antibodies were isolated from the serum of four patients with SLE. In these patients, 40%, 60%, 80%, and greater than 90% of the anti-DNA antibodies were 3I reactive.[2] The identification of a cross-reactive idiotype on a substantial percent of anti-DNA antibodies from a majority of patients with SLE suggests that unrelated individuals use the same germline gene or gene family to encode anti-DNA antibodies.

The genetic predisposition to the development of SLE has been demonstrated by epidemiologic studies of families with SLE (reviewed in reference 7) and by studies demonstrating higher concordance of disease in monozygotic compared with dizygotic twins.[8] While many factors have been identified that might contribute to this genetic predisposition, its molecular basis remains unclear. Because lupus is a disease of autoantibody production and most commonly production of anti-DNA antibodies, we thought it reasonable to ask whether the use of particular variable region genes might contribute to disease susceptibility. We, therefore, determined expression of the cross-reactive idiotype found on anti-DNA antibodies in family members of lupus patients.

Sera were obtained from three families where two or more members had SLE.[9,10] There were 8 patients with SLE and 19 family members with no clinical lupus. A radioimmunoassay for 3I reactivity revealed that 6 of 8 lupus patients and 15 of 19 family members had high-titered 3I reactivity (FIGURE 1).

To determine if it was possible to distinguish the 3I-reactive antibodies of lupus patients from those of family members, sera were displayed on isoelectric focusing gels, transferred to nitrocellulose, and then incubated with the 3I anti-idiotype, followed by enzyme-linked anti-mouse immunoglobulin and substrate. Two patterns of 3I reactivity emerged: either 3I-reactive bands were restricted to pH 5–7 or additional cationic bands were present at pH >7. Lupus patients showed both patterns of reactivity and 4 of 8 patients had cationic 3I-reactive bands. Family members also showed both patterns, but only 4 of 19 had cationic 3I-reactive bands.

In order to see which pattern associated with anti-DNA activity, all sera were examined by Millipore filter assay for DNA binding. Four lupus patients showed elevated anti-DNA activity. Two family members had high-titered anti-DNA activity. Because we had previously shown that anti-DNA activity can be masked presumably because the anti-DNA antibodies are complexed in the serum to antigen or autologous anti-idiotype, we examined all sera for DNA binding under conditions that dissociate immune complexes. The sera were displayed on isoelectric focusing gels, transferred to nitrocellulose, and probed with radiolabeled DNA. This revealed that 2 additional patients and 2 additional family members had anti-DNA activity.

All individuals (4 patients and 4 family members) with high-titered 3I reactivity and cationic 3I-reactive bands had anti-DNA antibodies in their serum either free or in masked form. One lupus patient and 11 family members had high-titered 3I reactivity, no anti-DNA antibodies, and no cationic 3I-reactive bands.[11]

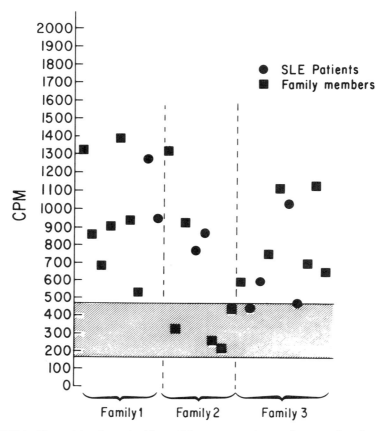

FIGURE 1. 3I reactivity determined by radioimmunoassay in sera from members from three human kindreds with SLE. Mean 3I reactivity of serum for 20 normal individuals is indicated by the shaded area. Six of 8 SLE patients (indicated by ●) and 15 of 19 family members (indicated by ■) have high-titered 3I reactivity.

These data had three conclusions:

(1) It is possible to have high-titered anti-DNA antibodies and no clinical disease. In this study, serum samples were analyzed at a single time point, so it is not known whether anti-DNA antibodies were chronically present in the four individuals without clinical lupus.

(2) All individuals, both SLE patients and family members, who had cationic 3I-reactive bands had anti-DNA activity. This suggests that both the charge of the antibody molecule as well as the primary amino-acid sequence help determine its affinity for DNA. The 3I-reactive antibodies that bind DNA are more likely to be positively charged than the 3I-reactive non-DNA binding immunoglobulin.

(3) There seems to be a genetic regulation of idiotype expression, but no necessary association with anti-DNA activity, thus indicating that idiotype expression is

regulated independently of antigen binding. We do not know what regulates idiotype expression. While some studies in mice suggest an association between idiotype expression and histocompatibility antigens, we found in our study no correlation between high-titered 3I reactivity and particular HLA alleles.[11]

Our finding of individuals with high-titered 3I reactivity, but no anti-DNA activity leads us to ask whether DNA is the antigen that elicits high-titered expression of the 3I idiotype. Several lines of study have suggested that DNA may not be the eliciting antigen for autoimmune anti-DNA antibodies, but that these antibodies represent a pathogenic cross-reactivity of antibodies elicited by a microbial antigen.[12-14]

Analyses of monoclonal murine anti-DNA antibodies have shown that they use variable region genes from the gene families used in the normal immune response.[14,15] One anti-DNA antibody from an NZB/NZW hybridoma sequenced by Rudikoff *et al.* was shown to have a heavy-chain variable region similar to one of the T15 variable region genes.[14] T15 is an idiotype expressed in response to immunization with phosphorylcholine, the dominant antigen on the pneumococcal cell wall.[16]

In an effort to understand the role of somatic mutation in the generation of antibody diversity, M. Scharff's laboratory has been generating variant progeny of the S107 cell line. S107 is a mouse myeloma line making a T15 positive anti-phosphorylcholine antibody.[17] The variants his laboratory has isolated make immunoglobulins differing by one or two amino acids, but they have markedly diminished affinity for phosphorylcholine.[18,19]

We examined these mutants for reactivity to DNA.[20] One of them, U4, differs from the parent by a single amino-acid substitution in the first hypervariable region of the heavy-chain variable region. It has lost reactivity with phosphorylcholine, but has acquired reactivity with double-stranded DNA, as well as with a number of other phosphorylated macromolecules, including protamine and cardiolipin (TABLE 1). This pattern of antigenic cross-reactivity has been described for autoimmune anti-DNA antibodies.[1]

Stollar and Schwartz and their colleagues have suggested that anti-DNA antibodies bind to a phosphodiester bond present in the backbone of DNA and in a number of phospholipids.[21] In order to determine if U4 recognizes a phosphate epitope, we examined its reactivity with rainbow-trout protamine. Rainbow-trout protamine is nonphosphorylated and it was not recognized by the U4 protein; however, when rainbow-trout protamine was phosphorylated, U4 bound to it, thus suggesting that a phosphate epitope was indeed crucial in determining its antigenic specificity.

The U4 protein has a glutamic acid to alanine substitution at residue 35 in the heavy chain. X-ray crystallographic studies of the McPC 603 myeloma, closely related to S107, suggest that the glutamic acid in the parental S107 forms a hydrogen bond with the tyrosine at residue 94 in the light chain.[22] This bond forms the pocket in which choline sits. It appears that the lack of the hydrogen bond in the mutant U4 causes an

TABLE 1. Binding of U4 and S107 to Phosphorylated Macromolecules

	PC-KLH	dsDNA[a] (×10)	Protamine	Cardiolipin
S107	4945	280	158	39
U4	781	1388	677	433
MRL Serum 1/100	1425	1808	1545	2274
BALB/c Serum 1/100	348	381	510	1043

[a]Done by a filter assay with radioactive dsDNA.

opening of the antigen binding site such that U4 now binds a variety of phosphorylated macromolecules that are unable to fit into the binding site of S107. However, the special pocket for choline is no longer present and the affinity for phosphorylcholine is thereby diminished.[20]

These data suggest that somatic mutation may be a mechanism for generating autoantibodies. Somatic mutation is a feature of the normal immune response and seems crucial in generating the higher affinity antibodies that characterize a secondary response to antigen. It may be that somatic mutation periodically generates clones to make autoreactive antibodies that are eliminated as they arise by the cellular network that prevents autoimmunity.

It is our hypothesis that anti-DNA antibodies may represent somatic mutants of antibodies made in response to a microbial antigen. The genetic predisposition to SLE that has been so abundantly documented may, in part, consist of the use of a germline gene in the response to a microbial antigen that lies only a few mutations from anti-DNA activity. The families with familial SLE preferentially express the 3I idiotype. Whether they also have anti-DNA activity may be a chance phenomenon and will depend on whether randomly occurring somatic mutations in the 3I germline gene(s) have generated a variable region now capable of forming an anti-DNA antibody. The mutations that lead to DNA binding may be associated with a change in charge such that the 3I-reactive anti-DNA antibody is now cationic.

The study of murine and human monoclonal anti-DNA antibodies within idiotypically defined systems should help determine whether somatic mutation is indeed one mechanism in the generation of anti-DNA antibodies.

REFERENCES

1. SCHWARTZ, R. S. & B. D. STOLLAR. 1985. Origins of anti-DNA antibodies. J. Clin. Invest. **75:** 321–327.
2. SOLOMON, G., J. SCHIFFENBAUER, H. D. KEISER & B. DIAMOND. 1983. Use of monoclonal antibodies to identify shared idiotypes on human antibodies to native DNA from patients with systemic lupus erythematosus. Proc. Natl. Acad. Sci. USA **80:** 850–854.
3. SHOENFELD, Y., D. A. ISENBERG, J. RAUCH, M. P. MADAIO, B. D. STOLLAR & R. S. SCHWARTZ. 1983. Idiotypic cross-reactions of monoclonal human lupus autoantibodies. J. Exp. Med. **158:** 718–730.
4. ZOUALI, M. & A. EYQHEM. 1984. Idiotype restriction in human autoantibodies to DNA in systemic lupus erythematosus. Immunol. Lett. **7:** 187–190.
5. DIAMOND, B. & G. SOLOMON. 1983. A monoclonal antibody that recognizes anti-DNA antibodies in patients with systemic lupus. Ann. N.Y. Acad. Sci. **418:** 379–385.
6. HALPERN, R., J. SCHIFFENBAUER, G. SOLOMON & B. DIAMOND. 1984. Detection of masked anti-DNA antibodies in lupus sera by a monoclonal anti-idiotype. J. Immunol. **133:** 1852–1856.
7. ARNETT, F. C., J. D. REVEILLE, R. W. WILSON, T. T. PROVOST & W. B. BIAS. 1984. Systemic lupus erythematosus: Current state of the genetic hypothesis. Semin. Arthritis Rheum. **14:** 24–35.
8. BLOCK, S. R., J. B. WINFIELD, M.D. LOCKSHIN, W. A. D'ANGELO and C. L. CHRISTIAN. 1975. Studies of twins with systemic lupus erythematosus: a review of the literature and presentation of 12 additional sets. Am. J. Med. **59:** 533–552.
9. LAHITA, R. G., N. CHIORAZZI, A. GIBOFSKY, R. J. WINCHESTER & H. G. KUNKEL. 1983. Familial systemic lupus erythematosus in males. Arthritis Rheum. **26:** 39–44.
10. WINCHESTER, R. S. & H. G. KUNKEL. 1979. The human Ia system. Adv. Immunol. **28:** 221–292.
11. HALPERN, R., A. DAVIDSON, A. LAZO, G. SOLOMON, R. G. LAHITA & B. DIAMOND. 1985. Familial SLE: presence of a cross-reactive idiotype in healthy family members. J. Clin. Invest. **76:** 731–736.

12. MADAIO, M. P., S. HODDER, R. S. SCHWARTZ & B. D. STOLLAR. 1984. Responsiveness of autoimmune and normal mice to nucleic acid antigens. J. Immunol. **132:** 872–876.
13. ATKINSON, P. M., G. W. LAMPMAN, B. C. FURIE, Y. NAPARSTEK, R. S. SCHWARTZ, B. D. STOLLAR & B. FURIE. 1985. Homology of the NH_2-terminal amino acid sequences of the heavy and light chains of human monoclonal lupus autoantibodies containing the dominant 16/6 idiotype. J. Clin. Invest. **75:** 1138–1143.
14. EILAT, D., M. HOCHBERG, J. POMPHREY & S. RUDIKOFF. 1984. Monoclonal antibodies to DNA and RNA from NZB/NZW F_1 mice: antigenic specificities and NH_2 amino acid sequences. J. Immunol. **133:** 489–494.
15. KOFLER, R., D. J. NOONAN, D. E. LEVY, M. C. WILSON, N. P. H. MOLLER, F. J. DIXON & A. N. THEOFILOPOULUS. 1985. Genetic elements used for a murine lupus anti-DNA autoantibody are closely related to those for antibodies to exogenous antigens. J. Exp. Med. **61:** 805–815.
16. BRILES, D. E., E. FORMAN, S. HODAK & J. C. CLAFLIN. 1983. Anti-phosphoryl choline antibodies of the T15 idiotype are optimally protective against *Streptococcus* pneumoniae. J. Exp. Med. **156:** 1172–1185.
17. CREWS, S., J. GRIFFIN, H. HUANG, K. CALAME & L. HOOD. 1981. A single V_H gene segment encodes the immune response to phosphorylcholine: somatic mutation is correlated with the class of the antibody. Cell **25:** 59–66.
18. RUDIKOFF, S., A. M. GIUSTI, D. N. COOK & M. D. SCHARFF. 1982. Single amino acid substitutions altering antigen-binding specificity. Proc. Natl. Acad. Sci. USA **79:** 1979–1983.
19. GIUSTI, A. M. 1984. Dissertation. Albert Einstein College of Medicine, Bronx, New York.
20. DIAMOND, B. & M. SCHARFF. 1984. Somatic mutation of the T15 heavy chain gives rise to an antibody with autoantibody specificity. Proc. Natl. Acad. Sci. USA **81:** 5841–5844.
21. LAFER, E. M., J. RAUCH, C. ANDRZEJEWSKI, JR., D. MUDD, B. FURIE, R. S. SCHWARTZ & B. D. STOLLAR. 1981. Polyspecific monoclonal lupus autoantibodies reactive with both polynucleotides and phospholipids. J. Exp. Med. **153:** 897–909.
22. PADLAN, E. A., D. R. DAVIES, S. RUDIKOFF & M. POTTER. 1976. Structural basis for the specificity of phosphorylcholine binding immunoglobulins. Immunochemistry **13:** 945–949.

DISCUSSION OF THE PAPER

B. H. HAHN (*University of California, Los Angeles, CA*): I want to discuss the definition of cationic. In all of our studies of the MRL and B/W mouse antibodies, what we isolate from glomeruli has a pI of 8.2 to 8.8, depending on the gel. That is a lot more cationic than your definition, which has a pI between 7 and 8.

B. DIAMOND (*Albert Einstein College of Medicine, Bronx, NY*): You are right. Our definition is different than yours. Some of the sera have 3I-reactive bands at a pI greater than 8, but we are interpreting 7.5 and above as cationic. We do not have renal studies on these people in the family studies and we never eluted the antibodies out of human kidneys, but we do know that the 3I anti-idiotype will react with lupus kidneys.

R. S. SCHWARTZ (*Tufts University School of Medicine, Boston, MA*): We have been studying an analogous human idiotype family with a different number. It is called 16/6. Your findings of an idiotype related to an anti-DNA antibody in healthy family members have been independently confirmed with the 16/6 system in three different laboratories: a joint study between the group at the Middlesex Hospital in London and one in Tel Aviv, and then one in our own laboratory. We also found a statistical correlation in the healthy family members between the presence of the 16/6 idiotype and suppressor T-cell function. Therefore, it seems that even though somewhat different markers are being used, genetic control of the expression of idiotypic families of anti-DNA antibodies occurs in human families.

Now, I would like to ask you two questions. The first is whether the idiotype-positive, non-DNA antibodies are immunoregulatory, and do they prevent the development of disease-producing antibodies in the family members? The second question concerns your *in vitro* myeloma system, where there was no antigen selection involved. Do you envision that in the patient with lupus there is a mutation that occurs after contact with some environmental antigen or does it occur independently of antigen?

DIAMOND: Let me answer your second question first. I believe that mutations are constantly occurring in idiotype systems, whether it is the T15 that M. D. Scharff has been studying or in the CRI system that Malcolm Gefter has been studying. In M. D. Scharff's system, there was specific selection for low affinity binding to antigen. Those clones had spontaneous or mutagen-induced V gene mutations. *In vivo,* antibodies that have autoreactivity are probably suppressed, but I think that in lupus, there is in addition some kind of immunoregulatory defect that permits the mutated autoreactive clones to survive. I believe that all of us have the ability to generate them, with perhaps some germline genes being more likely to generate them than others. However, we have no data bearing on your first question. We have looked at family members to see if there are anti-idiotypes to anti-DNA antibodies, but we cannot find them.

UNIDENTIFIED DISCUSSANT (*Stanford University, Stanford, CA*): Do you really think that anti-DNA antibodies are involved in the pathogenesis of lupus, especially given the fact that the family members have antibodies with similar idiotypes, similar affinities, and similar pI values?

DIAMOND: I cannot answer that. I suppose a prospective study on these family members might answer that. We have recently found, though, that if you immunize BALB/c mice with phosphocholine, you get some T15 anti-DNA antibodies that rapidly disappear. A similar event may occur again in all animals in the course of particular immune responses, but this rapidly gets regulated down.

Human Pemphigus Autoantibodies Are Pathogenic to Squamous Epithelium[a]

LUIS A. DIAZ, JUSTIN T. ROSCOE, N. FRED EAGLSTEIN,
RAMSY S. LABIB, HARISH P. PATEL, DIYA F. MUTASIM,
AND GRANT J. ANHALT

Immunodermatology Unit
Department of Dermatology
The Johns Hopkins University
Baltimore, Maryland 21218

INTRODUCTION

The term "pemphigus" refers to a group of cutaneous diseases that are characterized by the spontaneous development of intraepidermal blisters and mucosal erosions. These diseases are (a) pemphigus vulgaris, (b) pemphigus vegetans, (c) pemphigus foliaceus, (d) Brazilian pemphigus foliaceus or Fogo Selvagem, and (e) pemphigus erythematosus.[1] All forms of pemphigus are characterized by epidermal cell-cell detachment (acantholysis) leading to intraepidermal vesicle formation, along with the presence of IgG autoantibodies directed against antigenic determinants present on the cell surfaces of differentiating keratinocytes (FIGURE 1).[2] The underlying mechanisms in triggering this autoantibody formation are essentially unknown.

Pemphigus vulgaris is the most common form of pemphigus. It is a potentially lethal disease in which the blister formation in the epidermis occurs just above the basal cell layer. Pemphigus vegetans is an uncommon variant of pemphigus with verrucous lesions that are predominantly localized to flexural areas. Pemphigus foliaceus is a less serious disorder in which the blister formation is superficial, occurring just below the stratum corneum of the epidermis. Brazilian pemphigus foliaceus (Fogo Selvagem) is a form of pemphigus foliaceus that occurs in endemic areas of Brazil. Pemphigus erythematosus (the Senear-Usher syndrome) is a clinical syndrome in which pemphigus foliaceus occurs in patients with the clinical and serological features of lupus erythematosus.[3]

The precise etiology of all forms of pemphigus is unknown. There is strong epidemiological evidence suggesting an infectious agent as the cause of Brazilian pemphigus foliaceus.[4] Interestingly, recent reports implicate penicillamine[5,6] and rifampin[7] as potential etiologic factors in certain forms of pemphigus; however, the incidence of pemphigus in patients receiving these drugs is rare. There do appear, though, to be genetic factors that predispose individuals to developing the disease. Although pemphigus vulgaris is found in all ethnic and racial groups, it has a higher incidence in Jews and is associated with an increased prevalence of the HLA-DRw4 phenotype.[8,9]

Pemphigus has been associated with other autoimmune disorders such as lupus

[a]This investigation was supported in part by U.S. Public Health Service grant nos. RO1-AM 32081, RO1-AM 32599, R23-AM 32079, and R23-AM 32490 from the National Institutes of Health, a grant from the Andrew W. Mellon Foundation, and a gift from the Estee Lauder Corporation.

erythematosus (Senear-Usher syndrome), rheumatoid arthritis, myasthenia gravis, pernicious anemia, Hashimoto's thyroiditis, and benign thymomas.[10,11] Usually the course of pemphigus is not affected by the presence of these disorders. Pemphigus has also been associated with various malignancies; however, the incidence of malignancy is not high and temporal relationships are rare.

PATHOGENIC ROLE OF PEMPHIGUS AUTOANTIBODIES IN PATIENTS

There are several clinical observations to support the pathogenic role of pemphigus autoantibodies in the formation of the blisters of pemphigus patients. These include: (a) consistent demonstration of pemphigus autoantibodies in lesional skin and the patients' sera, (b) correlation between pemphigus autoantibody titer and disease activity, (c) passive transfer of pemphigus from mother to neonates, and (d) therapeutic response to plasmapheresis.

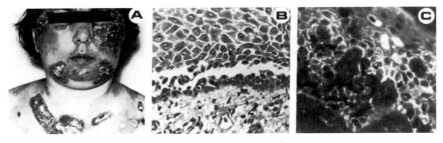

FIGURE 1. Pemphigus vulgaris: (A) Clinical photograph demonstrates bullae and crusted erosions; (B) Histologic examination of a bulla demonstrates acantholysis in the suprabasilar epidermal cells; (C) Direct immunofluorescence examination of the border of a blister using fluorescein-labeled antihuman IgG reveals IgG antibodies bound to the intercellular spaces and surface of keratinocytes.

Almost all patients have IgG autoantibodies bound to the surface of the epidermal cells both in and around lesions, as shown by direct immunofluorescence (IF) techniques.[12] Interestingly, complement proteins have also been detected in similar areas where pemphigus antibodies are bound,[13] suggesting *in vivo* complement activation and probable involvement in inducing epidermal injury.

In addition, the serum of the majority of these patients contains antiepithelial cell surface autoantibodies, which can be demonstrated by indirect IF procedures using cryosections of stratified epithelium as tissue substrate.[2,12] The indirect IF titer of pemphigus autoantibodies detected in the patient's serum correlates well with the clinical activity and extent of disease.[2,12,14,15] The antigen(s) to which these autoantibodies bind is not restricted to human skin alone, for these autoantibodies will bind to the cell surface of stratified squamous epithelium from all mammals and birds.[16] Pemphigus antigens have been partially characterized from different sources such as saliva,[17] human epidermis,[18,19] and epidermal cell cultures.[20] They appear to be glycoproteins with a molecular weight that varies among the different sources reported.

There are several reported cases in which a mother with pemphigus vulgaris has given birth to a child during a period when her disease was active and the child was born with the lesions typical of pemphigus vulgaris.[21,22] These infants were shown to have antiepidermal autoantibodies that were bound to the epidermal cell surface of lesional epidermis and that were circulating in their serum. In the months following birth, the antiepidermal autoantibodies disappear and the cutaneous disease improves spontaneously, suggesting that transplacentally transferred pathogenic maternal antiepidermal autoantibodies are responsible for the neonatal cutaneous disease.

Plasmapheresis has been employed for the treatment of patients with pemphigus.[23-25] The rationale for this treatment is that the removal of circulating autoantibodies with the subsequent decrease in their IF titer will lead to clinical improvement of the disease. In fact, with intensive plasmapheresis, it is possible to produce both a decrease in circulating autoantibody titers, as well as an improvement in the disease activity of the patient. The major drawback of this technique is that the improvement is very short-lived. With the cessation of plasmapheresis, the autoantibody titers quickly rebound (sometimes to a higher level) and the patient's disease flares once again.[25]

PATHOGENICITY OF PEMPHIGUS ANTIBODIES TO EXPERIMENTAL ANIMALS

Our laboratory has demonstrated that, given in sufficient doses, IgG fractions purified from the sera of patients with pemphigus vulgaris[26] and Brazilian pemphigus foliaceus[27] induce a disease in neonatal BALB/c mice that reproduces the clinical, histological, and immunological features of these human diseases (FIGURE 2). The neonatal mouse was chosen as a model for several reasons: first, primary epidermal cell cultures derived from neonatal BALB/c mice have proven to be a very reliable system for testing various effects of the autoantibodies *in vitro*.[28] Second, neonatal mice have been shown to be immunologically tolerant to injected foreign serum proteins.[29] This eliminates the concern that the animal may mount an antibody response against injected human IgM that alters the subsequent reaction. Third, because of their very small size, relatively large amounts of human IgG can be administered to these animals. In the study we reported, we used IgG doses from 1.5 to 16.0 mg per gram body weight of mouse per day. These injections were given intraperitoneally in two divided doses daily. Within 18 to 72 hours of the beginning of injections, mice injected with pemphigus IgG developed cutaneous blisters and erosions. These lesions had the same clinical, histological, ultrastructural, and immunological features of those seen in the human disease. These pathological changes were not observed in animals that received comparable doses of pooled normal human IgG. We found that the severity of disease produced in these animals was dependent on both the total dose of IgG administered and the titer of human pemphigus autoantibody detected in the mouse serum by indirect IF. In addition, lesions would occur only as long as injections were continued, but once the injections were discontinued, new lesions would cease to appear and previous lesions would begin to resolve.

Induction of disease in mice also depends on the pemphigus autoantibody titer in the serum used. IgG fractions obtained from the sera of patients with extensive cutaneous disease and high titers of pemphigus autoantibodies produced disease in these mice reproducibly. IgG fractions from those patients who had limited disease and low titers of pemphigus autoantibodies did not produce significant disease in the mice when given in comparable doses. We also had the opportunity to obtain multiple samples of plasma from a single patient with untreated pemphigus prior to treatment, during his courses of therapy (with prednisone and cyclophosphamide), and when his disease was in clinical remission. The indirect IF titer for pemphigus autoantibodies

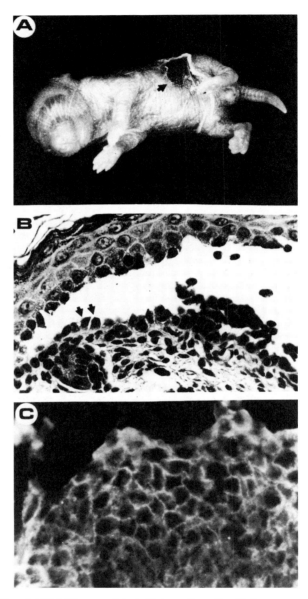

FIGURE 2. Neonatal BALB/c mouse injected intraperitoneally with human pemphigus vulgaris IgG: (A) Epidermal injury occurring 48 hours after the initial dose of IgG manifested clinically by an impending Nikolski's positive dermatosis; (B) The epidermal vesicles are intraepidermal and show acantholysis (Hematoxylin and Eosin, ×400); (C) Direct immunofluorescence studies of the skin of these animals show binding of pemphigus IgG to the epidermal intercellular spaces (×400).

was initially high (1:400) and fell to 1:100 during the early convalescent phase. The IgG fraction from his pretreatment serum was most effective in inducing cutaneous lesions in mice, while the IgG from the convalescent phase was ineffective. The IgG fraction from serum obtained during treatment was intermediate in potency.

The role of complement in the epidermal injury produced by pemphigus antibodies in the skin of these animals has been recently studied by Eaglstein *et al.*[30] They found that the bivalent $F(ab')_2$ fragments from pemphigus IgG are able to produce cutaneous disease in the mice. It is interesting that the monovalent Fab' fragments from pemphigus IgG retain their ability to bind the epidermal cell surface both *in vivo* and *in vitro*, but cannot induce lesions. Pemphigus autoantibodies can also produce cutaneous lesions in mice that are genetically deficient in C5 and in BALB/c mice that are depleted of complement components by pretreatment with cobra venom factor. When mice are injected with small doses of the pemphigus IgG, those animals that are normal complementemic develop lesions faster than those that are complement depleted. With larger doses of pemphigus IgG, this effect is not observed and both groups of animals develop extensive disease at the same time points. Altogether, these findings suggest that complement activation may not be crucial in the epidermal injury induced by pemphigus autoantibodies, but that it may enhance or perpetuate the cutaneous disease. These results also suggest that the initial binding of pemphigus autoantibodies to the epidermal cell surfaces may trigger cross-linking of the antigen, which may be the signal that precipitates the events leading to epidermal cell-cell detachment.

In a recent study, Takahashi *et al.*[31] examined the ultrastructural changes that occur in mice following injections with pemphigus IgG. These changes include widening of the intercellular spaces, separation of the desmosomes into split desmosomes, dissolution and disappearance of attachment plaques, and perinuclear tonofilament retraction. These findings are similar to those reported previously in pemphigus in humans[32] and in the experimentally induced epidermal cell-cell detachment in human skin explants.[33] Patel *et al.*[34] studied the changes that occur in the epidermal desmosomes of these animals during the development of pemphigus lesions after the injection of pemphigus IgG. They showed that there is a two-step process leading to a decrease in the number of desmosomes per cell. The first is the widening of the ICS between desmosomes, which is associated with an increase in the surface area of epidermal cells, and the second is a marked decrease in desmosomal assembly, which leads to the apparent disappearance of these organelles.

PATHOGENIC ROLE OF PEMPHIGUS AUTOANTIBODIES *IN VITRO*

In vitro studies strongly support the pathogenic role of pemphigus autoantibodies in the induction of acantholysis. Bellone and Leone,[35] Schiltz and Michel,[36] and Morioka *et al.*[37] demonstrated that the pemphigus serum or the IgG fractions from pemphigus serum induce acantholysis in human skin explant cultures. Farb *et al.*[38] and Diaz and Marcelo[39] showed that pemphigus IgG will cause epidermal cell detachment when added to murine primary epidermal cell cultures. This cell detachment is highly reproducible and quite specific for pemphigus autoantibodies. The cell detachment does not occur when cultures are treated with normal human IgG, IgG fractions isolated from the serum of patients with other autoimmune diseases such as bullous pemphigoid, and lupus erythematosus or IgG containing antibodies specific for blood groups A and B, which are expressed on the epidermal cell surfaces.[28] Although cell detachment is produced by pemphigus IgG in epidermal cultures maintained in complement-depleted media, restoration of complement in these cultures markedly enhances the cell detachment probably by a complement-dependent cytotoxicity.[40]

MECHANISMS OF EPIDERMAL CELL INJURY
BY PEMPHIGUS AUTOANTIBODIES

The mechanisms by which pemphigus autoantibodies induce this unique form of cell-cell detachment have not been fully elucidated. However, there have been some interesting observations made on possible pathogenetic mechanisms. Schiltz et al.[41] found that the supernatants of cultured skin explants treated with human pemphigus IgG contained a proteolytic enzyme that could cause acantholysis when added to fresh skin explants. It has also been shown that the increase in cell detachment that is observed in epidermal cell cultures treated with pemphigus IgG can be abolished by certain proteinase inhibitors.[28,38] This would suggest that pemphigus autoantibodies may cause the activation or release of certain proteolytic enzymes following their binding to the epidermal cell surface. The released enzymes may be responsible for the cell detachment. Recently, Hashimoto et al.[42] have identified a plasminogen activator (PA) in the supernatant of human epidermal cell cultures incubated with pemphigus IgG. According to these investigators, the increase in PA after pemphigus antibody binding, along with the subsequent activation of plasmin, may be responsible for the epidermal cell-cell detachment seen in pemphigus. This is strengthened by the fact that treatment of these cell cultures with dexamethasone will abolish PA activity. This would presumably explain the mechanisms by which corticosteroids assert their therapeutic effect in vivo. Unfortunately, they did not show that the incorporation of dexamethasone produced any change in cell detachment or acantholysis, thus failing to prove if this increase in the PA activity was a primary event or a secondary phenomenon resulting from cell detachment.

Our laboratory has made some observatons that seem to indicate that this system may not be of primary importance in the induction of acantholysis. In murine epidermal cell cultures treated with pemphigus IgG, we have demonstrated that the incorporation of dexamethasone can abolish PA activity almost completely; however, quantitative cell detachment remains unaffected.[43]

We have also examined the relationship between PA activity and cutaneous disease in the in vivo mouse model of pemphigus. In this study, one group of mice received pemphigus IgG alone, while the other was treated with dexamethasone in a dose of 20 μg per g daily and an identical dose of pemphigus IgG. The steroid treatment did not decrease the extent of the disease produced or delay the onset of the lesions. PA activity in epidermal extracts from animals treated with pemphigus IgG alone showed an elevation over control values and dexamethasone treatment reduced PA activity by 80%. Despite this reduction in PA activity, the extent of the cutaneous disease was not affected.[44] This would indicate that corticosteroids produce their major therapeutic effect in vivo by reducing autoantibody production rather than by modifying events that occur after autoantibody binding to the cells. The role of PA in this disease needs careful reevaluation.

We have proposed and tested other possible mechanisms that could be involved in the epidermal cell-cell detachment induced by pemphigus autoantibodies. It is possible that the cell surface antigen bound by pemphigus autoantibodies may be a molecule important in epidermal cell-cell adhesion.[39] Cross-linking of this antigen induced by pemphigus autoantibodies could alter the adhesion properties of the antigen or trigger intracellular events leading to alteration in cell adhesiveness. Some initial observations on such intracellular events have been reported by Patel et al.[45] They studied the fate of pemphigus antibodies after binding to the cell surface of cultured murine keratinocytes *in vitro*. By immunoelectron microscopy, they showed that there is a dynamic sequence of events that occurs following antibody binding to the cell membrane. Within 30 minutes, the pemphigus antibodies that were initially evenly distributed on the cell surface had become clustered. Subsequently, these antibodies were internalized into submembranous vesicles via surface pits and fused with lysosomes within the cell (FIGURE 3). These changes coincided with the development of a widening of the intercellular spaces between adjacent keratinocytes. Similarly, when pemphigus F(ab')$_2$ fragments were used instead of whole pemphigus IgG, binding, clustering, and internalization were also seen. However, although pemphigus Fab' fragments were bound to the epidermal cell surfaces, they did not cluster or internalize. It is conceivable therefore that binding, cross-linking, and internalization of the pemphigus antigen-antibody complexes may be an important step in the pathophysiology of the detachment process induced by pemphigus autoantibodies.

The *in vivo* studies on the epidermis of BALB/c mice after injections of pemphigus IgG show epidermal cell membrane ruffling, retraction of tonofilaments, and loss of desmosomes. These findings are similar to those reported in human skin explants treated with pemphigus IgG and would suggest that the fully developed acantholytic vesicle may represent the end result of several cytopathological processes that perhaps are operating within the keratinocyte itself rather than in the extracellular milieu alone. It is interesting that the fate of split desmosomes (attachment plaques and tonofilaments) in pemphigus-antibody-induced acantholysis is unique and quite different from that observed in epidermal cells that are detached from each other by proteases such as trypsin.[46] The difference in behavior of the attachment plaques and tonofilaments in the detachment of epidermal cells induced by pemphigus antibodies, as opposed to that observed with trypsin dissociation, would suggest that in the acantholysis seen in the human disease as well as in the animal model, intracellular events may play an important role in the rounding up and detachment of the epidermal cells. Furthermore, the initial signal that initiates acantholysis may be the binding, cross-linking, and internalization of pemphigus antigens. This hypothesis is supported by the observations that whole pemphigus IgG and its F(ab')$_2$ fragments bind the keratinocyte cell surface, are internalized, and produce disease *in vivo,* whereas Fab' fragments bind the keratinocyte cell surface, but do not internalize or produce disease *in vivo.*

SUMMARY

In 1957, Witbesky *et al.*[47] put forward several criteria that ideally should be fulfilled in order to prove the pathogenic role of an autoantibody in a putative autoimmune disease. There can now be very little doubt of the autoimmune nature of this disease and of the primary role of autoantibodies in its pathogenesis. The evidence that supports the concept that pemphigus autoantibodies are of primary pathogenic importance in the disease is as follows:

(a) IgG class autoantibodies can be found both circulating in the serum and bound to the epithelial cell surfaces in and around lesions in patients with pemphigus.

(b) These autoantibodies, purified from the serum of pemphigus patients, can induce acantholytic lesions typical of pemphigus both in experimental animals (neonatal mice) and in human and murine epidermal cell cultures.

(c) These autoantibodies react with a specific antigen of the epidermal cell. This

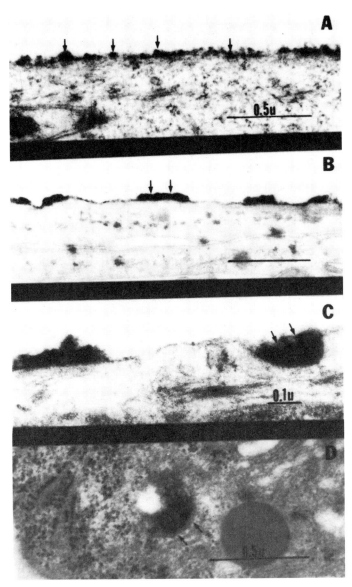

FIGURE 3. Distribution and fate of pemphigus antigen-antibody complexes in 48-hour murine epidermal cell cultures as shown by immunoelectron microscopy. Pemphigus antigen-antibody complexes are seen bound diffusely on the cell surface at time zero (A - arrows). After 30 minutes, the antigen-antibody complexes are seen clumping on the cell surface (B - arrows), within pits (C - arrows), and within secondary lysosomes (D - arrows). Magnifications: (A) ×45,000, (B) ×22,000, (C) ×90,000, and (D) ×52,000.

purified antigen has been used to immunize rabbits and the resulting antibodies are capable of inducing pemphigus-like lesions in neonatal mice.[18]

REFERENCES

1. LEVER, W. F. 1965. Pemphigus vulgaris. *In* Pemphigus and Pemphigoid, 1st edition. W. F. Lever, Ed.: 15. C. C. Thomas. Springfield, Illinois.
2. BEUTNER, E. H. & R. E. JORDON. 1964. Proc. Soc. Exp. Biol. Med. **117:** 505–510.
3. SENEAR, F. E. & B. USHER. 1926. Arch. Dermatol. **113:** 761–781.
4. CASTRO, M. C., J. T. ROSCOE & S. A. P. SAMPAIO. 1983. Brazilian pemphigus foliaceus. *In* Clinics in Dermatology, vol. 1(2), 1st edition. A. R. Ahmed, Ed.: 22–41. J. B. Lippincott. Philadelphia.
5. DEGOS, M. M. R., R. TOURAINE, S. BELAICH & J. REVUS. 1969. Bull. Soc. Fr. Dermatol. Syphiligr. **76:** 751–753.
6. TAN, S. G. & N. R. ROWELL. 1976. Br. J. Dermatol. **95:** 99–100.
7. LEE, C. W., J. H. LIM & H. J. KANG. 1984. Br. J. Dermatol. **III:** 619–622.
8. PARK, M. S., P. I. TERASAKI, A. R. AHMED & J. L. TIWARI. 1979. Lancet **2:** 441–442.
9. BRAUTBAR, C., M. MOSCOVITZ, T. LIVSHITS, S. HAIM, S. HACHAM-ZADEH, H. A. COHEN, R. SHARON, D. NELKEN & T. COHEN. 1980. Tissue Antigens **16:** 238–243.
10. DIAZ, L. A., R. W. GLAMB & J. SILVA, JR. 1980. Arch. Dermatol. **116:** 77–79.
11. MAIZE, J. C., D. GREEN & T. T. PROVOST. 1982. J. Am. Acad. Dermatol. **7:** 736–741.
12. BEUTNER, E. H., W. F. LEVER, E. WITEBSKY, R. E. JORDON & B. CHERTOCK. 1965. JAMA **192:** 682–688.
13. JORDON, R. E., A. L. SCHROETER, R. S. ROGERS III & H. O. PERRY. 1974. J. Invest. Dermatol. **63:** 256–259.
14. FITZPATRICK, R. E. & V. D. NEWCOMER. 1980. Arch. Dermatol. **116:** 285–290.
15. SAMS, W. J., JR. & R. E. JORDON. 1971. J. Invest. Dermatol. **56:** 474–479.
16. DIAZ, L. A., H. J. WEISS & N. J. CALVANICO. 1979. Acta Derm. Venereol. (Stockholm) **58:** 537–540.
17. DIAZ, L. A., H. PATEL & N. J. CALVANICO. 1980. J. Immunol. **124:** 760–765.
18. PETERSON, L. L. & K. D. WUEPPER. 1984. J. Clin. Invest. **73:** 1113–1120.
19. KOULU, L., A. KUSUMI, M. S. STEINBERG, V. KLAUS-KOVTUN & J. R. STANLEY. 1984. J. Exp. Med. **160:** 1509–1518.
20. STANLEY, J. R., L. KOULU & C. THIVOLET. 1984. J. Clin. Invest. **74:** 313–320.
21. MONCADA, B., S. KETTELSEN, J. L. HERNANDEZ-MONTEZUMA & F. RAMIREZ. 1982. Br. J. Dermatol. **106:** 465–468.
22. STORER, J. S., W. K. GALEN, L. T. NESBITT, JR. & V. A. DELCO. 1982. J. Am. Acad. Dermatol. **6:** 929–932.
23. AUERBACH, R. & J. BYSTRYN. 1979. Arch. Dermatol. **115:** 728–730.
24. SWANSON, D. L. & M. V. DAHL. 1981. J. Am. Acad. Dermatol. **4:** 325–328.
25. ROUJEAU, J. C., C. ANDRE, M. J. FABRE, P. LAURET, M. L. FLECHET, B. KALIS, J. ROVUZ & R. TOURAINE. 1983. Arch. Dermatol. **119:** 215–221.
26. ANHALT, G. J., R. S. LABIB, J. J. VOORHEES, T. F. BEALS & L. A. DIAZ. 1982. N. Engl. J. Med. **306:** 1189–1196.
27. ROSCOE, J. T., L. A. DIAZ, S. A. P. SAMPAIO, R. M. CASTRO R. S. LABIB, Y. TAKAHASHI, H. P. PATEL & G. J. ANHALT. 1985. J. Invest. Dermatol. **85:** 538–541.
28. WOO, T. Y., V. HOGAN, H. PATEL, G. J. ANHALT, R. S. LABIB, J. J. VOORHEES & L. A. DIAZ. 1983. J. Invest. Dermatol. **81:** 115–121.
29. BACH, J. F. 1978. Immunologic tolerance. *In* Immunology, 1st edition, chapter 20. J. F. Bach, Ed.: 508. J. Wiley & Sons. New York.
30. EAGLSTEIN, N. F., G. TILL, L. A. DIAZ, R. S. LABIB, H. P. PATEL & G. J. ANHALT. 1985. Clin. Res. **33:** 297A.
31. TAKAHASHI, Y., H. P. PATEL, R. S. LABIB, L. A. DIAZ & G. J. ANHALT. 1985. J. Invest. Dermatol. **84:** 41–46.
32. HASHIMOTO, K. & W. F. LEVER. 1967. J. Invest. Dermatol. **48:** 540–552.

33. HU, C-H., B. MICHEL & J. R. SCHLITZ. 1978. Am. J. Pathol. **90:** 345–362.
34. PATEL, H. P., L. A. DIAZ, G. J. ANHALT, R. S. LABIB & Y. TAKAHASHI. 1985. Clin. Res.
      33: 773A.
35. BELLONE, A. G. & V. LEONE. 1956. G. Ital. Dermatol. Sifilol. **97:** 97–109.
36. SCHLITZ, J. R. & B. MICHEL. 1976. J. Invest. Dermatol. **67:** 254–260.
37. MORIOKA, S., K. NAITO & H. OGAWA. 1981. J. Invest. Dermatol. **76:** 337–341.
38. FARB, R. M., R. DYKES & G. S. LAZARUS. 1978. Proc. Natl. Acad. Sci. USA **75:** 459–
      463.
39. DIAZ, L. A. & C. L. MARCELO. 1978. Br. J. Dermatol. **98:** 631–637.
40. KAWANA, S., W. D. GEOGHEGAN & R. E. JORDON. 1985. Clin. Exp. Immunol. **61:** 517–
      525.
41. SCHLITZ, J. R., B. MICHEL & R. PAPAY. 1979. J. Invest. Dermatol. **73:** 575–581.
42. HASHIMOTO, K., K. M. SHAFRAN, P. S. WEBBER, G. S. LAZARUS & K. H. SINGER. 1983. J.
      Exp. Med. **157:** 259–272.
43. WOO, T. Y., P. A. BAROUSKI-MILLER, T. D. GELEHRTER, G. J. ANHALT & L. A. DIAZ.
      1982. Clin. Res. **30:** 719A.
44. ANHALT, G. J., H. P. PATEL, R. S. LABIB, L. A. DIAZ & D. PROUD. 1985. Clin. Res.
      33: 623A.
45. PATEL, H. P., L. A. DIAZ, G. J. ANHALT, R. S. LABIB & Y. TAKAHASHI. 1984. J. Invest.
      Dermatol. **83:** 409–415.
46. OVERTON, J. 1968. J. Exp. Zool. **168:** 203–214.
47. WITEBSKY, E., N. R. ROSE, K. TERPLAN & J. R. PAINE. 1957. JAMA **164:** 1439–1447.

DISCUSSION OF THE PAPER

E. KHOURY (*University of California, San Francisco, CA*): You have shown that there is a direct correlation between the titer of the transferred human autoantibodies and the severity of the lesion in the mouse.

L. A. DIAZ (*John Hopkins University, Baltimore, MD*): It all depends on the time that you sacrifice the animal to test the serum. The animals are injected with extremely large doses of human IgG and titers of human pemphigus antibody. However, we have not done any correlation between time of injection and titers of autoantibody.

A. R. PACHNER (*Yale University, New Haven, CT*): Did you try your transfer system with adult mice?

DIAZ: Yes. In adult hairless mice, we found that we needed extremely large doses of human IgG to induce localized, small lesions of pemphigus.

PACHNER: Do you think that it is just a matter of amount and nothing else?

DIAZ: Yes. The larger the doses of antibody, the worse the disease.

PACHNER: Was the disease in adult mice diffuse?

DIAZ: It was localized.

D. B. DRACHMAN (*Johns Hopkins University, Baltimore, MD*): Have you taken the myasthenia cross-linking analogy as the next step? When we used piggyback antibodies that cross-linked with F(ab), we could induce the same accelerated degradation of acetylcholine receptors as F(ab')$_2$ fragments. Have you tried to do that?

DIAZ: We tried, but the animals did not survive the large doses of antibodies we gave them.

DRACHMAN: The interesting thing that you have shown is that the F(ab) fragments are not endocytosed. Thus, if you could get endocytosis by cross-linking, it may very well produce a lesion.

DIAZ: Perhaps the mechanism that holds epidermal cells together involves cell surface molecules and organelles like desmosomes. The idea we are exploring is that the antibody affects the assembly of desmosomes.

UNIDENTIFIED DISCUSSANT: What is the antigenic specificity of antibody you are studying.

DIAZ: The antigen is found by immunofluorescence in most mammalian squamous epithelium. Pemphigus antibody does seem to react with a 140-K epidermal protein. The antibody from pemphigus foliaceus (a clinical variant of pemphigus) may bind to a desmosomal protein.

I. MACKAY (*Hall Institute for Medical Research, Melbourne, Australia*): Are there any other disease sera that reliably reproduce the disease in the mouse?

DRACHMAN: There is another one. The Eton-Lambert syndrome, which can be passively transferred by serum.

MACKAY: Is that by one shot or do you need to give it repeatedly?

DRACHMAN: It takes months of passive transfer before you can transfer the Eaton-Lambert syndrome.

H. S. LUTHRA (*Mayo Medical School, Rochester, MN*): We and others also have shown that serum from animals who have developed arthritis after injection with type 2 collagen can transfer disease passively.

UNIDENTIFIED DISCUSSANT: Have you been able to immunize mice with cells that have undergone acantholysis?

DIAZ: The antigen is extremely sensitive to manipulation, so when we immunize mice, we do not get the antibody that we are looking for.

Monoclonal Anti-DNA Antibodies

The Targets and Origins of SLE Autoantibodies

B. DAVID STOLLAR AND ROBERT S. SCHWARTZ

Department of Biochemistry and Pharmacology
and
Department of Medicine
Tufts University Health Science Schools
and
the New England Medical Center Hospitals
Boston, Massachusetts 02111

The formation of antinuclear autoantibodies is a hallmark of systemic lupus erythematosus and a group of related diseases. Although the presence of anti-DNA antibodies in SLE sera was discovered nearly 30 years ago,[1-4] their true nature and origin remain a mystery. Certain findings have led to suggestions that some altered form of DNA may serve as an immunogen in these patients. For example, DNA fragments have been found in serum of SLE patients[5,6] and certain differences in DNA metabolism have been identified in comparisons of lymphocytes from SLE patients with those of normal subjects.[7,8] To date, however, no specific immunizing stimulus has been proven to be the cause of anti-DNA autoantibody formation in SLE. The same is true for other autoantibodies that are correlated with a variety of clinical syndromes or diseases that may be related to SLE.

One approach to testing the possible role of DNA immunogens has been the deliberate immunization of experimental animals with nucleic acids. Until 1960, DNA was considered to be nonantigenic and attempts to immunize animals with purified DNA were nonproductive. Several procedures that did lead to anti-DNA antibody formation (usually involving carrier proteins) became available after Murakami *et al.* demonstrated the first clear experimental anti-DNA system, which was directed against denatured DNA of the T-even bacteriophages.[9] Since then, it has been possible to induce antibodies to denatured DNA of any source,[10] to physically[11] or chemically[12,13] modified DNA, and to a number of synthetic polynucleotides,[14] including helical structures of double-stranded RNA,[15-17] RNA-DNA hybrids,[16,18,19] left-handed Z-DNA,[20-22] and certain right-handed polydeoxyribonucleotides.[23,24] None of the antibodies induced by these immunogens, however, react with native helical B-DNA, whereas some of the autoantibodies of SLE serum do so.[25-28] Furthermore, attempts to immunize normal animals with native DNA, even in complexes with carrier proteins, have generally not yielded antibody above the level induced by adjuvant alone.[29] This picture applies also to transfer RNA, which can react with some SLE antibodies,[30] but which has not been immunogenic in normal animals except for the induction of antibodies to some modified bases of bacterial tRNA.[31]

Therefore, the experience of experimental immunization is that it has not been possible to duplicate reproducibly the antinative DNA antibody production of SLE by immunization of normal animals with DNA, DNA fragments, DNA analogues, or chemically or physically modified DNA. On the other hand, small amounts of antibody that react with DNA (usually with only the denatured form, but in some cases with native DNA also) can be formed in animals given certain polyclonal activators such as lipopolysaccharide[32,33] or complete Freund's adjuvant.[29] In addition, certain naturally occurring antibodies in normal individuals can react with DNA,[34] as can a number of myeloma proteins that arose without relation to SLE.[35,36]

In view of these puzzling features of the immune response to DNA, it has been important to examine the autoantibodies carefully so as to determine whether they resemble any of the induced antibodies, whether DNA is truly the preferred antigen, or whether DNA may cross-react with antibodies targeted primarily against some other antigen. This was attempted with whole lupus serum and a complex picture emerged. SLE serum antibodies could be fractionated into populations that reacted with denatured DNA only, with denatured and native DNA equally, and with native DNA preferentially.[25,37] The complexity was demonstrated further in the reactions of individual sera with a variety of synthetic polynucleotides.[38] SLE sera reacted with a number of other antigens as well, but with polyclonal sera it was not clear how many separate antibody populations were involved in all of the reactions observed. It appeared that a large number of different anti-nucleic-acid antibodies were present and that they were part of a very diverse autoantibody formation in SLE.

Examination of the nature of anti-DNA antibodies has been facilitated greatly by analysis of monoclonal autoantibodies.[39,40] These have been obtained from hybridomas derived from both human and murine subjects with autoimmune disease. A study of their serological reactions, idiotypes, and primary structures has made it necessary to examine the relationship between anti-DNA autoantibodies and the development of immune responses to exogenous antigens such as those of bacteria.

A striking early finding in the study of both human and murine autoantibodies to DNA was the ability of a single monoclonal antibody to react with a number of polynucleotides of very different composition.[41–46] Prominent among the reactive forms were poly(dT), poly(dG), or poly(I), Z-DNA, and denatured DNA; in some cases, the synthetic polynucleotides reacted much more strongly than did denatured DNA, which was the antigen that was used to select the hybridomas.[41–43] This suggested that DNA itself may not be a primary immunogen for this response. It was also clear that the autoantibodies differed from induced anti-nucleic-acid antibodies in the extent of cross-reactivity. Induced anti-Z-DNA (including monoclonal examples[20,47]) did not show the cross-reactivity seen with autoantibodies that reacted with Z-DNA.[42,48] Induced antibodies to poly(ADP-ribose)[49] were also much more selective than autoantibodies that reacted with this structure.[50] These findings, comparable to those made in several laboratories, also indicated that the total number of antibody populations may not bear a simple relationship to the number of antigens with which the lupus sera reacted.

The cross-reactions of monoclonal anti-DNA antibodies extended beyond the realm of polynucleotides. Some reacted with cardiolipin and other phospholipids[51,52] in a cross-reaction that could be visualized as involving recognition of appropriately spaced phosphodiester groups (FIGURE 1).[51] Reaction with phospholipid may also have been responsible for the lupus anticoagulant activity of at least one monoclonal antibody.[41]

Other cross-reactions of monoclonal anti-DNA antibodies have been more difficult to understand in structural terms. Some of the antibodies selected because of their anti-DNA reactivity also caused immunofluorescent staining of cytoskeletal intermediate filaments due to reaction with vimentin (TABLE 1).[53] Others reacted with platelets[54] and with surface antigens of other cells.[55] The anti-DNA antibodies, therefore, include examples that simultaneously demonstrate several other reactions that have been observed with sera of autoimmune subjects. They also demonstrate a polyreactivity that has been observed with autoreactive antibodies isolated from normal human sera[34] and with certain myeloma proteins.[35,36]

It was important to determine whether the monoclonal antibodies were related to

TABLE 1. Cross-Reactions of 24 Monoclonal Human Lupus Autoantibodies[a]

Hybridoma	sDNA	nDNA	Cardiolipin	Cytoskeleton	Platelets
2/113b	+++	0	+	+++	+++
2/19b	+++	0	---	++	+++
2/1-17	+		0	0	++
2/1-43	+	0	---	+++	+
2/12-6	+++	+	0	+	++
2/12-33	++	0	+	+++	0
2/12-11a	+	0	+	+	+
2/18-2	++	++	0	+++	+
2/18-7	++	±	0	+	+
2/18-9	+	±	0	+++	+
6/21-28	++	+	0	++	+
6/21-29	+++	+	0	+	+
6/21-37	++	+	---	+	0
6/32-9	+	+	0	+++	+
6/32-15	++	+	0	0	+
6/3-1	++	+	+	0	+
3/3-47	+	+	+++	+	+
3/13-3	+++	±	---	---	---
3/15-2	++	+	---	---	---
3/15-6	++	+	---	---	---
3/15-13	++	0	++	---	---
3/15-17	+++	++	---	---	+
3/16-6	+++	±	0	++	+
14/134	++	+++	---	++	++

[a]Results are summarized from references 42, 53, and 54, and from unpublished experiments. All values are approximated for comparative purposes, ranging from +++ (strong) to 0 (negative); (- - -), not done. Reprinted with permission from *J. Clin. Invest.* 1985. **75:** 321–327 (Table III, pg. 322).

the anti-DNA antibodies present in lupus serum. For this purpose, anti-idiotype antibodies were raised. The corresponding idiotypes of the monoclonal antibodies were indeed found in serum in relation to the development of active disease, both in mice[56] and humans[57] (TABLE 2).

Anti-idiotype reagents were also used as a first step in determining the extent to which the monoclonal antibodies were structurally related to each other; that

TABLE 2. Detection of Autoantibody-Related Idiotypes in Serum[a]

Subjects	No.	No. Positive for 16/6	No. Positive for 32/15
Active SLE	74	40	21
Inactive SLE	26	6	1
Rheumatoid arthritis	38	9	4
Normal	96	4	0

[a]Rabbit anti-16/6 idiotype antibodies and murine monoclonal anti-32/15 anti-idiotype were prepared as described by Shoenfeld *et al.* Dilute samples of human sera (1:25,000 for 16/6 assay and 1/5000 for 32/15 assay) were used to coat wells of polystyrene plates and idiotype was detected by the anti-idiotype antibody followed by enzyme-linked goat anti-Ig. Ninety-six normal human subjects had a mean absorbane reading of 0.043 ($\pm$0.028) for anti-16/6 and 0.027 ($\pm$0.024) for anti-32/15. Values exceeding the normal mean by more than 2SD were considered positive. Data are from reference 57.

is, whether they were products of a limited number of germline genes. An anti-idiotype induced by the human monoclonal antibody 16/6 cross-reacted very strongly with several of the other antibodies, including some derived from different unrelated subjects.[58] The heavy and light chains of five monoclonal anti-DNA antibodies were subjected to partial amino acid sequence analysis. Four of them, from two different patients, were identical in the first 40 residues of the light chain and showed 90% homology in this portion of the heavy chain.[59] These results indicated that the anti-DNA antibodies could be products of genes that were not greatly modified from

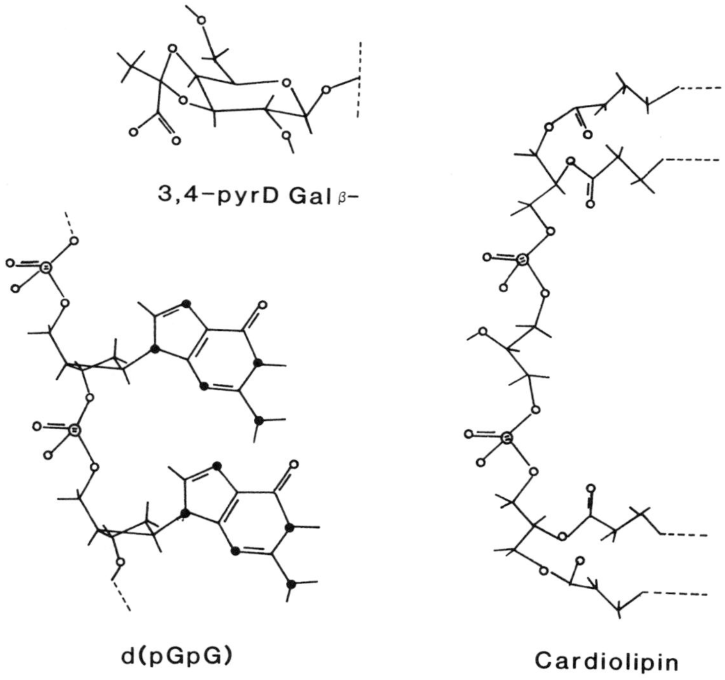

3,4-pyrD Gal β-

d(pGpG)   Cardiolipin

FIGURE 1. Portions of structures bound by monoclonal anti-DNA autoantibodies and related immunoglobulins. Certain antibodies selected for antidenatured DNA reactivity also recognize cardiolipin. The Waldenstrom's protein WEA binds 3,4-pyruvylated D-Galactose of *Klebsiella* K30 antigen[60] and the polynucleotide poly(G).[61]

conserved and widely distributed germline genes and that they could, therefore, represent an early stage in the development of immune responsiveness.

It was then observed that the shared light-chain sequence was identical, in 39 of the first 40 residues (including all, but one position of the first complementarity determining region), with a Waldenstrom's protein that had been studied for its binding to a pyruvylated galactose determinant of a *Klebsiella* antigen (FIGURE 1).[60] That Waldenstrom's IgM also showed an idiotypic cross-reactivity with the anti-idiotype reagent raised against the 16/6 monoclonal anti-DNA.[59,61] Furthermore, the Waldenstrom's protein bound the polynucleotide poly(G) and the 16/6 bound the *Klebsiella* antigen (though weakly).[61] Thus, there was a clear structural relationship between an autoantibody selected for anti-DNA activity and an immunoglobulin that showed weak nucleic acid binding and stronger activity against a bacterial antigen.

The possible association of anti-DNA antibody with antibacterial reactivity was tested directly. Several murine monoclonal anti-DNA antibodies were found to be bound to the surface of several kinds of bacteria isolated from the mouse intestine (FIGURE 2).[62] This binding was competed by DNA, but this was not due to DNA adsorbed to the bacterial surface because it was not susceptible to the action of DNase. It was a property of the Fab portion of the monoclonal antibody. At least one kind of target may have been phospholipid of the bacterial surface because the antibodies did react with phospholipids identified in a chloroform-methanol extract of the bacteria.

Human monoclonal anti-DNA antibodies also reacted with bacterial antigens. In this case, they were tested with mycobacteria because it was found that sera of patients

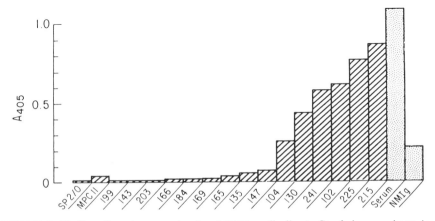

FIGURE 2. Binding of murine monoclonal anti-DNA antibodies to *Staphylococcus* bacteria. Monoclonal antibodies derived from MRL-lpr/lpr mice were selected on the basis of antidenatured DNA binding activity. Bacteria were isolated from intestines of 6-month-old MRL mice. Antibody binding to bacteria was detected with enzyme-labeled anti-mouse Ig.[62] Individual hybridoma products are designated at the base of the bars. Negative controls were: culture medium from growth of parental SP2/0 cells, mouse myeloma MPC11 IgG, and normal mouse IgG. The positive serum sample was from an MRL-lpr/lpr mouse.

with leprosy contained significant levels of anti-DNA antibody (D. Mudd and K. P. W. J. McAdam, unpublished data). In addition, certain of the monoclonal anti-DNA antibodies were found to bind to the mycobacteria and, again, with phospholipids extracted from them.

Could immunization with antigens related to bacteria stimulate anti-DNA antibodies? It had been observed earlier that immunization of rabbits with cardiolipin induced antibodies that could react with DNA incorporated into liposomes.[63] We confirmed this with serum antibodies induced by injection of cardiolipin into mice[64] and prepared hybridomas from the immunized animals. Most important, the resulting monoclonal antibodies resembled the autoantibodies to DNA in their polyreactivity and they cross-reacted with anti-idiotype antibodies raised against anti-DNA monoclonal antibodies.[64]

The analysis of monoclonal anti-DNA antibodies has raised new questions and insights concerning their true nature. Monoclonal antibodies that are idiotypically related to antibodies present in lupus serum demonstrate polyreactivity, an unexpectedly high degree of idiotypic cross-reactivity (even when obtained from unrelated individuals), and structural and functional relationships to antibodies that are more strongly reactive with bacterial antigens. This could mean that the anti-DNA reactivity is a property of a small portion of the repertoire that is derived from conserved germline genes for antibacterial responses. It could also mean that immunoglobulins with this polyreactivity represent an early stage in the normal maturation of responses to bacterial or other antigens. It will be important to determine whether the principles discovered for anti-DNA autoantibodies apply to the other characteristic autoantibodies of SLE-related diseases as well.

The studies carried on so far do not answer the question of the immediate stimulus that leads to expression of the potential for production of anti-DNA antibodies in subjects with SLE. This could still be the exposure to nucleic acid or nucleoprotein, to bacterial antigen, or to polyclonal activator. It could also result from a basic disorder of regulation rather than from a specific immunizing stimulus. Access to the responding cells, in any case, can help to answer these questions and could provide a more specific target for therapy and control than has been available; analyses of monoclonal antibody products help in the identification of these cells.

REFERENCES

1. SELIGMANN, M. 1957. C.R. Acad. Sci. Paris **245:** 243.
2. CEPELLINI, R., C. POLLI & F. CELADA. 1957. Proc. Soc. Exp. Biol. Med. **96:** 572.
3. ROBBINS, W. C., H. R. HOLMAN, H. R. DEICHER & H. G. KUNKEL. 1957. Proc. Soc. Exp. Biol. Med. **96:** 575.
4. MIESCHER, P. & R. STRASSLE. 1957. Vox Sang. **2:** 283.
5. SANO, H. & C. MORIMOTO. 1982. J. Immunol. **128:** 1341–1345.
6. RAPTIS, L. & H. A. MENARD. 1980. J. Clin. Invest. **66:** 1391–1399.
7. GOLAN, D. T. & Y. BOREL. 1983. Eur. J. Immunol. **13:** 430–433.
8. SANO, H., M. IMOKAWA, A. D. STEINBERG & C. MORIMOTO. 1983. J. Immunol. **130:** 187.
9. LEVINE, L., W. T. MURAKAMI, H. VAN VUNAKIS & L. GROSSMAN. 1960. Proc. Natl. Acad. Sci. USA **46:** 1038–1043.
10. PLESCIA, O., W. BRAUN & N. PALCZUK. 1964. Proc. Natl. Acad. Sci. USA **52:** 279–283.
11. SEAMAN, E., H. VAN VUNAKIS & L. LEVINE. 1972. J. Biol. Chem. **247:** 5709–5715.
12. SEAMAN, E., L. LEVINE & H. VAN VUNAKIS. 1966. Biochemistry **5:** 1216–1223.
13. STRICKLAND, P. T. & J. M. BOYLE. 1984. Prog. Nucleic Acid Res. Mol. Biol. **31:** 1–58.
14. SEAMAN, E., H. VAN VUNAKIS & L. LEVINE. 1965. Biochemistry **4:** 1312.
15. NAHON, E., A. M. MICHELSON & F. LACOUR. 1967. Biochim. Biophys. Acta **149:** 127–139.
16. STOLLAR, B. D. 1970. Science **169:** 609.
17. GUIGUES, M. & M. LENG. 1976. Eur. J. Biochem. **69:** 615–624.
18. KITAGAWA, Y. & B. D. STOLLAR. 1982. Mol. Immunol. **19:** 413–420.
19. NAKAZATO, H. 1979. Anal. Biochem. **98:** 74–80.
20. LAFER, E. M., A. MÖLLER, A. NORDHEIM, B. D. STOLLAR & A. RICH. 1981. Proc. Natl. Acad. Sci. USA **78:** 3546–3550.
21. MALFOY, B. & M. LENG. 1981. FEBS Lett. **132:** 45–48.
22. ZARLING, D. A., D. J. ARNDT-JOVIN, M. ROBERT-NICOUD, L. P. MCINTOSH, R. THOMAE & T. M. JOVIN. 1984. J. Mol. Biol. **176:** 369–415.
23. LEE, J. S., M. L. WOODSWORTH & L. J. P. LATIMER. 1984. Biochemistry **23:** 3277–3281.
24. LAFER, E. M. & B. D. STOLLAR. 1984. J. Biomol. Struct. Dyn. **2:** 487–494.
25. ARANA, R. & M. SELIGMANN. 1967. J. Clin. Invest. **46:** 1867–1882.
26. AARDEN, L. A., F. LAKMAKER & T. E. W. FELTKAMP. 1976. J. Immunol. Methods **10:** 39–48.

27. PICAZO, J. J. & E. M. TAN. 1975. Scand. J. Rheumatol. Suppl. **11:** 35–41.
28. PAPALIAN, M., E. LAFER, R. WONG & B. D. STOLLAR. 1980. J. Clin. Invest. **65:** 469–477.
29. MADAIO, M. P., S. HODDER, R. S. SCHWARTZ & B. D. STOLLAR. 1984. J. Immunol. **132:** 872.
30. ELIAT, D., A. D. STEINBERG & A. N. SCHECHTER. 1978. J. Immunol **120:** 550–557.
31. AHARONOV, A., S. FUCHS, B. D. STOLLAR & M. SELA. 1974. Eur. J. Biochem. **42:** 73–79.
32. FOURNIÉ, G. J., P. H. LAMBERT & P. A. MIESCHER. 1974. J. Exp. Med. **140:** 1189–1206.
33. DZIARSKI, R. 1982. J. Immunol. **128:** 1026–1030.
34. GUILBERT, B., G. DIGHIERO & S. AVRAMEAS. 1982. J. Immunol. **128:** 2779–2787.
35. FERMAND, J. P., F. DANON & J. C. BROUET. 1985. Clin. Exp. Immunol. **59:** 467–474.
36. ZOUALI, M., J. M. FINE & A. EYQUEM. 1984. Eur. J. Immunol. **14:** 1085–1089.
37. GILLIAM, A. C., D. LANG & J. J. LOSPALLUTO. 1980. J. Immunol. **125:** 874–885.
38. KOFFLER, D., R. CARR, V. AGNELLO, R. THOBURN & H. G. KUNKEL. 1971. J. Exp. Med. **134:** 294–312.
39. EILAT, D. 1982. Mol. Immunol. **19:** 943–955.
40. SHOENFELD, Y., J. ANDRÉ-SCHWARTZ, B. D. STOLLAR & R. S. SCHWARTZ. 1986. Anti-DNA antibodies. *In* Autoimmunity. R. Lahita, Ed. Wiley. New York. In press.
41. ANDRZEJEWSKI, C., J. RAUCH, E. LAFER, B. D. STOLLAR & R. S. SCHWARTZ. 1981. J. Immunol. **126:** 226–231.
42. SHOENFELD, Y., J. RAUCH, H. MASSICOTTE, S. K. DATTA, J. ANDRÉ-SCHWARTZ, B. D. STOLLAR & R. S. SCHWARTZ. 1983. N. Engl. J. Med. **308:** 414–420.
43. LEE, J. S., J. R. LEWIS, A. R. MORGAN, T. R. MOSMANN & B. SINGH. 1981. Nucleic Acids Res. **9:** 1707–1721.
44. MUNNS, T. W., M. K. LISZEWSKI & B. H. HAHN. 1984. Biochemistry **23:** 2964–2970.
45. PISETSKY, D. S. & S. A. CASTER. 1982. Mol. Immunol. **19:** 645–650.
46. BALLARD, D. W. & E. W. VOSS, JR. 1982. Mol. Immunol. **19:** 793–799,
47. MÖLLER, A., J. E. GABRIELS, E. M. LAFER, A. NORDHEIM, A. RICH & B. D. STOLLAR. 1982. J. Biol. Chem. **257:** 12081–12085.
48. GAVALCHIN, J., J. A. NICKLAS, J. W. EASTCOTT, M. P. MADAIO, B. D. STOLLAR, R. S. SCHWARTZ & S. K. DATTA. 1985. J. Immunol. **134:** 885–894.
49. KANAI, Y., M. MIWA, T. MATSUSHIMA & T. SUGIMURA. 1974. Biochem. Biophys. Res. Commun. **59:** 300–306.
50. KANAI, Y., T. AKATSUKA, T. KUBOTA, S. GOTO & B. D. STOLLAR. 1985. Clin. Exp. Immunol. **59:** 139–145.
51. LAFER, E. M., J. RAUCH, C. ANDRZEJEWSKI, JR., D. MUDD, B. FURIE, B. FURIE, R. S. SCHWARTZ & B. D. STOLLAR. 1981. J. Exp. Med. **153:** 897–909.
52. KOIKE, T., N. MARUYAMA, H. FUNAKI, H. TOMIOKA & S. YOSHIDA. 1984. Clin. Exp. Immunol. **57:** 345–350.
53. ANDRÉ-SCHWARTZ, J., S. K. DATTA, Y. SHOENFELD, D. A. ISENBERG, B. D. STOLLAR & R. S. SCHWARTZ. 1984. Clin. Immunol. Immunopathol. **31:** 261–271.
54. SHOENFELD, Y., S. C. HSU-LIN, J. E. GABRIELS, L. E. SILBERSTEIN, B. C. FURIE, B. FURIE, B. D. STOLLAR & R. S. SCHWARTZ. 1982. J. Clin. Invest. **70:** 205–208.
55. JACOB, L., M. A. LETY, D. LOUVARD & J. F. BACH. 1985. J. Clin. Invest. **75:** 315–317.
56. RAUCH, J., E. MURPHY, J. B. ROTHS, B. D. STOLLAR & R. S. SCHWARTZ. 1982. J. Immunol. **129:** 236–241.
57. ISENBERG, D. A., Y. SHOENFELD, M. P. MADAIO, J. RAUCH, M. REICHLIN, B. D. STOLLAR & R. S. SCHWARTZ. 1984. Lancet **2:** 418–421.
58. SHOENFELD, Y., D. A. ISENBERG, J. RAUCH, M. MADAIO, B. D. STOLLAR & R. S. SCHWARTZ. 1983. J. Exp. Med. **158:** 718–730.
59. ATKINSON, P. M., G. LAMPMAN, B. C. FURIE, Y. NAPARSTEK, R. S. SCHWARTZ, B. D. STOLLAR & B. F. FURIE. 1985. J. Clin. Invest. **75:** 1138–1143.
60. KABAT, E. A., G. LIAO, H. BRETTING, E. C. FRANKLIN, D. GELTNER, B. FRANGIONE, M. E. KOSHLAND, J. SHYONG & E. F. OSSERMAN. 1980. J. Exp. Med. **152:** 979–995.
61. NAPARSTEK, Y., D. DUGGAN, A. SCHATTNER, M. P. MADAIO, B. D. STOLLAR, E. A. KABAT & R. S. SCHWARTZ. 1985. J. Exp. Med. **161:** 1525–1538.
62. CARROLL, P., D. STAFFORD, R. S. SCHWARTZ & B. D. STOLLAR. 1985. J. Immunol. **135:** 1086–1090.

63. GUARNIERI, M. & D. EISNER. 1974. Biochem. Biophys. Res. Commun. **58:** 347–353.
64. RAUCH, J., H. TANNENBAUM, B. D. STOLLAR & R. S. SCHWARTZ. 1984. Eur. J. Immunol.
    14: 529–534.

DISCUSSION OF THE PAPER

B. F. ERLANGER (*Columbia University, New York, NY*): I want to suggest that not just monoclonal autoantibodies, but all antibodies are multivalent. About twenty years ago, Talmadge suggested that the reason why antisera are so specific is that they are composed of populations of monoclonal antibodies that have different ranges of specificity, but that share the specificity for the antigen that was used for immunization. What you have then in immune serum is a population that amplifies specificity for your immunogen, but when examined individually, the antibodies in the serum show very significant cross-reactions. Therefore, what you showed may not be confined to autoantibodies.

B. D. STOLLAR (*Tufts University School of Medicine, Boston, MA*): There are differences between anti-nucleic-acid autoantibodies and induced anti-nucleic-acid antibodies. For example, if we make hybridomas after immunizing with Z-DNA, the monoclonal antibodies do not have the polyreactivity that we find in spontaneously produced autoantibodies.

Studies of the Effects of Y Chromosome Factors on the Expression of Autoimmune Disease

ALFRED D. STEINBERG,[a] KATHLEEN H. TRIEM,[a]
HOWARD R. SMITH,[a] CARL A. LASKIN,[b] YVONNE J.
ROSENBERG,[c] DENNIS M. KLINMAN,[a] J. FREDERIC
MUSHINSKI,[d] AND JOHN D. MOUNTZ[a]

[a]Cellular Immunology Section
Arthritis and Rheumatism Branch
National Institute of Arthritis, Diabetes,
and Digestive and Kidney Diseases
National Institutes of Health
Bethesda, Maryland 20205

[b]Toronto General Hospital
Toronto, Ontario, Canada

[c]Columbia University
New York, New York 10027

[d]National Cancer Institute
National Institutes of Health
Bethesda, Maryland 20205

INTRODUCTION

Systemic lupus erythematosus (SLE) is a multisystem autoimmune disease that has been characterized by the production of antibodies reactive with nuclear antigens. As a result of the diagnostic specificity of large amounts of antinuclear antibodies, as well as the evidence for their role in the pathogenesis of lupus glomerulonephritis, a major emphasis has been placed upon such autoantibodies. In the late 1950s, sera from patients with SLE were found to contain antibodies reactive with DNA.[1-6] Such antibodies were distinguishable from lower avidity DNA binding proteins in normal serum at alkaline pH;[2] they could induce passive cutaneous anaphylaxis[7] and bind DNA via the Fab fragment.[8] The anti-DNA antibodies from SLE patients bound to DNA from several species[1,5,9] and were not isotype restricted.[10,11] Antibodies to heat-denatured DNA were also abundant in lupus sera.[9,12-15] The immune response to DNA appeared also to include cell-mediated immunity on the basis of skin tests,[16-18] *in vitro* proliferation of lymphocytes,[17,19,20] and migration inhibition factor production.[19,21,22] In addition to antibodies to DNA, lupus patients were also found to produce antibodies to RNA, including double-stranded RNA,[23-25] tRNA,[26] single-stranded RNA,[25-27] and ribosomal RNA.[28,29]

Although patients with SLE spontaneously produced large amounts of antibodies to native nucleic acids, it was very difficult to induce such antibodies in experimental animals. This led to the concept that nucleic acids were not in themselves immunogenic, but rather acted as haptens.[30] This view of the nonimmunogenic nature of nucleic acids was challenged by Steinberg and co-workers, who demonstrated that nucleic acids could be recognized by the immune system without a carrier protein.[24,31,32] It was demonstrated that nucleic acids could induce specific immune tolerance, antibody, delayed type hypersensitivity, passive cutaneous anaphylaxis, and acute anaphylaxis.[30-37] These studies also suggested that there were genetic as well as environmental factors that could predispose towards or against the development of antibodies to nucleic acids.

Subsequent genetic studies have demonstrated that different types of genes underlie the phenotypic expression of induced or spontaneous anti-nucleic-acid autoantibody production. One type of predisposing gene occurs in NZB mice as a single codominant trait.[38-40] A second type of gene is an accelerating gene on the BXSB Y chromosome.[41,42] This Y-chromosome gene will not induce anti-nucleic-acid antibody production on most nonautoimmune backgrounds; however, it will lead to accelerated autoantibody production on an autoimmune background. A third type of gene is a recessive anti-DNA inducing gene such as *lpr* or *gld*.[42-45] The various genes that predispose to anti-DNA are all substantially interfered with in terms of phenotypic expression by the *xid* gene.[46-49]

In our studies of the multiple factors that predispose to or retard the development of autoimmunity, we have been struck by the similarity between the Y-chromosome accelerating factor in mice and the evidence for a similar factor in some families of humans in which SLE predisposition appears to be passed from father to son.[50] As a result, we have endeavored to better understand the Y-chromosome factor in mice so as to shed light on the apparently comparable human situation. The present paper summarizes many of our results, including a number of which that have not been previously published.

MATERIALS AND METHODS

Animals

NZB, NZW, and CBA/N mice were obtained from colonies maintained at the National Institutes of Health, Bethesda, Maryland. BXSB, MRL-*lpr/lpr*, C57BL/6-*lpr/lpr*, SB/Le, and CBA/J mice were originally obtained from The Jackson Laboratory, Bar Harbor, Maine. Consomic mice bearing either the BXSB or the SB/Le Y chromosome with background genes of another strain were obtained by mating the background-strain female with a BXSB or SB/Le male and repeatedly backcrossing the male offspring with a background-strain female. Mice bearing the *xid* gene originally derived from the CBA/N mouse were produced as described previously.[46-49] Castration of males was performed at 12–20 days of age as described.[38] Recombinant inbred mice (NZB X NFS) have been described previously;[39,40] some of these inbred lines were mated with BXSB males and the F_1 offspring studied. Additional F_1 mice were produced by mating consomic mice bearing the BXSB Y chromosome with BXSB females.

Anti-Erythrocyte Autoantibodies

Antibodies bound to circulating erythrocytes were measured by the direct Coombs test.[39] Blood was obtained from individual mice and placed into heparinized saline. After washing, the extent of agglutination was measured in microtiter plates using a previously titered anti-mouse Ig that was serially diluted twofold.[39]

Anti-DNA

Antibodies reactive with native DNA or heat-denatured DNA were initially measured by an ammonium sulfate precipitation (Farr) assay as described previously.[39,40] Briefly, the percentage of 25 ng of ^{14}C-labeled human KB DNA (native or heat-denatured) bound by 25 μl serum was determined after an overnight incubation at room temperature and a subsequent 24-hour incubation at 4°C (the reaction mixture was a total of 100 μl in borate buffered saline, pH 8.0). In order to determine the IgG and IgM contributions to the anti-DNA, an ELISA assay was performed as described,[49] using anti-IgG or anti-IgM as the reagent to which the enzyme was linked. Standards with known amounts of IgG and IgM anti-DNA were run in some of the assays to allow a determination of the relative amounts of IgG and IgM anti-DNA in each serum.

Survival Studies

Mice were usually observed at least every other day and the deaths were recorded. These were summarized and checked every two weeks. Moribund mice were not sacrificed so that true survival data could be obtained. In most instances, mice studied for survival were not those studied for other measures. This was done so that the survival would not be influenced by bleeding, mating, etc.

Measure of Plaque-Forming Cells

Antibody-producing plaque-forming cells were enumerated by the Cunningham and Szenberg modification of the Jerne and Nordin method of local hemolysis; total class specific plaques were assayed by the reverse hemolytic plaque assay using isotype-specific sheep anti-mouse Ig coupled to sheep erythrocytes (via chromic chloride) as targets, isotype-specific rabbit anti-mouse antibodies as developers, and guinea pig serum as complement.[51]

Cell Sorter Studies

Two types of flow cytometry studies were performed as described.[48,52,53] One analyzed DNA content using propidium iodide. The second analyzed cell surface markers. For two-color studies, one reagent was labeled with fluorescein (green) and the second with Texas red avidin (red).

RNA Isolation, Blotting, and Hybridization

Organs or purified cells were homogenized with a polytron for one minute at high speed in guanidine thiocyanate to rupture cells and denature ribonuclease simultaneously.[54] The RNA was separated from DNA and proteins by cesium chloride centrifugation and was extracted once in chloroform/phenol and once in chloroform only.[54] The poly-(A)$^+$ fraction of RNA was obtained by passing purified RNA over an oligo-(dT)-cellulose column and by elution with low salt buffer.[54] Ten micrograms of poly-(A)$^+$ RNA were denatured in 14 mM methylmercury hydroxide and subjected to electrophoresis in 1.5% agarose/5 mM methylmercury hydroxide gels.[54] The RNA was then blotted onto O-diazophenyl thioether paper, prehybridized, and hybridized with (1–3) × 10^6 cpm/ml of different DNA probes that had been labeled with ^{32}P by nick-translation to a specific activity of approximately 2 × 10^8 cpm/μg.[54] Essentially equal amounts of RNA were blotted to the paper, as demonstrated by ethidium bromide staining of the gel before and after transfer and equal degrees of hybridization with control probes. After washing at 65°C in 0.1 × SSC, the hybridized blots were exposed to Kodak XAR-2 film at −70°C in the presence of an intensifying screen. In some cases, after photography of the radiographs, certain lanes were cut out and juxtaposed so as to more clearly illustrate relevant comparisons. The RNA blots were later stripped with 100% formamide at 65°C for 2–6 hours in order to remove traces of radioactive probes; the blots were then prehybridized and hybridized with other probes.

Subtraction Hybridization

Complementary DNA (cDNA) was synthesized in a final reaction volume of 0.2 ml that contained 5 μg poly-(A)$^+$ RNA, 2 μg of oligo-(dT), and 60 U reverse transcriptase (Life Sciences, St. Petersburg, Florida). It also contained 1 mM each of dATP, dGTP, dTTP, and ^{32}P dCTP (Amersham, Arlington Heights, Illinois, 10 mCi/ml; 3000 Ci/mMole), plus cold dCTP at a concentration of 75 μM, 5 μM dithiothreitol, 20 μg actinomycin D, 6 mM MgCl$_2$, 90 mM KCl, and 50 mM Tris (pH = 8.1 at 42°C). After incubation at 42°C for 2 hours and base hydrolysis of the mRNA in 0.1 M NaOH at 70°C for 20 minutes, the cDNA was separated from the reaction mixture components on a column of Sephadex G-50 fine in a Pasteur pipet and ethanol-precipitated with 50 μg of carrier tRNA.

A 20-fold excess of poly-(A)$^+$ RNA was mixed with the ^{32}P cDNA in an ultracentrifuge tube, precipitated in ethanol, and pelleted together. The pellet was resuspended in 5 μl of water, 1.5 μl of 2.0 M phosphate buffer, 0.1 μl of 20% SDS, and 0.1 μl of 0.1 M EDTA. The reaction volume was hybridized by heating it (in a sealed 20-μl capillary tube) up to 98°C for 30 seconds and then heating it at 68°C for 20 hours.[55] Hybridization was followed by hydroxyapatite chromatography at 60°C to allow isolation of the unhybridized single-stranded cDNA, which was then followed by elution of double-stranded cDNA poly-(A)$^+$ RNA at 98°C. The single-stranded cDNA was hybridized to RNA blots at a final specific activity of (1–3) × 10^6 cpm/ml of hybridization solution as described above, except that 1 mg yeast tRNA, 100 μg poly-A, 100 μg poly-C, and 50 μg sheared *E. Coli* DNA were added during prehybridization and hybridization. Hybridization was carried out at 45°C for 8 hours. The blots were stringently washed twice in 2 × SSC for 30 minutes at 37°C and then twice in 0.1 × SSC for 30 minutes at 65°C.

In Vitro *Translation*

In vitro translation was carried out with micrococcal nuclease-treated rabbit reticulocyte lysates (New England Nuclear)[56] in a volume of 50 μl using 1 μg mRNA, 1 mM dithiothreitol, 19 amino acids, ^{35}S-methionine (10 mCi in a 30-μl reaction), and the reticulocyte lysate system (optimized for translating B-cell mRNA), with incubation for 90 minutes at 30°C. An aliquot was removed for counting and for electrophoresis on a 10% polyacrylamide gel.

RESULTS

Variation in BXSB Mice from The Jackson Laboratory

The initial BXSB mice we obtained were from the research colonies of Murphy and Roths.[41] We were impressed that the male BXSB mice were especially small and wondered if that might not reflect an abnormality on the Y chromosome that correlated with accelerated autoimmunity. Subsequently, we received mice from The Jackson Laboratory that originated from the same BXSB colony, but which were from a larger production colony. We found that the males were no longer very small; a comparison of the body weights and survival of the original and subsequent BXSB males is shown in TABLE 1. The much smaller original BXSB males died significantly more rapidly than did the larger BXSB males. The larger males, nevertheless, had accelerated disease relative to their female littermates. Moreover, when mated with NZB females, these males transmitted to their male offspring accelerated disease relative to both female littermates and reciprocal male crosses; thus, there was strong evidence that the larger, more recent BXSB males did have a Y-chromosome accelerating factor.

Variation in NZW · BXSB-Y Consomic Mice

Alerted to the possibility that there might be changes in the phenotype of the offspring of mice carrying the BXSB Y chromosome, we monitored our consomic mice. Our original NZW · BXSB-Y consomic mice studied from 1982–83 had less than 0.06% genetic material from the original BXSB mouse. They demonstrated acceler-

TABLE 1. Variation in the Pace of the Autoimmune Process over Time in Inbred Male Mice

(A) BXSB Mice from The Jackson Laboratory		
Group[a]	Mean Weight (grams) at 4 Months ± SEM	Median Survival (months)
Mice obtained 1979–80	18 ± 2^{b}	5.5^{c}
Mice obtained since 1982	28 ± 2^{b}	9.5^{c}

(B) NZW.BXSB-Y Mice Produced at the NIH		Pathology at 6 Months	
Group[a]	Median Survival (months)	Renal	Cardiac
1982–83 NZW	24	0.6 ± 0.3	0.4 ± 0.2
NZW.BXSB-Y	7	2.9 ± 0.5^{e}	2.2 ± 0.4^{e}
1984–85 NZW	22	0.5 ± 0.2	0.3 ± 0.2
NZW.BXSB-Y	14^{d}	1.1 ± 0.3^{e}	0.5 ± 0.3

[a]Twenty to forty-five mice per group.

[b]Significantly different, p less than 0.01, Student's t test.

[c]Significantly different, p less than 0.01, Kolmogorov-Smirnov test.

[d]Significantly different from 1982–83 NZW.BXSB-Y mice as well as consomic NZW controls, each $p < 0.01$, Kolmogorov-Smirnov test.

[e]Significantly different from comparable NZW consomic mice, $p < 0.01$, Student's t test for 1982–83 mice; $p < 0.05$ for 1984–85 mice.

TABLE 2. Comparison of NZB.BXSB-Y and NZB.SB/Le-Y Consomic Mice

Group[a]	Anti-RBC Titer at 3.5 Months[b]	Anti-ssDNA at 4.5 Months[c]	Median Survival (months)
NZB Males	0.6 ± 0.3	18 ± 4	18
NZB.BXSB-Y Males	5.2 ± 1.0^d	23 ± 5	14
NZB.SB/Le-Y Males	6.1 ± 1.1^d	45 ± 4^e	6[f]

[a]Twenty-five to fifty mice per group.
[b]Measured by the direct Coombs test.
[c]Measured by the ammonium sulfate (Farr) assay.
[d]Significantly different from NZB males, p less than 0.01, Student's t test.
[e]Significantly different from the other two groups, p less than 0.01, Student's t test.
[f]Significantly less than the other two groups, p less than 0.01, Kolmogorov-Smirnov test.

ated immunopathology[57] and reduced survival (TABLE 1). These mice have been maintained by continuing to backcross them to NZW females. The result has been the emergence of consomic mice that have less accelerated disease (TABLE 1).

Comparison of NZB · BXSB-Y and NZB · SB/Le-Y Consomic Mice

In the process of studying consomic mice on the several autoimmune backgrounds, we were especially surprised to find that the highly inbred NZB · BXSB-Y mouse failed to manifest accelerated anti-DNA[58] or markedly accelerated mortality. This was especially surprising since John Roths had indicated (personal communication) that he had once made such mice and that they had accelerated death. We therefore compared consomic NZB · BXSB-Y and NZB · SB/Le-Y to determine whether a disease accelerating factor present on the Y chromosome of the original SB/Le mouse might have been "lost" somewhere in the breeding processes. Evidence in favor of that possibility was derived from those studies (TABLE 2). Both NZB · BXSB-Y and NZB · SB/Le-Y consomic males had accelerated anti-erythrocyte autoantibody production relative to NZB males; however, only the NZB · SB/Le-Y males had accelerated anti-DNA or accelerated mortality (TABLE 2). However, continued inbreeding of these mice led to more prolonged survival. We had noted a similar phenomenon early in the breeding of the NZB · BXSB-Y strain. Therefore, it appears that the BXSB-Y acts on a gene in NZB mice that is lost during the inbreeding process.

Effect of the BXSB-Y on Offspring of Crosses with NZB, NZW, and BXSB Mice

Since the NZB · BXSB-Y consomic mice had accelerated anti-RBC, but not anti-DNA, we wondered whether those mice had a factor on the Y chromosome that caused accelerated anti-RBC, but had also lost a factor that caused accelerated anti-DNA. To test for an anti-DNA accelerating factor, NZB · BXSB-Y mice were mated with BXSB or NZW females and the male offspring were compared with both their female littermates and reciprocal male crosses. In all cases, the males with the Y chromosome derived from the NZB · BXSB-Y male had accelerated anti-DNA production and reduced survival (TABLE 3). Therefore, the NZB · BXSB-Y consomic male did have a factor on the Y chromosome that could lead to both anti-DNA production and accelerated death; however, that factor required non-Y genes from the BXSB or NZW for expression.

TABLE 3. Effect of Castration or Androgen Administration on (NZB × NZW) F$_1$ Mice with and without BXSB Y Chromosomes

Group[a]	Sex and Treatment	Anti-DNA[b]	Survival[c]
(NZB × NZW) F$_1$	M	17	16
(NZB × NZW) F$_1$	Castrated M	64[d]	9[d]
(NZB × NZW · BXSB-Y) F$_1$	M	39[e]	11.5[e]
(NZB × NZW · BXSB-Y) F$_1$	Castrated M	71[d]	6[d]
(NZB × NZW) F$_1$	F	47	10
(NZB × NZW) F$_1$	F + Androgens	10[d]	18[d]
(NZW × NZB · BXSB-Y) F$_1$	M	32[e]	12[e]
(NZW × NZB · BXSB-Y) F$_1$	Castrated M	59[d]	7[d]
(NZW × NZB) F$_1$	M	21	17
(NZW × NZB) F$_1$	Castrated M	66[d]	9[d]

[a] Fifteen to thirty mice per group.
[b] Mean percent binding of 25 ng ^{14}C-labeled DNA by 25 μl serum; standard errors were ≤4.
[c] Median survival in months.
[d] Significantly different from control mice without hormone alterations.
[e] Significantly different from consomic mice without the BXSB Y chromosome.

Effect of the BXSB-Y on Survival of lpr/lpr Mice

We next asked what effect, if any, the BXSB-Y might have on the pace of illness in *lpr/lpr* mice. We found that MRL-*lpr/lpr* males with either the BXSB-Y or the SB/Le-Y had insignificant reductions in survival. In contrast, the more long-lived C57BL/6-*lpr/lpr* males demonstrated accelerated disease with either the BXSB or the SB/Le Y chromosome (TABLE 4).

Effect of Castration

In our original study of MRL-*lpr/lpr* mice,[59] we found that androgens retarded the disease of MRL-*lpr/lpr* mice. We have also found that sex hormones might play a role in modulating the pace of disease in C57BL/6-*lpr/lpr* mice (TABLE 4) and in

TABLE 4. Effect of the BXSB Y Chromosome on Survival of Male *lpr/lpr* Mice

Group[a]	Sex	Median Survival (months)
MRL-*lpr/lpr*	F	7
MRL-*lpr/lpr*	M	9
MRL-*lpr/lpr*.BXSB-Y	M	8
MRL-*lpr/lpr*.SB/Le-Y	M	7
C57BL/6-*lpr/lpr*	F	10.5
C57BL/6-*lpr/lpr*	F testosterone	17
C57BL/6-*lpr/lpr*	M	15.5[b]
C57BL/6-*lpr/lpr*	Castrated M	10[c]
C57BL/6-*lpr/lpr*.BXSB-Y	M	12[c]
C57BL/6-*lpr/lpr*.SB/Le-Y	M	9[c]

[a] Twenty-eight to sixty mice per group.
[b] Significantly different from females, p less than 0.01, Kolmogorov-Smirnov test.
[c] Significantly less than C57BL/6-*lpr/lpr* males, p less than 0.01.

(NZB × NZW · BXSB-Y) F_1 and (NZW × NZB · BXSB-Y) F_1 males (TABLE 3). Thus, in addition to a clear-cut accelerating factor on the Y chromosome of BXSB mice, an additional effect of androgens may be demonstrated in certain crosses.

The BXSB-Y and SB/Le-Y Increase IgG Anti-DNA

In NZB · BXSB-Y mice whose deaths were not markedly accelerated, there was very little IgG anti-DNA. This stood in contrast to the increased IgG anti-DNA found in the (BXSB × NZB · BXSB-Y) F_1 males.[57] This observation has been extended herein. When the relative and absolute amounts of IgG anti-DNA were measured in consomic mice and in F_1 crosses, it became apparent that there was a strong association between accelerated death and the production of IgG anti-DNA in autoimmune consomic mice bearing the BXSB-Y or the SB/Le-Y (TABLE 5). Of note, CBA/J ·

TABLE 5. Effect of BXSB-Y and SB/Le-Y on IgG Anti-DNA in Consomic and F_1 Males at 4.5 Months

Group	OD Units in ELISA[a]		% IgG[b] (corrected)
	IgM Anti-DNA	IgG Anti-DNA	
NZB	0.21	<0.1	<20
NZB.BXSB-Y	0.25	<0.1	<20
NZB.SB/Le-Y	0.32	0.16	51
(BXSB × NZB.BXSB-Y)F_1	0.46	0.43	69
MRL-*lpr/lpr*	0.41	0.83	82
MRL-*lpr/lpr*.BXSB-Y	0.48	1.09	91
MRL-*lpr/lpr*.SB/Le-Y	0.49	1.21	95
C57BL/6-*lpr/lpr*	0.44	0.26	55
C57BL/6-*lpr/lpr*.BXSB-Y	0.41	0.55	77
C57BL/6-*lpr/lpr*.SB/Le-Y	0.63	0.92	84
CBA/J	<0.1	<0.1	
CBA/J.BXSB-Y	<0.1	<0.1	
CBA/J.SB/Le-Y	<0.1	<0.1	

[a]Standard error less than 20%; OD units log normally distributed.
[b]Based upon standard curves.

BXSB-Y males with a normal survival[57] produced no anti-DNA. Thus, the BXSB-Y and SB/Le-Y chromosomal factors are truly accelerating factors rather than inducing factors.

Total Numbers of Antibody-Forming Cells

BXSB males had greater numbers of splenic antibody-forming cells of all isotypes than did their female littermates (TABLE 6). Consomic NZB · BXSB-Y males did not demonstrate greater numbers of Ig-secreting cells than did NZB males; they had an increase only in IgG_3 relative to both NZB males and their female littermates (TABLE 6). This result contrasted with the high levels of Ig-secreting cells in (NZB × BXSB) F_1 males. To demonstrate that the NZB · BXSB-Y did have a factor on the Y

TABLE 6. Effect of the BXSB Y Chromosome on Splenic Immunoglobulin Producing Cells

Strain or Cross[a]	Sex	Numbers of Ig-Secreting Cells $\times 10^{-3}$			
		IgM[b]	IgG$_1$	IgG$_2$	IgG$_3$
BXSB	M	198	141	222	98
BXSB	F	34	15	17	4
NZB	M	732	37	48	41
NZB.BXSB-Y	M	162	8	35	87
NZB.BXSB[c]	F	174	5	34	9
(NZB $\times$ BXSB)F$_1$	M	541	96	408	179
(BXSB $\times$ NZB.BXSB-Y)F$_1$	M	605	78	356	161
	F	173	22	31	21
(NZW $\times$ NZB.BXSB-Y)F$_1 \cdot +$	M	347	128	659	598
(NZW $\times$ NZB.BXSB-Y)F$_1 \cdot xid$[d]	M	8	2	3	2
(MRL-$lpr/lpr \times$ BXSB)F$_1$	M	493	293	385	506
	F	108	70	227	62

[a] Mice were approximately four months of age.

[b] Standard errors were originally expressed on log transformed data in the form of log $\times$ or $\div$ SEM. In this form, the errors varied from 0.10 to 0.34, with almost all less than 0.2.

[c] The female littermates of the NZB.BXSB-Y males that lacked the Y chromosome.

[d] These mice and the ones immediately above were prepared by mating NZW.$xid/+$ females with NZB.BXSB-Y consomic males and testing the male offspring; half of them were xid and the other half were $+$, but all of them were (NZW $\times$ NZB)F$_1$ with BXSB Y chromosomes.

chromosome that caused an increase in Ig-secreting cells, (BXSB $\times$ NZB $\cdot$ BXSB-Y) F$_1$ mice were studied. Indeed, the males had high levels of Ig-secreting cells that were comparable to those of (NZB $\times$ BXSB) F$_1$ males and that were substantially higher than littermate (BXSB $\times$ NZB $\cdot$ BXSB-Y) F$_1$ females (TABLE 6). The xid gene markedly reduced the number of Ig-secreting cells in F$_1$ crosses (TABLE 6).

Effect of Neonatal Thymectomy on BXSB Disease

Our studies of neonatal thymectomy on BXSB mice were carried out on male mice obtained from The Jackson Laboratory who were of larger size and who had life spans of approximately 7–10 months. Neonatal thymectomy led to a shortening of survival, a marked increase in lymphadenopathy, an increase in anti-DNA antibodies, a loss of

TABLE 7. Effect of Neonatal Thymectomy (Tx) of Male BXSB Mice

Group	Coombs Titer (log$_2$)	Anti-ssDNA (% bound)	LN Weight/ Body Weight	Number of Ly-1$^+$ B Cells in LN ($\times 10^{-7}$)	Median Survival (months)
Sham BXSB	1.4	31	0.007	0.08	9
Tx BXSB	8.9[a]	60[a]	0.026[a]	5.0[a]	5.5[a]
BXSB.xid Congenics	<0.5[b]	8[b]	<0.003[b]	<0.03[b]	>18[b]

[a] Significantly worse than sham controls, $p < 0.05$.

[b] Significantly better than controls, $p < 0.05$.

Lyt-2$^+$ cells, and an increase in Ly-1$^+$ B cells (TABLE 7). The increase in B cells and decrease in T cells was not only demonstrated by flow cytometry, but also by probing poly-(A$^+$) RNA with Thy-1 and other probes (e.g., see FIGURE 1).

Effect of xid on BXSB Disease

The *xid* gene caused a marked retardation of disease in BXSB males with regard to survival, anti-DNA production, and Ig production (TABLE 7). This effect was also observed in (NZB × BXSB) F$_1$, (NZW × BXSB) F$_1$, (NZW × NZB · BXSB-Y) F$_1$, and (NZW × NZB · BXSB-Y) F$_1$ males.

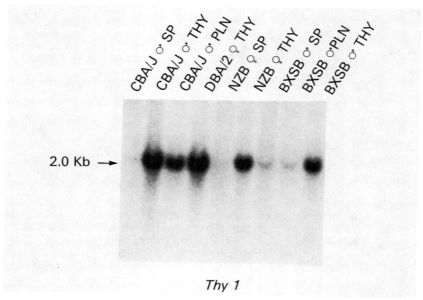

FIGURE 1. Northern blot, 10 μg poly-(A)$^+$ RNA per lane, of spleen (SP), thymus (THY), or peripheral lymph nodes (PLN) from various strains. This was probed with a Thy-1 specific probe. A reduction in Thy-1 expression was noted in BXSB male peripheral lymph nodes consistent with the increase in B cells in those nodes, especially Ly-1$^+$ B cells.

Proto-Oncogene Expression in Mice with the BXSB Y Chromosome

We recently have found that the *myb* proto-oncogene is strongly expressed in the peripheral T cells of the MRL-*lpr/lpr* mice.[54] This result led to a search for abnormal proto-oncogene expression in the lymphoid tissues of BXSB and other autoimmune strains and crosses. The *myc, ras/bas,* and *raf* proto-oncogenes were found to be strongly expressed in the B cells of BXSB mice, the splenic B cells, and especially the lymph-node B cells. The increase in these oncogenes was prevented by the *xid* gene in congenic mice (FIGURE 2).

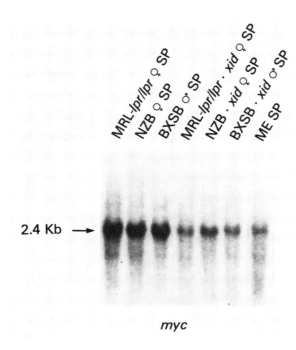

FIGURE 2. Northern blot of spleen from various autoimmune strains with and without the *xid* gene (congenic mice). Ten micrograms of poly-(A)$^+$ RNA per lane were probed with a c-*myc* probe. All of the autoimmune stains except *me* (moth-eaten) had increased c-*myc* RNA. In those mice with the *xid* gene, this increased *myc* expression was not observed.

Expression of Thy-1 Message by BXSB Cells

The cellular immunology studies suggested that the great majority of the lymph-node cells of BXSB males were B cells. To confirm the cell surface marker studies, poly-(A$^+$) RNA was probed with a Thy-1 probe (FIGURE 1). Indeed, whereas there was substantial Thy-1 message in control CBA/J lymph nodes and in several thymuses, including BXSB, there was very little Thy-1 message in male BXSB nodes.

Abnormal Proto-Oncogene Expression in Male BXSB Lymphoid Tissue

Male BXSB spleen and lymph-node cells were found to have very strong expression of the *raf* proto-oncogene (FIGURE 3). This expression was essentially eliminated by the *xid* gene in the congenic mice. These data suggest that the B cells of the BXSB mice are responsible for the very high *raf* expression. As a control for this experiment, we show the results from C3H/HeJ and C3H/HeJ-*gld/gld* mice. The *gld/gld* lymph nodes had strong expression of *raf*, which was not the case for the +/+ controls. We believe that this increase in *raf* in *gld/gld* mice is associated primarily with T cells.

The *myc* expression was found to be elevated in all of the autoimmune spleens except for moth-eaten (me/me). This elevated *myc* expression was reduced by the *xid* gene in congenic mice (FIGURE 2). A number of other oncogene probes were studied including *bas* and *fms*. The *xid* gene decreased expression of these as well. Of interest, the NZB consomic mice with BXSB Y chromosomes had very high *fms* expression (FIGURE 4).

Study of a Probe Prepared by Subtraction Hybridization

The above data suggest that BXSB males have increased expression of a number of different genes that are also expressed in normals, but at lower levels. We wondered whether there might be genes in BXSB mice that were expressed uniquely or expressed to an extraordinary high degree relative to normal mice. In order to test this possibility, poly-(A^+) RNA was obtained from the spleens of male BXSB mice and cDNA labeled with ^{32}P was prepared. This was annealed to a 20-fold excess of poly-(A^+) RNA from male CBA/J spleens. All of the expression in common between the two strains would result in the annealing of the cDNA of the BXSB and the mRNA of the CBA/J. This double-stranded material was removed on hydroxyapatite columns. Those genes unique to the BXSB male would come through as single-stranded unannealed material

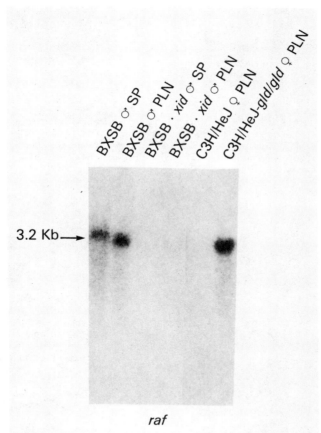

raf

FIGURE 3. Spleen (SP) and peripheral lymph nodes (PLN) from various mice were studied for *raf* expression by Northern analysis, 10 μg poly-$(A)^+$ RNA per lane. There was substantial *raf* expression in BXSB male tissues, but not in congenic BXSB · *xid*. Nonautoimmune-prone C3H PLN had little *raf* expression, whereas congenic mice bearing the *gld* mutation had substantial *raf* expression.

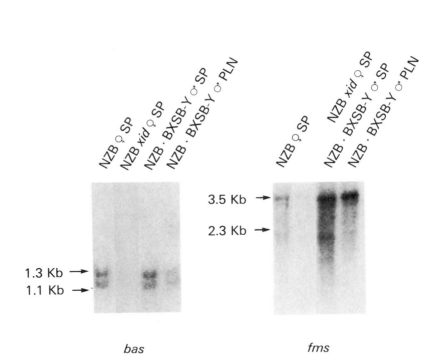

bas   fms

FIGURE 4. Effect of the *xid* and BXSB-Y genes on *bas* and *fms* expression in NZB mice. Northern analysis of 10 μg poly-(A)⁺ RNA from spleen (SP) and peripheral lymph nodes (PLN) demonstrated a loss of *bas* expression by spleen of NZB mice bearing either *xid* or the BXSB-Y. In contrast, *xid* led to a decrease in *fms* RNA, while the BXSB-Y led to a marked increase in *fms* expression on the NZB background.

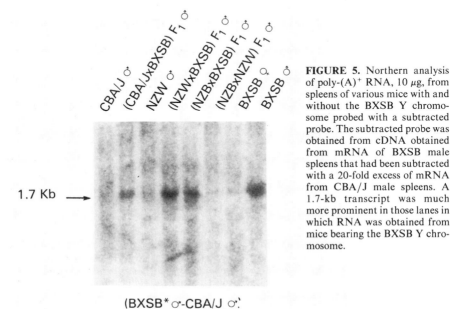

(BXSB* ♂-CBA/J ♂)

FIGURE 5. Northern analysis of poly-(A)⁺ RNA, 10 μg, from spleens of various mice with and without the BXSB Y chromosome probed with a subtracted probe. The subtracted probe was obtained from cDNA obtained from mRNA of BXSB male spleens that had been subtracted with a 20-fold excess of mRNA from CBA/J male spleens. A 1.7-kb transcript was much more prominent in those lanes in which RNA was obtained from mice bearing the BXSB Y chromosome.

and, by virtue of its ^{32}P label, could be used as a probe. This probe was used to probe poly-(A^+) RNA from several strains and crosses (FIGURE 5). The probe demonstrated substantial expression of a 1.7-kilobase message in BXSB males, but not BXSB females. This message was also abundant in three crosses that had the BXSB Y chromosome—(CBA/J × BXSB) F_1, (NZW × BXSB) F_1, and (NZB × BXSB) F_1—but not in mice without the BXSB-Y—(NZB × NZW) F_1 or NZW.

In Vitro *Translation*

The above study suggested that a large amount of message was produced under control of a gene on the BXSB Y chromosome. In order to try to determine if a unique protein might result from such a message, mRNA from BXSB males were used in an *in vitro* translation system. In this study, both the male BXSB and the MRL-*lpr/lpr* mRNA appeared to direct the synthesis of a protein of approximately 80 kDa (FIGURE 6). This result was obtained in several experiments. A number of less prominent bands were seen with MRL-*lpr/lpr* above or also with BXSB (FIGURE 6). Additional studies will be necessary to determine whether additional unique proteins may be uncovered.

DISCUSSION

The pioneering studies of Murphy and Roths and those of Theofilopoulos and Dixon and their colleagues clearly demonstrated that a factor or factors on the Y chromosome of the BXSB mouse led to accelerated autoimmune disease in male as compared with female offspring.[41,42] This effect was not dependent upon sex hormones and was transferrable with stem cells.[60,61] In our attempt to better understand factors that modify the expression of generalized autoimmune disease, we have extended those studies and have found that the BXSB mouse is less straightforward than the initial literature would suggest: There is considerable variability in highly inbred mice bearing the BXSB Y chromosome. This variability appears to represent rapid genetic drift, which may relate, in part, to a selective breeding efficiency by less severely afflicted males and a selective breeding disadvantage among more severely affected males. It is conceivable that there is more than one factor on the SB/Le Y chromosome that is capable of accelerating autoimmune disease and that there is incomplete inheritance of these factors, such that some, but not all, are inherited. Against this last possibility is the observation that the less autoimmune BXSB males or NZB · BXSB-Y males are fully capable in crosses with other autoimmune strain females of passing on to their male offspring severe accelerated disease. This observation would suggest that other genetic elements (such as non-Y genes or possibly virus genetic material) are critical to the full expression of Y-chromosome accelerated disease in the inbred strain and that they can be rapidly lost by selective breeding.

In addition to the problems generated by the consomic mice and the variable BXSB males, they have also provided insights. The BXSB-Y appears to be an accelerating factor rather than an inducing factor (such as *lpr* or *gld*). The BXSB-Y can accelerate disease on certain genetic backgrounds, including NZW, but not others (e.g., CBA/J). It can even conspire with the *lpr* gene to accelerate disease in C57BL/6 · *lpr/lpr* males. The acceleration of disease is most often associated with a marked augmentation in serum IgG concentrations, with no consistent changes in IgM. This increase in IgG extends to a marked increase in IgG anti-DNA, with only variable effects on IgM anti-DNA.

Of special note, the *xid* gene completely prevents the expression of disease in BXSB males and all of the various crosses examined. This result is accompanied by a marked reduction in IgG production as well as the expected reduction in IgM production. Neonatal thymectomy of the larger variety of BXSB males led to augmented

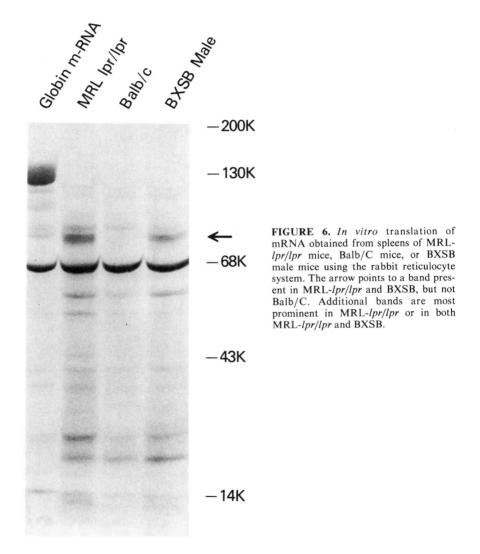

FIGURE 6. *In vitro* translation of mRNA obtained from spleens of MRL-*lpr/lpr* mice, Balb/C mice, or BXSB male mice using the rabbit reticulocyte system. The arrow points to a band present in MRL-*lpr/lpr* and BXSB, but not Balb/C. Additional bands are most prominent in MRL-*lpr/lpr* or in both MRL-*lpr/lpr* and BXSB.

lymphadenopathy. It is possible that a factor present in the original Murphy and Roths BXSB mice and that has been lost from the current Jackson Laboratory production colony of BXSB mice might be responsible for an abnormality in the immune system, which we now can reproduce by neonatal thymectomy. If this were the case, we would expect that the more severely affected BXSB males would not be worsened by neonatal thymectomy as has been found by the Scripps group.[62] In our hands, the massive lymphadenopathy of the thymectomized BXSB males was associated with a marked increase in Ly-1$^+$ B cells, which have also been associated with autoantibody production in NZB mice.[63] The predominance of B cells in the lymph nodes of BXSB mice was demonstrated both by flow cytometry and by molecular probing of mRNA. The c-*myc* proto-oncogene in the BXSB males was associated with B-cell activation; the increased expression was prevented by the *xid* gene, further pointing to a B-cell defect in BXSB mice as well or a regulatory T-cell defect.

Additional attempts to understand the differential gene expression included creation of a probe obtained by the technique of subtraction hybridization that has been used to obtain chains of the T-cell receptor for antigen[55] and to characterize the X-chromosome gene family.[64,65] This experiment demonstrated that BXSB males have an abundant 1.7-kilobase message that is absent from BXSB females and CBA/J males. Moreover, other autoimmune strains and crosses bearing the BXSB Y chromosome also strongly express this gene. Further work will be necessary to characterize this and possibly other genes very strongly or uniquely expressed as a result of an action of the BXSB Y chromosome.

The *in vitro* translation system demonstrated that the BXSB Y chromosome directs the expression of special mRNA, which can be synthesized into proteins. One very abundant protein was of approximately 80 kilodaltons and this protein was also made by MRL-*lpr/lpr* mice. It is possible that this represents the 70-kilodalton glycoprotein that is characteristic of several autoimmune strains and that is of retroviral origin.[66,67] Additional experiments are under way in an attempt to characterize this and other proteins unique to the BXSB mouse and to other autoimmune mice.

In the late 1960s, we found that polyclonal B-cell activators could accelerate the autoimmune disease of New Zealand mice[24] and lead to substantial immunopathology.[35,68] The BXSB Y-chromosome factor bears a substantial resemblance to those polyclonal activators: both accelerate the production of immunoglobulin, the production of anti-DNA (especially IgG anti-DNA), and the induction of widespread immunopathology. In what manner the BXSB Y chromosome leads to polyclonal B-cell activation remains to be determined. However, our more recent studies indicate that the *xid* gene can prevent the B-cell proto-oncogene expression of BXSB and MRL-*lpr/lpr* mice, but not the abnormal T-cell proto-oncogene expression of *lpr/lpr* mice. Therefore, the abnormality in BXSB males is expressed, at least in part, in the B cell. This conclusion is in harmony with that of Theofilopoulos and co-workers.[69]

We believe that generalized autoimmune disease in murine and human lupus is characterized by accelerated proliferation and maturation of B-cell precursors and B cells. This B-cell activation is what ultimately results from such genes as *lpr, gld*, and the SB/Le Y-chromosome accelerator. Defects in T-cell regulation either underlie or contribute importantly to the perpetuation, if not the initiation, of the process. Thus, polyclonal B-cell activation, which in a nonautoimmune background might be self-limited by normal T-cell regulation, is perpetuated by defects in T-cell regulation.[53] The abnormalities tend to be additive: background genes that predispose to autoimmunity[39,40] plus SB/LE-Y plus polyclonal immune activators. Acceleration of B-cell maturation reduces the ability of B cells to be tolerized. Acceleration of their proliferation increases the total number of B cells, thereby increasing the ultimate capacity for immunoglobulin produced. We suggest that polyclonal activation also increases the expansion of B cells that express genes of or close to germline, which may include many anti-self specificities. The polyclonal B-cell activation induced by the SB/Le-Y includes autoantibody production; however, the induction appears to work through non-Y genes. Isolation of the responsible gene(s) on the SB/Le Y chromosome and the resulting product(s) should shed further light on these processes.

REFERENCES

1. CEPELLINI, R., E. POLLI & F. CELEDA. 1957. Proc. Soc. Exp. Biol. Med. **96:** 572.
2. DEICHER, H. R., H. R. HOLMAN & H. G. KUNKEL. 1959. J. Exp. Med. **109:** 97.
3. MIESCHER, P. & R. STRAESSLE. 1957. Vox Sang. **2:** 283.
4. PEARSON, C. M., C. G. CRADDOCK & N. S. SIMMONS. 1958. J. Lab. Clin. Med. **52:** 588.
5. ROBBINS, W. C., H. R. HOLMAN, H. DEICHER & H. G. KUNKEL. 1957. Proc. Soc. Exp. Biol. Med. **96:** 575.
6. SELIGMANN, M. 1957. C. R. Soc. Biol. (Paris) **245:** 243.
7. DEICHER, H. R., H. R. HOLMAN, H. G. KUNKEL & Z. OVARY. 1960. J. Immunol. **84:** 106.
8. PINCUS, T. & A. P. KAPLAN. 1970. Nature **227:** 304.
9. STOLLAR, D., L. LEVINE & J. MARMUR. 1962. Biochem. Biophys. Acta **61:** 7.
10. SELIGMANN, M. & R. ARANA. 1968. The various types of DNA antibodies in SLE area. *In* Nucleic Acids in Immunology. O. J. Plescia & W. Braun, Eds.: **98.** Springer-Verlag. New York.
11. SELIGMANN, M., R. ARANA & A. CANNAT. 1968. The heterogeneity of DNA antibodies in SLE and their clinical significance. *In* Rheumatic Diseases. J. J. Duthie & W. R. M. Alexander, Eds.: 211. Williams & Wilkins. Baltimore.
12. BARBU, E., M. SELIGMANN & M. JOLY. 1960. Ann. Inst. Pasteur (Paris) **99:** 695.
13. LEVINE, L. & B. D. STOLLAR. 1968. Prog. Allergy **12:** 161.
14. LEVINE, L., W. T. MURAKAMI, H. van VANAKIS & L. GROSSMAN. 1960. Proc. Natl. Acad. Sci. USA **46:** 1038.
15. STOLLAR, B. D. & L. LEVINE. 1961. J. Immunol. **87:** 477.
16. AZOURY, F. J., H. E. JONES, V. J. DERBES & O. B. GUM. 1966. Ann. Intern. Med. **65:** 1221.
17. GOLDMAN, J. A., A. LITWIN, L. E. ADAMS, R. C. KRUEGAR & E. V. HESS. 1972. J. Clin. Invest. **51:** 2669.
18. ORES, R. O. & K. LANGE. 1964. Am. J. Med. Sci. **248:** 562.
19. BARTFIELD, H. & T. ATOYNATAN. 1971. Abstr. Arthritis Rheum. **14:** 369.
20. PATRUCCO, A., N. F. ROTHFIELD & K. HIRSCHHORN. 1967. Arthritis Rheum. **10:** 32.
21. GALANUD, P., J. DORMONT, J. CROSSNIER & J. P. H. MERY. 1971. Lancet **2:** 923.
22. MOULIAS, R., J. M. GOUST, P. REINERT, A. DEVILLECHABROLLE, C. N. M. BERAT, C. HEREMAN & P. GODEAU. 1972. Nouv. Presse Med. **1:** 1403.
23. SCHUR, P. H., B. D. STOLLAR, A. D. STEINBERG & N. TALAL. 1971. Arthritis Rheum. **14:** 342.
24. STEINBERG, A. D., S. BARON & N. TALAL. 1969. Proc. Natl. Acad. Sci. USA **63:** 1102.
25. TALAL, N., A. D. STEINBERG & G. G. DALEY. 1971. J. Clin. Invest. **50:** 1248.
26. EILAT, D., A. D. STEINBERG & A. N. SCHECHTER. 1978. J. Immunol. **120:** 550.
27. PILLARISETTY, R. J., M. J. BECKER, D. W. PALMER & N. TALAL. 1975. Clin. Exp. Immunol. **22:** 419.
28. LAMON, E. W. & J. C. BENNET. 1970. Immunology **19:** 439.
29. SCHUR, P. H., L. A. MOROZ & H. G. KUNKEL. 1967. Immunochemistry **4:** 447.
30. YACHNIN, S. 1962. Nature (London) **195:** 1319.
31. STEINBERG, A. D., T. M. CHUSED, M. E. JACOBS & N. TALAL. 1970. Nature **228:** 1090.
32. STEINBERG, A. D., G. G. DALEY & N. TALAL. 1970. Science **167:** 870.
33. HYMAN, L., K. KOVACS & A. D. STEINBERG. 1975. Int. Arch. Allergy Appl. Immunol. **48:** 248.
34. PARKER, L. M. & A. D. STEINBERG. 1973. J. Immunol. **110:** 742.
35. POWELL, D. E. & A. D. STEINBERG. 1972. Clin. Exp. Immunol. **12:** 419.
36. SCHER, I., A. D. STEINBERG, A. D. BERNING & W. E. PAUL. 1975. J. Exp. Med. **142:** 637.
37. van BOXEL, J. A., A. D. STEINBERG & I. GREEN. 1972. J. Immunol. **108:** 446.
38. RAVECHE, E. S. & A. D. STEINBERG. 1978. J. Exp. Med. **147:** 1487–1502.

39. RAVECHE, E. S., E. A. NOVOTNY, C. T. HANSEN, J. H. TJIO & A. D. STEINBERG. 1981. J. Exp. Med. **153:** 1187–1197.
40. MILLER, M. L., E. S. RAVECHE, C. A. LASKIN, D. M. KLINMAN & A. D. STEINBERG. 1984. J. Immunol. **133:** 1325–1331.
41. MURPHY, E. D. & J. B. ROTHS. 1979. Arthritis Rheum. **22:** 1188.
42. THEOFILOPOULOS, A. A. & F. J. DIXON. 1981. Immunol. Rev. **55:** 179.
43. MURPHY, E. D. & J. B. ROTHS. 1977. Fed. Proc. (Fed. Am. Soc. Exp. Biol.) **36:** 1246–1252.
44. MORSE, H. C., III, W. F. DAVIDSON, R. A. YETTER, E. MURPHY, J. B. ROTHS & R. L. COFFMAN. 1982. J. Immun. **129:** 2612–615.
45. ROTHS, J. B., E. D. MURPHY & E. M. EICHER. 1984. J. Exp. Med. **159:** 1.
46. TAUROG, J. D., E. S. RAVECHE, P. A. SMATHERS, L. H. GLIMCHER, D. P. HUSTON, C. T. HANSEN & A. D. STEINBERG. 1981. J. Exp. Med. **153:** 221–234.
47. STEINBERG, B. J., P. A. SMATHERS, K. FREDERIKSEN & A. D. STEINBERG. 1982. J. Clin. Invest. **70:** 587–597.
48. SMITH, H. R., T. M. CHUSED & A. D. STEINBERG. 1983. J. Immunol. **131:** 1257–1262.
49. STEINBERG, E. B., T. J. SANTORO, T. M. CHUSED, P. A. SMATHERS & A. D. STEINBERG. 1983. J. Immunol. **131:** 1789–2795.
50. LAHITA, R. G., N. CHIORAZZI, A. GIBOFSKY, R. J. WINCHESTER & H. G. KUNKEL. 1983. Arthritis Rheum. **26:** 39–44.
51. ROSENBERG, Y. J. & A. D. STEINBERG. 1984. J. Immunol. **132:** 1261–1264.
52. SMITH, H. R., T. M. CHUSED, P. A. SMATHERS & A. D. STEINBERG. 1983. J. Immunol. **130:** 1200–1204.
53. SMITH, H. R. *et al.* 1983. J. Immunol. **131:** 1257–1262.
54. MOUNTZ, J. D., A. D. STEINBERG, D. M. KLINMAN, H. R. SMITH & J. F. MUSHINSHI. 1984. Science **225:** 1087–1089.
55. DAVIS, M. M., D. I. COHEN, E. A. NIELSEN, A. L. DEFRANCO & W. E. PAUL. 1982. The isolation of B and T cell-specific genes. *In* B and T Cell Tumors. U.C.L.A. Symposia in Molecular and Cellular Biology, vol. 24, E. S. Vitetta, Ed.: 215. Academic Press. New York.
56. PELHAM, R. B. & R. J. JACKSON. 1976. Eur. J. Biochem. **67:** 247–256.
57. HUDGINS, C. C., R. T. STEINBERG, D. M. KLINMAN, J. P. REEVES & A. D. STEINBERG. 1965. J. Immunol. **134:** 3849–3854.
58. STEINBERG, R. T., M. L. MILLER & A. D. STEINBERG. 1985. Clin. Immunol. Immunopathol. **35:** 67–72.
59. STEINBERG, A. D., J. B. ROTHS, E. D. MURPHY, R. T. STEINBERG & E. S. RAVECHE. 1980. J. Immunol. **125:** 871–873.
60. EISENBERG, R. A. & F. J. DIXON. 1980. J. Immunol. **125:** 1959.
61. EISENBERG, R. A., S. IZUI, P. J. MCCONAHEY *et al.* 1980. J. Immunol. **125:** 1032.
62. HANG, L., A. N. THEOFILOPOULOS, R. S. BALDERAS, S. J. FRANCIS & F. J. DIXON. 1984. J. Immunol. **132:** 1809–1813.
63. HAYAKAWA, K., R. R. HARDY, M. HONDA, L. A. HERZENBERG, A. D. STEINBERG & L. A. HERZENBERG. 1984. Proc. Natl. Acad. Sci. USA **81:** 2494–2498.
64. COHEN, D. I., S. M. HEDRICK, E. A. NIELSON, P. D'EUSTACHIO, F. RUDDLE, A. D. STEINBERG, W. E. PAUL & M. M. DAVIS. 1985. Nature **314:** 369–372.
65. COHEN, D. I., A. D. STEINBERG, W. E. PAUL & M. M. DAVIS. 1985. Nature **314:** 372–374.
66. MORSE, H. C., III, T. M. CHUSED, S. O. SHARROW & J. W. HARTLEY. 1979. J. Immunol. **122:** 2345.
67. IZUI, S., J. H. ELDER, P. J. MCCONAHEY & F. J. DIXON. 1981. J. Exp. Med. **153:** 1151.
68. CARPENTER, D. F., A. D. STEINBERG, P. H. SCHUR & N. TALAL. 1970. Lab. Invest. **23:** 628–634.
69. PRUD'HOMME, G. J., R. S. BALDERAS, F. J. DIXON & A. N. THEOFILOPOULOS. 1983. J. Exp. Med. **157:** 1815.

DISCUSSION OF THE PAPER

UNIDENTIFIED DISCUSSANT: Do you have any information on what happens to *myb* expression in *lpr* mice during therapy?

A. D. STEINBERG (*National Institutes of Health, Bethesda, MD*): Treatment with either cyclophosphamide or cyclosporine normalizes *myb* expression; that is, expression of the gene by peripheral lymph-node cells declines, while in thymocytes, it remains high or rises.

UNIDENTIFIED DISCUSSANT: Does the alteration in *myb* expression precede the lymphadenopathy?

STEINBERG: Yes. Maximal *myb* expression precedes maximal lymphadenopathy. At about 11 weeks of age, when lymphadenopathy appears, there is a marked increase in the expression of *myb* and the gene for the beta chain of the T-cell receptor in the peripheral lymph nodes.

F. DIXON (*Scripps Clinic and Research Foundation, La Jolla, CA*): You suggested that either the thymus in the MRL mouse is not doing its job or that some of the cells in the bone marrow are escaping from the thymus. How then do you explain the fact that thymectomy prevents the disease?

STEINBERG: Treatment with poly-rI · rC after neonatal thymectomy causes lymphadenophathy in many of the mice. Therefore, we think that it may be possible to drive the T cells directly from the marrow to the lymph nodes. There is no question, though, that under ordinary circumstances, the thymus is important in the early expression of the disease. However, thymectomy at three weeks of age does not retard subsequent disease expression. At three weeks of age, the thymus and lymph nodes are normal in terms of the cellular oncogene and T-cell receptor studies.

C. A. BONA. (*Mount Sinai Medical Center, New York, NY*): Do you believe that the disease in MRL mice is an inborn defect in the immune system that does not need an environmental agent?

STEINBERG: Yes. I do not believe that environmental factors are necessary. That does not mean that environmental stimuli cannot alter the degree of expression. We first published such an effect in 1969 (*Proc. Natl. Acad. Sci. USA.* 1969. **63:** 1102–1107). Polyclonal B-cell activators can accelerate the disease, so environmental factors can, in fact, worsen a genetic disease.

The Auto-Anti-Idiotypic Route to Antireceptor Antibodies[a]

BERNARD F. ERLANGER,[b] W. L. CLEVELAND,[b]
N. H. WASSERMANN,[b] H. H. KU,[b] B. L. HILL,[b]
K. K. WAN,[c] R. SARANGARAJAN,[b]
AND A. S. PENN[d]

[b]Department of Microbiology
Cancer Center
Columbia University
College of Physicians and Surgeons
New York, New York 10032

[c]Department of Biochemistry
University of Toronto
Toronto, Canada M5S 1A8

[d]Department of Neurology
Columbia University
College of Physicians and Surgeons
New York, New York 10032

INTRODUCTION

Data will be presented in support of the view that the products of a functioning anti-idiotype network can cause an autoimmune disease, specifically, the experimental form of myasthenia gravis (MG). We will describe how the disease can be induced in the rabbit by active immunization with an antiligand[1-3] and in the mouse by passive administration of hybridoma cells that secrete a monoclonal anti-idiotypic antibody specific for the acetylcholine binding site of the nicotinic acetylcholine receptor (AChR).

EARLY EXPERIMENTS IN RABBITS

Our experiments began with the synthesis of a potent agonist of AChR, trans-3, 3'-bis [α-(trimethylammonio)methyl] azobenzene (Bis Q).[4] This compound is constrained in structure[5] and we concluded from its very high activity as an agonist that its molecular "topography" must be complementary to that of the combining site of AChR.

A derivative of Bis Q was prepared that could be linked to a protein carrier (FIGURE 1) to produce antibodies specific for Bis Q. We predicted that the specificity of these antibodies would resemble the specificity of AChR when the latter is in its

[a]This work was supported by NIH grant no. NS-15581, a grant from the Muscular Dystrophy Association, and a postdoctoral fellowship in the laboratory of J. Lindstrom to K.K.W. from the Canadian Medical Research Council.

219

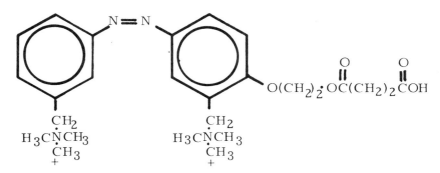

FIGURE 1. Compound linked to bovine serum albumin (BSA) for immunization: 4-(succinoyloxy)-3,3′-bis[α-(trimethylammonio)methyl]azobenzene.

activated state,[6] i.e., the antibodies would bind agonists, but not antagonists, and the hierarchical order of binding to agonists would be like that of AChR. This is precisely what was found.[1-3]

Specifically purified anti–Bis Q was then prepared by affinity chromatography and it was used to immunize rabbits. It was our hope that since anti–Bis Q mimicked AChR, anti-anti–Bis Q might mimic anti-AChR. If we were successful, the rabbits should show signs of experimental MG since it was shown[7] that experimental MG was produced in rabbits immunized with purified Torpedo AChR.

Of five rabbits immunized with anti–Bis Q, four showed signs of experimental MG after the first booster injection. The signs were severe to mild and in all cases the signs disappeared after subsequent booster injections. In one case, severe signs were seen when the rabbit was reimmunized after a "rest" of several months.

The same transient phenomenon was seen when sera of the rabbits were examined for the presence of antibodies to AChR (FIGURE 2); that is, after the first booster immunization, an elevated titer of antireceptor was seen; after subsequent boosts, the titer fell.

In order to be sure that the signs of MG in the rabbits were induced by an anti-idiotypic response directed at the combining site of anti–Bis Q, we examined several samples of sera taken from a rabbit when it was showing signs of experimental MG to determine whether they inhibited the binding of [³H]–Bis Q to anti–Bis Q. Inhibition was seen with three sera. One sample of serum, however, caused enhanced binding. Indeed, this serum, itself, could bind [³H]–Bis Q. We reasoned that an auto-anti-idiotypic response had been stimulated in this rabbit, resulting in the expression of anti-anti-anti–Bis Q, which would resemble anti–Bis Q in its binding specificity.[8]

EXPERIMENTS IN MICE

As we had concluded that an auto-anti-idiotypic response had been induced in the rabbits (yielding anti-anti-anti–Bis Q), we reasoned that it would be feasible to obtain anti-anti–Bis Q antibodies (= anti-AChR) in a one-step procedure by immunizing with Bis-Q-BSA and allowing the idiotypic network of the immunized animal to produce anti-anti–Bis Q; that is, we would rely upon the naturally occurring auto-anti-idiotypic response.[9] We chose the monoclonal route for these experiments because we could then avoid the complicating factor of idiotype–anti-idiotype interactions that would occur in sera.

Upon immunization of BALB/c mice with Bis-Q-BSA, fusion with a nonsecreting myeloma cell line, and screening for anti-anti–Bis Q antibodies in hybridoma cell supernatants using rabbit anti–Bis Q, we found a very substantial auto-anti-idiotypic response.[10] We were able to isolate three hybridomas that secreted anti-anti–Bis Q, which cross-reacted with AChR from Torpedo, *Electrophorus electricus,* and rat muscle. One of these monoclonal antibodies (F8-D5, an IgM, kappa) was examined in

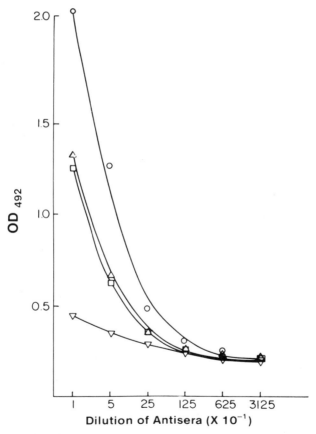

FIGURE 2. Transient response of rabbit 522 to immunization with Bis Q immunogen as seen by an ELISA in which plastic wells were coated with AChR at: O——O, 21 days after first boost (animal shows severe muscle weakness); △——△, 7 days after second boost (minimal signs of muscle weakness); □——□, 32 days after second boost (animal appears normal); ▽——▽, 6 days after fourth boost (animal appears normal).

detail. It had the following properties:

(1) Binding to AChR from rat muscle, *Electrophorus electricus,* and Torpedo was inhibited by decamethonium ($I_{50} = 5 \times 10^{-5} M$) and by α-bungarotoxin ($I_{50} = 0.7 \times 10^{-6} M$).

(2) When tested in J. Lindstrom's laboratory in a vesicle system containing reconstituted Torpedo AChR,[11] it inhibited ^{134}Cs flux in the presence of $10^{-3} M$ carbamylcholine (FIGURE 3).

(3) Immunofluorescence experiments showed binding to Torpedo electric tissue (FIGURE 4), with the pattern of binding being identical to that seen with rabbit antibody raised by immunization with Torpedo AChR.

(4) When hybridoma cells producing F8-D5 were allowed to multiply intraperitoneally in three male and three female BALB/c mice, all of the females showed signs of experimental MG, which could be temporally alleviated by injection of neostigmine (FIGURE 5).

The last experimental finding is a most significant one. We had shown earlier (above) that experimental MG could be produced actively in rabbits by an anti-idiotypic route. We have now shown that a monoclonal product of an auto-anti-idiotypic response can also produce experimental MG by passive transfer. Taken together, we conclude that it is time to take seriously the possibility of an anti-idiotypic etiology for MG and other autoimmune diseases. Questions that must be answered, however, include the nature of the primary antigen responsible for the subsequent pathological auto-anti-idiotypic response. In MG, it could be a molecule, either endogenous or exogenous, that shares idiotypic features with acetylcholine. Examples might be other naturally occurring choline-containing compounds, such as the lecithins, or components of bacterial cell walls, such as the phosphocholine of pneumococcal C carbohydrate. Another possibility is a virus that enters the cell via AChR. Anti-idiotypic antibodies to the antiviral antibody would then be specific for

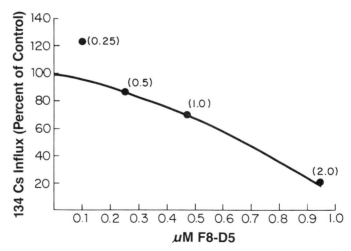

FIGURE 3. Effect of F8-D5 on ^{134}Cs flux in reconstituted liposomes with purified Torpedo AChR. Carbachol is at $10^{-3} M$. Numbers in parentheses represent ratio of antibody to receptor. At an equimolar ratio, about 30% inhibition was seen.

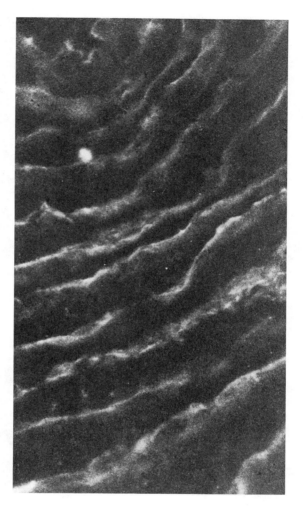

FIGURE 4. Immunofluorescence of sectioned tissue of the electric organ of *Torpedo californica* using F8-D5 and fluorescein-tagged rabbit anti-mouse globulin.

AChR. The highly interesting studies with rabies virus support this suggestion,[12,13] although we are not proposing that rabies virus is the primary antigen in MG.

Finally, if the auto-anti-idiotypic mechanism for MG is to be taken seriously, it is most important that evidence for anti-idiotypic antibodies reactive with AChR be seen in patients with MG. In this respect, there is good evidence that antibodies specific for the combining site of AChR are found in patients with MG, particularly when they are severely ill.[14] Anti-idiotypic antibodies would have this specificity. Although it is true that the majority of antibodies in the serum of patients with MG are directed at a "main immunogenic region" (MIR) on the α subunit of AChR,[15] which is a region that does not include the acetylcholine binding site, these antibodies could have arisen after the primary damage was caused by the anti-idiotypic (anti-binding-site) antibodies, with subsequent release of AChR-containing membrane fragments into the circulation.

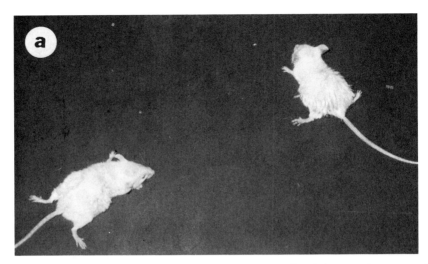

FIGURE 5a. Six 37-day-old BALB/c mice (three males, three females) were pristane-treated. Seven days later, they were irradiated with 500 rads and on the next day, 10^6 cells of F8-D5 were administered i.p. Ascites fluid appeared in the abdomens of both sexes by the 12th day and was collected. By the 14th day, the female mice showed signs of severe muscle weakness. Two are shown in the figure.

FIGURE 5b. The mice in FIGURE 5a were treated as follows: The one on the right was given neostigmine (66 μg/kg) i.p. and the one on the left was injected i.p. with an equal volume of water. After an interval of 30 minutes, the mice appeared as shown; that is, the mouse on the right showed sufficient strength to stand and to attempt to approach the food. The mouse on the left showed no improvement. After about an additional 40 minutes, the mouse on the right weakened and resembled the other one.

REFERENCES

1. WASSERMANN, N. H., A. S. PENN, P. I. FREIMUTH, N. TREPTOW, S. WENTZEL, W. L. CLEVELAND & B. F. ERLANGER. 1982. Proc. Natl. Acad. Sci. USA **79:** 4810–4814.
2. ERLANGER, B. F., N. H. WASSERMANN, W. L. CLEVELAND, A. S. PENN, B. L. HILL & R. SARANGARAJAN. 1984. *In* Monoclonal and Antibodies: Probes for Receptor Structure and Functions, pp. 163–176. A. R. Liss. New York.
3. ERLANGER, B. F., W. L. CLEVELAND, N. H. WASSERMANN, B. L. HILL, A. S. PENN, H. H. KU & R. SARANGARAJAN. 1985. *In* Molecular Basis of Nerve Activity, pp. 523–536. W. de Gruyter. Berlin/New York.
4. BARTELS, E., N. H. WASSERMANN & B. F. ERLANGER. 1971. Proc. Natl. Acad. Sci. USA **68:** 1820–1823.
5. WASSERMANN, N. H., E. BARTELS & B. F. ERLANGER. 1979. Proc. Natl. Acad. Sci. USA **76:** 256–259.
6. HEIDMANN, T. & J-P. CHANGEUX. 1978. Annu. Rev. Biochem. **47:** 317–357.
7. PATRICK, J. & J. LINDSTROM. 1973. Science **180:** 871–872.
8. OUDIN, Y. & M. MICHAEL. 1963. C. R. Acad. Sci. (Paris) **257:** 805–808.
9. JERNE, N. K. 1974. Ann. Immunol. (Inst. Pasteur Paris) **125C:** 373–389.
10. CLEVELAND, W. L., N. H. WASSERMANN, R. SARANGARAJAN, A. S. PENN & B. F. ERLANGER. 1983. Nature **305:** 56–57.
11. SUAREZ-ISLA, B. A., K. K. WAN, J. LINDSTROM & M. MONTAL. 1983. Biochemistry **22:** 2319–2323.
12. BURRAGE, T. G., G. H. TIGNOR & A. L. SMITH. 1985. Virus Res. **2:** 273–289.
13. LENTZ, T. L., T. G. BURRAGE, A. L. SMITH, J. CRICK & G. H. TIGNOR. 1982. Science **215:** 182–184.
14. FULPIUS, B. W., A. K. LEFVERT, S. CUEONOUD & A. MOUREY. 1981. Ann. N.Y. Acad. Sci. **377:** 307–315.
15. LINDSTROM, J., S. TZARTOS & W. GULLICK. 1981. Ann. N.Y. Acad. Sci. **377:** 1–19.

DISCUSSION OF THE PAPER

A. R. PACHNER (*Yale University, New Haven, CT*): We tried to reproduce the phenomenon you described with cobra venom neurotoxin and reproduced it almost exactly. Thus, it does not seem that Bis Q is a special ligand. I think it can be done with other ligands of the acetylcholine receptor.

I. R. COHEN (*Weizmann Institute of Science, Rehovot, Israel*): An example of another ligand is insulin. We found that mice immunized to insulin make antibodies to the insulin receptor. Our monoclonals show similar prevalence to yours; out of about 700 wells, we found that 40 made anti-insulin and 5 made anti-idiotype. However, of the 5 anti-idiotypes, 4 were actually antireceptor antibodies. Thus, there seems to be a bias for those anti-idiotypes that bind to the receptor. We recently studied a young child suffering from hypoglycemia, in whom we found antibodies to the insulin receptor. Upon treatment with immunosuppressive agents, the antireceptor antibodies disappeared along with the hypoglycemia. Upon cessation of the immunosuppressive therapy, those antireceptor antibodies did not reappear; however, what did appear for the first time were antibodies to insulin. We affinity-purified the anti-insulin antibodies and found that they interacted with the antireceptor antibodies. Therefore, in support of your conclusion, this kind of phenomenon can go both ways. Antibody 1 or antibody 2 (either of them) can mimic the ligand or the ligand receptor.

B. F. ERLANGER (*Columbia University, New York, NY*): I was interested in the discussion about whether antibodies found in patients with myasthenia gravis are directed at the binding site of receptor. The main reason why they were not found in the early studies is that the assay was done with a receptor to which bungarotoxin was bound. Thus, we were screening out any antibodies that might react with the receptor binding site. Any time you find antibodies to the combining site of a receptor, there is a possibility that they may be anti-idiotypic antibodies.

I. R. MACKAY (*Hall Institute of Medical Research, Melbourne, Australia*): The choline molecule seems to crop up in all sorts of surprising ways. Anaphylactic reactions can occur to succinylcholine (which is a short-acting anesthetic) even before any prior exposure to this agent takes place. Perhaps an anti-idiotypic antibody has not only sensitized them, but even raised an IgE antibody response, which is enough to cause the immediate hypersensitivity response.

D. B. DRACHMAN (*John Hopkins School of Medicine, Baltimore, MD*): Antisite antibodies in myasthenia may be sterically hindering rather than being against the site itself.

ERLANGER: Once you start the disease process, you are going to get antibodies to other things. If, for example, there is necrosis of an organ, autoantigens may enter the circulation in a form that could be immunogenic. The real problem, though, is what starts it going in the first place.

Immune Response Potential and Its Genetic Regulation in Autoimmune Diseases

Alterations in Systemic Lupus Erythematosus and Thyroid Autoimmune Diseases

ZVI BENTWICH,[a] Y. SHALEV,[a] R. SEGAL,[b] D. KATZ,[c]
AND E. MOZES[c]

[a]R. Ben Ari Institute of Clinical Immunology
Kaplan Medical Center
[b]Assaf Harofe Medical Center
[c]Department of Chemical Immunology
Weizmann Institute of Science
Rehovot, 76100 Israel

INTRODUCTION

An attractive approach for the study of immune responsiveness and genetic regulation in autoimmune diseases is through antigen-specific T-cell factors that either enhance or suppress the immune response to a specific antigen and are genetically controlled.[1] In recent years, we have developed such systems in humans with the synthetic polypeptide antigen, poly(Tyr,Glu)-poly(DL Ala)--poly(Lys) [abbreviated as (T,G)-A--L], and have shown that the T cells of about 50% of normal individuals produce active (T,G)-A--L specific factors that have a helper effect in the generation of antibodies to (T,G)-A--L. Furthermore, we were able to show that the generation of factors specific to (T,G)-A--L and to poly(His,Glu)-poly(DL Ala)--poly(Lys)[(H,G)-A--L] was genetically regulated and inherited as autosomal dominant traits linked with HLA, though distinct for each antigen.[3,4] Structural studies of these factors have suggested that they consist of a specific antigen binding moiety that is linked to MHC determinants.[5] Using this system, we have investigated the immune response potential of patients with autoimmune diseases and its regulation in comparison to that observed in normals. These studies have shown a significant defect in regulation of the immune response potential in patients with systemic lupus erythematosus (SLE).[6] This loss of normal regulation was not observed in patients with autoimmune diseases of the thyroid (TAD) nor in the family members of the SLE patients. These findings are the subject of this report and their significance is discussed.

MATERIALS AND METHODS

Human Subjects and Patients

Thirty-five patients with SLE and 35 patients with TAD attending the rheumatology clinic and thyroid clinic of the Kaplan Medical Center, respectively, participated in the study. The characterization and criteria for analyzing the SLE patients have been previously described.[6] The TAD patients consisted of two groups: Group I - Graves' Disease ($n = 22$). All the patients in this group had sufficient clinical and laboratory criteria for the diagnosis of Graves' disease and about half (13 patients) were euthyroid, while the rest (9 patients) had clinical and laboratory signs of hyperthyroidism about one to nine months prior to this study; Group II - Hashimotos' Thyroiditis ($n = 13$). All had a high to moderate enlargement of the thyroid gland and an increase in serum levels of antimicrosomal antibodies. First-degree relatives in 14 families of the SLE patients (altogether 80 subjects), as well as 14 normal controls, were also studied.

Generation and Assay of Antigen-Specific T-Cell Factors

The generation of (T,G)-A--L specific T-cell helper factors and their assay were performed as previously described.[2] Briefly, peripheral blood lymphocytes (PBL), after *in vitro* education to (T,G)-A--L, were rechallenged with 2 μg/ml of the antigen for 12–18 hours at 37°C. The cells were then removed and their supernatants were tested for (T,G)-A--L specific helper activity in an *in vitro* antibody production system using murine NIP-OVA primed B cells, 50 μl of the factor, and 0.01 μg of NIP-(T,G)-A--L. NIP-HGG was used as a specificity control for the factor. The number of plaque-forming cells in the culture was determined on day 5 in Cunningham chambers using NIP-conjugated sheep red blood cells. All factors were tested at least twice for their helper activity.

RESULTS

Generation of (T,G)-A--L Specific Helper Factor

PBL obtained from patients with autoimmune diseases, either SLE or TAD, produced antigen-specific helper factors that were able to replace (T,G)-A--L primed T cells for the generation of antibodies to (T,G)-A--L. Representative results of these studies on one patient with TAD and one patient with SLE are depicted in TABLE 1. That the factors generated were antigen-specific is shown by the absence of significant helper effect when cultured with the nonrelated antigen. Screening of patients with SLE and TAD for the capacity of their T cells to produce (T,G)-A--L specific helper factors indicated that all patients with SLE produced the factor, whereas only 57% (20/35) of the patients with TAD produced the factor, similar to the rate of response found among normals. It is of special interest that the rate of response and the mode of inheritance among the first-degree relatives of the SLE patients were also similar to that found among normals (TABLE 2). No effect of disease activity or type on factor generation was observed either among the SLE patients or among the TAD patients.

DISCUSSION AND CONCLUSIONS

We have demonstrated that educated T cells obtained from patients with autoimmune diseases are able to produce antigen-specific T-cell helper factors. The regulation of this response was profoundly altered in SLE patients in whom enhanced helper effects or loss of suppression was thought to have taken place. We were also able to

TABLE 1. Helper Activity of (T,G)-A--L Specific Factors of Educated PBL of Patients with Autoimmune Disorders

NIP-OVA Primed Spleen Cells Cultured with[a]	NIP-Specific PFC/Culture[b]
Graves' Patient	
Medium	900 ± 300
NIP-OVA	2850 ± 726
(T,G)-A--L primed T cells + NIP-HGG	1750 ± 792
(T,G)-A--L primed T cells + NIP-(T,G)-A--L	6750 ± 3000
Factor[c] + NIP-HGG	733 ± 249
Factor + NIP-(T,G)-A--L	6100 ± 1100
SLE Patient	
Medium	1630 ± 130
NIP-OVA	4480 ± 360
Factor[c] + NIP-HGG	510 ± 130
Factor + NIP-(T,G)-A--L	3750 ± 640

[a] NIP-OVA primed spleen cells were cultured in microtiter plates together with the factor and 0.01 μg of antigen.

[b] Indirect PFC were determined by using NIP-SRBC. Results are expressed as the mean ± SD of quadriplicate tests.

[c] Fifty microliters of factor were added to each well. One milliliter of factor is the equivalent of 10^7 (T,G)-A--L educated PBL of the patients.

show for the first time that the altered regulation in SLE is at the level of the specific immune response and not only a result of polyclonal stimulation.[6] Furthermore, our SLE family studies suggest that it is an acquired characteristic that is not determined genetically and that is not related to disease activity. At the same time, we were able to show that in TAD the aberrant immune reaction focuses on the one organ and probably on one antigen without affecting the whole immune system. It remains to be seen whether this distinction between SLE and TAD is indeed characteristic of systemic versus organ-specific autoimmune diseases or rather a unique characteristic of SLE.

This study lends further support to the concept that T cells are a major determinant in autoimmunity. However, it would be of great interest to study in the same manner the specific immune response potential of T cells to the putative antigens important in the causation of these autoimmune diseases, e.g., DNA in SLE and thyroglobulin or TSH in Hashimoto's thyroiditis and Grave's disease, respectively.

TABLE 2. Segregation of HLA Haplotypes and the Immune Response Potential to (T,G)-A--L in Families of SLE Patients[a]

Family	Father	Mother	Children 1 (Patient)	2	3
1	a/b	c/d	a/d	b/d	b/c
	+	+	+	+	−
2	a/b	c/d	b/c		
	−	−	+		

[a] The immune response potential tested by the ability of antigen-activated T cells to secrete helper T-cell factors is indicated by the plus and minus signs.

REFERENCES

1. MOZES, E. 1976. The nature of antigen specific T cell factors involved in the genetic regulation of immune response. *In* The Role of Products of the Histocompatibility Gene Complex in Immune Responses. D. H. Katz & B. Benaceraff, Eds.: 485–505. Academic Press. New York.
2. KATZ, D., Z. BENTWICH, N. ESHHAR, I. LÖWY & E. MOZES. 1981. Proc. Natl. Acad. Sci. USA **78:** 4505–4509.
3. SUEZ, D., D. KATZ, C. BRAUTBAR, T. COHEN, Z. WEISMAN, Z. BENTWICH & E. MOZES. 1985. Hum. Immunol. **13:** 219–230.
4. KATZ, D., D. SUEZ, C. BRAUTBAR, T. COHEN, Z. BENTWICH & E. MOZES. 1986. Hum. Immunol. **15:** 75–84.
5. KATZ, D., C. BRAUTBAR, Z. BENTWICH & E. MOZES. 1983. Hum. Immunol. **7:** 217–227.
6. SHALEV, Y., Z. BENTWICH, D. KATZ, C. BRAUTBAR & E. MOZES. 1985. Clin. Exp. Immunol. **60:** 355–362.

The Questionable Role of Anti-DNA Antibodies in the Pathogenesis of Systemic Lupus Erythematosus

JEAN-FRANÇOIS BACH, LAURENT JACOB,
GILLES FEUTREN, AND FRANÇOIS TRON

Hopital Necker
INSERM-CNRS
161 Rue de Sèvres
Paris 15, France

Systemic lupus erythematosus (SLE) is characterized by the production of a variety of antinuclear antibodies, notably, antibodies specific for native double-stranded (ds) DNA. Several lines of arguments have been assembled to support the pathogenic role of anti-dsDNA antibodies in the pathogenesis of SLE.

ROLE OF DNA–ANTI-DNA IMMUNE COMPLEXES

Koffler *et al.*[1,2] and Krishnan and Kaplan[3] in man and Lambert and Dixon[4] in B/W mice have demonstrated the presence of anti-DNA antibodies, DNA, and complement in kidney eluates, thus suggesting the deposit and pathogenetic role of DNA–anti-DNA immune complexes. Moreover, most authors have observed a significant correlation (before treatment) between high anti-DNA serum titers and the severity of the disease, particularly that associated with glomerulonephritis,[5,6] as well as with the amount and the diffuse character of immunoglobulin glomerular deposits.[7]

However, the common occurrence of high titers of anti-DNA antibodies in patients with mild disease activity favors the hypothesis that only subpopulations of anti-DNA antibodies are particularly deleterious. Conflicting results have been reported concerning the affinity and the precipitating character of anti-DNA antibodies.[8–10] The lack of homogeneity of the DNA used as antigen, the large variety of autoantibodies in SLE sera, and mainly the lack of standardization of experimental conditions used in the techniques may account for these conflicting results.[11]

In contrast, most studies agree on correlation between the immunoglobulin classes and the severity of the disease. DNA antibodies of the IgG classes that fix complement are more pathogenic than noncomplement-fixing or IgM antibodies.[12–14] DNA antibodies of the IgG class are detectable in kidney eluates of patients with SLE.[15] In murine lupus, Talal *et al.*[16] have shown that the IgM/IgG switch of anti-DNA antibodies occurs earlier in females than in males, who develop the disease later and inconstantly. The pathogenic role of anti-DNA antibody subpopulations is further suggested by the demonstration of anti-DNA antibodies present in glomerular eluates from MRL/1 and B/W mice showing a more restricted heterogeneity than serum antibodies in isoelectric focusing studies.[17]

More recent studies have indicated that the antibody pI could be of major importance in the pathogenic effect: acidic antibodies are clearly more toxic than basic antibodies.[17,18]

Clinical and experimental observations have also been accumulated to support the contention that DNA–anti-DNA complexes play a major role in the development of renal lesions. However, direct evidence of circulating DNA–anti-DNA complexes has been reported in only a few studies. Several groups have failed to detect circulating DNA–anti-DNA complexes.[19,20] This finding, as well as the demonstration of a particular affinity of DNA for the basal membrane[21] and the results in experimental glomerulonephritis in mice,[22] have led to the formulation of a new concept of lupus glomerulonephritis. This hypothesis suggests that DNA–anti-DNA complexes form *in situ* after the binding of the antigen in the glomerular basal membrane.

Conversely, several groups have demonstrated the existence of circulating DNA–anti-DNA complexes in sera from SLE patients.[23,24] We have ourselves specifically demonstrated the presence of such complexes by using monoclonal anti-DNA antibodies to reveal the DNA present within the complexes.[25] However, these complexes are detected in only a few patients. Moreover, the lack of correlation with the tests detecting whole immune complexes suggests that other antigen-antibody systems constitute the major immune complex components in SLE sera.

CORRELATIONS BETWEEN ANTI-DNA ANTIBODY LEVEL AND CLINICAL STATE

It is of importance to determine the predictive value of anti-DNA antibodies for the disease activity. Severe SLE with diffuse glomerulonephritis is associated with a high titer of anti-DNA antibodies, a high amount of immune complexes and cryoglobulinemia, and a low level of the C3 fraction of complement. In an untreated group of SLE patients, a correlation between immunologic abnormalities and the severity of the disease was observed.[6] Conflicting results dealing with this point have been published; this could be the consequence of studying treated and untreated patients as a whole.[26] However, when isolated, not one of these immunologic abnormalities indicates a severe form of the disease. A high titer of anti-DNA antibodies and the presence of immune complexes and/or cryoglobulinemia can be demonstrated in mild forms of the disease. In contrast, a low C3 level is a more reliable index and often indicates major tissue damage. The best way to define the severity of the disease is to consider simultaneously the different assays described above. We already have mentioned the importance of works aimed at defining the immunochemical properties of anti-DNA antibodies; some of these properties could constitute a better index of disease activity. More rarely, severe forms of the disease are associated with a low titer of anti-DNA antibodies or with even the absence of antinuclear antibodies. This case could be the consequence of an excess of antigen. This hypothesis is supported by the finding that in these cases DNA–anti-DNA immune complexes can be demonstrated in the sera by a technique using murine monoclonal anti-DNA antibody.[25]

In any case, it still is questionable whether these immunologic tests can predict a favorable outcome after treatment and whether their normalization constitutes a criterion of recovery. The study of the DNA binding capacity and the histologic data obtained through treatment showed that no correlation was observed when these data were compared to immunologic tests performed on the day of examination.[26] The lack of correlation might be explained by a different timing of the evolution of the various parameters. However, in most cases, the clinical histologic and immunologic remittance were parallel even if not simultaneous.[27] In a few patients, immunologic abnormalities persisted after the disappearance of clinical and histologic signs of disease activity. In contrast, it was uncommon to observe immunologic remittance with the persistence of clinical disease activity.

The majority of patients with stable remission have normal immunologic tests. An increase in anti-DNA titer is followed, in more than 50% of the cases, by the reappearance of disease activity within an interval ranging from several weeks to several months. When a decrease in complement levels is associated with increased anti-DNA antibody titers, the clinical relapse occurs more frequently (90% of the cases) and earlier (one to three months). In some patients, the rise in anti-DNA titer is not associated with or followed by clinical relapse.[27,28] In contrast, it is quite uncommon to observe clinical exacerbation without previous reappearance of immunologic abnormalities. These data are summarized in TABLE 1, which shows that a correlation is seen between clinical activity and the presence of immunologic abnormalities. However, exceptions occur that limit the value of this test as a therapeutic guideline in SLE. It is interesting to note that in the seven patients with complete clinical long-lasting remission who had been followed for severe lupus nephritis at Necker Hospital and who had been seen for more than five years after the last clinical symptom (5–21 years), only two out of the seven patients showed anti-DNA binding over 20%. In fact, even in these two cases, the binding values were moderate (<40%). These patients, however, still presented antinuclear factors (detected by immunofluorescence). In conclusion, these studies indicate an overall correlation between DNA binding activity and clinical course. Enormous exceptions are observed, though, and it is still questionable whether anti-DNA antibodies are pathogenic or only represent a marker of the disease.

TABLE 1. Correlation between the Occurrence of Clinical Relapse and the Reappearance of Immunologic Abnormalities

Immunologic Abnormalities		Clinical Relapse[a]	No Clinical Relapse[a]
None		2	52
Increase of DNA binding activity (>4 µg/ml)	without hypocomplementemia	6 ⌉ 16	5 ⌉ 6
	with hypocomplementemia	10 ⌋	1 ⌋

[a]Number of patients.

THE UNEXPECTED EFFECTS OF CYCLOSPORINE

The treatment of severe forms of systemic lupus resistant to steroid therapy is still unsatisfactory. The risks of the life-threatening manifestations of the disease are not abrogated and chronically administered high doses of corticosteroids generate major side effects. The efficacy of other immunosuppressive drugs (azathioprine and cyclophosphamide) is not clearly established.

Cyclosporine (CyA) is a potent immunosuppressive drug that has been shown to improve the life span of (NZB × NZW)F$_1$ female mice with lupus and to decrease anti-DNA antibody production in male mice of the same strain.[29,30] It is also active on a number of other autoimmune diseases. These data have prompted us to initiate an open trial of cyclosporine in steroid-resistant or steroid-dependent forms of lupus.

Twelve patients with systemic lupus erythematous were studied in an open trial. All of them had a severe form of lupus, as defined either by steroid resistance (dosage ≥ 1 mg/kg/d prednisone) or by steroid dependence (dosage ≥ 0.5 mg/kg/d prednisone for more than six months). All these patients showed severe side effects of steroid therapy.

Cyclosporine was given orally once daily at an initial dosage of 5 to 10 mg/kg/d in five cases and only at 5 mg/kg/d in seven cases because of the poor tolerance of the higher doses observed in the first five patients. The treatment was continued for six months at full dosage and thereafter tapered with a 20% decrease every month. Additionally, the dosage was decreased in case of side effects or when CyA blood-through level (RIA kit Sandoz) was above 750 ng/ml. Steroid therapy was maintained with the aim of decreasing their dosage. Prednisone dosage was plateaued after it had reached 0.2 mg/kg/d, which is a dose not known to induce major chronic side effects.

The treatment could only be applied at full dosage for six months in eight patients. In the eight patients who were treated with cyclosporine for six months, all but one was clinically improved. Two young females with severe central neurological manifestations completely recovered with return to normal life. A vespertilio that had been resistant to steroids and antimalarial drugs for one year completely disappeared within a week of cyclosporine therapy. One patient with pulmonary hypertension due to pulmonary vasculitis and suffering from a severe exertional dyspnea was clearly improved, as well as the patient with severe arthritis and skin vasculitis. One patient with a lupus-related pulmonary interstitial fibrosis has received to date three months of cyclosporine and is improving. In patients with nephritis, biological signs (proteinuria and hematuria) regressed. Iterative kidney biopsies were performed in four cases: three had proliferative nephritis, while activity of the disease had clearly declined in two and was unchanged in one. The fibrosis index remained unchanged in three (including a case with membranous nephritis) and worsened in one. No vascular lesions were noted. These favorable results were substantiated by the decrease in the steroid doses (0.76 ± 0.08 mg/kg/d prednisone before CyA treatment versus 0.21 ± 0.02 mg/kg/d after six months, $p < 0.001$). Limited data are available on the disease course after six months, when the dosage of cyclosporine is tapered. It is important to note, however, that mild signs of lupus (fever, arthritis, skin rash) recurred in three patients after, respectively, 9, 14, and 16 months, when CyA dosage became lower than 2.5–3.0 mg/kg/d.

In contrast with the clinical improvement observed in most cases, anti-DNA antibody titers remained unchanged; the titers of antinuclear antibodies (detected by immunofluorescence) also remained unaltered. The false positive syphilis test remained positive in the patient in whom it was initially present. Similar resistance to cyclosporine was noted for the abnormalities of the complement fractions, especially the decreased level C4 (FIGURE 1). Interestingly, IgG plasma levels were significantly increased at six months, which is an effect probably linked to the decrease in the steroid dosage allowed by the clinical improvement.

Initially, the low percentage of OKT3$^+$ lymphocytes progressively increased with time under CyA. The helper/suppressor ratio, which was initially in the range of normal values, was not significantly modified. *In vitro* production of IL-2 was initially low, although not significantly. No clear changes in IL-2 production were noted during CyA treatment. Finally, not one of the immunological tests performed was clearly correlated with the clinical evolution.

Data obtained in this limited series of patients indicate that cyclosporine is beneficial in a majority of steroid-resistant or steroid-dependent forms of systemic lupus, thus allowing a significant reduction in the steroid dosage. The heterogeneity of patients studied does not permit us to draw general conclusions. In most cases, the improvement was assessed on clinical grounds. In two out of the three subjects with proliferative glomerulonephritis, the improvement was substantiated by a clear decrease of activity indexes on iterative kidney biopsies.

At variance with the favorable clinical effect, immunological abnormalities were not corrected: anti-DNA and antinuclear antibodies, as well as complement, decreased or remained unchanged, while IgG levels increased probably due to a diminution of steroid dosage. This contrasted effect of cyclosporine on clinical activity and immuno-logical parameters is at variance with the data observed with steroids that usually induce simultaneously a clinical improvement and a decrease in anti-DNA antibody titer. This does not mean that cyclosporine will not depress anti-DNA antibodies in other cases of lupus as it can do at high doses in (NZB × NZW)F$_1$ mice since the cases studied here represent a particular subpopulation selected for its resistance to steroids. In any case, it remains that patients were clinically improved in spite of the persistence of high antibody titers. This discrepancy may be explained in several ways: (1) pathogenic antibodies or immune complexes are not detected by the tests that are currently used, so a decreased production of such antibodies or complexes could have been missed; (2) cyclosporine acts on immune complex-induced inflammation in a way that could involve a cyclosporine-sensitive T-cell contribution; (3) cell-mediated immunity could play a direct (although still unknown) role in the pathogenesis of systemic lupus.

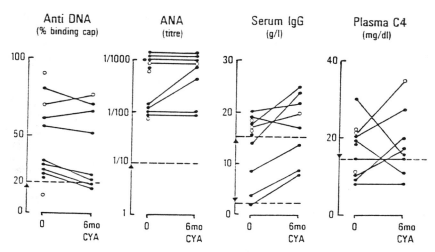

FIGURE 1. Immunological parameters (anti-dsDNA, antinuclear antibodies, C4 plasma level, and IgG level) before and after six months of cyclosporine in patients with systemic lupus. Symbols: ● = clinically improved; ○ = unchanged; dotted lines and arrows = normal values.

A NEW MAJOR CROSS-REACTIVITY OF ANTI-DNA ANTIBODIES

The production of monoclonal anti-DNA autoantibodies by the hybridoma tech-nique has permitted a new approach to the specificity of anti-DNA antibodies that were impossible to study analytically in the serum of lupus patients where they are present as a polyclonal mixture of antibodies. We have thus been able to show that monoclonal anti-dsDNA antibodies (screened on the double criteria of reactivity with dsDNA in the Farr assay and positivity in the Crithidia Luciliae test) were strictly specific for dsDNA.[31] To be more precise, they were specific for the conformational structure of the B form.

In the course of these specificity studies, we made the fortuitous observation by indirect immunofluorescence that several of these monoclonals were bound to Raji cell membranes.[32] Binding inhibition by DNA excluded nonspecific attachment to Fc receptors. Absence of binding inhibition by DNAse I and inhibition by proteinase K (100 µg/ml) indicated that the antibodies recognized a membrane protein rather than protein-bound DNA.

This protein membrane component was characterized by immunoblot analysis of Raji cell membranes.[33] The same five polypeptides, with respective molecular weights of 14, 16, 17, 33, and 34 kD, were characterized with all antibodies tested, including an antibody provided by B. Hahn. As previously mentioned for studies on intact cells, treatment of cell membrane with proteinase K induced total disappearance of the five polypeptides; similarly, the monoclonal antibodies lost their reactivity when preincubated with native DNA (1 ng/ml). It is not yet known whether the five polypeptides are distinct molecular species or whether they represent the split products of a single protein.

To further characterize the protein(s) in question, immunoprecipitation studies were performed with Raji cells internally labeled with ^{35}S-methionine. Cells were submitted to mild treatment with elastase, which is known for its specific action on membranes. They were then centrifuged and the supernatant was studied by SDS polyacrylamide gel electrophoresis. Two of the five polypeptides previously cited were detected after precipitation by the anti-DNA monoclonal antibodies (14 and 17 kD).

Immunoblot analysis was also applied to other cell types.[34] The five polypeptides were found on the membrane of human glomerular cells, B and T cell lines, erythrocytes, platelets, rat neuronal tissue, and mouse teratocarcinoma. Conversely, human liver, intestine, and pancreas remained negative. One could thus explain the reaction of several lupus sera with erythrocytes and lymphocytes.

Finally, these data indicate that anti-dsDNA antibodies may react strongly with a structure totally unrelated to DNA or nucleic acids, namely, a protein. This, in keeping with other data, indicates that such antibodies react with IgG,[35] phospholipids,[36] and microfilaments.[37] The pathogenetic significance of the polypeptides described above might be of particular importance because the DNA antibodies used to reveal them are strictly specific of dsDNA, which is a criterion not demonstrated for other cross-reactivities mentioned.

CONCLUSIONS

Anti-dsDNA antibodies have been known to be tightly and specifically correlated with SLE. Consequently, they represent a unique marker of the disease. The data presented above indicate that, in defined conditions, they also provide an index of activity that could suggest that they directly participate in the pathogenesis of the disease, particularly in the case of renal involvement where the clinical correlations are the best. There are, however, major exceptions to these correlations, such as patients in remission with high antibody titer. The absence of effect on anti-DNA antibody titers of cyclosporine, which is a T-cell selective immunosuppressive agent, is also intriguing. It could be thought that either pathogenic antibodies only represent a minor subpopulation of total anti-DNA antibodies or that other mechanisms operate at least in some cases, notably, cell-mediated immunity.

The antigenic molecular species, recognized by anti-dsDNA antibodies, is also questionable. The data presented above, as well as the works by others, indicate the existence of strong cross-reactivities of anti-DNA antibodies with proteins and phospholipids. The question is thus posed of the primary antigenic stimulus and of the main immunological target in SLE. One has to consider the possibility that the anti-DNA reactivity is only secondary to cross-reactions and not the primary event.

These considerations are not mere speculations. The DNA cross-reacting proteins will be isolated. It will then be possible to evaluate the effects of autoimmune reactions against them. Also to be evaluated are the effects of the respective pathogenic role of antibodies and the cell-mediated immunity directed against them. These studies will be probably easier to handle and interpret than those using DNA itself, which, in any case, remains a unique and elusive autoantigen.

REFERENCES

1. KOFFLER, D., P. H. SHUR & H. G. KUNKEL. 1967. Immunologic studies concerning the nephritis of SLE. J. Exp. Med. **126:** 607–624.
2. KOFFLER, D., V. AGNELLO & H. G. KUNKEL. 1974. Polynucleotide immune complexes in serum and glomeruli of patients with systemic lupus erythematosus. Am. J. Pathol. **74:** 109–124.
3. KRISHNAN, C. S. & M. H. KAPLAN. 1967. Immunopathologic studies of systemic lupus erythematosus. II. Antinuclear reaction of globulin eluted from homogenates and isolated glomeruli of kidneys from patients with lupus nephritis. J. Clin. Invest. **46:** 569–579.
4. LAMBERT, P. H. & F. J. DIXON. 1968. Pathogenesis of glomerulonephritis of NZB/W mice. J. Exp. Med. **127:** 507–522.
5. PINCUS, T., P. H. SCHUR, J. A. ROSE, J. L. DECKER & N. TALAL. 1969. Measurement of serum DNA-binding activity in systemic lupus erythematosus. N. Engl. J. Med. **281:** 701–705.
6. TRON, F. & J. F. BACH. 1977. Tests immunologiques pour le diagnostic du LED avant le traitement. Intérêt et limites. Nouv. Presse Med. **6:** 2573–2578.
7. HILL, G. S., N. HINGLAIS, F. TRON & J. F. BACH. 1978. Systemic lupus erythematosus. Morphologic correlations with immunologic and clinical data at the time of biopsy. Am. J. Med. **64:** 61–79.
8. GERSHWIN, M. E. & A. D. STEINBERG. 1974. Qualitative characteristics of anti-DNA antibodies in lupus nephritis. Arthritis Rheum. **17:** 947.
9. LEON, S. A., G. E. GREEN, E. EHRLICH, M. POLAND & B. SHAPIRO. 1977. Avidity of antibodies in SLE. Relationship to severity of renal involvement. Arthritis Rheum. **20:** 23–29.
10. TRON, F. & J. F. BACH. 1977. Relationships between antibodies to native DNA and glomerulonephritis in systemic lupus erythematosus. Clin. Exp. Immunol. **28:** 426–432.
11. TAYLOR, R. P., D. WEBER, A. V. BROCCOLI & J. B. WINFIELD. 1979. Stability of DNA–anti-DNA complexes. J. Immunol. **122:** 115–120.
12. HUBER, O., M. L. GREENBERG & J. HUBER. 1979. Complement-fixing anti-double-stranded DNA with the Crithidia method is a better indicator of active SLE than anti-DNA with the Farr method. J. Lab. Clin. Med. **93:** 32–39.
13. PENNEBAKER, J. B., J. N. GILLIAM & M. ZIFF. 1977. Immunoglobulin classes of DNA binding activity in serum and skin in systemic lupus erythematosus. J. Clin. Invest. **60:** 1331–1338.
14. ROTHFIELD, N. F. & B. D. STOLLAR. 1967. The relation of immunoglobulin class, pattern of antinuclear antibody, and complement-fixing antibodies to DNA in sera from patients with systemic lupus erythematosus. J. Clin. Invest. **46:** 1785–1794.
15. WINFIELD, J. B., I. FAIFERMAN & D. KOFFLER. 1977. Avidity of anti-DNA antibodies in serum and IgG glomerular eluates from patients with systemic lupus erythematosus. J. Clin. Invest. **59:** 90–96.
16. TALAL, N., J. F. ROUBINIAN, H. SHEAR, J. T. HOM & N. MIYASAKA. 1980. Mechanisms of autoimmune disease. *In* Progress in Immunology. M. Fougereau & J. Dausset, Eds.: 889–905. Academic Press. New York.
17. EBLING, F. & B. H. HAHN. 1980. Restricted subpopulations of DNA antibodies in kidneys

of mice with systemic lupus: comparison of antibodies in serum and renal eluates. Arthritis Rheum. **23:** 392–403.

18. GAVALCHIN, J., J. A. NICKLAS, J. W. EASTCOTT, M. P. MADAIO, B. D. STOLLAR, R. S. SCHWARTZ & S. K. DATTA. 1985. Lupus prone (SWR × NZB)F$_1$ mice produce potentially nephritogenic autoantibodies inherited from the normal SWR parent. J. Immunol. **134:** 885–894.

19. FELTKAMP, T. E. W. 1975. The significance of the determination of DNA anti-DNA complexes. Scand. J. Rheum. **11:** 33.

20. IZUI, S., P. H. LAMBERT & P. A. MIESCHER. 1977. Failure to detect circulating DNA: Anti-DNA complexes in systemic lupus erythematosus. Clin. Exp. Immunol. **30:** 388–392.

21. CUKIER, R. & F. TRON. 1985. Monoclonal anti-DNA antibodies: an approach to studying SLE molecules. Clin. Exp. Immunol. **62:** 143–149.

22. IZUI, S., P. H. LAMBERT, H. TÜRLER & P. A. MIESCHER. 1977. Features of systemic lupus erythematosus in mice injected with bacterial lipopolysaccharides. Identification of circulating DNA and renal localization of DNA anti-DNA complexes. J. Exp. Med. **145:** 1115–1130.

23. BRUNEAU, C. & J. BENVENISTE. 1979. Circulating DNA: Anti-DNA complexes in systemic lupus erythematosus. Detection and characterization by ultracentrifugation. J. Clin. Invest. **64:** 191–198.

24. HARBECK, R. J., E. J. BARDANA, P. F. KOHLER & R. I. CARR. 1973. DNA complexes: Their detection in systemic lupus erythematosus sera. J. Clin. Invest. **52:** 789–795.

25. TRON, F., J. LETARTE, M. C. ROQUE-ANTUNES BARREIRA & P. LESAVRE. 1982. Specific detection of DNA-anti-DNA immune complexes in human SLE sera using murine monoclonal antibody. Clin. Exp. Immunol. **49:** 481–487.

26. CAMERON, J. S., M. H. LESSOF, B. D. WILLIAMS & P. G. WILLIAMS. 1976. Disease activity in the nephritis of systemic lupus erythematosus in relation to serum complement concentrations. Clin. Exp. Immunol. **25:** 418–427.

27. TRON, T., P. JUNGERS, D. DROZ & J. F. BACH. 1980. Valeur des tests immunologiques dans la surveillance du traitement du lupus érythémateux disséminé. Nouv. Presse Med. **9:** 2319–2323.

28. LIGHTFOOT, R. W. & G. V. HUGUES. 1976. Significance of persisting serologic abnormalities in SLE. Arthritis Rheum. **19:** 837–843.

29. ISRAEL-BIET, D., L. H. NOEL, M. A. BACH, M. DARDENNE & J. F. BACH. 1983. Marked reduction of DNA antibody production and glomerulopathy in thymulin (FTS-Zn) or cyclosporine A treated (NZB × NZW)F$_1$ mice. Clin. Exp. Immunol. **54:** 359–365.

30. JONES, M. G., G. HARRIS & G. COWING. 1983. Response of murine autoimmune disease to cyclosporine and thiols. Transplant. Proc. **15**(suppl. 1): 2904–2908.

31. JACOB, L. & F. TRON. 1982. Monoclonal anti-deoxyribonucleic antibodies. I. Isotype and specificity studies. J. Immunol. **128:** 895–898.

32. TRON, F., L. JACOB & J. F. BACH. 1984. Binding of a murine monoclonal anti-DNA antibody to Raji cells. Implications for the interpretation of the Raji cell assay for immune complexes. Eur. J. Immunol. **14:** 283–286.

33. JACOB, L., F. TRON, J. F. BACH & D. LOUVARD. 1984. A monoclonal anti-DNA antibody also binds to cell-surface protein(s). Proc. Natl. Acad. Sci. USA **81:** 3843–3845.

34. JACOB, L., M. A. LETY, D. LOUVARD & J. F. BACH. 1985. Binding of a monoclonal anti-DNA autoantibody to identical protein(s) present at the surface of several human cell types involved in lupus pathogenesis. J. Clin. Invest. **75:** 315–317.

35. RUBIN, R. L., R. S. BALDERAS, E. M. TAN, F. J. DIXON & A. N. THEOFILOPOULOS. 1984. Multiple autoantigen binding capabilities of mouse monoclonal antibodies selected for rheumatoid factor activity. J. Exp. Med. **159:** 1429–1440.

36. LAFER, E. M., J. RAUCH, C. ANDRZEJEWSKI, JR., D. MUDD, B. FURIE, R. S. SCHWARTZ & B. D. STOLLAR. 1981. Polyspecific monoclonal lupus autoantibodies reactive with both polynucleotides and phospholipids. J. Exp. Med. **153:** 897–909.

37. DIGHIERO, G., P. LEMBERI, J. C. MAZILE, S. ROUYRE, G. S. BUTLER-BROWNE, R. G. WHALEN & S. AVRAMEAS. 1983. Murine hybridomas secreting natural monoclonal antibodies reacting with self antigens. J. Immunol. **131:** 2267–2272.

DISCUSSION OF THE PAPER

A. D. STEINBERG (*National Institutes of Health, Bethesda, MD*): There may be a difference between anti-DNA antibodies that are pathogenic and anti-DNA antibodies that do not involve the kidneys. Patients who have the highest levels of anti-DNA antibodies are very easily treated, whereas the patients who have intermediate levels have more clinical problems. This suggests that it may not be the level, but the quality of the antibody.

J-F. BACH (*Hopital Necker, Paris, France*): I agree with that very much. It is obvious that the patients we have tested are not representative of the whole disease. I would like to stress, in line with what you say, that the best correlation between DNA antibody titer and clinical activity occurs within the particular subgroup of patients with the acute form of nephritis.

B. H. HAHN (*University of California, Los Angeles, CA*): Do you know if the antigen on your Raji cell is phosphorylated?

BACH: We have no data indicating that it is phosphorylated.

Y. BOREL (*Harvard Medical School, Boston, MA*): Most of the monoclonal antibodies you tested are IgM antibodies that are known to cross-react extensively. Therefore, we have to be careful in our conclusions about whether DNA or some other antigen is the immunogen in SLE.

BACH: In our case, the antibodies we have tested are IgG antibodies, not IgM. It is certainly true that we have no evidence that the protein antigens or the phospholipids are the initial antigen. The data, though, indicate that this is a possibility.

Z. BENTWICH (*R. Ben Ari Institute of Clinical Immunology, Rehovot, Israel*): Did you see such interactions by anti-DNA antibodies with proteins in the spontaneously occurring anti-DNA antibodies from lupus patients?

BACH: No. Our studies have been done with monoclonal antibodies that have been made by fusing myeloma cells with the spleen cells from B/W mice.

UNIDENTIFIED DISCUSSANT: Is it possible that there is a constellation of different nuclear antigens that do not necessarily cross-react? Is there, in SLE, an immune response with specificity for certain nuclear components?

BACH: My hypothesis is that there may be similarities among apparently unrelated nuclear antigens, but that is an open question.

UNIDENTIFIED DISCUSSANT: I do not think the question is quite as open as you say. There are two easily recognized sets of nuclear antigens: DNA and the set of the RNPs. Now, in the case of DNA, the antibody is to the nucleic acid, but in the case of RNP, the antibody is directed against protein and not the nucleic acid. Therefore, one must assume that in these two sets of antinuclear antibodies, the epitopes must be rather different.

BACH: I agree, but that again poses the problem of if there are two very different types of antigens, why should one individual react against both types?

B. D. STOLLAR (*Tufts University School of Medicine, Boston, MA*): The question as to whether there is some connection between anti-DNA and some of the other antibodies is very important. That connection may be that they are all directed against very highly conserved antigens. The RNP determinants are present all the way down to insects. The histones and the determinants are also very highly conserved. Another kind of connection might be found in the report of D. Pisetsky, where there is some idiotypic cross-reactivity between an anti-Sm antibody and an anti-DNA antibody. Is it possible that these antibodies derive from a limited number of related genes?

R. S. SCHWARTZ (*Tufts University School of Medicine, Boston, MA*): There never has been any a priori reason for believing that DNA is an antigen in systemic lupus. The situation in SLE is completely different from that in Hashimoto's disease, where it is virtually self-evident that there must be some thyroid antigen involved. However, in systemic lupus, the discovery that DNA is an antigen was serendipitous.

HLA-D/DR Expression on Epithelial Cells: The Finger on the Trigger?[a]

I. TODD,[b] M. LONDEI,[c]

R. PUJOL-BORRELL,[b] R. MIRAKIAN,[b] M. FELDMANN,[c]

AND G. F. BOTTAZZO[b]

[b]*Department of Immunology*
Middlesex Hospital Medical School
London W1P 9PG, United Kingdom

[c]*The Charing Cross Sunley Medical Research Center*
London W6 8LW, United Kingdom

HLA-D/DR EXPRESSION IN AUTOIMMUNITY

Investigations of the immune system have indicated a variety of mechanisms whereby self-tolerance could be maintained and whose breakdown or bypass might therefore lead to autoimmunity.[1] Our present knowledge is insufficient to fully discriminate between the possibilities, although it seems reasonable that where potential autoantigens are normally inaccessible to the immune system, T cells specific for these self-determinants will not be detected. One example of a "hidden" antigen is the thyroid-associated microsomal/microvillar antigen (TMAg) of the follicular epithelial cells (thyrocytes).[2] The surface expression of this molecule is normally restricted to the apical border facing the interior of the thyroid follicles where it is not exposed to cells of the immune system.[3] However, in the autoimmune thyroid disease (ATD) of Graves' thyrotoxicosis, follicles can be isolated expressing TMAg on their basal vascular border where it would be available for immune presentation.[4]

Immunization against an antigen requires not only that it can be seen by lymphocytes, but that it be seen in an immunogenic form. The presentation of foreign antigen to helper T cells is usually accomplished in the context of major histocompatibility complex (MHC) class II molecules.[5] These molecules are of restricted tissue distribution. They are mainly associated with cells of the immune system, of which the class II+ macrophages and dendritic cells have been principally implicated in antigen presentation. It might be assumed that these cell types must also function in the presentation of autoantigens. However, expression of class II molecules has been noted on other cells not principally associated with immune functions, including capilliary endothelium and a variety of epithelia either in normal tissues (e.g., mammary, small intestine)[6] or in skin and/or gut in circumstances such as graft-versus-host disease, dermatoses, and parasitic infestation.[7]

With regard to organ-specific autoimmunity, we found that human thyrocytes, which are normally HLA-D/DR[d] negative, could be induced to express HLA-D/DR antigens by culture with mitogenic plant lectins.[8] Yet even more significant was our

[a]I. Todd is supported by the Wellcome Trust Foundation, and M. Londei and R. Pujol-Borrell are supported by the Juvenile Diabetes Foundation International.
[d]The term HLA-D/DR is used in this article to indicate any or all of the products of the HLA-D region (i.e., DR, DQ, DP).

observation that thyrocytes in sections or monolayers of thyroid glands from patients with autoimmune thyroid disease (ATD, Graves' disease, or Hashimoto's thyroiditis) expressed HLA-D/DR antigens in the vast majority of cases.[9] (In all of our experiments, class II expression is detected by indirect immunofluorescence using monoclonal anti-HLA-D/DR antibodies.) These findings raised the possibility that the class II molecules expressed by thyrocytes may play an active role in the autoimmune process. We accordingly proposed that endocrine epithelial cells can present their own surface autoantigens in association with inappropriately expressed HLA-D/DR molecules, thus perpetuating, and possibly initiating, the T-cell activation that eventuates in autoimmune disease.[10] The wide applicability of this hypothesis is suggested by the inappropriate HLA-D/DR expression that has been noted in other human tissues undergoing autoimmune attack. These include bile duct epithelium in patients with primary biliary cirrhosis (PBC),[11] surviving insulin-producing islet cells in pancreas obtained from newly diagnosed type I diabetics[12] (Foulis et al., in preparation), and enterocytes in autoimmune protracted diarrhea of infancy (PDI).[13] In this last case, it is worth noting that the jejunal enterocytes of the villi and upper crypts normally express HLA-DR (but not DQ or DP molecules) because they are presumably concerned with protective immunity against pathogens present in the gut lumen. However, in some cases of autoimmune PDI, DP and possibly DQ molecules are synthesized by the enterocytes, with DR expression being more intense and extending to cells of the lower crypts.[13]

The above findings in different autoimmunities are consistent with the hypothesis that inappropriate MHC class II expression in a particular organ might facilitate the presentation of organ-specific autoantigens (e.g., TMAg) and hence give rise to autoimmunity restricted to that organ. This could account for the organ-specific nature of many autoimmune diseases.

ANTIGEN PRESENTATION BY HLA-D/DR⁺ EPITHELIUM

Although essential for antigen presentation, the expression of HLA-D/DR molecules by epithelial cells does not of itself prove that these cells can effectively present antigen. We therefore examined the antigen presenting ability of HLA-D/DR⁺ thyrocytes.[14] As responding T cells, the cloned human T cell line HA1.7 was used, which is specific for a defined peptide (p20, residues 306–329) of the hemagglutinin molecule of influenza virus A presented in a MHC class II restricted fashion.[15,16] We found that class II⁺ thyrocytes from a Graves' disease patient of the appropriate HLA type were indeed able to effectively present peptide antigen in an antigen-specific, MHC-restricted fashion, as measured by incorporation of tritiated-thymidine by HA1.7. However, unlike peripheral blood mononuclear cells (PBMC), the thyrocytes were unable to present whole flu virus. This suggests that they are unable to catabolize or "process" antigen, which would not be required for an antigen fragment like p20. HLA-D/DR⁺ epithelial cells may therefore be restricted in vivo to presenting autoantigens that require no modification for their stable expression at the cell surface.[17] The cells' own surface molecules would clearly fulfill this requirement.

The ability of epithelial cells to present autoantigens was directly tested following the derivation of cloned T cell lines from the activated lymphocytes infiltrating the thyroid glands from Graves' disease patients.[18] The specificity of each clone was tested by examining proliferation in response to autologous or allogeneic (HLA mismatched) class II⁺ thyrocytes, or autologous PBMC. Apart from those clones proliferating only to interleukin-2 (IL-2), two types of response patterns were found (FIGURE 1). Some clones (e.g., clone 51) showed the type of reactivity typified by the autologous mixed lymphocyte reaction in that they responded to autologous thyrocytes or PBMC, but not to allogeneic cells; such lymphocytes may play an important role in autoimmune pathogenesis.[19] Another 10–15% of the clones were activated only by autologous thyrocytes (e.g., clone 17) and this could be blocked by an anti-HLA-D/DR monoclonal antibody. These experiments thus demonstrate, firstly, the presence in the lymphocytic infiltrates of autoimmune-diseased thyroids of activated autoreactive T cells whose stimulation occurs in an antigen-specific, MHC-restricted fashion. Secondly, HLA-D/DR$^+$ thyrocytes are capable of mediating this stimulation by presenting their own autoantigens. Consistent with these findings are experiments in mice in which the Ia restricted sensitization of lymphocytes on monolayers of thyroid cells generates thyroid-specific autoimmunization.[20]

The T-cell clones derived from Graves' disease glands were of the "helper" phenotype (T3$^+$, T4$^+$, T8$^-$). Recently, a line with the "cytotoxic/suppressor" phenotype (T3$^+$, T4$^-$, T8$^+$) has been derived from a thyroid affected by Hashimoto's disease.

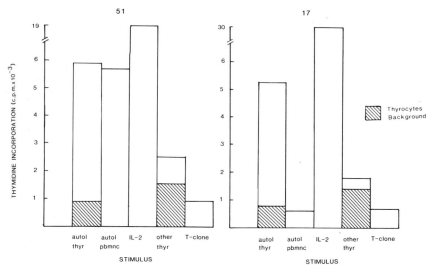

FIGURE 1. Proliferative response of cloned T cell lines derived from the infiltrate of a Graves' disease thyroid. Clone 51 (left) responds equally well to autologous thyrocytes and autologous PBMC, but not to allogeneic thyrocytes. Clone 17 (right) responds to autologous thyrocytes, but not to autologous PBMC or allogeneic thyrocytes.

Because T8$^+$ cells recognize antigen in the context of MHC class I, it is relevant to note that, as well as expression of class II molecules, increased expression of class I is found on epithelial cells in ATD,[9] PBC,[11] type I diabetes,[12] and autoimmune PDI.[13] Such enhanced class I expression could facilitate recognition by autoreactive cytotoxic T cells,[21] which probably play a major destructive role in, for example, type I diabetes where T8$^+$ cells predominate in the pancreatic infiltrate.[12]

INDUCTION OF HLA-D/DR EXPRESSION

Since class II expression by epithelial cells may play a central role in the pathogenesis of organ-specific autoimmunity, it was important to investigate the nature of the *in vivo* stimulus for this expression. In view of results with other cell types,[22] this was postulated to be interferon (IFN);[10] indeed, we found that recombinant human IFN-gamma induced strong surface and cytoplasmic expression of HLA-D/DR by cultured normal human thyrocytes.[23] The surface expression was detectable within 24 hours of culture and doses of IFN-gamma as low as 1 U/ml were effective, thus being within the physiological range. By contrast, IFN-alpha, IFN-beta, and interleukin-2 (IL-2) were unable to induce HLA-D/DR expression by thyrocytes, although all three interferon species (but not IL-2) enhanced expression of class I molecules.

These results suggest that IFN-gamma is an inducer of the class II expression seen by thyrocytes in ATD. Furthermore, one may envisage this lymphokine as being an important intermediary in the potentiation and propagation of the autoreactive attack. This is because T lymphocytes are a prime source of IFN-gamma, and thus its secretion by activated autoreactive T cells infiltrating the thyroid would stimulate thyrocyte HLA-D/DR expression and hence the presentation of autoantigens (FIGURE 2).

Further investigations have shown that other factors as well as IFN-gamma probably play a role in determining the quantity and quality of class II expression by thyroid epithelium (Todd *et al.,* in preparation). We have found that thyroid-stimulating hormone (TSH) enhances the induction of class II expression in cultured thyrocytes by IFN-gamma, although TSH alone has little or no effect (FIGURE 3). Concentrations of the order of 0.1–1 mU bovine TSH/ml (equivalent to 100–1000 mU/L) were found to be optimal. This is at least as high as serum TSH concentrations even in severe hypothyroidism (maximum about 100 mU/L), but local *in vivo*

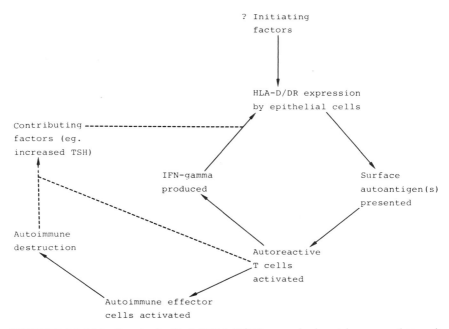

FIGURE 2. Model for the role of epithelial HLA-D/DR expression in autoimmune pathogenesis and the possible factors contributing to this expression.

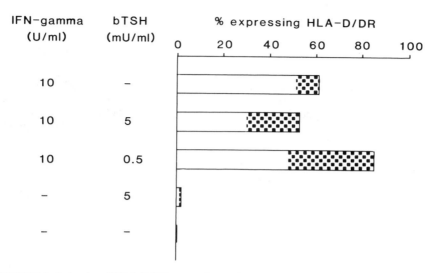

FIGURE 3. Induction of HLA-D/DR expression on the surface of human thyrocytes cultured for seven days with *E. coli*–derived purified recombinant human IFN-gamma (Genentech/Boehringer-Ingelheim) and/or bovine TSH (bTSH: "Thytropar," Armour Pharmaceutical). HLA-D/DR detection was by indirect immunofluorescence using murine monoclonal anti-HLA-D/DR (MID-3: provided by G. Guarnotta and P. Lydyard), followed by fluoresceinated rabbit anti-mouse immunoglobulin (Dako). Intensity of HLA-D/DR expression was scored as weak to moderate (☐) or strong (▦) on each thyrocyte.

concentrations at the thyroid follicular surface may well be greater than that found in serum. Enhancing effects similar to that of TSH were obtained both with $10^{-3}M$ isobutyl-methyl xanthine (IBMX), which inhibits cyclic-AMP phosphodiesterase, and with dibutyryl-cyclic-AMP itself. This suggests that this activity of TSH is mediated by intracellular cyclic-AMP, as has been demonstrated for several other effects of TSH on thyrocytes.[24]

The involvement of other factors apart from IFN-gamma in qualitative aspects of thyrocyte class II expression was suggested by indirect immunofluorescent staining with monoclonal antibodies specific for DR or DP subregion products (Todd *et al.*, in preparation). Examination of thyroid sections from patients with ATD indicated similar strong expression of both DR and DP molecules by the thyrocytes. By contrast, normal thyrocytes cultured with a limiting concentration of IFN-gamma showed much weaker expression of DP than DR. However, parity of DP/DR induction could be approached by culturing the thyrocytes with a much higher concentration of IFN-gamma or possibly, more significantly, with a low concentration of IFN-gamma together with TSH or IBMX as an additional signal (FIGURE 4).

The raised levels of TSH accompanying hypothyroid autoimmunity (e.g., as in Hashimoto's disease) might therefore contribute to pathogenesis by enhancing HLA-D/DR induction on thyrocytes (FIGURE 2). Whether thyroid-stimulating antibodies in Graves' disease have similar activity is presently under investigation. Furthermore, appropriately stimulated lymphocytes have been reported to produce immunoreactive TSH,[27] which raises the possibility of infiltrating lymphocytes producing by themselves an enhancing factor (FIGURE 2).

A PRIMARY ROLE FOR EPITHELIAL HLA-D/DR?

The above findings indicate that IFN-gamma is not the sole agent involved in epithelial class II expression, but that other factors play a modulatory role. Indeed, one may go further and ask whether other factors may induce class II expression by epithelial cells independently of IFN-gamma. The occurrence of such is indicated by investigations of the pancreas. As discussed above, human beta cells do express HLA-D/DR in the pancreas of newly diagnosed type I diabetics[12] (Foulis *et al.*, in preparation). However, recombinant IFN-gamma (with or without possible cofactors)

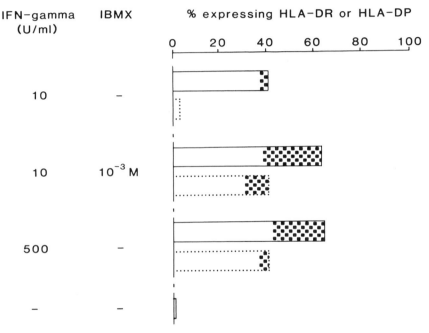

FIGURE 4. Induction of HLA-DR and HLA-DP on the surface of human thyrocytes cultured for six days with recombinant human IFN-gamma with or without IBMX (Sigma). Class II detection was by indirect immunofluorescence using murine monoclonal anti-DR (DA6.164) (□)[25] or anti-DP (B7/21) (⋮⋮⋮),[26] which was followed by fluoresceinated rabbit anti-mouse immunoglobulin. Intensity of class II expression was scored as weak to moderate (□) or strong (▦) on each thyrocyte.

is unable to induce HLA-D/DR expression by cultured, insulin-positive human islet cells (Pujol-Borrell *et al.*, in preparation) and similar observations have been made in mice.[28]

One might also favor a requirement for other stimuli on the basis that IFN-gamma production must be associated with an ongoing immune response. In the autoimmune situation, this is clearly compatible with the model depicted in FIGURE 2, where epithelial class II expression is implicated in a propagatory capacity. This, though, is a closed circuit in which the induction of HLA-D/DR expression on epithelium cannot be singled out as an event in the initiation of the pathogenesis. Because we consider the possibility of such a triggering role to be high, we proposed that epithelial HLA-D/DR might be initially induced by local IFN-gamma production in an immune response unrelated to autoimmunity (e.g., one against a local infection).[10] However, a number of observations in different autoimmunities point to factors or conditions other than ones directly related to immune events being implicated in the initial induction of epithelial class II expression. This indirect evidence comes from analyses of the relationship between epithelial HLA-D/DR expression and mononuclear infiltration of the gland in question. For example, in ATD we find the correlation between follicular HLA-D/DR expression and local infiltration to be incomplete; that is, occasional follicles strongly express HLA-D/DR, despite very few lymphocytes being within their vicinity.[9] Of course, the majority of follicular HLA-D/DR expression is accompanied by infiltration, as would be expected in glands surgically removed when the disease is at a relatively advanced stage. This could account for reports by other workers that follicular HLA-D/DR expression is almost always accompanied by infiltration.[29,30]

In this respect, studies of PBC have the advantage that biopsies are available from patients in different disease stages; indeed, bile ducts of specimens taken at stage I and II of the disease have shown the most intense HLA-D/DR expression without necessarily exhibiting massive lymphocytic infiltration.[11]

Perhaps the most convincing example is again provided by type I diabetes. Here, examinations of the pancreas from one recent onset diabetic by ourselves,[12] along with several more cases by others (Foulis *et al.*, in preparation), have revealed that the only epithelial cells expressing HLA-D/DR are the insulin-positive islet cells; the glucagon, somatostatin, and exocrine cells being HLA-D/DR-negative. What is more, the majority of islets containing HLA-D/DR-positive beta cells show no insulitis; conversely, in other diseases involving pancreatic infiltration, namely, chronic pancreatitis and cystic fibrosis, no HLA-D/DR expression by the islet cells is observed.

It is also worth noting that the physiological class II expression by epithelium of the small intestine seen in normal rats also occurs in nude rats (which are deficient in T cells). This indicates that T cells, which are a major source of IFN-gamma, are not obligatory for this class II expression.[31]

The above findings in various autoimmune diseases are consistent with epithelial HLA-D/DR expression being at least initially induced by presently unknown mechanisms that are independent of lymphocytic infiltration. This permits us to suggest that the circuit in FIGURE 2 may be initiated at the point of epithelial HLA-D/DR expression. This event would precede and would therefore be the stimulus for the initial attraction and activation of autoreactive T cells. A role of this type involving the activation of unprimed T cells may require other stimuli in addition to MHC-restricted antigen presentation, such as interleukin-1 (IL-1). It is therefore significant that certain epithelial cells (e.g., keratinocytes and corneal epithelium) have been shown to produce an IL-1-like molecule.[32]

Also important in these triggering events could be the local capillary endothelium through which infiltrating lymphocytes must pass. It is striking that the endothelium surrounding the islets of diabetic pancreas is swollen and much more strongly HLA-D/DR-positive than normal[12] (Foulis *et al.*, in preparation). This, again, is independent of local insulitis. One is tempted to view these dramatic changes as an invitation to autoreactive lymphocytes to enter the tissues and mount their attack.

SUMMARY

The findings we have described here show a clear association between epithelial HLA-D/DR expression and autoimmunity. Furthermore, the ability of class II$^+$ thyrocytes to present both exogenous antigens and autoantigens indicates an active role for these HLA-D/DR molecules in autoimmune pathogenesis. IFN-gamma is capable of inducing HLA-D/DR expression by thyroid epithelium, but a number of observations suggest the involvement of other inducers as well. Overall, we conclude that epithelial class II expression very probably plays a key role in the propagation and also in possibly the initiation of autoimmune attack. This is in accord with the proposal of a more general relationship between inappropriate or excessive class II expression and pathogenesis.[33]

ACKNOWLEDGMENTS

We thank D. Doniach and I. M. Roitt for useful discussions, encouragement, and support.

REFERENCES

1. ROITT, I. M. 1984. Prevailing theories in autoimmune disorders. Triangle (Engl. Ed.) **23:** 67–76.
2. KHOURY, E. L., L. HAMMOND, G. F. BOTTAZZO & D. DONIACH. 1981. Presence of the organ-specific microsomal autoantigen on the surface of human thyroid cells in culture: its involvement in complement-mediated cytotoxicity. Clin. Exp. Immunol. **45:** 316–328.
3. KHOURY, E. L., G. F. BOTTAZZO & I. M. ROITT. 1984. The thyroid "microsomal" antibody revisited. Its paradoxical binding *in vivo* to the apical surface of the follicular epithelium. J. Exp. Med. **159:** 577–591.
4. HANAFUSA, T., R. PUJOL-BORRELL, L. CHIOVATO, D. DONIACH & G. F. BOTTAZZO. 1984. *In vitro* and *in vivo* reversal of thyroid epithelial polarity: its relevance for autoimmune thyroid disease. Clin. Exp. Immunol. **57:** 639–646.
5. UNANUE, E. R. 1984. Antigen presenting function of the macrophage. Ann. Rev. Immunol. **2:** 395–428.
6. WIMAN, K., B. CURMAN, U. FORSUM, L. KLARESKOG, U. MALMNAS-TJERNLUND, L. RASK, J. TRAGARDH & P. A. PETERSON. 1978. Occurrence of Ia antigens on tissues of non-lymphoid origin. Nature **276:** 711–713.
7. BARCLAY, A. N. & D. W. MASON. 1983. Graft rejection and Ia antigens—paradox resolved? Nature **303:** 382–383.
8. PUJOL-BORRELL, R., T. HANAFUSA, L. CHIOVATO & G. F. BOTTAZZO. 1983. Lectin-induced expression of DR antigen on human cultured follicular thyroid cells. Nature **303:** 71–73.
9. HANAFUSA, T., R. PUJOL-BORRELL, L. CHIOVATO, R. C. G. RUSSELL, D. DONIACH & G. F. BOTTAZZO. 1983. Aberrant expression of HLA-DR antigen on thyrocytes in Graves' disease: relevance for autoimmunity. Lancet **ii:** 1111–1115.
10. BOTTAZZO, G. F., R. PUJOL-BORRELL, T. HANAFUSA & M. FELDMANN. 1983. Role of aberrant HLA-DR expression and antigen presentation in induction of endocrine autoimmunity. Lancet **ii:** 1115–1119.
11. BALLARDINI, G., R. MIRAKIAN, F. B. BIANCHI, E. PISI, D. DONIACH & G. F. BOTTAZZO. 1984. Aberrant expression of HLA-DR antigens on bile duct epithelium in primary biliary cirrhosis: relevance to pathogenesis. Lancet **ii:** 1009–1013.
12. BOTTAZZO, G. F., B. M. DEAN, J. M. MCNALLY, E. H. MACKAY, P. G. F. SWIFT & D. R. GAMBLE. 1985. *In situ* characterization of autoimmune phenomena and expression of HLA molecules in the pancreas in diabetic insulitis. N. Engl. J. Med. **313:** 353–360.
13. MIRAKIAN, R., A. RICHARDSON, P. J. MILLA, J. UNSWORTH, J. A. WALKER-SMITH, M. O. SAVAGE & G. F. BOTTAZZO. 1985. Protracted diarrhoea of infancy: evidence in support of an autoimmune variant. Submitted for publication.
14. LONDEI, M., J. R. LAMB, G. F. BOTTAZZO & M. FELDMANN. 1984. Epithelial cells expressing aberrant MHC class II determinants can present antigen to cloned human T cells. Nature **312:** 639–641.
15. LAMB, J. R., D. D. ECKELS, P. LAKE, J. N. WOODY & N. GREEN. 1982. Human T cell clones

recognize chemically synthesized peptides of influenza haemagglutinin. Nature **300:** 66–67.

16. LAMB, J. R. & M. FELDMANN. 1983. Essential requirement for major histocompatibility complex recognition in T-cell tolerance induction. Nature **308:** 72–74.

17. GREY, H. M. & R. CHESNUT. 1985. Antigen processing and presentation to T cells. Immunol. Today **6:** 101–106.

18. LONDEI, M., G. F. BOTTAZZO & M. FELDMANN. 1985. Human T cell clones from autoimmune thyroid glands: specific recognition of autologous thyroid cells. Science **228:** 85–89.

19. WILSON, D. B. 1984. Idiotypic regulation of self-reactive and alloreactive T cells in autoimmunity and graft-versus-host disease. Immunol. Today **5:** 228–230.

20. SALAMERO, J. & J. CHARREIRE. 1983. Syngeneic sensitization of mouse lymphocytes on monolayers of thyroid epithelial cells. V. The primary syngeneic sensitization is under I-A subregion control. Eur. J. Immunol. **13:** 948–951.

21. BEVAN, M. 1984. High determinant density may explain the phenomenon of alloreactivity. Immunol. Today **5:** 128–130.

22. TRINCHIERI, G. & B. PERUSSIA. 1985. Immune interferon: a pleiotropic lymphokine with multiple effects. Immunol. Today **6:** 131–136.

23. TODD, I., R. PUJOL-BORRELL, L. J. HAMMOND, G. F. BOTTAZZO & M. FELDMANN. 1985. Interferon-gamma induces HLA-DR expression by thyroid epithelium. Clin. Exp. Immunol. **61:** 265–273.

24. CARAYON, P. & S. AMR. 1985. Mechanisms of thyroid regulation. *In* Endocrinology (2nd Edition). L. J. DeGroot, Ed. Grune & Stratton. Orlando, Florida.

25. GUY, K., V. VANHEYNINGEN, B. B. COHEN, D. L. DEANE, D. N. CRICHTON & C. M. STEEL. 1981. Subsets of human D-locus products identified by a series of monoclonal antibodies. Protides Biol. Fluids Proc. Colloq. **29:** 729–732.

26. WATSON, A. J., R. DeMARS, I. S. TROWBRIDGE & F. H. BACH. 1983. Detection of a novel human Class II HLA-Ag. Nature **304:** 358–361.

27. SMITH, E. M., M. PHAN, T. E. KRUGER, D. H. COPPENHAVER & J. E. BLALOCK. 1983. Human lymphocyte production of immunoreactive thyrotropin. Proc. Natl. Acad. Sci. USA **80:** 6010–6013.

28. CAMPBELL, I. L., G. H. W. WONG, J. W. SCHRADER & L. C. HARRISON. 1985. Interferon-gamma enhances the expression of the major histocompatibility class I antigens on mouse pancreatic beta cells. Diabetes **34:** 1205–1209.

29. JANSSON, R., A. KARLSSON & U. FORSUM. 1984. Intrathyroidal HLA-DR expression and T lymphocyte phenotypes in Graves' thyrotoxicosis, Hashimoto's thyroiditis and nodular colloid goitre. Clin. Exp. Immunol. **58:** 264–272.

30. AICHINGER, G., H. FILL & G. WICK. 1984. *In situ* immune complexes, lymphocyte subpopulations, and HLA-DR-positive epithelial cells in Hashimoto thyroiditis. Lab. Invest. **52:** 132–140.

31. MAYRHOFER, G., C. W. PUGH & A. N. BARCLAY. 1983. The distribution ontogeny and origin in the rat of Ia-positive cells with dendritic morphology and of Ia antigen in epithelia, with special reference to the intestine. Eur. J. Immunol. **13:** 112–122.

32. DURUM, S. K., J. A. SCHMIDT & J. J. OPPENHEIM. 1985. Interleukin 1: an immunological perspective. Ann. Rev. Immunol. **3:** 263–287.

33. UNANUE, E. R., D. I. BELLER, C. Y. LU & P. M. ALLEN. 1984. Antigen presentation: comments on its regulation and mechanism. J. Immunol. **132:** 1–5.

DISCUSSION OF THE PAPER

E. KHOURY (*University of California, San Francisco, CA*): An alternative explanation of your data is that aberrant expression of DR on the islet cells is not the primary reason for the autoreaction, but a consequence of those cells being the target for an immune response, as in the case of graft rejection.

G. F. BOTTAZZO (*Middlesex Hospital Medical School, London, United Kingdom*): I do not think we can compare an allogeneic graft with an autorejection process. Moreover, an aberrant expression of DR antigens can occur in melanoma cells, but they are not rejected. You must have an open mind on this because it is possible that focal thyroiditis can be a very early event.

B. D. STOLLAR (*National Institutes of Health, Bethesda, MD*): Have you been able to stimulate thyroglobulin-specific T cells with Ia-expressing thyroid cells?

BOTTAZZO: No. We do not know yet because we have not tried it.

STOLLAR: Do you think that interferon is the only factor that stimulates thyroid cells to express Ia?

BOTTAZZO: Gamma-interferon has such an effect on normal thyroid cells, but not on normal human islet cells. Thus, even if it is an important inducer of HLA-DR expression, it is selective for certain cells. Our effort now is to find out what is actually causing aberrant HLA-DR expression on pancreatic beta cells.

STOLLAR: What do you think triggers Ia expression in human thyroid disease to start off the disease, as you postulate?

BOTTAZZO: I do not know yet.

B. E. WENZEL (*University of Lübeck, Lübeck, Federal Republic of Germany*): We have evidence that, *in vitro,* normal thyroid cells can express DR if TSH is present in the medium.

BOTTAZZO: Yes, Ian Tudol also has evidence that TSH enhances the effect of gamma-interferon on aberrant expression of DR.

I. R. MACKAY (*Royal Melbourne Hospital, Victoria, Australia*): You have picked a very tricky disease in primary biliary cirrhosis because it is the one disease in which you have not yet got an organ-specific antigen expressed on the surface of the cell. Therefore, I do not see what use it is in primary biliary cirrhosis for the biliary epithelium to present class II antigens because the autoantigen of primary biliary cirrhosis is, of course, a mitochondrial antigen. Do you think there is a surface antigen on the cell in primary biliary cirrhosis?

BOTTAZZO: Is it possible that mitochondrial antigen can be expressed on the surface of bile ducts?

MACKAY: Yes, it is possible.

Ia Antigen Expression and Autoimmunity in MRL-*lpr/lpr* Mice

YVONNE J. ROSENBERG,[a,d] PAUL K. GOLDSMITH,[b]
JUNICHI OHARA,[c] ALFRED D. STEINBERG,[a] AND
WILLIAM OHRINER[a]

[a]*Arthritis and Rheumatism Branch*
[b]*Metabolic Diseases Branch*
National Institute of Arthritis, Diabetes, and Digestive Disease
[c]*Laboratory of Immunology*
National Institute of Allergy and Infectious Diseases
National Institutes of Health
Bethesda, Maryland 20205

Major histocompatibility complex (MHC) class II glycoprotein antigens expressed on antigen-presenting cells play a critical role in L3T4$^+$ T-cell proliferation and T-B interactions. As such, they are important regulatory molecules. In functional terms, Ia antigens constitute the target antigens for the large frequency of alloreactive T cells or they serve as restriction elements for the induction of syngeneic helper cells that recognize these determinants in association with nominal antigen (reviewed in reference 1). The particular class II determinants recognized and, consequently, the specificity repetoire of peripheral T cells are known to be determined by the MHC phenotype of the thymic APC.[2,3] Although autoreactive T cell clones specific for syngeneic Ia antigens have been frequently demonstrated in *vitro*[4] and recognition of self-Ia antigens is known to form the basis of the *in vitro* autologous mixed lymphocyte reaction (AMLR),[5] it is generally thought that such cells are not commonly activated *in vivo*. Thus, as a result of negative selection of high-affinity self-Ia reactive T cells in the thymus, or changes in the antigen receptor or activation requirements of post-thymic T cells, triggering of T cells in the periphery of normal mice optimally occurs following corecognition of class II determinants with antigen. It is clear, however, that because of the frequent demonstration of autoreactive cells *in vitro,* any changes in the conditions that might lead to enhanced activity of these cells [for example, increased Ia expression by antigen-presenting cells (APC) or aberrant expression by Ia$^-$ tissues] could be potentially harmful to the animal. If unregulated, this could be an important factor in the development of autoimmune disease.

MRL-*lpr/lpr* mice spontaneously develop an autoimmune disease manifested clinically by arthritis, vasculitis, and immune complex glomerulonephritis. As such, this represents a murine model for systemic lupus erythematosus (SLE).[6,7] Because strains homozygous for the *lpr* gene exhibit a profound T-cell lymphadenopathy associated with polyclonal B-cell activation, autoantibody production, and specific B-cell unresponsiveness,[8,9] such mice also serve as useful models for studying the mechanisms underlying this B-cell hyperactivity, which, in addition to *lpr*-linked disease, is observed following infections with parasites (e.g., malaria)[10] and viruses (e.g., acquired immune deficiency syndrome).[11] Although the marked lymphoprolifer-

[d]Yvonne J. Rosenberg's present affiliation is the Institute for Cellular and Molecular Oncology, New York, New York 10014.

ation that occurs within an unusual dull Lyt-1$^+$, 2$^-$, Thy-1$^+$, L3T4$^-$, 6B2$^+$, Ig$^-$, Ia$^-$ T-cell population[12] is known to be central to the development of autoimmunity in MRL-*lpr/lpr* mice,[13] the immunological abnormalities that result in severe disease are not clearly defined.

In the context of Ia antigen expression and disease association, these mice are particularly interesting because they have been shown to exhibit an age-related increase in both the percent and number of Ia$^+$ macrophages that appear coincident with lymphoid hyperplasia and lupus.[14,15] Thus, they may provide appropriate conditions for the abnormal induction of autoreactive T cells. To investigate the signals required for induction and growth of *lpr/lpr* T cells, the lymphokines they produce, their role in B-cell activation, proliferation, and differentiation, and a role for the

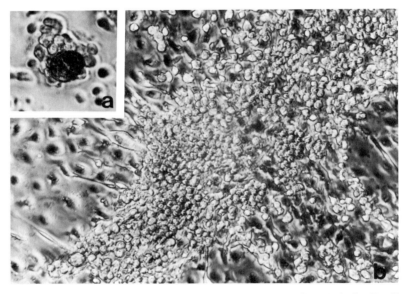

FIGURE 1. Binding of lymphocytes to self-cells in early cultures of MRL-*lpr/lpr* T cells: (a) typical rosette formation around a large granular cell; (b) binding to adherent dendritic cells.

elevated Ia antigen levels in the disease process, T cell lines from MRL-*lpr/lpr* mice were established and the properties of the cells and their factors studied.

UNUSUAL FEATURES OF MRL-*lpr/lpr* T CELL LINES

Several features about the growth of autoimmune *lpr/lpr* T cells appear to be unique:

(1) During the first two weeks of culture of nylon-wool-passaged MRL-*lpr/lpr* splenic T cells (and to a lesser extent, lymph node), many lymphocytes appear to bind to other cell types in the culture. For example, in FIGURE 1b, lymphocytes are shown to bind to and outline the dendritic processes of large

adherent cells, while FIGURE 1a shows a typical rosette comprised of lymphocytes, often in a state of division, bound to a large granular cell.

(2) Despite the marked impairment in the ability of fresh MRL-*lpr/lpr* T cells to
produce interleukin-2 (IL-2) in Concanavalin A (Con A) stimulated culture *in
vitro,* following an initial culture period in the presence of IL-2-containing
supernatant (SN), these T cells continue to grow spontaneously as slowly
growing lines (e.g., 50,000 cpm in five days) in the absence of added growth
factor, antigen, or mitogen. Analysis of SN from these cultures demonstrate
constitutive IL-2 synthesis.[16] In addition, T-cell proliferation of the slowly
growing lines can be prevented by anti-IL-2 receptor (IL-2R) antibody. In
some cases, it is blocked by anti-Ia^k (10.2.16), but not anti-Ia^d antibody (not
shown).

(3) In contrast to normal T cells that require antigenic or mitogenic stimulation
for lymphokine production, cultured MRL-*lpr/lpr* T cells appear to synthesize
a variety of lymphokines (e.g., colony stimulating factor (CSF), IL-2, interferon (IFN), and B-cell directed factors) without exogenous stimuli.

(4) Recent studies[17,18] using *lpr/lpr* T cells or rapidly growing clones derived from
the above cultures show greatly elevated levels of both c-*myb* and c-*raf*
oncogene mRNA compared to other mouse strains. Whether this high
expression affects the growth and transformation of these cells is currently
under study.

The relevance of these unusual properties will be discussed in later sections.

Ia ANTIGEN EXPRESSION IN MRL-*lpr/lpr* MICE

As mentioned, one of the unique features of MRL-*lpr/lpr* mice is an increase in the
expression of Ia$^+$ peritoneal macrophages concomitant with the development of
autoimmunity. In normal animals, expression of such determinants by macrophages is
not a constitutive property, but is regulated positively by IFN-γ[19] and negatively by
agents such as prostaglandin E$_2$ (PGE$_2$)[20] and α-fetoprotein (AFP).[21] Abnormal
MRL-*lpr/lpr* splenic T cells, however, are extremely unusual in being able to secrete
an IFN-like mediator spontaneously,[15] which probably accounts for the serologically
detectable levels in these mice.[6] Furthermore, despite a marked defect in the ability of
lpr/lpr T cells to produce IL-2 in Con A stimulated cultures, their capacity to generate
IFN in the same culture is intact, demonstrating an interesting dissociation between
the two lymphokines.[22]

It is of interest that despite the lymphadenopathy, B-cell activation, and abnormal
IL-2 responses in the *lpr/lpr*-bearing C3H, B6, and AKR strains,[8,14,23] only those that
are genetically predisposed toward autoimmunity (e.g., MRL-*lpr/lpr* and NZB-
lpr/lpr) develop severe disease and exhibit the increased levels of macrophage Ia
antigens. Thus, T-cell lymphoproliferation does not necessarily lead to IFN production
sufficient for hyper-Ia expression. Whether the Ia-inducing levels of IFN detected in
the serum of the latter mice reflect an intrinsic ability of T cells to hypersynthesize this
lymphokine or whether the antagonists to macrophage Ia expression are reduced is not
known. It has been shown, however, that regulation of IFN production is defective in
MRL-*lpr/lpr* mice.[24]

Several other observations suggest a link between the excess IFN-γ synthesis,
hyper-Ia expression, and the development of disease. For example, injection of
two-month-old MRL-*lpr/lpr* with PGE$_1$ has been shown to prevent the increase in Ia
expression, lymphoid hyperplasia, and lupus nephritis,[9] while in the case of NZB mice,

another high Ia$^+$ lupus strain, accelerated autoimmunity following IFN treatment has been observed.[25]

In addition to macrophages, B cells from all *lpr/lpr* mice exhibit enhanced class II antigen expression.[26,27] FIGURE 2 shows the Ia antigen profiles from spleens of both MRL-*lpr/lpr* and the congeneic control MRL-+/+ mice. Although the relative increase for all anti-Ia^k staining B cells was only around 2.5-fold, the *lpr/lpr*-bearing mice contained many more brightly staining cells (e.g., above channel 500, 20% in the *lpr* versus 5% in the control). Despite the potency of IFN-γ at inducing Ia antigens on macrophages and several other cell types (such as myeloid cells and B-cell lymphomas),[28] it surprisingly does not appear to augment increased Ia expression on B cells,[29] which, instead, is induced by another T-cell-derived lymphokine.

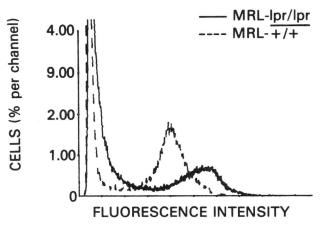

FIGURE 2. Ia antigen expression of MRL-*lpr/lpr* and MRL-+/+ spleen cells following staining with biotinylated anti-Ia^k (10.2.16) and FITC-avidin.

THE PRODUCTION OF B-CELL Ia-INDUCING FACTOR BY MRL-*lpr/lpr* T CELLS

To study the mechanisms leading to hyper-Ia expression by *lpr/lpr* B cells, SN from the MRL-*lpr/lpr* T cell lines were tested for B-cell Ia-inducing activity. The ability of a 10% SN from the 14.1.7 T cell line to induce a tenfold increase in Ia antigen expression on resting B cells in 18 hours is shown in FIGURE 3. Such a factor, which is present to varying degrees in SN from short- or long-term T-cell cultures, functions in the absence of antigen, mitogen, or anti-immunoglobulin (Ig) and is MHC unrestricted. Purification of this lymphokine using a 70–100% ammonium-sulfate precipitate and C18 reverse-phase high performance liquid chromatography (HPLC) indicated that the Ia-inducing activity was eluted at 44–48% acetonitrile and is therefore identical biochemically to the T-cell-derived B-cell stimulating factor (BSF-1, originally B-cell growth factor, BCGF-1), which was previously described as a growth factor and said to act only on activated B cells.[30] However, the results from this laboratory and those of Vitetta and colleagues indicate that BCGF-1 is not a growth factor, but instead provides an early activation signal to resting B cells to induce, among other things, increased Ia expression and receptors for another growth factor.

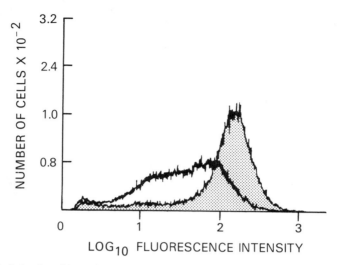

FIGURE 3. Induction of Ia antigen expression by MRL-*lpr/lpr* T-cell SN. MRL-+/+ B cells (3 × 10⁵/ml) were cultured for 16 hours alone or with 10% SN from the MRL-*lpr/lpr* T cell line 1.T34. Cells were stained as in FIGURE 2. The shaded profile represents the increased Ia expression on B cells with SN.

For example, as shown in TABLE 1, Ia induction on normal B cells by *lpr* SN is inhibited by the anti-BSF-1 monoclonal antibody (11B11). This Ia expression, induced by factor, occurs in the absence of any increase in RNA or DNA, although increases are observed if crude 14.1.7 SN is used (see FIGURE 4). In addition, B cells first stimulated with anti-Ig and then washed do not respond to BSF-1.[30] Whether Ia-inducing factor causes an increase in cell size or an entry into cell cycle is debatable. While no increases are observed using MRL-+/+ or some BALB/c B cells,[31] different results have been obtained using similar mice,[32] which probably reflect different activation states of the starting B-cell populations. However, the effects of this factor do appear to be pleiotropic, because in addition to Ia induction, BSF-1 is shown to selectively induce the synthesis of IgG1 secretion in LPS-activated B-cell blasts.[33]

To analyze the possible functional significance of enhanced Ia expression in MRL-*lpr/lpr* B cells and macrophages, experiments were done based on two assumptions: (i) Following Ia induction and activation by BSF-1, B cells are the targets for other proliferation and differentiation factors, which lead to the polyclonal B-cell

TABLE 1. Inhibition of Ia Induction by Anti-BSF-1[a]

Cells	T-Cell SN	Anti-BSF-1	% Bright Ia⁺ Cells (50)
MRL-+/+	—	—	10.43
MRL-+/+	14.1.7	—	33.78
MRL-+/+	14.1.7	+	13.49
MRL-+/+	70–100% ppte	—	32.9
MRL-+/+	70–100% ppte	+	11.03

[a]MRL-*lpr/lpr* spleen cells were cultured for 18 hours at 3 × 10⁵ cells/ml/well alone or with 10% 14.1.7 MRL-*lpr/lpr* T-cell line SN in the presence or absence of anti-BSF-1(1/5000). A 70–100% ammonium sulfate precipitate of 14.1.7 was also tested.

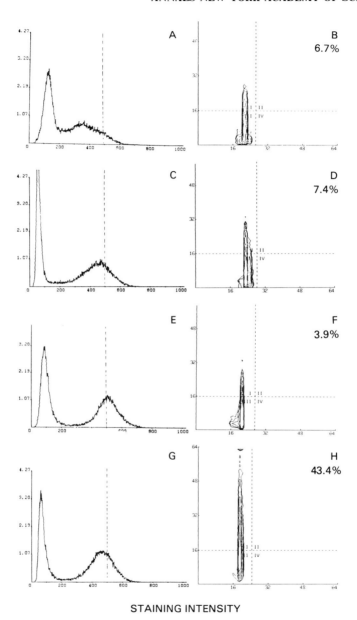

STAINING INTENSITY

FIGURE 4. Analysis of changes in Ia antigen levels and RNA and DNA content of MRL-$+/+$ spleen cells cultured alone or with purified or crude 14.1.7 SN. (A,B): no SN; (C,D): HPLC purified 14.1.7 SN; (E,F): affinity purified 14.1.7 SN; (G,H): crude SN. Cells ($3 \times 10^5/ml$) were cultured for 18 hours, aliquoted, and stained with either biotinylated anti-Ia^k and FITC-avidin (A,C,E,G) or with the metachromatic dye acridine orange (OA) (B,D,F,H,) to estimate RNA and DNA content. They were analyzed using a fluorescence-activated cell sorter (FACS 440, Becton Dickinson, Mountain View, California).

activation and autoantibody production and the immune complex formation observed in these mice; (ii) Such high Ia$^+$ macrophages and B cells could also stimulate low-affinity self-Ia-reactive T cells that, following activation, would elaborate many lymphokines, including those maintaining the high Ia antigen levels (e.g., IFN, BSF-1), as well as those responsible for the T-cell lymphadenopathy.

MECHANISMS UNDERLYING B-CELL HYPERACTIVITY IN *lpr/lpr* MICE

Several reports have demonstrated the greatly increased numbers of Ig-secreting cells, particularly IgG, in *lpr/lpr* strains.[8,9] To test for the helper-cell properties of these abnormal T cells, 5×10^6 MRL-$+/+$ B cells were cultured with 2×10^4–10^5 T cells from the *in vitro* cultured lines. TABLE 2 indicates that in the absence of mitogen or antigen, such T cells can induce B cells to terminally differentiate into IgM- and IgG-secreting cells and therefore provide all the B-cell Ia-inducing, activation, proliferation, and differentiation signals required for IgG secretion.

TABLE 2. Helper Cell Activity of MRL-*lpr/lpr* T Cell Lines[a]

T Cell Line	T (*lpr*)	B (+/+)	Number of Class-Specific IgFC				
			IgM	IgG1	IgG2	IgG3	IgA
1.AB4	10^5	5×10^6	36,160	6800	3400	120	60
1.AB6	10^5	5×10^6	8620	3240	16,360	500	120
1.Bot5	10^5	5×10^6	22,190	5620	15,800	320	380
1.T34	5×10^4	5×10^6	11,000	4960	7600	200	60
—	—	5×10^6	4080	700	1100	200	200

[a]In this study, 5×10^6 anti-Thy1 treated MRL-$+/+$ B cells were cultured alone or with MRL-*lpr/lpr* T cells grown for 2–4 months *in vitro*. Total numbers of class-specific IgFC were scored at day 5.

The Production of B-Cell Proliferation/Differentiation Factors by MRL-lpr/lpr T Cells

In addition to expressing increased amounts of Ia antigen, B cells of any haplotype also proliferate when cultured for 60 hours with 10–40% SN from the T cell lines. That such factors act directly on B cells was demonstrated when single B-cell cultures were induced to form colonies by SN alone.[26] Thus, in addition to BSF-1, such T cells spontaneously make a B-cell growth factor. The properties of such a factor were examined by culturing a sample of the fractions from a SORBAX G250 HPLC column with MRL-$+/+$ resting B cells and ten units of purified BSF-1. The experiments shown in FIGURE 5 indicate (i) BSF-1 (in FCS containing medium) is sufficient to prepare B cells to receive proliferation signals (i.e., to induce BCGF receptors) and (ii) the B-cell growth factor eluted from the column between albumin and ovalbumin ($M_r = 45$–$67,000$) is similar to both of the previously described BCGF-II,[34] the B-cell growth and differentiation factor (BGDF),[35] and T-cell replacing factor-1 (TRF-1).[36] In terms of B-cell maturation, it is now clear that proliferation factors also induce Ig synthesis. TABLE 3 compares the relative increase in proliferation and Ig production, as measured by an ELISA assay, in cultures of 10^5 B cells and a variety of *lpr/lpr* T-cell SN. These experiments, however, also indicate that another differentiation signal (BCDF) may be required because, in order to generate good IgG

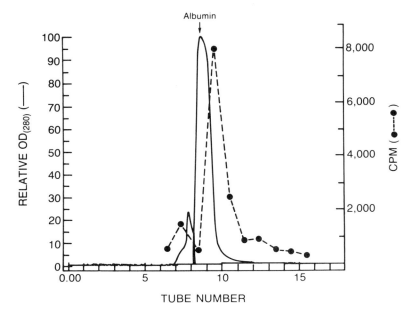

FIGURE 5. Identification of the BCGF produced by MRL-*lpr/lpr* T cell lines. Here, 10^5 MRL-+/+ B cells were cultured with 10 U purified BSF-1 and 30 μl from each 2-ml fraction from a SORBAX G250 HPLC column (Dupont, New Jersey), onto which 250 μl of a pool of T-cell SN was loaded. Cultures were pulsed at 48 hours with 1 μC ^{3}(H)-TdR and harvested 12 hours later. Data represent CPM. No significant counts were found in cultures containing B cells and HPLC fractions only.

PFC responses, T cells not merely their factors are required. Whether this signal would be qualitatively different for each Ig isotype is not determined. A differentiation factor produced by MRL-*lpr/lpr* T cells that induces large IgG responses in LPS-stimulated cultures has previously been reported,[37] but how it relates to the two described here is not known.

TABLE 3. Ability of MRL-*lpr/lpr* T-Cell SN to Induce Both Proliferation and Differentiation[a]

T-Cell Supernatant	Relative Increase in Proliferation	Relative Increase in Ig Synthesis
B cells only	1	1
14.1.7	42.6	32
4.3	4.8	4
D42	18	16
D28	30.8	32

[a]In this study, 10^5 MRL-+/+ B cells were cultured with 40% SN from the above MRL-*lpr/lpr* T-cell cultures or long-term lines. At 48 hours, one set of duplicate cultures were pulsed with 1 μC ^{3}(H)-TdR and harvested 12 hours later. SN from the other set was removed at day 6 and tested for Ig production by an ELISA assay. Cultures containing only B cells had 2400 ± 289 CPM (D3) and 1.7 μg/ml (D6).

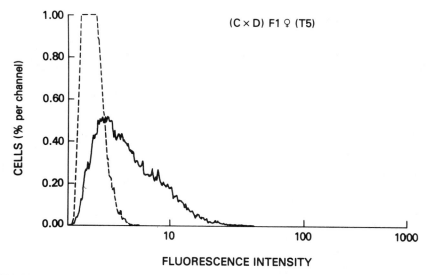

FIGURE 6. Profile of IgM⁺ cells present in four-week cultures of $(CBA/N \times DBA/2)F_1$ female B cells cultured with the 10% MRL-*lpr/lpr* T-cell SN 1.T5 and stained with FITC-anti-IgM. Control profile represents unstained cells.

B-Cell Growth in Vitro Induced by lpr/lpr T-Cell SN

Due to the presence in these SN of both the activation (Ia-inducing) and growth factors essential for proliferation, attempts were made to establish B cell lines in the presence of 10% SN. FIGURE 6 represents a profile of IgM⁺ cells following a four-week culture of $(CBA/N \times DBA/2)F_1$ female B cells in the presence of 1.T5 SN. Clearly, with no other addition to the culture, these SN can sustain B-cell growth through many rounds of division. Defective male $(CBA/N \times DBA/2)F_1$ B cells also grew in similar conditions. Experiments are in progress to study whether these B-cell cultures that already synthesize Ig can be further induced.

In summary, these experiments indicate that, in the absence of antigen, mitogen, anti-Ig, or other cross-linking agents, two lymphokines are sufficient, although perhaps

TABLE 4. Responses of MRL-*lpr/lpr* T Cell Lines in an Autologous Mixed Lymphocyte Reaction[a]

T-Cell Line	³(H)-TdR Incorporated Following Stimulation with		
	—	MRL-+/+	CBA/J
1.B2	1302 ± 388	$14{,}960 \pm 2660$	$16{,}335 \pm 1242$
1.Bot2	3188 ± 2786	$12{,}157 \pm 1921$	$48{,}685 \pm 1302$
1.T2	1131 ± 600	2929 ± 902	7258 ± 940
4.1.1	410 ± 137	1935 ± 589	5867 ± 899

[a]In this study, 4×10^4 T cells were cultured with 5×10^4 2500R irradiated anti-Thy1.2 treated spleen cells from congeneic MRL-+/+ or syngeneic CBA/J mice. After four days, wells were pulsed with 1 μC ³(H)-TdR and harvested 12 hours later. Data represent the mean CPM $\pm$ SEM of triplicate cultures.

not optimal, to induce B cells to terminal differentiation (IgM secretion) from a resting cell. Thus, it is thought that *in vivo* B cells emerging from the bone marrow are continuously activated by BSF-1, which by inducing BCGF receptors and increasing Ia antigens, facilitates T-B interactions and the delivery of later-acting T-cell-derived growth and differentiation signals; the latter resulting in the elevated numbers of Ig- and autoantibody-secreting cells characteristic of autoimmune disease. It should be noted that IFN and IL-2, made by the MRL-*lpr/lpr* T cells and known to cause B-cell differentiation in some systems,[38,39] may play roles in the polyclonal B-cell activation in these mice.

Ia ANTIGEN EXPRESSION, SELF-Ia REACTIVE T CELLS, AND AUTOIMMUNITY

The ability of nonmalignant MRL-*lpr/lpr* T cells to spontaneously proliferate and synthesize lymphokines both *in vitro* and *in vivo* suggests that either these cells are "semitransformed" (requiring no stimulation for these functions) or that self-Ia determinants on presenting cells in the culture serve as stimulatory molecules for their induction. The binding of lymphocytes to dendritic cells in the culture and the inhibition by anti-IL-2R and anti-Ia^k antibodies would support the latter. It should be noted that although the rapidly growing T-cell clones established from MRL-*lpr/lpr* spleen and LN are transformed and are IL-2 receptor bearing, they are no longer inhibitable by the IL-2 receptor antibody.[18]

To test directly whether autologous stimulation of MRL-*lpr/lpr* T cells could account for these observations, T cell lines were tested for their ability to recognize and be triggered by self-Ia antigens in two types of experiments. First, 4×10^4 T cells from the lines were cultured with 5×10^4 congeneic MRL-+/+ and syngeneic CBA/J non-T-cells irradiated with 2500R. TABLE 4 indicates that many lines responded to self-Ia molecules in these AMLR cultures. Secondly, T cells of the 14.1.7 line were irradiated (3300R) and cultured with 5×10^4 MRL-+/+ B cells because it has been shown that following recognition, nondividing Ia-reactive T cells can produce factors that result in B-cell activation.[40] The large responses seen in TABLE 5 would therefore again indicate self-recognition. Finally, in order to determine that MRL-*lpr/lpr* APC were competent to induce T-cell responses, 2×10^4 to 6×10^5 MRL-*lpr/lpr* or MRL-+/+ spleen or B cells were given 500R irradiation and cultured with 10^4 B10.BR anti-Ia^k reactive cloned T cells (kindly provided by Allison Finnegan). While *lpr/lpr* whole spleen cells were slightly less efficient than +/+ cells (due to the higher proportion of splenic T cells), B cells plus macrophages from the former presented equally as well (TABLE 6). Experiments are in progress to evaluate the antigen-presenting ability of the different cell types, which appears to be complex and highly regulated.

TABLE 5. B-Cell Proliferation Induced by the Irradiated MRL-*lpr/lpr* T Cell Line 14.1.7^a

14.1.7 T Cell Line	MRL-+/+ B Cells	^{3}(H)-TdR Incorporated
2×10^4	2×10^5	$139,598 \pm 14,283$
2×10^4	—	1036 ± 355
—	2×10^5	2203 ± 511

^{a}MRL-+/+ B cells were cultured alone or with 3300R irradiated T cells from the 14.1.7 T cell line. Cultures were pulsed at 24 hours with 1 μC ^{3}(H)-TdR and harvested at 48 hours.

TABLE 6. The Ability of MRL-*lpr/lpr* Spleen to Present Ia^k Antigens^a

Type of Stimulator	^{3}(H)-TdR Incorporation by an Anti-Ia^k Specific Clone Following Stimulation with	
	MRL-*lpr/lpr*	MRL-+/+
6×10^5 spleen cells	9370 ± 900	8536 ± 1677
2×10^5	15,137 ± 1982	27,379 ± 1692
0.6×10^5	10,560 ± 3381	17,388 ± 1058
0.2×10^5	3918 ± 1480	6589 ± 679
6×10^5 B cells	15,053 ± 2573	34,442 ± 4700
2×10^5	32,251 ± 2090	27,619 ± 1856
0.6×10^5	19,578 ± 3728	16,807 ± 5010

^{a}In this study, 10^4 T cells from the B10.BR anti-Ia^k (BR5) clone were cultured with varying numbers of MRL-*lpr/lpr* or MRL-+/+ spleen cells or B cells given 500R irradiation. Cultures were pulsed with 1 μC ^{3}(H)-TdR at 48 hours and harvested 12 hours later. Data represent the mean CPM ± SEM of triplicate cultures.

Ia ANTIGEN EXPRESSION AND OTHER AUTOIMMUNE MODELS

A linkage between Ia antigen expression and onset of autoimmunity has been demonstrated in both human disease and their murine counterparts. For example, HLA-DRw2 and HLA-DRw3 individuals are at higher risk for SLE than the general population.[43] Similarly, in the SLE strain of mice (NZB × NZW)F$_1$, the immune complex glomerulonephritis that develops is tightly linked to a gene in the H-2^z complex and can be prevented by *in vitro* treatment with anti-Ia^z antibody.[44] In addition, injection of the appropriate anti-Ia antibody has been shown to prevent both experimental allergic encephalomyelitis (EAE)[45] and myasthenia gravis.[46]

Although such antibodies may act by inducing suppression of T-lymphocyte function, it is also possible that they may prevent the activation of autoreactive T cells by interfering with antigen presentation. Recent studies have suggested that aberrant induction of Ia by tissues and subsequent presentation of autoantigens to self-reactive T cells may be important in the etiopathogenesis of organ-specific diseases in genetically susceptible individuals. For example, abnormal expression of HLA-DR by thyroid cells, detected from the early stages of autoimmune lymphocytic thyroiditis, is thought to stimulate thyroid-specific T cells, which, if unregulated, could mediate tissue damage and lead ultimately to disease.[47] The establishment of autoreactive T-cell clones from infiltrating cells in the thyroid glands of two patients with Graves' disease offers strong support for such a mechanism.[48] However, although aberrant Ia expression may indeed lead to stimulation of autologous T cells by autoantigens and constitute an early event in pathogenesis of certain autoimmune disease, clearly other physiological properties of the cells are critical because the mere presence of Ia antigens does not always confer cells with antigen-presenting function (Cowing, personal communication).

CONCLUDING REMARKS

Although the *lpr* (lymphoproliferation) gene and the precise defect it controls are not identified, the immunological abnormalities associated with the lymphoadenopathy seen in homozygous *lpr/lpr* mouse strains are well characterized. These mice exhibit autoantibody production against DNA, RNA, GP70, IgG, and thymocytes, along with polyclonal B-cell activation, elevated B-cell Ia expression, defective IL-2 synthesis in Con A stimulated cultures, and T-cell hyporesponsiveness; the extent to which these features exist being dependent on the background strain. Interestingly, similar abnormalities are also observed following infectious diseases. Alone, such manifestations are accompanied by mild nephritis (5–17% of mice develop severe glomerular lesions) and reduced longevity.[49] However, it is clear that additional genetic factors present in the spontaneously autoimmune strains of MRL and NZB are required for the development of early onset disease. To date, several features appear unique to these strains and may contribute to the more severe form of the disease. For example, the number and percent of Ia^+ macrophages and levels of IFN-γ are both

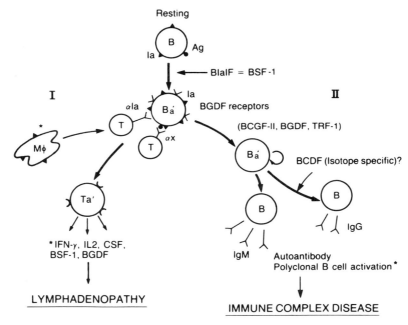

FIGURE 7. Scheme depicting the possible interactions between autologous lymphocytes and T-cell-derived factors leading to lupus-like disease in MRL-*lpr/lpr* mice. It shows the roles for high Ia^+ B cells in MRL-*lpr/lpr* autoimmune disease.

increased in these mice. In addition, the particular IgG anti-DNA clonotypes produced are unusual and may be more pathogenic in the development of lupus nephritis.[49]

However, the common disease manifestations observed in the MRL-*lpr/lpr* and other *lpr/lpr* stains (e.g., elevated B-cell Ia expression, increased Ig secretion by B cells, self-reactive T cells, nonmalignant T-cell lymphoproliferation, and spontaneous lymphokine synthesis) suggest that the underlying basis for *lpr* disease may be similar to that operating in an *in vivo* AMLR.[50] The possible interactions between autologous cells and lymphokines involved in this regulatory circuit are shown in FIGURE 7. Thus, the increased level of Ia antigens on B cells and macrophages is thought to lead to stimulation of usually inactive autologous Ia-reactive T cells, which in turn produce the lymphokines responsible for the characteristic B-cell hyperactivity, the T-cell division, and the continued high Ia expression. To directly test the possible role of high Ia$^+$ B cells in the development of disease, young MRL-*lpr/lpr* mice have been injected with antibody against the factor that induces B-cell Ia (anti-BSF-1). Preliminary results indicate both a marked reduction in anti-DNA antibody and the total LN weight in these treated mice as compared to controls. These encouraging findings, in addition to those demonstrating impressive retardation in the development of lymphadenopathy in mice suppressed with anti-IgM from birth,[41] provide examples of how intervention in this self-perpetuating circuit may result in prevention or amelioration of disease.

REFERENCES

1. SCHWARTZ, R. H. 1984. The role of gene products of the major histocompatibility complex in T cell activation and cellular interactions. *In* Fundamental Immunology. W. E. Paul, Ed.: 379–438. Raven Press. New York.
2. FINK, P. J. & M. J. BEVAN. 1978. H-2 antigens of the thymus determine lymphocyte specificity. J. Exp. Med. **148:** 766–775.
3. KRUISBEEK, A. M., S. O. SHARROW, B. J. MATHIESON & A. SINGER. 1981. The H-2 phenotype of the thymus dictates the self-specificity expressed by thymic, but not splenic cytotoxic T lymphocyte precursors in thymus-engrafted nude mice. J. Immunol. **127:** 2168–2178.
4. FINNEGAN, A., B. NEEDLEMAN & R. J. HODES. 1984. Activation of B cells by autoreactive T cells: cloned autoreactive T cells activate B cells by two distinct pathways. J. Immunol. **133:** 78–85.
5. GLIMCHER, L. N., D. L. LONGO, I. GREEN & R. H. SCHWARTZ. 1981. Murine syngeneic mixed lymphocyte response 1. Target antigens are self Ia molecules. J. Exp. Med. **154:** 1652–1670.
6. STEINBERG, A. D., E. S. RAVECHE, C. A. LASKIN, H. R. SMITH, T. J. SANTORO, M. L. MILLER & P. H. PLOTZ. 1984. Systemic lupus erythematosus: insights from animal models. Ann. Int. Med. **100:** 714–727.
7. THEOFILOPOULOS, A. N. & F. J. DIXON. 1985. Murine models of splenic lupus erythematosus. Adv. Immunol. **37:** 268.
8. WARREN, R. W., S. A. CASTER, J. B. ROTHS, E. D. MURPHY & D. S. PISETSKY. 1984. The influence of the *lpr* gene on B cell activation: differential antibody expression in *lpr* congenic mouse strains. Clin. Immunol. Immunopathol. **31:** 65.
9. THEOFILOPOULOS, A. N., D. L. SHAWLER, R. A. EISENBERG & F. J. DIXON. 1980. Splenic immunoglobulin-secreting cells and regulation in autoimmune mice. J. Exp. Med. **151:** 446–466.
10. ROSENBERG, Y. J. 1978. Autoimmune and polyclonal B cell responses during murine malaria. Nature **274:** 170–172.
11. ZOLLA-PAZNER, S. 1984. B cells in the pathogenesis of AIDS. Immunol. Today **5:** 289–291.
12. MORSE, H. C., III, W. F. DAVIDSON, R. A. YETTER, E. MURPHY, J. B. ROTHS & R. L. COFFMAN. 1982. Abnormalities induced by the mutant gene *lpr:* expansion of a unique lymphocyte subset. J. Immunol. **129:** 2612–2615.
13. STEINBERG, A. D., J. B. ROTHS, E. D. MURPHY, R. T. STEINBER & E. S. RAVECHE. 1980. Effects of thymectomy or androgen administration upon the autoimmune disease of MRL-*lpr/lpr* mice. J. Immunol. **125:** 871–873.
14. KELLY, V. E. & J. B. ROTHS. 1982. Increase in macrophage Ia expression in autoimmune mice: role of the *lpr* gene. J. Immunol. **129:** 923–925.
15. LU, C. Y. & E. R. UNANUE. 1982. Spontaneous T cell lymphokine production and enhanced macrophage Ia expression and tumerocidal activity in MRL-*lpr/lpr* mice. Clin. Immunol. Immunopathol. **25:** 213–222.
16. ROSENBERG, Y. J., A. D. STEINBERG & T. J. SANTORO. 1984. T cells from autoimmune IL 2 defective MRL-*lpr/lpr* mice continue to grow *in vitro* and produce IL 2 constitutively. J. Immunol. **133:** 2545–2548.

17. MOUNTZ, J. D., A. D. STEINBERG, D. M. KLINMAN, H. R. SMITH & J. F. MUSHINSKI. 1984. Lymphoproliferation with autoimmunity is associated with increased c-*myb* transcription. Science **225**: 1087–1089.
18. ROSENBERG, Y. J., T. R. MALEK, D. E. SCHAEFFER, T. J. SANTORO, G. E. MARK, A. D. STEINBERG & J. D. MOUNTZ. 1984. Unusual expression of IL 2 receptors and both the c-*myb* and c-*raf* oncogenes in rapidly growing T cell clones derived from autoimmune MRL-*lpr/lpr* mice. J. Immunol. **134**: 3120–3123.
19. STEEG, P. S., R. N. MOORE, H. M. JOHNSON & J. J. OPPENHEIM. 1982. Regulation of macrophage Ia antigen expression by a lymphokine with immune interferon activity. J. Exp. Med. **156**: 1780–1793.
20. SNYDER, D. S., D. I. BELLER & E. R. UNANUE. 1984. Prostaglandins modulate macrophage Ia expression. Nature **299**: 163–165.
21. LU, C. Y., T. S. CHANGELIAN & E. R. UNANUE. 1984. α-Fetoprotein inhibits macrophage expression of Ia antigens. J. Immunol. **132**: 1722–1727.
22. SANTORO, T. J., W. R. BENJAMIN, J. J. OPPENHEIM & A. D. STEINBERG. 1983. The cellular basis for immune interferon production in autoimmune MRL-*lpr/lpr* mice. J. Immunol. **131**: 265–268.
23. DAVIDSON, W. F., J. B. ROTHS, K. C. HOLMES, E. RUDIKOFF & H. C. MORSE. 1984. Dissociation of severe lupus-like disease from polyclonal B cell activation and IL 2 deficiency in C3H-*lpr/lpr* mice. J. Immunol. **133**: 1048–1056.
24. SANTORO, T. J., T. R. MALEK, Y. J. ROSENBERG, H. C. MORSE III & A. D. STEINBERG. 1984. Signals required for activation and growth of autoimmune T lymphocytes. J. Mol. Cell. Immunol. **1**: 347–356.
25. HEREMANS, H., A. BILLIAU, A. COLOMBATTI, J. HILGERS & P. DeSOMER. 1978. Interferon treatment of NZB mice accelerated progression of autoimmune disease. Infect. Immun. **21**: 925–1024.
26. ROSENBERG, Y. J., P. K. GOLDSMITH, J. OHARA, D. A. STEPHANY, G. D. WETZEL, A. D. STEINBERG & W. OHRINER. Mechanisms underlying polyclonal B cell activation in autoimmunity: MRL-*lpr/lpr* T cells produce an Ia inducing factor and a B cell growth and/or differentiation factor in the absence of exogenous antigen or mitogen. Submitted for publication.
27. MONROE, J. G., J. C. CAMBIER, E. A. MODY & D. S. PIESETSKY. 1985. Hyper-Ia antigen expression on B cells from B6-*lpr/lpr* mice correlates with manifestations of the autoimmune state. Clin. Immunol. Immunopathol. **34**: 124
28. WONG, G. H. N., I. CLARK-LEWIS, J. L. MCKIMM-BRESCHKIN, A. W. HARRIS & J. W. SCHRADER. 1984. Interferon-γ induces enhanced expression of Ia and H-2 antigens on B lymphoid, macrophage, and myeloid cell lines. Nature **310**: 688.
29. NOELLE, R., P. H. KRAMMER, J. OHARA, J. W. UHR & E. S. VITETTA. 1984. Increased expression of Ia on resting B cells: an additional role B cell growth factor. Proc. Natl. Acad. Sci. USA **81**: 6149–6153.
30. HOWARD, M., J. FARRAR, M. HILFIKER, B. JOHNSON, K. TAKATSU, T. HAMAOKA & W. E. PAUL. 1982. Identification of a T-cell derived B cell growth distinct from interleukin 2. J. Exp. Med. **155**: 914–926.
31. OLIVER, K., R. J. NOELLE, J. W. UHR, P. H. KRAMMER & E. S. VITETTA. 1985. B cell growth factor (BCGF-1 or BSF-1) is a differentiation factor for resting B cells and may not induce cell growth. Proc. Natl. Acad. Sci. USA **82**: 2465–2467.
32. RABIN, E. M., J. OHARA & W. E. PAUL. 1985. B-cell stimulatory factor activates resting B cells. Proc. Natl. Acad. Sci. USA **82**: 2935–2939.
33. VITETTA, E. S., J. OHARA, C. MYERS, J. LAYTON, P. H. KRAMMER & W. E. PAUL. 1985. Serological, biochemical, and functional identity of a B cell-stimulatory factor (BSF-1) and B cell differentiation factor for IgG1 (BCDF). J. Exp. Med. **162**: 1726.
34. SWAIN, S. L. 1985. Role of BCGF II in the differentiation to antibody secretion of normal and tumour B cells. J. Immunol. **134**: 3934–3943.
35. PIKE, B. L., D. L. VAUX, I. CLARK-LEWIS, J. W. SCHRADER & G. J. V. NOSSAL. 1982. Proliferation and differentiation of single hapten-specific B lymphocytes is promoted by T cell factor(s) distinct from T cell growth factor. Proc. Natl. Acad. Sci. USA **79**: 6350–6355.
36. TAKATSU, K., K. TANAKA, A. TOMINAGA, Y. KUMAHRA & T. HAMAOKA. 1980. Antigen-

inducing T cell-replacing factor III. Establishment of T cell hybridoma clone continuously producing TRF and functional analysis of released TRF. J. Immunol. **125:** 2646–2653.

37. PRUD'HOMME, G. J., C. L. PARK, T. M. FIESER, R. KOFFER, F. J. DIXON & A. N. THEOFILOPOULUS. 1983. Identification of a B cell differentiation factor(s) spontaneously produced by proliferating T cells in murine lupus strains of the *lpr/lpr* genotype. J. Exp. Med. **157:** 630–740.

38. SANTORO, T. J., B. L. LOTZIN, T. R. MALEK & K. R. LEHMANN. 1985. Interleukin 2 as a proliferative signal for autoimmune B cells. Fed. Proc. **1129:** 603.

39. LEIBSON, H. J., M. GEFTER, A. PLOTNIK, P. MARRACK & J. W. KAPPLER. 1984. Role for γ-interferon in antibody producing responses. Nature **309:** 799–802.

40. ASHWELL, J. D., A. L. DEFRANCO, W. E. PAUL & R. H. SCHWARTZ. 1984. Antigen presentation by resting B cells. Radiosensitivity of the antigen-presentation function and two distinct pathways of T cell activation. J. Exp. Med. **159:** 881–905.

41. JANEWAY, C. A., JR., K. BOTTOMLY, J. BABICH, P. CONRAD, S. CONZEN, B. JONES, J. KAYE, M. KATZ, L. MCVAY, D. MURPHY & C. TITE. 1984. Quantitative variation in Ia antigen expression plays a central role in immunoregulation. Immunol. Today **5:** 99–105.

42. FROHMAN, M. & C. COWING. 1985. Presentation of antigen by B cells: functional dependence on radiation dose, interleukins, cellular activation, and differential glycosylation. J. Immunol. **134:** 2269–2275.

43. GIBOFSKY, A., R. T. WINCHESTER, M. PATARROYO, M. FONTINO & H. G. KUNKEL. 1978. Disease association of the Ia-like human alloantigens: Contrasting patterns in rheumatoid arthritis and systemic lupus erythematosus. J. Exp. Med. **148:** 1728–1732.

44. KNIGHT, J. G. & D. D. ADAMS. 1978. Three genes for lupus nephritis in NZB × NZW mice. J. Exp. Med. **147:** 1653–1660.

45. WALDOR, M., S. SRIRAM, H. O. MCDEVITT & L. STEINMAN. 1983. *In vivo* therapy with monoclonal anti-I-A antibody suppress immune responses to acetylcholine receptors. Proc. Natl. Acad. Sci. USA **80:** 2713–2717.

46. STEINMAN, L., J. T. ROSENBAUM, S. SRIRAM & H. O. MCDEVITT. 1981. *In vivo* effects of antibodies to immune response gene products: prevention of experimental allergic encephalitis. Proc. Natl. Acad. Sci. USA **78:** 7111–7114.

47. BOTTAZZO, G. F., R. PUJOL-BORRELL, T. HANAFUSA & M. FELDMAN. 1984. HLA-DR expression and antigen presentation in the induction of endocrine autoimmunity. Lancet **11:** 1115–1119.

48. LONEI, M., G. F. BOTTAZZO & M. FELDMAN. 1985. Human T-cell clones from autoimmune thyroid glands: specific recognition of autologous thyroid cells. Science **228:** 85–89.

49. IZUI, S., V. E. KELLY, K. MASUDA, H. YOSHIDA, J. B. ROTHS & E. D. MURPHY. 1984. Induction of various autoantibodies by mutant gene *lpr* in several strains of mice. J. Immunol. **133:** 227–233.

50. ROSENBERG, Y. J., A. D. STEINBERG & T. J. SANTORO. 1984. The basis of autoimmunity in MRL-*lpr/lpr* mice: a role for self-reactive T cells. Immunol. Today **5:** 64–67.

DISCUSSION OF THE PAPER

UNIDENTIFIED DISCUSSANT: Gleichmann produced many elements of autoimmunity by injecting allogeneic T cells into normal mice. His idea is that there are two signals: the allogeneic T cell recognizing Ia on the B cell and the cross-linking of the B-cell receptors by polymeric antigen. Now, if that applies to your system, then autoreactive anti-Ia cells would provide signal 1. The question is, do you need anything else to make B cells produce autoantibodies?

Y. J. ROSENBERG (*National Institutes of Health, Bethesda, MD*): In this case, the anti-DNA antibodies result from polyclonal activation. Therefore, you do not need an antigen. If you give any antigen to these mice, they never respond in an antigen-specific way once they have gotten sick.

UNIDENTIFIED DISCUSSANT: What sort of antigen are you thinking of?

ROSENBERG: One can use TNP or sheep red cells.

UNIDENTIFIED DISCUSSANT: That is a very late stage. I still think that the auto-anti-Ia may be one factor that would help polymeric autoantigens to trigger a B-cell response.

S. DATTA (*Tufts University School of Medicine, Boston, MA*): Have you treated your animals with anti-Ia?

ROSENBERG: No, but I am sure it will work.

UNIDENTIFIED DISCUSSANT: Have you compared MRL-*lpr/lpr* mice to MRL-+/+ mice, which also develop nephritis and anti-DNA antibodies?

ROSENBERG: I cannot grow MRL-+/+ T cells in tissue culture.

UNIDENTIFIED DISCUSSANT: Do B cells of NZB mice have high Ia expression?

ROSENBERG: Yes.

UNIDENTIFIED DISCUSSANT: Do they behave like MRL-*lpr/lpr* cells *in vitro?*

ROSENBERG: I do not know; I have not done the experiment.

UNIDENTIFIED DISCUSSANT: Do the T cells start producing BSF first or do the B cells produce large amounts of factors that then stimulate other B cells?

ROSENBERG: Everything happens after the T cells start to expand.

UNIDENTIFIED DISCUSSANT: Have you tried using supernatants from T cell lines other than the MRL-*lpr/lpr* T cells lines? I mean, other cell lines that produce BCGF?

ROSENBERG: I am sure they work. Mine just make more of it for fewer cells.

UNIDENTIFIED DISCUSSANT: Are you then suggesting that the abnormal MRL T cell that also expresses B-cell markers is producing the Ia-inducing factor?

ROSENBERG: Yes. My lines are all Ly-1, Ly-2 negative.

Vaccination against Experimental Autoimmune Diseases Using T Lymphocytes Treated with Hydrostatic Pressure

OFER LIDER,[a] MEIR SHINITZKY,[b] AND
IRUN R. COHEN[a]

[a]*Department of Cell Biology*
[b]*Department of Membrane Research*
The Weizmann Institute of Science
Rehovot, 76100 Israel

BACKGROUND

Diseases thought to involve autoimmune processes include multiple sclerosis, rheumatoid and other arthritides, type I diabetes mellitus, and various forms of thyroiditis. In these diseases, the particular target organ suffers irreparable damage from progressive or repeated insults by the individual's immune system. At present, there exists no specific therapy for the pathogenic process of these conditions. Nonspecific anti-inflammatory drugs are used symptomatically in arthritis, exogenous hormones are administered to replace endogenous insulin or thyroid hormones, and indiscriminant immunosuppression is used as a last resort in severe cases of multiple sclerosis or rheumatoid arthritis. (It is also used experimentally in early type I diabetes.) An ideal mode of therapy would be one that could selectively nullify those autoreactive lymphocytes responsible for the disease, while leaving intact the other, healthy components of the immune system.

The laboratory of one of us (I.R.C.) has initiated steps in the direction of this goal by deploying lines and clones of autoimmune T lymphocytes to vaccinate animals against particular experimental autoimmune diseases.[1] The strategy was to isolate and grow in long-term culture the T lymphocytes that caused autoimmune diseases in rats or mice. These include experimental autoimmune encephalomyelitis (EAE),[2,3] experimental autoimmune thyroiditis (EAT),[4] and adjuvant arthritis (AA).[5–7] The T-lymphocyte lines have been used successfully to investigate factors important in disease: identification of the target antigens of autoimmune attack,[8,9] migration of the T lymphocytes to their target organ,[10] their persistence in the body,[11] their pathogenic effects *in vivo*[12] and *in vitro*,[13] and their expression of enzymes[14] and surface markers[10] associated with function.

Relevant to the present communication was the observation that autoimmune T lymphocytes could induce resistance, that is, vaccinate animals against the specific disease. Rat T-lymphocyte lines reactive to the basic protein of myelin (anti-BP) will, upon intravenous inoculation, produce EAE in naive rats.[2,3] However, the virulence of the anti-BP line cells could be attenuated by irradiating them (1500R). Such line cells could no longer produce EAE, but rats receiving these attenuated cells acquired resistance to EAE induced later by active immunization to BP in complete Freund's adjuvant (BP/CFA).[10,15,16] Vaccination with irradiated T lymphocytes, though, has deficiencies; there was little resistance to EAE produced by passive transfer of virulent anti-BP line cells[17] and individual clones of the anti-BP line were incapable of vaccination.[18]

Anti-thyroglobulin (anti-Tg) T-lymphocyte lines were found to mediate EAT in mice.[4] Attenuated anti-Tg T lymphocytes vaccinated mice against EAT, produced either actively by immunization to Tg/CFA or passively by inoculation with virulent anti-Tg line cells.[4]

Adjuvant arthritis, unlike EAE or EAT, is not induced by immunization to a defined self-antigen, but by immunization to antigens of *Mycobacterium tuberculosis* (MT).[19] By raising rat T lymphocytes reactive to MT, we isolated a clone, A2b, that produced arthritis in heavily irradiated (750R) rats.[5,6] This arthritogenic clone responded *in vitro* both to MT and to a fraction of the proteoglycan of joint cartilage.[8] Thus, AA probably is caused by T lymphocytes that recognize an epitope of MT cross-reactive with rat joint cartilage. Clone A2b was not able to vaccinate rats against AA.[6] However, another clone, A2c, was not arthritogenic and the rats receiving A2c acquired resistance to AA (in preparation). Although the process of vaccination remains to be clarified, it is reasonable to suspect that the autoimmune receptors of the T-lymphocyte vaccine induce resistance to disease by activating antireceptor immunity.[1,20] If this is so, then procedures that increase the immunogenicity of the T-lymphocyte receptor might increase the potency of vaccination induced by T-lymphocyte line cells.

AUGMENTATION OF IMMUNOGENICITY BY HYDROSTATIC PRESSURE

The rationale behind our strategy for increasing the potency of vaccination by autoimmune T lymphocytes was derived from observations related to augmentation of immunogenicity of tumor cells. The laboratory of one of us (M.S.) has been investigating nonadversative means for augmentation of immunogenicity of tumor cells through lateral and vertical rearrangement of their membrane proteins (reviewed in reference 21). Currently two types of vaccines have been prepared from tumor cells: cholesterol-treated cells and pressure-treated cells. Pressure treatment of tumor cells was found to be very effective in enhancing the immunogenicity of tumor-associated antigens.[22] We therefore undertook to investigate whether hydrostatic pressure similarly would augment the potency of autoimmune T lymphocytes as vaccines against autoimmune disease.

PRESSURE TREATMENT INHIBITS PROLIFERATION OF T LYMPHOCYTES

T-lymphocyte lines treated with the pressure used to enhance the immunogenicity of tumor cells (1.2–1.5 kbar for 15 min) were found to remain intact and they excluded the vital dye, trypan blue (not shown). However, as shown in TABLE 1, pressure-treated line cells were unable to proliferate *in vitro* when stimulated by incubation with specific antigen or the T-cell mitogen, Concanavalin A. Irradiation with 1500R left the lymphocytes with a negligibly small response, yet with an apparent normal morphology. However, death and disintegration of both irradiated and pressure-treated line cells were observed after culture for 3–4 days (not shown). Thus, pressure rendered the T lymphocytes unresponsive and moribund.

TABLE 1. T-Lymphocyte Lines Are Unable to Proliferate after Treatment with Pressure[a]

T Lymphocyte Line		Proliferative Response (cpm $\times$ 10^{-3} $\pm$ SD)			
Specificity	Treatment	No. Antigen	BP	MT	Con A
Anti-BP	none	0.9 ± 0.2	115 ± 3	0.7 ± 0.3	140 ± 7
	irradiation	0.9 ± 0.1	2.3 ± 0.4	1.0 ± 0.2	2.5 ± 0.5
	pressure	0.4 ± 0.2	0.6 ± 0.2	0.4 ± 0.1	0.7 ± 0.3
Anti-MT	none	1.5 ± 0.4	0.9 ± 0.3	98.3 ± 1	138 ± 7
	irradiation	1.1 ± 0.5	1.2 ± 0.2	3.0 ± 0.3	2.9 ± 0.2
	pressure	0.8 ± 0.2	0.6 ± 0.2	0.7 ± 0.1	0.6 ± 0.3

[a]Anti-BP[3] and anti-MT lines[5] were developed and maintained as described. The line cells were irradiated as described[3] or treated with pressure as follows. The cells were suspended in PBS at a concentration of 7×10^7/ml and placed in a sterile Eppendorf centrifuge tube. A 22G needle was inserted through the cap of the tube and the tube was filled with cold PBS (0°C) and sealed. The tube was then placed in a cooled (4°C) pressure cylinder (American Instrument, Aminco., Silver Spring, Maryland) and the cylinder was introduced into a French Press. Pressure was applied over 7–8 min to a level of 1.5 kbars, where it was maintained for 15 min and then released over another 7–8 min. The pressure-treated cells were washed in PBS and used in a proliferative response assay as described.[3] Results are shown as the cpm of incorporated ³H-thymidine. Each well of a microtiter plate contained 25×10^3 line cells, 2×10^6 irradiated Lewis thymocytes (1500R), and 10 μg/ml of BP or MT, or 2.5 μg/ml Con A. Each group was cultured in quadruplicate for 72 hours. ³H-Thymidine was added for the last 12 hours of incubation. (BP = myelin basic protein, MT = *Mycobacterium tuberculosis,* irradiation = 1500R, pressure = 1.5 kbar.)

TABLE 2. Pressure Treatment of Lines or Clones Augments Vaccination against EAE[a]

Anti-BP Lymphocytes	BP Activation	Treatment	% Incidence of Passive EAE	Vaccination	
				% Inhibition of EAE Induced by:	
				BP/CFA	Anti-BP Line
Line Z1a	no	none	0	0	0
	yes	none	100	70	10
	yes	irradiation	0	70	0
	no	pressure	0	0	0
	yes	pressure	0	80	100
Clone D9	no	none	0	0	0
	yes	none	100	0	0
	yes	irradiation	0	0	0
	no	pressure	0	0	0
	yes	pressure	0	80	100

[a]Line Z1a and clone D9, both reactive against the 68–88 peptide of BP,[18] were activated or not by incubation with BP and irradiated accessory cells as described.[10] Line and clone cells were treated with irradiation[3] or pressure as described in the footnote to TABLE 1. Lewis rats (5–15 per group) were inoculated intravenously with 10^7 T lymphocytes as described[3] and the incidence of EAE mediated by the T lymphocytes was recorded. Rats to be tested for vaccination were inoculated with 2×10^7 treated T lymphocytes intraperitoneally in incomplete Freund's adjuvant. Thirty days later, the rats were challenged with BP/CFA to induce active EAE or with 5×10^6 Z1a line cells to induce passive EAE. (Irradiation = 1500R; pressure = 1.5 kbar, 15 min.)[3]

PRESSURE-TREATED T LYMPHOCYTES VACCINATE

TABLE 2 summarizes the effects of anti-BP line Z1a and clone D9 in producing EAE or vaccinating against EAE. Line Z1a, if not activated by incubation with BP before inoculation, neither caused EAE nor vaccinated against it.[20] Activated anti-BP line cells produced EAE in all recipient rats and those rats that recovered from acute disease showed resistance to active EAE induced by immunization to BA/CFA. However, there was little resistance to EAE mediated by a second injection of the Z1a line itself. As was reported, activated and irradiated line cells did not produce EAE, but recipient rats were vaccinated against active EAE.[10,15] However, these rats were not resistant to passive EAE produced by the anti-BP line.[17] In contrast, inoculation of rats with pressure-treated, activated anti-BP line cells induced resistance to both active and passive EAE. Moreover, the pressure-treated cells themselves did not produce EAE. Pressure-treated, nonactivated anti-BP line lymphocytes, though, did not vaccinate.

The results with anti-BP clone D9 were even more striking. Similar to the other anti-BP clones, D9 could only produce EAE, but could not vaccinate against either active or passive disease.[18] Nevertheless, activated anti-BP clone D9, when treated with pressure, vaccinated recipient rats against both active EAE and EAE produced by the Z1a line. Thus, pressure rendered anti-BP T lymphocytes nonvirulent and as superior vaccines against EAE.

VACCINATION IS SPECIFIC

The results of experiments designed to test the specificity of vaccination with anti-BP line cells are shown in TABLE 3. It can be seen that anti-BP line cells activated by Con A were as effective as those activated by BP in vaccinating rats against EAE. Thus, acquired resistance could not be explained by carryover of BP into the recipient rats. This conclusion was further supported by the failure of anti-MT line cells or normal thymocytes to vaccinate against EAE even after they had been cultured together with BP.

In additional experiments, we found that pressure-treated anti-BP line cells did not vaccinate against AA and that pressure-activated anti-MT line cells vaccinated rats

TABLE 3. Specificity of Vaccination[a]

Pressure-Treated Cells	Activation	Vaccination	
		% Inhibition of EAE Induced by:	
		BP/CFA	Anti-BP Line
Anti-BP	BP	73	93
Anti-BP	Con A	75	100
Anti-BP	none	0	0
Anti-MT	MT	0	0
Anti-MT	MT + BP	0	0
Thymocytes	BP	0	0

[a]Anti-BP[3] or anti-MT[5] line cells or Lewis thymocytes were activated by incubation with antigens or Con A as described. The cells were then treated with pressure as described in the footnote to TABLE 1. Rats were inoculated with 2×10^7 cells in incomplete Freund's adjuvant intraperitoneally, and one month later were challenged to induce EAE actively with BP/CFA or passively with 5×10^6 anti-BP line cells.[3]

TABLE 4. Pressure-Treated Anti-BP Lymphocytes Must Be Intact to Vaccinate[a]

Activated Anti-BP Line	Treatment	Subsequent EAE via Anti-BP Line		
		Incidence	Clinical Score	% Protection
none	none	15/15	4	0
yes	irradiation	5/5	2.8	0
yes	P	1/15	0.2	93
yes	P + sonication	3/3	3	0
yes	P membrane	3/3	3	0
yes	cholesterol	4/4	3.5	0

[a]Anti-BP line cells were activated as described[3] and rats were incubated intraperitoneally with 2×10^7 cells that had been irradiated (1500R) or treated with pressure (see footnote to TABLE 1). Some rats were inoculated with an equivalent number of pressure-treated cells (P) that had been disrupted by sonication or with membrane preparations of pressure-treated cells. Sonication was done using an Ultrasonic Model W325 at intervals of 5 sec × 8. Membranes were prepared by homogenizing the cells and centrifuging the homogenate in a 41% sucrose gradient at 90,000G. Cholesterol packing of cells was done using a solution of cholesterol hemisuccinate in a PVP solution. The clinical score was determined as follows: 1 = tail weakness; 2 = paralysis of hind limbs; 3 = paralysis of all limbs; 4 = moribund. (Pressure = 1.5 kbar, 15 min; irradiation = 1500R.)

against AA, but not against EAE (not shown). Thus, vaccination was immunologically specific and could not be attributed to transfer of antigen.

VACCINATION REQUIRES INTACT T LYMPHOCYTES

Experiments were done to learn whether augmented vaccination required that the pressure-treated anti-BP line cells be intact. TABLE 4 shows that pressure-treated, but not irradiated, activated anti-BP line cells vaccinated rats against passive EAE. However, sonication of the pressure-treated cells or membrane preparations of these cells failed to vaccinate. Enriching the anti-BP cells with cholesterol also failed to render them effective vaccines. Thus, the ability of pressure-treated T lymphocytes to induce resistance to disease appears to depend on the intactness of the cells. Moreover, augmented vaccination cannot be attributed to membrane ridigification alone as treatment with cholesterol had no effect.

MECHANISM OF VACCINATION

Two important questions must be answered: What are the critical effects of pressure on the T lymphocytes that render them vaccines and what are the mechanisms of resistance that they induce in the recipient? Hydrostatic pressure operates exclusively on compressible compartments, and in intact cells, these are comprised of the membrane lipid layer and the cytoskeletal polymers.[21] While under pressure in the range used in our study, the lipid layer becomes significantly more rigid and the cytoskeletal network practically disintegrates. These changes lead to aggregations of membrane proteins that are largely preserved after the pressure is released, and the lipid layer and the cytoskeletal return to their normal state.[21] Examination of the cell surface using a fluorescent antibody assay indeed indicated that the pressure treatment produced permanent aggregation of lymphocyte surface major histocompatibility class

I antigens (not shown) and Thy1, 2.[22] We suspect that similar aggregation of the T lymphocyte antigen receptor may also take place as a result of the pressure treatment. These antigen aggregates presumably increase considerably the immunogenic expression of the T-cell receptors. As the pressure-treated T lymphocytes are nonresponsive and moribund, it is not likely that they participate actively in the process of resistance. Vaccination, therefore, is probably accomplished by the response of the recipient to the rearranged membrane antigens of the inoculated T lymphocytes.

If, indeed, resistance is due to antireceptor immunity, then that immunity is unexpectedly comprehensive since a single clone can induce resistance to disease produced either by an uncloned line or by active immunization. Either all anti-BP T lymphocytes share a common receptor idiotype or immunization to a single receptor idiotype generates a mechanism that recognizes the antigen and suppresses all the receptor-bearing effector T lymphocytes that also see the antigen, irrespective of their idiotype. These possibilities are being explored. Whatever the mechanism turns out to be, it is now evident that pressure-treated T lymphocytes are a powerful tool for exciting resistance to experimentally induced autoimmune disease. The ultimate question is the feasibility of this strategy to produce resistance in clinical autoimmunity.

REFERENCES

1. COHEN, I. R., A. BEN-NUN, J. HOLOSHITZ, R. MARON & R. ZERUBAVEL. 1983. Vaccination against autoimmune disease using lines of autoimmune T lymphocyte. Immunol. Today **4:** 227–230.
2. BEN-NUN, A., H. WEKERLE & I. R. COHEN. 1981. The rapid isolation of clonable antigen-specific T lymphocyte lines capable of mediating autoimmune encephalomyelitis. Eur. J. Immunol. **11:** 195–199.
3. BEN-NUN, A. & I. R. COHEN. 1982. Experimental autoimmune encephalomyelitis (EAE) medicated by T cell lines: Process of selection of lines and characterization of the cells. J. Immunol. **129:** 303–308.
4. MARON, R., R. ZERUBAVEL, A. FRIEDMAN & I. R. COHEN. 1983. T lymphocyte line specific for thyroglobulin produces or vaccinates against autoimmune thyroiditis in mice. J. Immunol. **131:** 2316–2322.
5. HOLOSHITZ, J., Y. NAPARSTEK, A. BEN-NUN & I. R. COHEN. 1983. Lines of T lymphocytes induce or vaccinate against autoimmune arthritis. Science **219:** 56–58.
6. HOLOSHITZ, J., A. MATITIAU & I. R. COHEN. 1984. Arthritis induced in rats by cloned T lymphocytes responsive to mycobacteria, but not to collagen type II. J. Clin. Invest. **73:** 211–215.
7. HOLOSHITZ, J., A. MATITIAU & I. R. COHEN. 1985. Role of the thymus in induction and transfer of vaccination against adjuvant arthritis with a T lymphocyte line in rats. J. Clin. Invest. **75:** 472–477.
8. VAN EDEN, W., J. HOLOSHITZ, Z. NEVO, A. FRENKEL, A. KLAJMAN & I. R. COHEN. 1985. Arthritis induced by a T lymphocyte clone that responds to *Mycobacterium tuberculosis* and to cartilage proteoglycans. Proc. Natl. Acad. Sci. USA. **82:** 5117–5120.
9. COHEN, I. R., J. HOLOSHITZ, W. VAN EDEN & A. FRENKEL. 1985. T lymphocyte clones illuminate pathogenesis and effect therapy of experimental arthritis. Arthritis Rheum. **28:** 841–845.
10. NAPARSTEK, Y., A. BEN-NUN, J. HOLOSHITZ, T. RESHEF, A. FRENKEL, M. ROSENBERG & I. R. COHEN. 1983. T lymphocyte lines producing or vaccinating against autoimmune encephalomyelitis (EAE): Functional activation induces PNA receptors and accumulation in the brain and thymus of line cells. Eur. J. Immunol. **13:** 418–423.
11. NAPARSTEK, Y., Y. HOLOSHITZ, S. EISENSTEIN, T. RESHEF, S. RAPPAPORT, S. CHEMKE, A. BEN-NUN & I. R. COHEN. 1982. Effector T lymphocyte line cells migrate to the thymus and persist there. Nature **300:** 262–264.

12. HOLOSHITZ, J., Y. NAPARSTEK, A. BEN-NUN, P. MARQUARDT & I. R. COHEN. 1984. T lymphocyte lines induce autoimmune encephalomyelitis delayed hypersensitive and bystander encephalitis or arthritis. Eur. J. Immunol. **14:** 729–732.
13. YAROM, Y., Y. NAPARSTEK, V. LEV-RAM, J. HOLOSHITZ, A. BEN-NUN & I. R. COHEN. 1983. Immunospecific inhibition of nerve conduction in isolated rat optic nerve exerted by a line of T lymphocytes reactive to basic protein of myelin. Nature **303:** 246–247.
14. NAPARSTEK, Y., I. R. COHEN, Z. FUKS & I. VLODAVSKY. 1984. Activated T lymphocytes produce a matrix degrading heparan sulphate endoglycosidase. Nature **310:** 241–244.
15. BEN-NUN, A., A. WEKERLE & I. R. COHEN. 1981. Vaccination against autoimmune encephalomyelitis with T lymphocyte line cells reactive against myelin basic protein. Nature (London) **292:** 60–61.
16. HOLOSHITZ, J., A. FRENKEL, A. BEN-NUN & I. R. COHEN. 1983. Autoimmune encephalomyelitis (EAE) mediated or prevented by T lymphocyte lines directed against diverse antigenic determinants or myelin basic protein. Vaccination is determinant specific. J. Immunol. **131:** 2810–2813.
17. BEN-NUN, A. & I. R. COHEN. 1981. Vaccination against autoimmune encephalomyelitis (EAE). Attenuated autoimmune T lymphocytes confer resistance to induction of active EAE, but not to EAE mediated by intact T lymphocyte line. Eur. J. Immunol. **11:** 949–952.
18. VANDENBARK, A. A., H. OFFNER, T. RESHEF, R. FRITZ, C-H. J. CHOU & I. R. COHEN. 1985. Specificity of T lymphocyte lines for peptides of myelin basic protein. J. Immunol. **135:** 229–233.
19. PEARSON, C. M. 1964. Experimental models in rheumatoid disease. Arthritis Rheum. **7:** 80–86.
20. COHEN, I. R. 1984. Autoimmunity: Physiologic and pernicious. Adv. Intern. Med. **29:** 147–165.
21. SHINITZKY, M. 1984. Membrane fluidity in malignancy—adversative and recuperative. Biochim. Biophys. Acta **738:** 251–261.
22. RICHERT, L., A. OR & M. SHINITZKY. Promotion of tumor immunogenicity in EL4 cells subjected to hydrostatic pressure. Cancer Immunol. Immunotherapy. In press.

DISCUSSION OF THE PAPER

I. R. MACKAY (*Royal Melbourne Hospital, Victoria, Australia*): Have you followed cutaneous DTH reactions in parallel with the induction and suppression of disease? It appears from the time intervals that the apparent helper cells that you are injecting are in fact acting as effectors.

I. R. COHEN: (*Weizmann Institute of Science, Rehovot, Israel*): We have looked at DTH and these cells do, if they are activated, transfer DTH to their specific antigen.

Therapy of Autoimmune Diseases with Antibody to Immune Response Gene Products or to T-Cell Surface Markers[a]

LAWRENCE STEINMAN, MATTHEW K. WALDOR,
SCOTT S. ZAMVIL, MAE LIM, LEANORE HERZENBERG,
LEONARD HERZENBERG, HUGH O. McDEVITT, DENNIS
MITCHELL, AND SUBRAMANIAM SRIRAM

Departments of Neurology and Pediatrics
Stanford University School of Medicine
Stanford, California 94305

Over the past five years, the efficacy of monoclonal antibodies for the treatment of autoimmune disease has been demonstrated. Monoclonal antibodies directed against products of the immune response (IR) genes or against T-cell structures involved with recognition of these IR gene products are extraordinarily successful therapeutic agents against autoimmune diseases in experimental animals. In five models of autoimmune disease, monoclonal antibodies against products of the I-A subregion of the major histocompatibility complex or against the L3T4a molecule on helper/inducer T cells either prevented development of clinical signs (when given prior to autoimmunization) or reversed ongoing disease (when given after clinical signs were apparent).

TREATMENT WITH MONOCLONAL ANTI-I-A ANTIBODIES

Experimental allergic encephalitis (EAE) is an inflammatory disease of the central nervous system resulting in clinical paralysis. One of the primary pathologic events is the development of autoreactive T cells to myelin basic protein (MBP). Susceptibility to EAE and immune responsiveness to MBP is under control of IR genes in a variety of species. In the mouse, we have demonstrated that T-cell clones, which recognize MBP in the context of Ia molecules, can induce EAE.[1] In TABLE 1, we demonstrate that the encephalitogenic T-cell clone, designated 1_1, derived from immunization of SJL/J mice with bovine MBP, responds to MBP only when MBP is presented on spleen cells that express I-A^s.

The linkage of EAE to IR genes can be more precisely analyzed with the strains, PL/J(H-2^u) and (PL/J × SJL/J)F$_1$ [(PLSJ)F$_1$]. Following sensitization to guinea pig MBP, inbred mouse strains of SJL/J(H-2^s), PL/J(H-2^u), and (PLSJ)F$_1$ mice are all found to be susceptible to EAE.[2] Whereas sensitization to the N-terminal 1–37 amino-acid peptide of MBP induces EAE in PL/J mice, immunization to the C-terminal 89–169 peptide of MBP leads to EAE in SJL/J mice.[2] The immune response to MBP in the (PLSJ)F$_1$ is not codominant, with sensitization to the

[a]Financial support was derived from NIH grant no. NS18235, NIH contract no. NO1-NS-4-23178, an NIH Teacher Investigator Award, the National Multiple Sclerosis Society, the Kroc Foundation, the Kittredge Fund, the Fausel Foundation, and the Kramer Foundation.

N-terminal (but not the C-terminal) peptide inducing EAE.[2,3] We asked whether T-cell clones raised in (PLSJ)F$_1$ following sensitization to rat MBP would be reactive to N-terminal or C-terminal peptides on MBP and whether they would be restricted to Ia^s, Ia^u, or Ia$^{s/u}$ molecules. We showed that reactivity to self(mouse)-MBP occurs in all clones restricted to I-A^u or I-E$^{s/u}$. These mouse MBP reactive clones respond to the N-terminal peptide 1–37. An I-A^u restricted T-cell clone recognizing peptide 1–37 of MBP induces both classic clinical and histological EAE in the (PLSJ)F$_1$ mouse.[4] The clone-induced disease has three forms, namely, acute and fatal, chronic and stable, and relapsing and remitting. Demyelination is evident histologically, in addition to perivascular cuffing.

Because susceptibility to EAE is controlled in part by IR genes mapping to the I-A subregion, we first asked whether anti-I-A antibodies might prevent acute EAE. Acute EAE is a monophasic disease with high mortality. A small change in immunization protocol produces a chronic relapsing form of EAE (CR-EAE) that resembles multiple sclerosis (MS) in clinical presentation and histology. Like susceptibility to EAE, susceptibility to MS is associated with class II major histocompatibility gene products.

TABLE 1. MHC-Restricted Proliferation of Bovine BP SJL/J Clone 1$_1$

| Strain of APC | I-A Haplotype | Antigen | |
		None	BOV BP 100 μg/ml
SJL/J	(s)	1081 ± 778^a	101,268 ± 15,695
B10.S(9R)	(s)	256 ± 177	29,550 ± 5984
A.TH	(s)	310 ± 320	104,509 ± 10,791
B10.HTT	(s)	91 ± 28	29,811 ± 5012
BALB/c	(d)	3576 ± 1266	6329 ± 1932
C57BL/6	(b)	130 ± 43	524 ± 148
C3H	(k)	349 ± 80	405 ± 129
PL/J	(u)	903 ± 440	1988 ± 1020

^{a}Values represent mean ± SD of ^{3}H-thymidine cpm incorporated in quadruplicate cultures.

Prevention of acute EAE was demonstrated in SJL/J (H-2^s) mice by administering antibodies reactive with I-A^s prior to immunization with spinal-cord antigen.[5] Clinical disease was evident in 3/28 mice that received anti-I-A^s antibodies, compared to 19/28 mice that received a noncross-reactive anti-I-A^k antibody ($p < 0.0001$). Surprisingly, histologic disease was apparent in most of the mice that received anti-I-A^s, though the lesions were not as extensive. This observation indicated that although disease was prevented, autoimmunization to myelin antigens with subsequent entry of cells into the central nervous systems had occurred. Proliferation of T cells to MBP can be demonstrated in MBP-immunized, anti-I-A^s treated mice, and this corroborates our view that following immunization with MBP in complete Freund's adjuvant (CFA), autoimmunization is not prevented. In spite of the generation of autoreactive T lymphocytes, there was decreased migration of lymphocytes to the central nervous system in mice treated with I-A^s.[6] This was demonstrated by injecting ^{51}Cr-labeled lymphocytes intravenously into mice. The mice had been injected with anti-I-A^s prior to immunization with spinal cord in CFA. The homing of ^{51}Cr lymphocytes to brain and spinal cord was clearly diminished in mice given anti-I-A^s (TABLE 2).

In order to be clinically relevant, any putative therapy must be successful when given after disease onset. Thus, we investigated whether treatment with anti-I-A

TABLE 2. Accumulation of ^{51}Cr-Lymphocytes in Spinal Cords of Mice Treated with Anti-I-A^s

| Treatment | Clinical EAE | | | Mean Weight Loss |
	Mild	Severe	Total	
Anti-I-A^s	1/20	3/20	4/20^a	-0.3 ± 2.2 g^b
Anti-I-A^d	5/40	15/40	20/40^a	-1.1 ± 2.0 g^b

Treatment	^{51}Cr Accumulation (lymph-node cells)
Anti-I-A^s (clinically well)	6160 ± 1308^c
Anti-I-A^d (clinically well)	9357 ± 4239
Anti-I-A^d (severe disease)	$24,751 \pm 4331^c$

$^a\chi^2 = 3.84$ with continuity correction; $p < 0.05$.
$^bp < 0.07$, Student's t test.
$^cp < 0.00001$, Student's t test.

antibodies might prove effective in mitigating ongoing acute EAE and CR-EAE.[7] Anti-I-A antibodies were administered at the onset of paralytic signs and the subsequent clinical course was followed (see TABLE 3). In CR-EAE, mice first displayed the initial attack of paralysis around day 32. These SJL/L mice were then given either anti-I-A^s (0.6 mg weekly, intraperitoneally) or a control monoclonal anti-I-A that does not cross-react with I-A^s. During a 4½-month observation period, 18 clinical relapses were seen in a control group containing 18 mice, while 7 relapses were seen in a group of 18 mice given anti-I-A^s ($p < 0.001$). There was no mortality (0/18) in the anti-I-A^s treated group, while control mice had 7/23 deaths ($p < 0.04$), with 5 occurring in the first attack. Weekly measurement of antibody to MBP revealed a decrease in anti-MBP levels in mice given anti-I-A^s. The reduction occurred five weeks after treatment started and continued throughout the full period of observations. In acute EAE, mice were treated with anti-I-A antibody at the first signs of paralysis.

TABLE 3. Clinical Features of Anti-I-A Antibody Treatment in Chronic Relapsing EAE

	Number of Mice	Date of Onset (d) (mean $\pm$ S.D.)	Mortality
Initial Attack			
Group I	18	32 ± 9	0/18
Group II	23	32 ± 12	5/23
First Relapse			
Group I	5/18^a	78 ± 14^b	0/5
Group II	12/18^a	61 ± 20^b	2/12
Second Relapse			
Group I	2/18	105 ± 12	0/2
Group II	5/16^c	99 ± 16	0/5
Cumulative Totals	Number of Relapses		Mortality at Day 130
Group I	7^d		0/18^a
Group II	18^d		7/23^a

$^ap < 0.04$.
$^bp < 0.08$.
^{c}One mouse had a third relapse.
$^dp < 0.001$.

These mice showed a dramatic reversal of paralytic signs and a rapid recovery, sometimes over a period of as little as a few hours.[3]

These experiments with acute EAE and CR-EAE extend our view that anti-I-A therapy acts after the generation of autoreactive effector T lymphocytes. Though we can demonstrate that anti-I-A antibody blocks macrophage presentation of myelin basic protein to T-cell clones in an *in vitro* presentation assay, it is unlikely that this is the only mechanism of action for anti-I-A.[2,4] *In vivo* administration of anti-I-A antibody can induce suppressor T cells that abrogate a delayed type hypersensitivity response to tumor antigens.[8] Anti-I-A treatment may also lead to the induction of suppressor T cells that attenuate the autoimmune response to MBP.[9] However, the extreme rapidity of action of anti-I-A in acute EAE indicates that it probably plays a role in suppressing the immune response at the sites of inflammation. Thus, although lymphocytes and monocytes are observed in the central nervous system in mice given anti-I-A[s] antibody,[5,7] it is possible that their function is impaired or altered. Cerebral capillary endothelial cells may play an important role in the pathogenesis of EAE. These endothelial cells express I-A antigens in guinea pigs with EAE.[10] Following the binding of anti-I-A antibody to I-A positive endothelial cells, there may be an alteration in endothelial function with attenuation of local immune reactivity.

We have studied anti-I-A therapy in experimental autoimmune myasthenia gravis (EAMG), which is a model for human myasthenia gravis where antibodies to

TABLE 4. Anti-I-A Induces Suppressor T Cells

Cell Transferred	Antibody Titer (Anti-AChR Standard)	% Inhibition
Anti-I-A^{s}T	3.7 ± 1.7	66
Anti-I-A^{s}T + Anti-Thy + C	9.0 ± 1.3	17
Anti-I-A^{d}T	11.4 ± 1.2	− 6
Anti-I-A^{d}T + Anti-Thy + C	8.5 ± 1.1	21
No Monoclonal	10.8 ± 1.7	0

acetylcholine receptor (AChR) impair neuromuscular transmission by mediating the loss of AChR in the postsynaptic membrane. Increased susceptibility to myasthenia gravis is associated with HLA-DR3 in man, while in the mouse, immune responses to AChR map to the I-A region.

In two different strains of mice susceptible to EAMG, treatment with the appropriate strain-specific monoclonal anti-I-A abolished antibody responses to AChR, while the irrelevant anti-I-A had no effect.[11] Clinical manifestations of EAMG appeared to be suppressed. In addition, while antibody and proliferation responses to AChR were reduced in anti-I-A treated mice, reactivity to the purified protein derivative of tuberculin remained intact. Thus, there seems to be some specificity in the immune suppression that is induced by anti-I-A treatment.

It can be demonstrated, with an adoptive transfer system, that *in vivo* injection of anti-I-A induces a suppressor T cell capable of suppressing the antibody response to AChR. Thus, lethally irradiated SJL/J mice were reconstituted with AChR-primed spleen cells plus T cells from other groups of SJL mice that were given a primary and secondary immunization with AChR and given either (1) *in vivo* anti-I-A^s, (2) an irrelevant monoclonal anti-I-A^d, or (3) no monoclonal. In TABLE 4, it can be seen that T cells from anti-I-A^s treated mice could inhibit anti-AChR titers by 66%, while T cells from anti-I-A^d mice did not inhibit at all. The T suppressor cell was Thy positive.

Unlike EAE and EAMG, the autoimmune syndrome that develops in NZB/W F$_1$

mice is spontaneous. This disease bears a strong resemblance to the human disease of systemic lupus erythematosus (SLE) and is characterized by antibodies to nuclear antigens and an immune-complex-mediated glomerulonephritis. Susceptibility to SLE in humans is associated with HLA-DR2 and HLA-DR3. In NZB/W F_1 ($H-2^{d/z}$) mice, a gene closely linked to $H-2^z$ haplotype is associated with the development of renal disease. Hugh McDevitt and his colleagues, Nancy Adelman and David Watling, studied suppression of NZB/W F_1 disease with anti-I-A antibody. When monoclonal anti-I-A^z was administered to NZB/W F_1 mice that already exhibited signs of renal disease, there was a 90% increase in survival as compared to control mice receiving no monoclonal antibody.[12] Anti-I-A^d treatment also significantly increased the survival of treated mice.

Thus, therapy with antibody to IR gene products is clearly helpful in several experimental autoimmune conditions where susceptibility is linked to specific IR genes. These results with anti-I-A have been extended to include prevention of collagen-induced arthritis[13] and experimental autoimmune thyroiditis.[14]

Anti-I-A antibodies have been successful in disease prevention, as well as in ameliorating clinical deficits in acute and chronic situations. Therapy was successful in induced model systems like EAE, EAMG, collagen arthritis,[13] and experimental

TABLE 5. Anti-I-A Treatment Depletes IgM$^+$, IgD$^+$ B Cells from Spleen and Lymph Node

| Days After Anti-I-A Treatment | IgM$^+$, IgD$^+$ Cells (percents)[a] | | | |
| | SJL/J Mice | | CKB Mice | |
	Spleen	Lymph Node	Spleen	Lymph Node
untreated	31 ± 5	10 ± 3	42 ± 6	15 ± 3
2	11 (9,12,12)	3 (2,3,3)	24 (17,30)	10 (10,10)
5	5 ± 1	1 (1,1)	14 ± 3	6 (5,6)
14	18 ± 3	4 ± 2	36 (35,36)	8 (7.8)
49	34 (33,34)	10 (10,10)	36 (35,36)	11 (10,11)

[a]Means and individual mouse values are indicated except if four or more mice were tested, in which case standard deviations are given.

autoimmune thyroiditis,[14] where the disease provoking self-antigens is intentionally administered, and in spontaneous diseases like NZB/W F_1 nephritis, where the etiology of the autoimmune process remains unsolved.

One of the intriguing aspects of anti-I-A therapy is the haplotype specificity of its action. When an anti-I-A^k monoclonal antibody is administered to a (C3H-CWB)F_1 ($H-2^{k/b}$), antibody production to the synthetic polypeptide of (H,G)-A--L, which is regulated by I-A^k, is suppressed, while antibody production to (T,G)-A--L, which is controlled by I-A^b, is unaffected.[15] Because most humans are heterozygous at the critical HLA-D loci that play a role in conferring disease susceptibility, haplotype-specific therapy offers the possibility of suppressing autoimmune responses linked to particular alleles at HLA-D region loci without global immune suppression.

A note of caution should be raised regarding human therapy protocols based on injection of anti-Ia antibodies. Fluorescent-activated cell sorter (FACS) multiparameter analysis of the B-cell populations shows that anti-I-A treatment causes severe and prolonged depletions of splenic and lymph-node B cells (TABLE 5). Maximum depletion occurs around five days after treatment and recovery of some B-cell subpopulations is still incomplete one month later.[16] SJL mice are more sensitive to this

TABLE 6. Anti-I-A Treatment Impairs IgG$_1$ Anti-DNP Responses More Severely than IgG$_{2a}$ and IgG$_{2b}$ Anti-DNP Responses

Treatment[a]	DNP Immunization[b]	Splenic B Cells on Day of Immunization	IgG Anti-DNP Responses[c]		
			IgG1	IgG2b	IgG2a
	Day	Estimated percent	No. impaired/no. tested		
Anti-I-A	1	(24)	8/10	5/10	7/10
(Day 0,2,7,9)	8	(8)	6/10	0/5	2/10
	70	(39)	9/10	0/10	0/5
None	2	(39)	1/10	0/5	0/10
	8	(39)	0/10	0/5	0/10
	70	(39)	0/10	0/5	1/10

[a]Treated animals received 4 mg of anti-I-A antibody (0.5 ml 10-3.6 ascites) on days 0, 2, 7, and 9.

[b]DNP-KLH (100 μg) on alum on day 1 and day 8, and 50 μg of DNP-CGG on alum on day 70.

[c]Mice were bled one week after the first immunization and two weeks after the second and third immunizations. Anti-DNP responses, measured with a solid-phase radioimmune binding assay,[17] were scored as impaired if they were less than two standard deviations below the mean of the appropriate control (non-anti-I-A injected) anti-DNP responses.

B-cell depletion and recover more slowly than CKB mice. Despite the overall depletion of B cells, IgG responses to DNP and to KLH are not as severely impaired for the IgG2a and IgG2b isotypes as they are for the IgG1 isotype (TABLES 6 and 7).

TREATMENT WITH MONOCLONAL ANTIBODIES TO T-CELL SUBSET ANTIGENS

The L3T4 antigen expressed on helper T cells is near the site of the aspect of the T-cell receptor that recognizes I-A. Thus, anti-L3T4 antibody can block antigen-driven activation of antigen-specific T-cell clones.[1,17] We have demonstrated that administration of a mAb (GK1.5) directed against the L3T4 marker present on helper T cells prevents development of EAE. Furthermore, treatment with mAb GK1.5 reverses EAE when the antibody is given to paralyzed animals. *In vivo* injection of mAb GK1.5 also selectively depleted L3T4-bearing helper T cells from lymph node and spleen.[17]

Injection of mAb GK1.5 prevented the clinical and histologic manifestations of

TABLE 7. Impairment of Secondary IgG Anticarrier Responses by Anti-I-A Treatment

Treatment[a]	Immunization[a]	IgG Anti-KLH Responses[a]		
		IgG1	IgG2b	IgG2a
		No. impaired/no. tested		
Anti-I-A	DNP-KLH twice	10/10	4/5	5/10
None	DNP-KLH twice	0/10	0/5	1/10

[a]Treatment, immunization, and bleed schedules, as well as responses and scoring, are described in the footnote for TABLE 6.

EAE when the antibody was administered after autoimmune T cells capable of transferring EAE had already been generated (TABLE 8). Nine days after immunization with mouse spinal-cord homogenate (MSCH), mice have already developed a T-cell population that can transfer EAE to naive recipients. Such MSCH-immunized mice fail to develop EAE when injected repeatedly with mAb GK1.5 beginning on day 9. When mAb GK1.5 was injected on the two days preceding and the day following immunization for induction of EAE, no mice exhibited disease two weeks later—a time when nearly 90% of saline-injected controls were paralyzed (TABLE 8). Similar treatments with a monoclonal anti-Lyt2 antibody, which does not bind to L3T4[+]

TABLE 8. Prevention of Experimental Allergic Encephalomyelitis with mAb GK1.5[a]

Monoclonal Antibody Treatment of MSCH-Immunized Mice (day 0)		Clinical Disease			Perivascular Cuffs
Monoclonal Antibody[b]	Injection days %	Cumulative Incidence[c]	Significance[d] (p value)	Mean Onset[e] (day)	Frequency[f]
GK1.5 (anti-L3T4)	9, 10, 11, 12 12, 14, 16, 18, 20, 22	0/10	0.001	—	1/6
(anti-L3T4)	9, 10, 11, 12	8/18	0.02	19	1/8
(anti-L3T4)	−2, −1, 1	4/15	0.002	27	0/9
53-6.7 (anti-Lyt2)	−2, −1, 1	8/9	n.s.	12	5/5
(anti-Lyt2)	9, 10, 11, 12	17/19	n.s.	14	11/12
none (PBS)	−2, −1, 1	26/30	—	14	13/13

[a]On day 0, all mice were immunized with 5 mg of mouse spinal-cord homogenate (MSCH) in 0.1 ml of a 1:1 emulsion of complete Freund's adjuvant and phosphate-buffered solution (PBS) containing 4 mg/ml H37Ra mycobacteria in the hind footpads. *Bordetella pertussis* (30×10^9) organisms in 0.5 ml PBS were injected into the tail vein before immunization with MSCH on day 0 and again on day 2.

[b]Monoclonal anti-L3T4 and anti-Lyt2 antibodies were purified from culture supernatants of hybridomas GK1.5[17] and 53-6.7[17] grown in serum-free medium HB101. One hundred μg of antibody were given intraperitoneally on each day.

[c]Number of mice sick/total. Mice were examined at least through day 32. Mice were scored as sick if they exhibited any signs of illness.

[d]p values were computed by comparing the treated groups to the PBS group by utilizing the continuity correction and taking account of multiple comparisons (n.s. = nonsignificant).

[e]The standard deviation for all these values is ±2 days.

[f]Number of mice with perivascular cuffs/total number of mice examined histologically. Six standard sections of brain and spinal cord were examined for each mouse.[17] Slides were coded and read by an observer who was blind with regard to the treatment protocol.

peripheral T cells, but does bind to suppressor/cytotoxic T cells, did not significantly influence the incidence of EAE (TABLE 8).

Treatment with mAb GK1.5 was effective even when mice were injected with the antibody after the first signs of EAE were apparent (on days 12–14). In this protocol, mice were observed daily and were randomly selected to receive mAb GK1.5 or phosphate-buffered saline (PBS) injection once the first signs of EAE (tail weakness, paraparesis, and weight loss) appeared. Unlike the control mice, the mAb GK1.5 treated mice did not progress to hind-limb paralysis, quadriplegia, or death, and by 72

TABLE 9. Reversal of EAE with mAb GK1.5

Treatment[a]	Before Treatment (mild)[b]	Number of Mice Exhibiting Clinical Symptoms			Deaths[c]
		72 Hours After Treatment			
		none	mild	severe	
mAb GK1.5	16	14	1	1	1
none (PBS)	16	1	2	13	6

[a]Treatment was initiated when mice exhibited mild EAE. At this time, mice received 300 μg of mAb GK1.5 intraperitoneally. Also, 100 μg of mAb GK1.5 were injected on each of the two days following treatment initiation.

[b]The clinical status of the mice was graded according to the following scale: none = no neurologic symptoms or residual tail weakness with weight gain; mild = a flaccid tail and paraparesis with weight loss and poor coat texture; severe = quadriplegia with hind-limb scissoring. The clinical conditions were graded by an observer who was blind with regard to the treatment protocol.

[c]Seven days after treatment initiation.

hours after the initiation of mAb GK1.5 treatment, 90% of the treated mice showed clinical improvement with no residual neurologic deficit (TABLE 9). Treatment of quadriplegic or moribund mice with mAb GK1.5 did not ameliorate paralysis or prevent death.

In TABLE 10, the potency of a monoclonal anti-I-A^s mouse (monoclonal 10-3.6) is compared to the anti-L3T4 antibody (the rat monoclonal GK1.5).

We used multiparameter fluorescent-activated cell sorter (FACS) analyses to investigate the changes in the frequencies of T cells belonging to different T-cell subsets following treatment with mAb GK1.5. We utilized the Ly1 and Lyt2 surface markers. T helper/inducer cells are Ly1$^+$Lyt2$^-$, while suppressor/cytotoxic cells are Ly1$^+$Lyt2$^+$. With dual immunofluorescence analyses, these surface markers provide a measure of L3T4$^+$ T-cell frequency since L3T4$^+$ cells are Ly1$^+$Lyt2$^-$ and L3T4$^-$ cells are Ly1$^+$Lyt2$^+$.[17]

Anti-L3T4 antibody treatment selectively depletes L3T4$^+$ T cells. Two injections of mAb GK1.5 at 24-hour intervals are sufficient to deplete about half of the splenic L3T4$^+$ cells and nearly all of this T-cell subset from lymph nodes. Similar depletions of the L3T4$^+$ subset occur in mice that have already been immunized for the induction of

TABLE 10. Comparison of Dose Response for Monoclonal Anti-I-A versus Monoclonal Anti-L3T4 in Prevention of EAE

Treatment[a]	Incidence of EAE	Number Dead
0	9/10	1/10
120 μg anti I-A	7/9	5/9
600 μg anti I-A	7/9	2/9
3,000 μg anti I-A	1/7	0/7
15,000 μg anti I-A	0/5	0/5
0	7/10	1/10
5 μg anti L3T4	7/8	1/8
20 μg anti L3T4	4/8	4/8
100 μg anti L3T4	0/8	0/8
500 μg anti L3T4	0/8	0/8

[a]One injection of mAb i.p. on the day prior to immunization with MSCH-CFA. Anti-I-A employed was 10-3.6, anti-I-A^s. Anti-L3T4 was GK1.5.

EAE and treated with mAb GK1.5 on days 9–12. The T-cell depletion was specific for the L3T4$^+$ subset since the numbers of Ly1$^+$Lyt2$^+$ (L3T4$^-$ T cells) were not altered by the mAb GK1.5 treatment. Interestingly, although nearly all thymocytes express L3T4,[17] the percentage of L3T4$^+$ thymocytes was not significantly changed in treated mice.

Similar results with anti-L3T4 antibodies in the suppression of NZB/W F$_1$ disease were reported by Seamens and Wofsey[18] and similar results in suppression of EAE in rats with W3/25 were reported by Brostoff and Mason.[19] These results in EAE and in NZB/W F$_1$ disease suggest that manipulation of the human equivalent of the L3T4$^+$ T-cell subset (namely, Leu-3 or OkT-4 T cells) with monoclonal antibodies may provide effective therapy for autoimmune diseases mediated by this cell subset.

Before either anti-Ia or anti-L3T4 antibody therapy can be tried in humans, the potential toxicities of these antibodies must be evaluated. Preliminary studies indicate that although treatment with anti-I-A antibodies substantially depletes B cells,[16] anamnestic antibody responses remain intact in treated mice. In addition, for therapy of chronic disease states in humans with these mouse monoclonal antibodies, overcoming the anti-mouse response may be critical. For this purpose, chimeric immunoglobulins, combining a human constant region with a mouse variable region,[20] may be a solution. We are also generating isotype switch variants of monoclonal antibodies for use in therapy.

Therapeutic trials with either anti-Ia or anti-Leu-3 antibodies for diseases like multiple sclerosis are currently being planned. Testing with anti-Ia and anti-Leu-3 reagents in the treatment of EAE in monkeys is under way. If the results seen in animal models prove relevant, then the promise of these therapies would seem great.

ACKNOWLEDGMENTS

The technical support of Teri Montgomery has facilitated this work.

REFERENCES

1. TROTTER, J., S. SRIRAM, L. RASSENTI, C. CHOU, R. B. FRITZ & L. STEINMAN. 1985. Characterization of T cell lines and clones from SJL/J and (BALB/c × SJL)F$_1$ mice specific for myelin basic protein. J. Immunol. **134:** 2322–2327.
2. FRITZ, R. B., C-H. J. CHOU & D. E. MCFARLIN. 1983. Induction of EAE in PL/J and (SJL/J × PL/J)F$_1$ mice by myelin basic protein and its peptides: Localization of a second encephalitogenic determinant. J. Immunol. **130:** 191.
3. CHOU, C-H. J., R. SHAPIRA & R. FRITZ. 1984. Further delineation of encephalitogenic determinant for PL/J and (SJL × PL)F$_1$ mice. In EAE: A Good Model for MS. M. Kies & E. A. Alvord, Eds.: 229–234. Alan Liss. New York.
4. ZAMVIL, S., P. NELSON, D. MITCHELL, R. FRITZ & L. STEINMAN. 1985. Unusual bias in repertoire of T cells primed to MBP from (PL/J × SJL/J)F$_1$ mice: Induction of EAE with T cell clones. Fed. Proc. Fed. Am. Soc. Exp. Biol. **44:** 1179.
5. STEINMAN, L., J. ROSENBAUM, S. SRIRAM & H. O. MCDEVITT. 1981. In vivo effects of antibodies to immune response gene products: Prevention of EAE. Proc. Natl. Acad. Sci. USA **78:** 7111–7114.
6. STEINMAN, L., D. SOLOMON, S. ZAMVIL, M. LIM & S. SRIRAM. 1983. Prevention of EAE with in vivo administration of anti-I-A antibody: Decreased accumulation of radiolabelled lymph node cells in the central nervous system. J. Neuroimmunol. **5:** 91–97.
7. SRIRAM, S. & L. STEINMAN. 1983. Anti-I-A antibody suppresses active encephalomyelitis: Treatment model for diseases linked to IR genes. J. Exp. Med. **158:** 1362–1367.

8. PERRY, L. & M. GREENE. 1982. Conversion of immunity to suppression by *in vivo* administration of I-A subregion specific antibodies. J. Exp. Med. **158**: 480–486.
9. STEINMAN, L., G. SCHWARTZ, M. WALDOR, M. O'HEARN, M. LIM & S. SRIRAM. 1984. Gene specific and antigen specific strategies for the induction of suppressor T cells to myelin basic protein. *In* EAE: A Good Model for MS. M. Kies & E. A. Alvord, Eds. Alan Liss. New York.
10. SOBEL, R., B. BLANCHETTE & R. COLVIN. 1984. Preinflammatory expression of fibronectin and Ia in acute EAE. *In* EAE: A Good Model for MS. M. Kies & E. A. Alvord, Eds. Alan Liss. New York.
11. WALDOR, M., S. SRIRAM, H. O. MCDEVITT & L. STEINMAN. 1983. *In vivo* therapy with monoclonal anti-I-A antibody suppresses immune responses to AChR. Proc. Natl. Acad. Sci. USA **80**: 2713–2717.
12. ADELMAN, N., D. WATLING & H. O. MCDEVITT. 1983. Treatment of NZB/W F₁ disease with monoclonal anti-I-A monoclonal antibodies. J. Exp. Med. **158**: 1350–1355.
13. WOOLEY, P. M., H. S. LUTHRA, W. P. LAFUSE, A. HUSE, J. STUART & C. S. DAVID. 1983. Type II collagen-induced arthritis in mice. III. Suppression of arthritis by using monoclonal and polyclonal anti-Ia antisera. J. Immunol. **134**: 2361–2371.
14. VLADUTIU, A. & L. STEINMAN. 1984. Inhibition of experimental allergic thyroiditis in mice by monoclonal anti-I-A. Fed. Proc. Fed. Am. Soc. Exp. Biol. **43**: 1991.
15. ROSENBAUM, J., N. ADELMAN & H. O. MCDEVITT. 1981. *In vivo* effects of antibodies to IR gene products: Haplotype specific suppression of humoral immune responses with monoclonal anti-I-A. J. Exp. Med. **154**: 1694–1701.
16. WALDOR, M., R. HARDY, K. HAYAKAWA, L. STEINMAN, L. A. HERZENBERG & L. A. HERZENBERG. 1984. Disappearance and reappearance of B cells following *in vivo* treatment with monoclonal anti-I-A antibody. Proc. Natl. Acad. Sci. USA **81**: 2855–2858.
17. WALDOR, M., S. SRIRAM, R. HARDY, L. A. HERZENBERG, L. A. HERZENBERG, L. LANIER, M. LIM & L. STEINMAN. 1985. Reversal of EAE with a monoclonal antibody to a T cell subset marker (L3T4). Science **227**: 415–417.
18. WOFSY, D. & W. E. SEAMAN. 1985. Successful treatment of autoimmunity in NZB/NZW F₁ mice with monoclonal antibody to L3T4. J. Exp. Med. **161**: 378–391.
19. BROSTOFF, S. W. & P. W. MASON. 1984. Experimental allergic encephalomyelitis: Successful treatment *in vivo* with a monoclonal antibody that recognizes T helper cells. J. Immunol. **133**: 1938–1942.
20. MORRISON, S. L., J. M. JOHNSON, L. A. HERZENBERG & V. T. OI. 1984. Chimeric human antibody molecules: Mouse antigen-binding domains with human constant region domains. Proc. Natl. Acad. Sci. USA **81**: 6851–6855.

DISCUSSION OF THE PAPER

UNIDENTIFIED DISCUSSANT: Do you think you are simply removing the cells responsible for inducing the disease or might you perhaps be allowing for the development of Ly2-3 positive cells that are involved in suppression?

S. SRIRAM (*Stanford University School of Medicine, Stanford, CA*): If you immunize animals that have been pretreated with anti-L3T4 with tetanus toxoid and abrogate the primary anti-tetanus antibody response, the secondary anti-tetanus is nevertheless intact. Therefore, I do not think that I am immunoregulating them with an Ly2-positive suppressor cell population.

UNIDENTIFIED DISCUSSANT: Have you checked to see if there is a compromise of the immune response against cells infected by virus when you use anti-Ia antibodies?

SRIRAM: I have not yet tested them against the antibody response to a specific virus like flu or measles. However, the animals that lived for four or five months following Ia treatment did not succumb to any unusual illnesses. The same is true of animals that received anti-L3T4. If you challenge them with tetanus toxoid when they are T4 deleted, antibody titers are lowered, but still present.

D. HAFLER (*Harvard Medical School, Boston, MA*): I have treated a number of MS patients with anti-T11, anti-T4 monoclonal antibodies. The major problem has been that the antibodies attach to the T-cell surface and remain there. Have you observed this in your animals?

SRIRAM: We do not find it.

UNIDENTIFIED DISCUSSANT: Is it true that monkeys given anti-Ia antibody died?

SRIRAM: I think I will ask E. A. Clark to answer this question because he is involved in these experiments.

E. A. CLARK (*University of Washington, Seattle, WA*): Three or four years ago Paul Martin at the Fred Hutchinson Cancer Center had given quite a few monkeys anti-Ia antibodies with no effect. We have given anti-Ia antibodies of all different types to primates with no toxic effect and are in the process of testing their efficacy in EAE in nonhuman primates. Therefore, I think that the report by Billings and Terisaki might have had some technical problems.

Treatment of Autoimmune Disease with Total Lymphoid Irradiation

Cellular and Humoral Mechanisms

S. STROBER, B. KOTZIN, E. FIELD, R. HOPPE, B. MYERS,
AND A. TANAY

Division of Immunology
Department of Medicine
Stanford University School of Medicine
Stanford, California 94305

INTRODUCTION

The rationale for using total lymphoid irradiation (TLI) as an immunosuppressive treatment originated from studies of patients with lymphoid malignancies. TLI has been an accepted form of therapy for Hodgkin's disease and non-Hodgkin's lymphoma for over 15 years.[1] This radiotherapy regimen induced profound immunologic abnormalities in these patients; however, it has proven to be relatively safe and well tolerated with few long-term side effects.[1] More recent studies in both experimental animals and humans have further documented the profound long-lasting immunosuppression and relative lack of toxicity. We review here the development of TLI as an immunosuppressive treatment in autoimmune disease.

SUPPRESSION OF THE LUPUS-LIKE DISEASE OF NZB/NZW MICE

A large group of NZB/NZW female mice, five to seven months old (mean age = 6.0 months), with documented proteinuria were randomly allocated to a treatment (TLI) or control group.[2] The mice tolerated the irradiation (3400 rad in 17 fractions of 200 rad each) extremely well and there were no deaths during irradiation in the treated group. At an age of 8 months, two months after irradiation, the difference in survival of the two groups became statistically significant in favor of the TLI group. The difference continued to widen so that by 12 months of age, 2 of the 24 treated animals and 18 of the 24 control animals had died ($p < 0.0001$). Neither death in the treated group was secondary to NZB/NZW renal disease. In contrast, 16 of the 18 control group deaths were secondary to the lupus-like kidney disease. There was a significant reduction in the progression to high grade proteinuria in the treated group. At 12 months of age, 75% of the controls had progressed to high grade proteinuria as compared to less than 10% in the irradiated group.[2] Suppression of anti-DNA antibodies was also observed in the treated group. The levels of antibody in the treated and control groups were significantly different at 8, 9, 10, and 11 months of age. By the completion of the study (16 months of age), there was no difference in the incidence of tumors between the irradiated and control groups.

In another study designed to demonstrate the potency of TLI, seven-month-old female NZB/NZW mice were selected for advanced proteinuria and placed in treatment or control groups.[2] Prolongation of survival and reversal of proteinuria was observed in the TLI group. Even clinically ill mice (ascitic or wasted) showed clinical improvement during the irradiation period, but all control mice died within six weeks.

Further studies were carried out to compare the effects of TLI and whole body irradiation (WBI) on NZB/NZW disease. Surprisingly, single dose WBI (500 rad) also induced a prolonged remission in the disease activity of adult female NZB/NZW mice with proteinuria (Kotzin *et al.,* manuscript in preparation). Eighty percent of mice given WBI survived one year as compared to over 90% of TLI-treated animals and 15% of control animals. At 14 months of age, only one-third of the WBI animals were alive compared to 75% of the TLI animals and none of the controls. The onset of high grade proteinuria was retarded by WBI, but unlike the remission induced by TLI, most of the WBI-treated animals that survived 12 months showed progression to marked proteinuria. Suppression of antinative DNA antibodies was also more profound and long-lasting after TLI, but significant suppression was seen in the WBI group as well.

In summary, we demonstrated that TLI reversed even well-expressed disease in NZB/NZW mice with a prolongation in survival, a decrease in proteinuria, and a decrease in anti-DNA antibodies as compared to control animals. Few side effects were observed in the treated groups. TLI also prolonged survival in animals with very advanced renal disease. Few studies have shown a similar suppression of disease after the development of proteinuria. WBI was also capable of disease suppression, but the suppression was greater and longer-lasting after TLI.

Although TLI reduced autoantibody production and disease activity, the response to mitogens and antigens eventually increased as compared to controls (Kotzin *et al.,* manuscript in preparation). Thus, a prolonged remission in autoimmunity is achieved in the absence of generalized immunosuppression. The cellular mechanisms that explain these changes, though, are unclear. One possibility is that TLI induced tolerance to autoantigens in the same way as has been described for alloantigens or heterologous antigens,[3,4] and thereby resolves the autoimmune disease without suppressing long-term normal immune functions. Another possibility is that TLI specifically eliminates subsets of T or B cells that mediate autoimmune disease by virtue of altered patterns of cellular repopulation. Residual subsets may carry out normal immune function. For example, the introduction of the xid gene into NZB/NZW mice prevents disease activity, presumably by eliminating the Lyb-5$^+$ subset of B cells.[5] Nevertheless, a variety of normal immune functions persist in the presence of the xid gene. Since TLI has been reported to reduce thymus-independent antibody responses to TI-2,[6] but not TI-1 antigens,[7,8] it is possible that a reduction of the Lyb-5$^+$ subset after TLI contributes to the remission of disease activity. Regardless of the mechanism by which autoimmunity is persistently decreased in the absence of generalized immunosuppression, this is a desirable therapeutic goal that can be achieved with a short-term radiotherapy regimen (four weeks).

SUPPRESSION OF THE AUTOIMMUNE DISEASE OF MRL/1 MICE

MRL/1 mice spontaneously develop massive nonmalignant T-cell proliferation and autoimmune disease that kills 50% of animals by five to six months of age.[9] Of such mice, 100% given TLI at three months of age (age of clinical onset of disease) and 82% given WBI (300 rad) remained alive at nine months of age when the experiment was terminated.[10] At that age, 92% of unirradiated controls were dead with massive lymph-node hyperplasia, splenomegaly, and severe glomerulonephritis. In contrast, none of the TLI or WBI animals had enlarged lymph nodes or splenomegaly and only

10 to 15% of them developed glomerulonephritis. Interestingly, whereas 20% of untreated animals develop an age-related inflammatory arthritis, none of the irradiated animals developed arthritis despite the markedly extended life span. Levels of antinative DNA antibodies were minimally reduced in irradiated animals as compared to controls, and anti-single-stranded DNA antibodies were the same in all groups.

Owing to the lack of T-cell proliferation, TLI and WBI mice had 10-fold fewer lymphocytes in their lymph nodes and 4- to 7-fold fewer mononuclear cells in their spleens than unmanipulated diseased mice. TLI and WBI mice had 14- and 33-fold, respectively, fewer spontaneous splenic Ig-secreting cells than controls. At six months postirradiation, treated animals had normal suppressor T-cell function (Con A induced), but the helper T-cell activity assayed on a cell-to-cell basis was much below that of the controls.[10]

SUPPRESSION OF ADJUVANT ARTHRITIS IN RATS

The effect of TLI with or without local joint irradiation on adjuvant arthritis (induced by a subcutaneous injection of mineral oil with *M. butyricum*) in rats was investigated.[11] Four groups of rats with adjuvant arthritis were studied:

(1) An untreated group;
(2) A group treated only with TLI;
(3) A group given only paw irradiation;
(4) A group given both TLI and paw irradiation.

There were no statistical differences between any of the groups at the time the groups were formed and treatment initiated (17 days after adjuvant injection). Inflammation and deformity steadily worsened in untreated animals from the time of the first appearance of clinical arthritis (11 to 15 days after adjuvant inoculation) until day 40 when the maximum mean score was recorded. At the conclusion of irradiation, the group receiving TLI had significantly less ($p < 0.001$) arthritis than the control group. However, very soon after the treatment ended, the arthritis scores of this group rose to pretreatment levels. The scores then stabilized at a modestly improved level (compared to controls) until the completion of the study. The time course of inflammation and deformity in the rats treated with only local joint irradiation paralleled that of the control rats, but the severity was reduced. The final effect of this treatment was significant, but modest. The arthritis scores of animals treated with both TLI and local paw irradiation fell dramatically when treatment was begun. The response was most pronounced during treatment, but appeared to continue during the first several months after treatment. For all four experimental groups, the arthritis scores remained at their respective levels after day 100.

Roentgenographic findings correlated very closely with the arthritis rating score.[11] The rats that received no irradiation treatments had rapid destructive changes (demineralization, bony erosions, and joint space narrowing) during the period between 17 and 40 days. By day 100, cartilage space narrowing and ankylosis of the involved joints were typical and little further change occurred on roentgenographs taken up to one year. In rats treated with either TLI or local joint irradiation only, joint abnormalities on X rays were similar to controls except that the changes were less marked and the areas of involvement were fewer. Rats treated with a combination of TLI and local joint irradiation had very few significant abnormalities, but those that did occur were similar to controls, except diminished in degree.

TREATMENT OF INTRACTABLE RHEUMATOID ARTHRITIS WITH TLI

Clinical manifestations of rheumatoid arthritis vary from mild inflammation of the joints and surrounding soft tissues with little bony change to severe inflammation with erosive disease of bone and marked deformities of the joints. Milder cases of the disease are adequately treated with nonsteroidal anti-inflammatory drugs (i.e., aspirin, indomethacin, ibuprofen, etc.). Patients with progressive destructive disease are commonly treated with gold compounds and/or penicillamine; at least 20 to 30% of the latter patients will be treatment failures as a result of the lack of efficacy of the two drugs or unacceptable side effects.[12] Cytotoxic drugs, such as azathioprine or cyclophosphamide, have been used to treat rheumatoid arthritis refractory to conventional therapy during the past two decades. Although these drugs may be efficacious in controlling even severe disease, the frequency of dangerous side effects was so great that it restricted their widespread use.[13-17] In a literature comparison, complications associated with the use of TLI in the treatment of Hodgkin's disease are substantially less than that associated with the chronic use of cytotoxic drugs such as cyclophosphamide in rheumatoid arthritis.

RESULTS FROM UNCONTROLLED AND CONTROLLED STUDIES OF TLI IN THE TREATMENT OF INTRACTABLE RHEUMATOID ARTHRITIS

Two uncontrolled studies suggested that TLI is effective in the treatment of patients with intractable rheumatoid arthritis.[18,19] However, neither the patients nor the observers were blinded, so that placebo effects of the treatment procedure, biased observations, and regression to the mean in the follow-up period may have played some role in the measured improvement. Therefore, to determine the efficacy of TLI in a controlled trial, 26 patients with intractable rheumatoid arthritis were randomized to receive either a high (immunosuppressive) dose (2000 rad total; 200 rad per fraction) or a low dose (200 rad total; 20 rad per fraction).[20] Patients and observers were blinded with regard to the treatment group. Of the patients entered, 13 completed high-dose and 11 completed low-dose therapy. One patient dropped out due to transportation difficulties and another due to a recurrence of a chronic urinary tract infection. The patients in the two groups were well matched prior to treatment in regard to age, duration of disease, disease activity (i.e., morning stiffness, joint scores, and global composite score), prednisone dose, functional class (American Rheumatism Association), and rheumatoid factor titer.

Patients were evaluated twice before and at three and six months after TLI by blinded observers.[20] Significant improvements in morning stiffness, joint tenderness, joint swelling, and global composite scores were observed in the high-dose group at three and six months after TLI as compared to pretreatment values. No significant change was observed in any parameter in the low-dose group. When the percentage improvements in the high- and low-dose groups were compared, the former showed significantly greater improvement in three of the four clinical parameters. While 10 of 13 patients in the high-dose group had more than a 25% improvement in three of the four parameters, only 3 of 11 patients in the low-dose group had such improvement ($p < 0.05$). These results indicate that TLI (2000 rad) is an effective treatment for patients with intractable rheumatoid arthritis.

Both patients given high-dose and low-dose irradiation experienced constitutional symptoms during TLI, which resolved within two months after TLI. Furthermore, three patients in each group developed herpes zoster. Other complications observed in the high-dose group included transient severe leucopenia with white cell counts less than 2000/mm³ (three patients), transient thrombocytopenia (one patient), pleuritis (one patient), and gastric ulcer (one patient). Two deaths in the high-dose group at 9 and 18 months after TLI (secondary to myocardial infarction and pulmonary embolism) appeared to be unrelated to radiotherapy.

As expected, marked changes of *in vitro* lymphocyte function were noted in the high-dose group. Proliferative responses of peripheral blood lymphocytes to mitogens, allogeneic cells, and soluble antigens were reduced 60 to 90%. *In vitro* immunoglobulin synthesis (pokeweed mitogen-stimulated) was also reduced by 90% in the high-dose group. In contrast, no significant changes of *in vitro* T-cell function were observed in the low-dose group. The functional deficits in the high-dose group were associated with a marked T lymphopenia, primarily due to the reduction of the number of helper/inducer (Leu-3) cells. While the Leu-2/Leu-3 ratio rose from 0.72 to 1.95 after high-dose TLI, no decrease in Leu-3 cells or increase in this ratio occurred after low-dose TLI.

LONG-TERM FOLLOW-UP OF PATIENTS WITH RHEUMATOID ARTHRITIS TREATED WITH TLI

Twenty-four of 32 patients given TLI at the Stanford University Medical Center showed a marked improvement in clinical disease activity as measured by morning stiffness, overall functional activities, joint tenderness, and joint swelling (Tanay *et al.*, manuscript in preparation). The mean improvement in disease activity was maximal at 6 months after TLI and persisted at about the same level during the follow-up period of 12 to 48 months. Eight of the 32 patients received adjunctive drug therapy during the 48-month follow-up period due to continued or persistent worsening of disease activity. The mean percent improvement in the disease activity observed in the patients with adjunctive drug therapy was not significantly different from that of the 24 patients who never received adjunctive drugs after TLI. Complications included severe fatigue and other constitutional symptoms transiently during radiotherapy in most patients, development of Felty's syndrome in one patient, severe transient neutropenia in three patients, severe transient thrombocytopenia in one patient, chronic xerostomia with tooth decay in two patients, transient xerostomia in six patients, exacerbation of rheumatoid lung disease in two patients, cutaneous vasculitis in one patient, staphylococcal septicemia in one patient, and rectal abscess in one transiently neutropenic patient. Four patients died at 9, 10, 18, and 48 months after TLI due to acute myocardial infarction, pulmonary embolism, and respiratory insufficiency complicated by respiratory infection in two patients with severe rheumatoid lung disease, respectively.

After therapy, all patients exhibited a profound T lymphopenia, along with a reversal in their T suppressor/cytotoxic to helper/inducer cell ratio. Proliferative responses of peripheral blood mononuclear cells to phytohemagglutinin and to allogeneic lymphocytes (mixed leukocytes reaction) were profoundly reduced, as was the *in vitro* immunoglobulin secretion after stimulation with pokeweed mitogen. The alteration in T-cell numbers and function persisted during the entire follow-up period.

The sustained improvement in clinical disease activity observed during a four-year follow-up indicates that TLI is an effective therapeutic regimen for patients with intractable rheumatoid arthritis. However, further controlled clinical studies comparing the efficacy and the short-term and long-term complications of TLI to other drugs are needed to determine the role of TLI in the management of rheumatoid arthritis.

EFFECT OF TLI ON ANTIBODY AND AUTOANTIBODY FORMATION IN RA

An important aspect of the initial studies of TLI in the treatment of rheumatoid arthritis was the correlation of various immunological laboratory parameters with the clinical changes observed after TLI. Despite the improvement in joint disease activity, there was no appreciable change in serum rheumatoid factor titer or in antinuclear antibodies.[18,19,21] This was especially interesting in light of the marked reduction in T helper cell numbers and function after TLI.

The effect of TLI on T-cell-dependent and T-cell-independent humoral immune responses in patients with rheumatoid arthritis was further studied by Tanay et al.[22] The serum levels of antibodies to diphtheria (DT) and tetanus (TT) toxoids and to pneumococcal polysaccharide (PPS) were studied before and after TLI. In addition, TLI-treated patients were studied after a booster injection of DT and TT, as well as after a single injection of pneumococcal vaccine. Antibody levels of DT and TT decreased about twofold after TLI and did not rise significantly after a booster injection. However, there was no reduction in antibody levels to PPS after TLI, and a significant rise in titers was observed after a single vaccination. Thus, as previously demonstrated in rodents,[7,8] TLI appeared to selectively decrease T helper cell-dependent antibody responses (i.e., antibodies to DT and TT), while leaving intact (or even augmenting) T helper cell-independent antibody responses (i.e., antibodies to PPS) in patients with rheumatoid arthritis.

TREATMENT OF LUPUS NEPHRITIS WITH TLI

TLI (total dose = 2000 rad) was used to treat ten patients with systemic lupus erythematosus (SLE) who had severe intractable glomerulonephritis.[23] All patients had biopsy-proven diffuse proliferative disease and the nephrotic syndrome. Before TLI, all patients could not be tapered below 0.5 mg/kg prednisone per day for six months without an exacerbation of nephritis. Azathioprine was discontinued at the initiation of TLI in three patients who were receiving this drug in combination with prednisone. Patients have thus far been followed 4 to 48 months after the initiation of TLI.

All ten patients had a decrease in 24-hour protein excretion and/or an increase in serum albumin concentration. The serum creatinine values improved in five patients and were unchanged in three patients. The daily prednisone dosage was tapered by a mean of 60% in six patients followed for more than one year. Side effects of radiotherapy were confined to herpes zoster in two patients.

In contrast to the changes in autoantibody levels in rheumatoid arthritis after TLI, elevated anti-DNA antibody levels in these SLE patients returned to the normal range immediately following treatment with TLI.[23] This suggests that anti-nDNA antibody production may be T helper cell dependent. Similar to the above studies of rheumatoid arthritis patients treated with TLI, a number of alterations of cellular immune function were noted after TLI, including (1) T-cell lymphocytopenia, (2) a decrease in the number of helper (Leu-3) cells and a reversal of the Leu-2/Leu-3 ratio, (3) a decrease of in vitro lymphocyte proliferative responses to mitogens and allogeneic cells, (4) a decrease of spontaneous and PWM-stimulated immunoglobulin production in vitro, and (5) the appearance of circulating suppressor cells of PWM-stimulated immunoglobulin production.

It is of interest that the levels of serum anti-DNA antibodies and leakage of protein in the urine continued to decrease with time after completion of TLI in the lupus patients (FIGURE 1). Simultaneously, the level of serum complement gradually increased with time. This suggests that the disease activity is declining as the duration of time after TLI is increasing. This notion is confirmed by the continued gradual decrease in the mean daily dose of prednisone during the first two years after TLI and the complete elimination of steroid drugs in some patients after two years. This pattern is different from that observed in rheumatoid arthritis because a gradual worsening of disease activity was noted in 8 of 32 patients, necessitating the use of "second line" drugs. In addition, the mean improvement of disease activity in rheumatoid arthritis did not increase beyond six months after TLI.

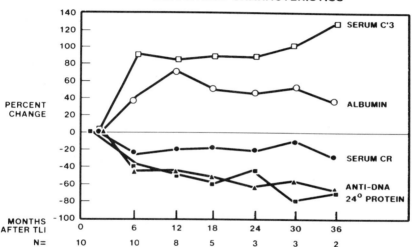

FIGURE 1. Changes in lupus disease activity parameters with time after TLI. The mean levels of serum C′3, albumin, anti-DNA antibodies, and creatinine (CR) at various time points after TLI were compared to the mean immediate pretreatment values. Similar comparisons were made for the mean 24-hour urinary protein excretion values (24° protein). Data is expressed as the percent change of the posttreatment value as compared to pretreatment. Reductions in posttreatment values resulted in negative percent changes. *N* = the number of patients who had been followed up to the indicated time point.

CONCLUSIONS

We have reviewed the development of TLI as an immunosuppressive regimen in autoimmune disease. The rationale for its use originated from studies of Hodgkin's disease patients, where this radiotherapy regimen was noted to induce profound and long-lasting immune suppression and yet was well tolerated with few long-term side effects. TLI is an unique immunosuppressive regimen that produces a selective (and long-lasting) reduction in the number and function of helper T cells and certain subsets of B cells. Conventional immunosuppressive drugs show little selectivity and their effects are short-lived. The lack of severe infectious side effects associated with 4400 rad in Hodgkin's patients and 2000 rad in autoimmune patients may be related to its selectivity. The early (repopulation) period after radiotherapy has also been associated with the appearance of antigen-nonspecific suppressor cells. These "natural" suppressor cells may be important in the induction of tolerance to allogeneic bone marrow grafts, as well as to organ grafts after TLI.[24]

TLI produced a marked and prolonged reduction in the activity of the lupus-like disease of NZB/NZW and MRL/1 mice, as well as in adjuvant arthritis in rats. In initial feasibility studies, a marked suppression of disease activity in patients with refractory rheumatoid arthritis was observed in association with a selective reduction in the number and function of the Leu-3 (helper subset) cells. These results have been recently confirmed in a controlled study. Initial feasibility studies of TLI in the treatment of refractory lupus nephritis have been equally encouraging. The future role of TLI in the treatment of these autoimmune diseases will depend on longer follow-up studies for both continued efficacy and side effects. Nevertheless, initial results with TLI suggest that selective regulation of lymphocyte subsets may provide a means of modifying autoimmune disease with fewer untoward costs than with conventional immunosuppressive drugs, such as steroids, azathioprine, and cyclophosphamide.

REFERENCES

1. KAPLAN, H. S. 1980. Hodgkin's Disease (2nd edition), pp. 366–441. Harvard University Press. Cambridge, Massachusetts.
2. KOTZIN, B. L. & S. STROBER. 1979. Reversal of NZB/NZW disease with total lymphoid irradiation. J. Exp. Med. **150:** 371–378.
3. SLAVIN, S., S. STOBER, Z. FUKS & H. S. KAPLAN. 1977. Induction of specific tissue transplantation tolerance after fractionated total lymphoid irradiation in adult mice: long-term survival of allogeneic bone marrow and skin grafts. J. Exp. Med. **146:** 34–48.
4. ZAN-BAR, I., S. SLAVIN & S. STROBER. 1978. Induction and mechanism of tolerance to bovine serum albumin in mice given total lymphoid irradiation (TLI). J. Immunol. **121:** 1400–1404.
5. STEINBERG, E. B., P. A. SMATHERS, K. FREDERICKSON & A. D. STEINBERG. 1982. Ability of the *Xid* gene to prevent autoimmunity in (NZB/NZW)F$_1$ mice during the course of their natural history, after polyclonal stimulation or following immunization with DNA. J. Clin. Invest. **70:** 587–597.
6. ZAN-BAR, I. 1983. Modulation of B and T cell subsets in mice treated with fractionated total lymphoid irradiation. III. Spleen and thymus dependency of B cell maturation processes. Eur. J. Immunol. **13:** 236–240.
7. TANAY, A. & S. STROBER. 1984. Opposite effects of total lymphoid irradiation on T cell-dependent and T cell-independent antibody responses. J. Immunol. **132:** 979–984.
8. TANAY, A. & S. STROBER. 1985. T cell regulation of the thymus-independent antibody response to trinitrophenylated-Brucella abortus (TNP-BA). J. Immunol. **134:** 3669–3674.
9. ANDREWS, B. S., R. A. EISENBERG, A. N. THEOFILOPOULOS, S. IZUI, C. B. WILSON, P. J. MCCONAHEY, E. D. MURPHY, J. B. ROTHS & F. J. DIXON. 1978. Spontaneous murine lupus-like syndromes. Clinical and immunopathological manifestations in several strains. J. Exp. Med. **148:** 1198–1215.
10. THEOFILOPOULOS, A. N., R. BALDERAS, D. L. SHAWLER, S. IZUI, B. L. KOTZIN, S. STROBER & F. J. DIXON. 1980. Inhibition of T cell proliferation and SLE-like syndrome of MRL/1 mice by whole body or total lymphoid irradiation. J. Immunol. **125:** 2137–2142.
11. SCHURMAN, D. J., P. HIRSHMAN & S. STROBER. 1981. Total lymphoid irradiation and local joint irradiation in the treatment of adjuvant arthritis. Arthritis Rheum. **24:** 38–45.
12. MCCARTY, D. J. 1979. Arthritis and Allied Conditions (9th edition), pp. 355–374. Lea & Febiger. Philadelphia.
13. FOSDICK, W. M., J. L. PARSONS & D. F. HILL. 1968. Long-term cyclophosphamide therapy in rheumatoid arthritis. Arthritis Rheum. **11:** 151–161.

14. FOSDICK, W. M., J. L. PARSONS & D. F. HILL. 1969. Long-term cyclosphosphamide therapy in rheumatoid arthritis, a progress report, six years' experience. Arthritis Rheum. **12:** 663.
15. SCHWARTZ, R. S. & J. D. GOWANS. 1971. Guidelines for the use of cytotoxic drugs in rheumatic disease. Arthritis Rheum. **14:** 134–137.
16. TOWNES, A. S., J. M. SOWA & L. E. SHULMAN. 1976. Controlled trial of cyclophosphamide in rheumatoid arthritis. Arthritis Rheum. **19:** 563–573.
17. DAVIS, J. D., H. B. MUSS & R. A. TURNER. 1978. Cytotoxic agents in the treatment of rheumatoid arthritis. Southwest. Med. J. **71:** 58–64.
18. KOTZIN, B. L., S. STROBER, E. G. ENGLEMAN, A. CALIN, R. T. HOPPE, G. S. KANSAS, C. P. TERRELL & H. S. KAPLAN. 1981. Treatment of intractable rheumatoid arthritis with total lymphoid irradiation. N. Engl. J. Med. **305:** 969–976.
19. TRENTHAM, D. E., J. A. BELLI, R. J. ANDERSON, J. A. BUCKLEY, E. J. GOETZL, J. R. DAVID & K. F. AUSTEN. 1981. Clinical and immunologic effects of fractionated total lymphoid irradiation in refractory rheumatoid arthritis. N. Engl. J. Med. **305:** 976–982.
20. STROBER, S., A. TANY, E. FIELD, R. T. HOPPE, A. CALIN, E. G. ENGLEMAN, B. KOTZIN, B. W. BROWN & H. S. KAPLAN. 1985. Efficacy of total lymphoid irradiation in intractable rheumatoid arthritis: a double-blind, randomized trial. Ann. Intern. Med. **102:** 441–449.
21. FIELD, E. H., S. STROBER, R. T. HOPPE, A. CALIN, E. G. ENGLEMAN, B. L. KOTZIN, A. S. TANAY, H. J. CALIN, C. P. TERRELL & H. S. KAPLAN. 1093. Sustained improvement of intractable rheumatoid arthritis after total lymphoid irradiation. Arthritis Rheum. **26:** 937–946.
22. TANAY, A., S. STROBER, G. L. LOGUE & G. SCHIFFMAN. 1984. Use of total lymphoid irradiation (TLI) in studies of the T cell dependence of autoantibody production in rheumatoid arthritis. J. Immunol. **132:** 1036–1040.
23. STROBER, S., E. FIELD, R. T. HOPPE, B. L. KOTZIN, O. SHEMESH, E. ENGLEMAN, J. C. ROSS & B. D. MYERS. 1985. Treatment of intractable lupus nephritis with total lymphoid irradiation. Ann. Intern. Med. **102:** 450–458.
24. STROBER, S. 1984. Natural suppressor (NS) cells, neonatal tolerance, and total lymphoid irradiation: exploring obscure relationships. Ann. Rev. Immunol. **2:** 97–115.

DISCUSSION OF THE PAPER

I. R. COHEN (*Weizmann Institute of Science, Rehovot, Israel*): Which antibodies are unaffected by the treatment?

S. STROBER (*Stanford University School of Medicine, Stanford, CA*): We have measured both the rheumatoid factors, IgM and IgG, in the serum, as well as antigranulocyte antibodies, which are IgG, and antinuclear antibodies, which are IgG.

COHEN: Therefore, in lupus patients, you found a decrease in antinuclear antibodies, while in patients with rheumatoid arthritis, there was no decrease.

STROBER: That is right. If anything, though, there can be an actual slight rise in antinuclear antibodies in RA.

THORBECKE (*New York University, New York, NY*): Do you think that induction of suppressor cells is also responsible for the improvement in NZB mice? What might be the antigen that induces the antigen-specific suppressor cells in this disease?

STROBER: I think that there may be a number of antigens involved in inducing the autoimmune disease in NZB/NZW mice. As long as these antigens are present and constantly stimulating the immune system in the presence of reduced numbers of helper cells, they stimulate the immune system to build up a pool of antigen-specific suppressor cells.

THORBECKE: However, you have not yet looked for specific suppressor cells?

STROBER: No.

UNIDENTIFIED DISCUSSANT: My impression from the literature is that, in RA, there are more side effects—sepsis, leukopenia, herpes—than in the Hodgkin's patients. Do you have any insight from the immunologic studies comparing these groups as to why that is the case?

STROBER: First, there are dose-dependent side effects. There are three groups that have done this: our group at Stanford, the Harvard group, and the group in Dublin, Ireland. The Harvard group used a total of 3000 rads, we used a total of 2000 rads, and the Dublin group compared 2000 rads with 750 rads. There is no question that as you reduce the number of rads given, the number of side effects is reduced very substantially. Very few side effects occurred with 750 rads, but that dose is still efficacious. I agree that even at the 3000 rad dose, patients with rheumatoid arthritis developed more leukopenia and bacterial infections than patients with Hodgkin's disease, who were treated with at 4400 rads. My interpretation of this is that almost all of the patients we see have high levels of antineutrophil antibodies. After TLI, the antibodies slightly increase. I think that it is the presence of these antineutrophil antibodies in rheumatoid arthritis patients that produces side effects with regard to the neutropenia.

UNIDENTIFIED DISCUSSANT: With respect to the suppressor cells that you have observed after birth and also in the mice treated with irradiation, do you know if they have a cytotoxic effect on allo-T-cell blasts?

STROBER: We have not directly tested this hypothesis. However, what we do know is that the number of blasts in the culture are markedly reduced.

R. S. SCHWARTZ: (*Tufts University School of Medicine, Boston, MA*): It is true, as you said, that there is no evidence that TLI has an increased risk of malignant disease, but there is an increased risk of malignant disease in patients who have received radiotherapy plus chemotherapy. As you know, many patients with autoimmune diseases have previously received chemotherapy, including alkylating agents. Therefore, I do think there is a risk unless the patients are carefully screened to exclude those who have received alkylating agent therapy before they get the TLI. Would you agree with this?

STROBER: I think it is a very important point. There are two comments I would like to make on that, both of which are of equal importance. First, in all of our studies, we have done exactly what R. S. Schwartz has suggested. We have excluded anybody from that study that has had more than six months of therapy with any alkylating agent because we are concerned about cancer induction. We have not, though, excluded people previously treated with methotrexate or azathioprine because these have not been implicated in cancer induction. However, in studies of Hodgkin's disease, the risk of cancer after chemotherapy alone was statistically similar to that with TLI plus chemotherapy. Nevertheless, I still would be very cautious about giving alkylating agents.

SCHWARTZ: Is my impression correct that the lupus study you showed did not have a control group?

STROBER: We could not have a sham control group or placebo control group because these patients have severe nephritis and, according to the NIH study, they would lose their kidneys if treated with steroids alone. I do not think you can ethically withhold therapy from those people. Therefore, the only thing you can do is compare the patients in this group to an alternative therapy, which is what we are doing right now.

UNIDENTIFIED DISCUSSANT: I was not clear whether those ten patients you were showing were the only ones treated.

STROBER: Yes, those are the patients we entered into the study.

UNIDENTIFIED DISCUSSANT: How about the average creatinine level at the beginning?

STROBER: The average creatinine level was close to two.

UNIDENTIFIED DISCUSSANT: Then a 20% drop is not very much in the patients who survived.

A Possible New Therapy of Systemic Lupus Erythematosus (SLE)[a]

H. BOREL, D. BASTIAN, B. COOPER, AND Y. BOREL

Department of Pediatrics
Harvard Medical School
and
Department of Immunology
Children's Hospital
Boston, Massachusetts 02115

INTRODUCTION

It is increasingly apparent that the function of the immune system is to protect the host not only against foreign aggression, but also from self. Central to this issue is the concept that natural autoantibodies normally occur and that a powerful mechanism, that of immunologic tolerance, constantly keeps them in check. Consequently, when tolerance is lost, autoimmunity may ensue. Although, at first sight, this idea may seem controversial, one way to test it is to demonstrate that tolerance induction to autoantigens is beneficial for either the prevention or the treatment of autoimmune disease. Our long-term goal is to apply this approach as a specific therapy of SLE. However, before presenting some data consistent with this view, what are the criteria required to apply the principle of tolerance to the treatment of autoimmunity? At least three conditions should be met: (1) autoantibodies reacting with autoantigens (i.e., immune complexes) should cause tissue injury; (2) the immunogen or some antigenic determinant(s) (epitopes) on the immunogen should provide a disease stimulus; (3) these antigenic determinants should be able to be rendered tolerogenic; that is, one could transform an immunogen into a tolerogen, for example, by covalent linkage of epitopes to self-IgG.[1]

How does this apply to SLE? This autoimmune disease "par excellence" is extraordinarily complex not only because the etiology is unknown and the disease stimulus ill-defined, but also because autoantibodies to a wide variety of autoantigens can occur.[2] However, despite this complexity, DNA anti-DNA immune complexes have clearly been shown to cause tissue injury in SLE, particularly in the kidneys both in humans (by Kunkel *et al.*[3]) and mice (by Dixon *et al.*[4]). Therefore, we reasoned that induction of tolerance to DNA might provide an antigen-specific therapy of the disease. If so, not only will it test the hypothesis that the mechanism of tolerance can be applied to the treatment of autoimmunity, but also the role of immune complexes irrelevant to DNA can be ascertained in the pathogenesis of the disease.

Thus far, the practical realization of the concept of specific immunotherapy for SLE has been hampered not by the ability to induce tolerance, but by an inability to link DNA fragments larger than nucleosides to soluble protein carriers. This is so because a minimum size of at least 10–40 base pairs are necessary to accommodate the combining site of anti-DNA antibody made by SLE patients.[5,6] A two-stage method, with gluteraldehyde as linking agent, was developed to covalently link oligonucleotides to protein carriers.[7] Depending upon the choice of the carrier, either immunogen

[a]This work was supported by an NIH grant and in part by The Seragen Corp.

296

(oligonucleotide linked to keyhole limpet hemocyamin oligo-KLH) or tolerogen (oligonucleotide linked to isologous immunoglobulin oligo-HGG or oligo-MGG) can be prepared. We believe that the importance of this method bears on the finding that the wide variety of antibodies in lupus may be more restricted in specificity than originally thought because they recognized common epitopes among different antigens.[8] Because such epitopes like, for example, the phosphate-sugar backbone of the DNA bases are present on oligonucleotide DNA fragments, conjugates should be able to either elicit or suppress anti-DNA antibodies. We tested the immunogenicity and the tolerogenicity of these DNA-fragment conjugates both in humans *in vitro*[9] and in mice *in vivo*.[7] The data reported in this paper suggest that one can specifically immunomodulate antinative and antidenatured anti-DNA antibodies produced *in vitro* by cultured lymphocytes from SLE patients. In addition, administration of fragments of DNA linked to mouse IgG appears to improve murine lupus.

RESULTS

Studies in Human in Vitro

Induction of Anti-DNA Antibody in Cultured Lymphoid Cells

Initially, we studied the immunogenicity of DNA fragments (either oligonucleotide or total DNA digest) covalently linked to keyhole limpet hemocyamin in cultured peripheral blood lymphocytes from 63 system lupus patients *in vitro*. Peripheral blood lymphocytes (PBL) from 10 normal individuals and 11 rheumatoid arthritis patients (RA) served as controls. Antibodies to three nucleic acid antigens [oligonucleotide, denatured DNA (d-DNA), and native DNA (n-DNA)] were assayed in supernatants of cultured lymphoid cells by a sensitive solid-phase radioimmunoassay. More than 50% of the SLE and RA patients' lymphoid cells formed spontaneous antibodies to one or several nucleic acid antigens. In contrast, only two normals did. Following *in vitro* challenge with oligo-KLH or DNA-KLH, cultured lymphocytes of more than 50% of SLE patients formed antibodies to one or several nucleic acid antigens. Similar results were obtained in PBL from RA patients. In SLE patients, the response to both antigens was either monospecific or polyspecific, but DNA-KLH appeared to raise a greater proportion of antibody to n-DNA than oligo-KLH. A greater proportion of patients with active disease responded *in vitro* as compared with those with inactive disease. In contrast, a mixture of oligonucleotide together with KLH was not immunogenic *in vitro*. In addition, oligo-KLH or DNA-KLH did not raise antibody to an irrelevant antigen, namely, ovalbumin. Of particular interest, PBL from seven of ten normal subjects formed antibody to n-DNA following challenge *in vitro* with oligo-KLH.

These results support the view that DNA fragments could be an important immunogen in SLE. Furthermore, this study provides an *in vitro* model to test the tolerogenicity of similar fragments of DNA linked to self-carrier molecules such as gamma globulin. The next series of experiments were designed to examine this question.

Diminution of Spontaneous Antibody to DNA in Vitro in Peripheral Blood Lymphocytes from SLE Patients

Initially, we determined whether antinative or antidenatured DNA spontaneously produced can be specifically immunomodulated *in vitro*. The experimental design was the same as above. Briefly, unfractionated PBL were incubated for 18–24 hours *in vitro* with DNA-fragment conjugates. Then, the cells were washed three times and cultured in fresh medium. After four days, this procedure was repeated; six days later, the cells were harvested. Antibody to either native or denatured DNA present in the supernatant was tested using a sensitive solid-phase radioimmunoassay. Controls included not only testing the antibody activity of the tissue culture medium alone, but also testing the supernatant against an irrelevant antigen such as ovalbumin. We found that preincubation of cultured lymphocytes with oligonucleotide linked to human gamma globulin diminishes the production of either antidenatured or antinative DNA. This was dose dependent (i.e., 1 μg per culture of 1×10^6 cells was the most effective, whereas 10 μg was not).

Similar results were also obtained with total DNA digest linked to human gamma globulin in cultured lymphoid cells from other SLE patients. This appears to be specific since preincubation with free oligonucleotide or total DNA digest together with human gamma globulin failed to affect the spontaneous production of anti-DNA antibodies, thus ruling out that preformed antibodies were passively absorbed by DNA fragments. In addition, preincubation with the immunogen (i.e., the same DNA fragment linked to keyhole limpet hemocyamin DNA-KLH) failed to affect the spontaneous production of anti-DNA antibodies *in vitro*. We found that both IgM and IgG antibodies to either native or denatured DNA spontaneously produced *in vitro* can be specifically diminished by preincubation with tolerogens.

Suppression of Antigen-Induced Antibody Production in Peripheral Blood Lymphocytes from SLE Patients

In the next series of experiments, we determined whether the tolerogen diminished the antigen-induced response *in vitro*. The experimental protocol was the same as above, except that the immunogen (oligo-KLH or DNA-KLH at the dose of 1 μg/culture) was incubated for four days *in vitro* following the 24 hours of tolerogen incubation. Thereafter, the experimental design was identical. Preliminary experiments were performed to determine the optimal dose of tolerogen. As for spontaneous antibody, the maximum inhibition of the *in vitro* response to antigen was obtained with 1 μg of tolerogen per culture. In 90% of the cases, the response to antigen was reduced by more than 50%. An example is represented in FIGURE 1. In contrast, the controls, which were made of a mixture of human gamma globulin and oligonucleotide not covalently linked to each other, failed to inhibit the antigen-induced immune response. Rather, in 6 of the 30 experiments, this control mixture induced a priming effect; that is, the antigen-induced response of this group was greater than that which was untreated prior to antigen challenge.

In addition, we found that either IgM or IgG antibodies to both denatured and native DNA can be decreased *in vitro*. All together, these experiments suggest that either spontaneous or antigen-induced antibody to native or denatured DNA can be specifically suppressed in cultured lymphoid cells from some SLE patients.

Induction of Tolerance to DNA in (NZB × NZW)F₁ Mice

Female BWF₁ mice were chosen not only because, like women, they develop a faster and more severe disease than males, but also because it is the only autoimmune strain of mice with lupus nephritis in which the pathogenic role of immune complex to DNA was clearly documented.[4] Before applying the principle of carrier-determined tolerance to the treatment of murine lupus, it was critical to determine the optimal size of the DNA fragment recognized by BWF_1 anti-DNA antibodies in order to construct a tailor-made tolerogen. This was done by absorbing humoral anti-DNA antibody on sheep red cells covalently coated with DNA fragments of different size and testing the supernatant for the presence of residual anti-DNA antibody by a sensitive fluid-phase double-antibody radioimmunoassay. The results clearly show that a fraction somewhat larger than ten base pairs of oligonucleotide was the most effective in absorbing antinative anti-DNA antibody (FIGURE 2). Therefore, this fraction was selected to construct a tolerogen using mouse IgG2a as carrier.

In an attempt to influence the natural course of the disease, the experimental protocol was as follows: Three groups of ten littermates were used. At one month of age, the experimental group was injected intravenously with 0.2 mg of tolerogen (oligonucleotide–γ2a). Similar injections were given at monthly intervals until five

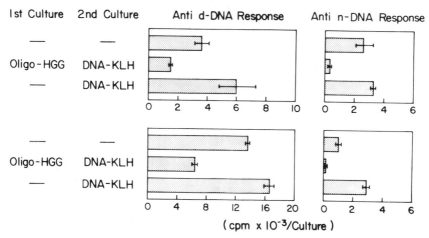

FIGURE 1. Diminution of antigen-induced anti-DNA *in vitro*. Each bar represents the genometric mean of triplicate culture ($\pm$ SE) of one patient's peripheral blood lymphocytes. Two different experiments are illustrated on this figure. The upper bar of each panel represents the spontaneous antibody production. The second bar of each panel represents the result following tolerance induction *in vitro*, whereas the last bar represents the antigen-induced response *in vitro*.

months of age. One group of control was similarly treated as the experimental, except that both components of the tolerogen (i.e., oligonucleotide and γ2a) were not covalently bound to each other. The last group of control was untreated. All animals were watched at regular intervals to assess clinical signs of disease activity, such as, for instance, increased proteinuria. They were also bled at monthly intervals to determine both the serum anti-DNA antibody and the blood urea nitrogen (BUN). Animals with high proteinuria and BUN were sacrificed to examine the kidney pathology. The experiment was discontinued at eight months of age because this is when it corresponds to the LD 50% of untreated female BWF_1 mice that will spontaneously die from murine lupus. The results show that not only the proportion of mice forming either antinative or antidenatured anti-DNA antibodies was reduced in the experimental group treated with tolerogen, but at five and six months of age, the level of antibody

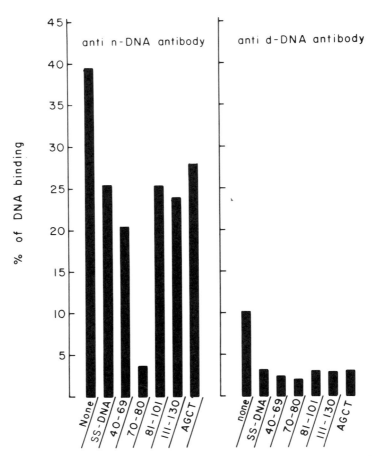

FIGURE 2. Size of DNA for tolerogen in mice. This figure represents anti-DNA antibody in BWF$_1$ sera following absorption of pooled sera with various fractions of DNA fragments on sheep red blood cells. Residual antibody, after absorbing the sera with sheep red cells covalently coated by gluteraldehyde with different sizes of DNA fragments, were measured by a double-antibody fluid-phase radioimmunoassay. On the left side are the largest fragments from total DNA digest, with individual nucleotides (AGCT) on the right side. Fraction 81–101 corresponds to about ten oligonucleotides. Fraction 70–90 is somewhat larger. The DNA fragment corresponding to the fraction 70–90 is the most effective to absorb antinative DNA antibody.

was also reduced as compared to the other two control groups (FIGURES 3 and 4). In contrast, at eight months of age, three months after the arrest of the therapy, this effect waned. However, despite the observation that anti-DNA antibodies appear to be high both in the experimental group and in the control-treated group, there was a dramatic difference in the kidney functions of these three groups of mice (FIGURE 5), which is also reflected in survival. At eight months of age, all experimental mice were alive. In contrast, 50% of either group of control were dead (FIGURES 6 and 7).

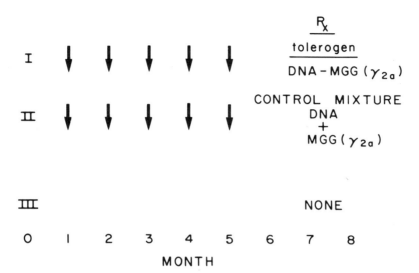

FIGURE 3. The experimental design in female BWF_1 mice to prevent murine lupus. There are ten mice in each group. I is the group treated with tolerogen, while groups II and III are controls.

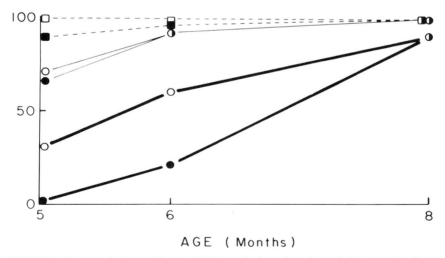

FIGURE 4. Percent of mice making anti-DNA antibody at five, six, and eight months of age: ●——●, antinative anti-DNA in the experimental group; ○——○, antidenatured anti-DNA in the experimental group; ●——●, ○——○, same as above, but in the group treated with the control mixture; ■– – – –■, □– – – –□, same as above, but in the untreated control group.

DISCUSSION

The above data are consistent with the view that the mechanism of immunologic tolerance can be applied to the treatment of autoimmunity; that is, one can induce tolerance to DNA both in human *in vitro* and in mice *in vivo*. Before discussing the implication of these findings for the development of a possible novel therapy of SLE, let us examine briefly the role of DNA in the mechanism of the disease. The significance of DNA as a disease stimulus, as well as anti-DNA antibody in the pathogenesis of the disease, have been recently debated in the literature.[10,11] In this symposium, both topics

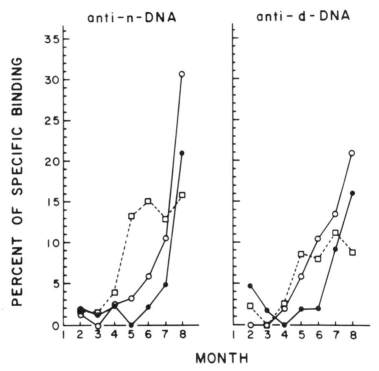

FIGURE 5. Anti-DNA antibody in BWF_1 mice: ●—●, experimental; ○—○, control mixture; □– – – –□, control untreated.

are discussed in the papers of B. D. Stollar *et al.* and J. F. Bach *et al.* The above data do not resolve this controversy. Rather, they add to it in two significant ways: First, they suggest that DNA fragments (when covalently linked to an immunogenic carrier) can elicit an antibody cross-reactive with native DNA in cultured lymphoid cells from both normal individuals and SLE patients.[9] Second, they suggest that DNA fragments (when linked to a tolerogenic carrier) can diminish anti-DNA antibody formation.

We have shown that oligonucleotide linked to KLH is immunogenic in human PBL *in vitro* as previously shown for animals *in vivo*.[7] In addition, we have confirmed other reports[12,13] by finding that antibodies to nucleic acid antigens are spontaneously formed

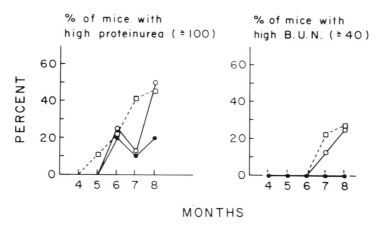

FIGURE 6. Kidney functions in BWF_1 mice: ●——●, experimental; ○——○, control mixture; □ – – – –□, control untreated.

by over 50% of SLE patients' lymphocytes. They appear to be specific for the nucleic acid antigen since oligonucleotide inhibited the spontaneous formation of antibody not only to oligonucleotide, but also to denatured DNA and native DNA.[9]

How can we explain that oligonucleotide linked to KLH raises antibodies not only to oligonucleotide, but also to denatured DNA and native DNA? Several possibilities that are not mutually exclusive can account for this observation: (a) the immunogen acts as a polyclonal activator; (b) there is an immunoregulatory defect in SLE; and (c) there is a common epitope among these various antigens. Although it is known that mitogens including EBV virus can raise antidenatured DNA antibody both in normal and SLE patient lymphocytes,[14] the *in vitro* response to pokeweed mitogen is decreased

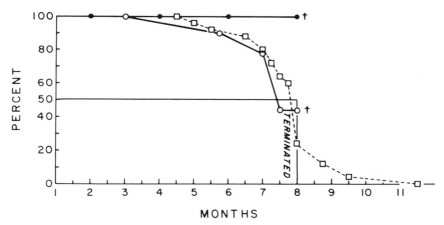

FIGURE 7. Survival in BWF_1 mice: □ – – – –□ represents the cumulative survival of control untreated female BWF_1 mice. LD 50% is at eight months of age; ○——○, control mixture; ●——●, experimental.

in SLE patients as compared to normal individuals.[15] Moreover, since oligo-KLH failed to raise antibody to an antigen irrelevant to nucleic acid, such as ovalbumin, it does not appear that it acts simply as a mitogen triggering B cells. On the other hand, the finding that normal individuals make antinative DNA antibody points against the possibility of an immunoregulatory defect in B lymphocytes of SLE patients only. Rather, it seems, depending upon a given population of B lymphocytes available at a certain time, that a single epitope can elicit either antibodies that cross-react with related antigens or that several antibodies are raised by different epitopes on the same antigen. It is known that monoclonal anti-DNA antibodies are polyspecific,[8] but whether DNA fragments elicit either polyspecific antibody or heterogeneous antibody with different specificity is unknown.

What is the implication of this finding for the pathogenesis of disease? First, it suggests that the capacity to make antinative DNA antibody is not unique to SLE and that the difference between normal and SLE might be more quantitative than qualitative. Second, it supports the view that the stimulus in SLE to make antinative DNA may be single-stranded DNA.[16] In contrast, others who have studied the specificity of monoclonal anti-DNA in murine and human SLE suggested that the immunogen may not be DNA because of the binding preference of these antibodies to antigens unrelated to DNA[10] This is not necessarily inconsistent with our interpretation. First, as suggested by Lafer et al.,[8] the common structure among these different antigens is the phosphate-sugar backbone, which is present in DNA fragments or oligonucleotide. Second, even if monoclonal anti-DNA antibody recognizes cross-reactive antigens unrelated to DNA, it does not rule out the possibility that the immunogen in SLE is denatured DNA. Finally, the capacity to raise antinative as well as antidenatured DNA by oligonucleotide linked to KLH in cultured lymphocytes of SLE patients might be of significance not only to understand the mechanism of the disease, but also for its treatment.

Studies are under way to determine whether DNA fragments linked to human gamma globulin can specifically diminish antibody to either denatured or native DNA spontaneously formed or produced after in vitro challenge with the corresponding immunogen. The preliminary data presented above suggest the feasibility of this approach.

Whereas spontaneous antibody to DNA can only be reduced by preincubation with DNA fragments linked to human gamma globulin, such treatment before in vitro challenge with the immunogen abrogate the antigen-induced immune response. Thus, anti-DNA antibody induced by exogenous nucleic acid antigens seems to be more easily suppressed than what is naturally produced either by autologous antigens or polyclonal activation. Caution should be applied in the interpretation of these results because the immune response to nucleic acid antigens is polyspecific and varies from patient to patient and time to time.

Many questions, though, are still open. For example, what are the relevant epitopes in oligonucleotides or the size and/or the base sequence of the DNA fragments that are the most important for tolerance induction? Does it vary from individual to individual or even at different times within the same SLE patient? These issues are critical to determine whether a few tolerogens or tailor-made tolerogens have to be synthesized to accommodate the combining sites of the family of antinucleic acid antibodies made by the SLE patients' lymphoid cells. Both horizontal study in a large population of SLE patients and longitudinal study within the same patients are needed to solve this question. Although the data are still preliminary, they clearly indicate that either IgM or IgG antibodies to both native and denatured DNA can be affected by tolerance induction in vitro. However, is it tolerance or a trivial mechanism? This phenomenon appears to be specific since neither a mixture of free oligonucleotide and human gamma globulin nor DNA fragments linked to an immunogenic protein carrier suppress anti-DNA antibody *in vitro*. Clearly, oligonucleotide or total DNA digest have to be covalently bound to human gamma globulin to be tolerogenic. What is the cellular mechanism? We have previously shown both in animals *in vivo* and in humans *in vitro* that hapten linked to IgG tolerized either T or B cells.[17,18] It is tempting to speculate that the mechanism of tolerance induction is similar to the one proposed by Lanzavecchia for antigen T-B cooperation.[19] Since the tolerogen is a hapten-IgG conjugate, it might provide a bridge between T and B cells. For instance, the antigenic determinant binds to the corresponding antigen receptor on B cells and Fc fragment on its corresponding receptor on T cells or vice versa. Whether the B cells are rendered unresponsive directly or whether they are made tolerant via the T cells is unclear. However, regardless of the cellular mechanism, we believe that it is important that T cells can be rendered unresponsive by hapten-IgG conjugate because natural tolerance is mediated by T cells only.[18]

To develop a specific immunotherapy of SLE in humans, it is important to demonstrate that this treatment is effective in animals that spontaneously develop the disease, such as female BWF_1 mice. Here again, the size of the DNA fragments that accommodate the combining site of antinative anti-DNA antibody appears to be critical for constructing a tolerogenic conjugate. The above data in BWF_1 need to be confirmed and extended, but they clearly indicate that monthly administration of tolerogen from one to five months of age has a dramatic effect. Not only does it reduce and delay anti-DNA antibody production particularly to native DNA, but also it improves kidney function and consequently survival. Studies are under way to determine the effect of this treatment on murine lupus nephritis. Further studies are needed to determine whether one can not only prevent the disease, but also influence murine lupus in adult mice.

In conclusion, it has to be shown initially that tolerance to nucleic acid antigens can be achieved in humans *in vivo*. Whether it will either prevent or treat SLE is another matter. As mentioned earlier, because the immune response in SLE is polyspecific, it might offer a unique opportunity to assess the role of immune complex to DNA in the pathogenesis of the disease. In addition, the principle of carrier-determined tolerance might be applicable to other autoimmune diseases (such as myasthenia gravis or pemphigus foliaceus) in which the immune response is monospecific.[21,22] The hope is not only to characterize relevant antigens that play a role in autoimmune disease, but to have them in sufficient amounts so as to test the principle of carrier-determined tolerance as a novel specific therapy of many immune diseases including allergy, juvenile diabetes, and multiple sclerosis.

REFERENCES

1. BOREL, Y. 1980. Immunol. Rev. **50:** 71.
2. TAN, E. M. 1982. Adv. Immunol. **33:** 167.
3. KOFFLER, D., P. H. SCHUR & H. G. KUNKEL. 1967. J. Exp. Med. **126:** 607.
4. LAMBERT, P. H. & F. J. DIXON. 1968. J. Exp. Med. **127:** 507.
5. PAPALIAN, M. E., R. LAFER, WONG & B. D. STOLLAR. 1980. J. Clin. Invest. **65:** 469.
6. STOLLAR, B. D. & M. PAPALIAN. 1980. J. Clin. Invest. **66:** 210.
7. BOREL, H., T. SASAKI, B. D. STOLLAR & Y. BOREL. 1984. J. Immunol. Methods **67:** 285.
8. LAFER, E. M., J. RAUSCH, C. ANDRZEJEWSKI, JR., D. MUDD, B. FURIED, R. S. SCHWARTZ & B. D. STOLLAR. 1981. J. Exp. Med. **153:** 897.
9. BASTIAN, D., H. BOREL, T. SASAKI, A. D. STEINBERG & Y. BOREL. J. Immunol. In press.
10. SCHWARTZ, R. S. & B. D. STOLLAR. 1985. J. Clin. Invest **75:** 321.
11. ELIAT, D. 1985. Immunol. Today **6:** 123.

12. KIYOTAKI, M., T. TONGUCHI, T. ABE, T. TAKEUCHI, C. MORIMOTO & M. HOMMA. 1981. Clin. Immunol. Immunopathol. **21:** 237.
13. TAKECHI, T., T. ABE, J. KOIDE, O. HOSONO, C. MORIMOTO & M. HOMMA. 1984. Arthritis Rheum. **27:** 766.
14. HOCH, S., P. H. SCHUR & J. SCHWABER. 1983. Clin. Immunol. Immunopathol. **27:** 28.
15. MORIMOTO, C., A. D. STEINBERG, S. F. SCHLOSSMAN & Y. BOREL. 1983. J. Clin. Invest. **71:** 1402.
16. KOFFLER, D., R. CARR, V. ANGNELLO, R. THOBURN & H. G. KUNKEL. 1971. J. Exp. Med. **1345:** 284.
17. BOREL, Y., C. L. REINISCH & S. F. SCHLOSSMAN. 1975. J. Exp. Med. **142:** 1254.
18. MORIMOTO, C. & Y. BOREL. 1983. Cell. Immunol. **82:** 415.
19. LANZAVECCHIA, A. 1985. Nature **314:** 537.
20. HARRIS, D. E., L. CAIRNS, F. S. ROSEN & Y. BOREL. 1982. J. Exp. Med. **156:** 567.
21. DRACHMAN, D. B., R. N. ADAMS & L. F. JOSEJEK. 1982. N. Engl. J. Med. **307:** 769.
22. STANLEY, J. R., L. KONLU & C. THIVOLET. 1984. J. Clin. Invest. **74:** 313.

DISCUSSION OF THE PAPER

Z. BENTWICH (*R. Ben Ari Institute of Clinical Immunology, Rehovot, Israel*): What is the evidence that this is indeed tolerance and not suppression?

Y. BOREL (*Harvard Medical School, Boston, MA*): We have never found a suppressor mechanism in any case.

S. DATTA (*Tufts University School of Medicine, Boston, MA*): How do you visualize the mechanism by which the tolerogen acts?

BOREL: I can tell you that it can tolerize B cells without the involvement of T cells, but it can also tolerize T cells in cultures lacking B cells.

Cyclosporine as a New Approach to Therapy of Autoimmune Diseases

J. F. BOREL AND H. C. GUNN

Preclinical Research
Sandoz Limited
CH-4002 Basel, Switzerland

INTRODUCTION

The fungal metabolite cyclosporine (CS) is a very hydrophobic, cyclic endecapeptide with a molecular weight of 1202.6.[1] Since the discovery of its powerful immunosuppressive properties in 1972,[2] much work has been done on a world-wide basis.[3] CS is the forerunner of a new generation of immunosuppressants, and it has made an impact as a drug in clinical organ transplantation as well as on fundamental immunology where it is used as a tool.

CS suppresses a wide spectrum of *in vitro* and *in vivo* reactions in which immunocompetent cells play a crucial role. Thus, it inhibits both humoral and cell-mediated immunity and is also effective in chronic inflammation.[4-7] However, the precise nature of events in the lymphocyte when it comes into contact with CS is still imperfectly understood. All the experimental data available suggest that the compound has a specific and reversible action on T cells. There is no evidence of functional influences on hemopoietic, phagocytic, and tumor cells.[8]

Today, CS has been registered under the trade name of SANDIMMUNE® in over 20 countries and is widely used in the field of organ transplantation (for review, see reference 9). Another potential area for the use of CS is in the conglomerate of ill-defined diseases considered to originate from underlying autoimmune disorders. Though the compound is known to be effective both preventively and therapeutically in a number of animal models for autoimmunity,[10,11] clinical progress has for obvious reasons been somewhat slow. However, a Workshop on Autoimmunity was held in Basel, Switzerland in March 1985 to update the clinical results obtained with CS in autoimmune diseases (for review, see reference 12).

RATIONALE FOR THE USE OF CS IN AUTOIMMUNITY

In order to evaluate the potential beneficial effects of CS in autoimmune disorders, its mechanism of action should be considered first. The steps in the transformation of resting T cells (T) into activated T cells (T') with receptors for interleukin-2 (IL-2), along with the function of these T' cells (such as the production of lymphokines), have different sensitivities to CS.[13]

Effect of CS on the Quiescent Lymphocyte

CS is known to affect the early cellular events that occur in the immunocompetent T cell in response to a mitogenic stimulus by halting it in the G_0 or early G_1 phase of the cell cycle.[14] In this activation reaction, signal 1 is provided by antigen or mitogen to a receptor on the T-cell surface, while signal 2 is provided by costimulator activity such as interleukin-1 (IL-1) or other postulated products of antigen-presenting cells (FIGURE 1). CS does not prevent cell interaction between the lymphocyte and the antigen-presenting cell; nor does it prevent the recognition of the antigen and the regulatory structure (MHC class I and II antigens) and the subsequent production of IL-1. The element suppressed is the reception of the message that the antigen recognition should trigger off. The result is that lymphokine production (e.g., of IL-2) fails to materialize. As long as CS is present in sufficient quantity, the T cell remains arrested in a very early phase of the cell cycle, though it does express IL-2 receptors at its surface.[15] Once the compound has disappeared, though, the cell can again be activated in a normal manner.

Effect of CS on the Activated Lymphocyte

What is the effect of adding CS to lymphocytes that have already been activated? Here, the therapeutic and not the preventive action is in the foreground of attention. Activated cells of this kind can, for instance, be driven into clonal expansion by the addition of exogenous IL-2 (signal 2) (FIGURE 2). This reaction is not prevented in the presence of CS. On the other hand, T′ cells can be induced to release lymphokines by the addition of antigen. This second antigen-specific reaction is markedly inhibited in the presence of CS. The compound thus acts on the antigen-specific message, suppresses it, and has the effect of "muzzling" the lymphocyte. This might explain why CS can effectively suppress an ongoing immune reaction such as, for example, a rejection crisis or an autoimmune relapse (for review, see reference 8).

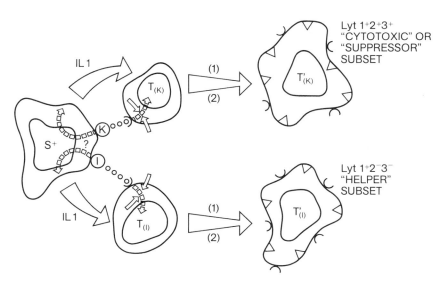

FIGURE 1. T-cell activation by alloantigen. Mechanism of action of CS: effect on the resting lymphocyte. The antigen transduction is inhibited, as indicated by the small arrows, and the cell is arrested in the G_0 or early G_1 phase of the cell cycle.

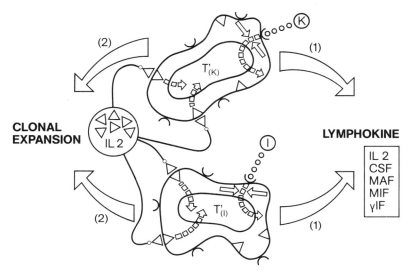

FIGURE 2. Triggering of clonal expansion and lymphokine release. Mechanism of action of CS: effect on the activated lymphocyte. In the presence of CS, only reactivation by antigen is suppressed (i.e., lymphokine production).

Effect of CS at the Level of Molecular Cell Biology

The following hypothesis commands the widest agreement (FIGURE 3). CS and prolactin bind to the same (yet undefined) binding protein, which is definitely not identical with the antigen recognition site or the T-cell receptor.[16,17] CS is then internalized and concentrated into the cytoplasm, where it is bound to cyclophilin.[18] This process bears some similarity with that of steroid hormones because both compounds appear to have receptors in the cytosol and appear to be able to penetrate into the nucleus. Here CS inhibits specifically the transcription of RNA coding for lymphokines, but not for the bulk of other proteins.[19-21] This might be the crucial CS-sensitive step because addition of the drug beyond this stage remains ineffective; for instance, the subsequent translation and lymphokine synthesis appear to proceed normally.[21] The advantage of this hypothesis is its simplicity and its compatibility with the *in vivo* findings. These demonstrate that CS not only prevents a primary response, but that it may also terminate an ongoing immune reaction. This might most likely occur through inhibition of continued lymphokine release,[22] as well as through suppression of further activation and recruitment of effector cells (see also reference 8).

Current Theories of T-Cell Biology

While there is agreement concerning the regulation of activation, clonal proliferation, and triggering of T cells expressing helper function, views diverge on the response of other T cells to CS. These divergencies lead to two theories of T-cell biology: The signaling model claims that all T cells are physiologically similar and have similar effector potential.[23] According to this hypothesis, CS affects all T cells in essentially the same way, but the expression of different functions of the cells is regulated by differing receptor sensitivities to CS. On the other hand, the subset model postulates that CS defines two T-cell subsets,[24] namely, those that are sensitive to CS (among

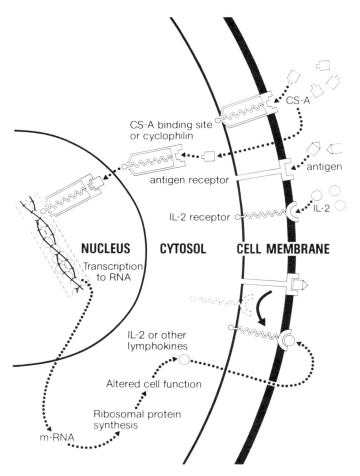

FIGURE 3. Mechanism of action of CS: effect at the intracellular level. The exact step of inhibition is unknown; however, it results in the suppression of transcription of m-RNA for lymphokines. Both IL-2 receptor expression and translation of m-RNA are CS-resistant processes.

which are helper and cytotoxic precursor cells) and those that are insensitive (including suppressor and cytotoxic cells). However, the knowledge available to us at present does not permit the rejection of either of these models, and there is need of further experimental work designed to distinguish between them.

Finally, it has been suggested that CS may affect B-cell function in a manner similar to that in which it regulates T cells; that is, either the signaling model, according to which CS would define B cells at various stages of differentiation on the way to immunoglobulin synthesis, or the subset model, in which only B cells of one of several physiologically different subsets are CS-sensitive, would also be applicable.[25-27]

RESULTS OF CS IN EXPERIMENTAL AUTOIMMUNE MODELS

Although there are ongoing clinical trials with CS in several autoimmune diseases, it is still important to review the effect of the drug in various animal models for the following reasons. First, CS is often used clinically to treat patients who have failed to respond to various other treatments. These patients may belong to the subset who would not respond to treatment of any kind and who may also have irreversible pathological damage even when the immune response would be suppressed. In animal experiments, treatment with CS may be started at various stages after the onset of disease to provide a theoretical knowledge of how late into the clinical course of a disease the drug can produce an effect. Secondly, the heterogeneity of patients in terms of age, sex, HLA type, and clinical picture, in addition to the heterogeneity of the treatment protocols, may provide a very confusing picture. Animal experiments produce much more controlled situations. Finally, various manipulations of the animal models may provide some insight into immune defects in the various diseases. These manipulations are not ethically possible in patients.

TABLE 1 summarizes the results obtained with CS in both induction and genetic models. Induction models comprise those test systems in which autoimmunity is elicited by the artificial introduction of an autoantigen or a related antigen, usually in combination with enhancing measures as, for instance, complete Freund's adjuvant (CFA). The latter promotes sensitization by rendering the antigen more immunogenic. Genetic models are mainly the results of the genetic selection of particular animal strains known to spontaneously develop certain autoimmune disorders.

The efficacy of a drug to modify the course of an autoimmune disease can be tested in at least two ways: It can be used preventively to inhibit the onset of the disease, that is, when it is administered before or from the start of sensitization; on the other hand, in the therapeutic treatment, drug administration starts only after sensitization has occurred or it is delayed until the first pathological symptoms are seen to be appearing. Length of treatment, discontinuation, or reinstitution of drug administration and other parameters (e.g., solvent, dose, route of administration) may be adjusted in several ways.

Induction Models

An experimental condition of possible autoimmune character is Freund's adjuvant arthritis in rats, which represents an experimentally induced polyarthritis model. CS strongly reduced the chronic inflammatory symptoms when given either preventively (days 1–18) or therapeutically (days 14–20).[7,28] In acute inflammation, however, this compound was completely inactive.

Another similar induction model is the collagen type II arthritis in the rat. CS was also active in suppressing the developing collagen arthritis. When the drug was given therapeutically, it exerted only a weak to moderate inhibition effect on the edematous

TABLE 1. Summary of Results Obtained with Cyclosporine in Experimental Autoimmune Models

Experimental Models[a]	Species	Preventive versus Therapeutic Treatment[b]	References
Induced Animal Models:			
Freund's adjuvant arthritis (rheumatoid arthritis)	rat	+/+	7, 28
Collagen type II arthritis (rheumatoid arthritis)	rat	+/+	28–31
Streptococcal cell-wall-induced arthritis (rheumatoid arthritis)	rat	+/+	32
Allergic encephalomyelitis (multiple sclerosis)	rat, guinea pig, monkey	+/+[c]	5, 7, 11, 33–38
Allergic neuritis (Guillain-Barré syndrome)	rat, guinea pig	+/+[c]	41, 42
Uveitis (human uveitis)	rat	+/+	43, 44
Autoimmune myasthenia gravis (myasthenia gravis)	rat	+/+[c]	45
Autoimmune thyroid disease (Graves' and Hashimoto's thyroiditis)	rat	+/+[c]	46, 47
	mouse	+/–	48
Diabetes (type I insulin-dependent diabetes) —endomyocarditis virus-induced	mouse	–/–	49
—streptozotocin-induced	mouse	–/nd	50
Autoimmune hemolytic anemia (autoimmune hemolytic anemia)	mouse	+/nd	51
Autoimmune glomerulonephritis (autoimmune nephritis) —Heymann nephritis	rat	+/–	52
—mercuric chloride-induced	rat	+/+	53
Genetic Models:			
Spontaneous autoimmune thyroiditis (Hashimoto's thyroiditis)	obese chicken	–/–	54
Spontaneous autoimmune diabetes (type I insulin-dependent diabetes)	BB/W rat	+/–	55, 56
Murine autoimmune lupus (systemic lupus erythematosus)	NZB/W mouse	+/+[c]	57–61
Murine autoimmune lpr disease (SLE, arteritis, arthritis)	MRL/lpr mouse	+/nd	62

[a]The human correlates to the animal models are indicated in the parentheses.
[b]Positive sign (+): beneficial effect; negative sign (–): detrimental effect of CS; nd: experiment not done.
[c]Relapse of symptoms following discontinuation of CS treatment.

swelling of the paws. However, at the end of the curative treatment, when the skeleton of the tarsi was evaluated by X ray and compared to those of the solvent-treated controls, a clear prevention of cartilage destruction closely resembling the normal state was observed.[28]

CS was further shown to prevent the development of group A streptococcal cell-wall-induced arthritis in the rat. Therapeutic treatment inhibited the chronic, proliferative, and erosive synovitis. Histology revealed significantly less synovial proliferation and joint destruction. Hepatic granuloma formation was completely inhibited.

Experimental allergic encephalomyelitis (EAE), which serves as the model for multiple sclerosis and also for naturally occurring postinfectious encephalomyelitis in humans since there are similarities in the pathological picture of demyelination, is the model on which most work has been carried out. If given during the sensitization phase, CS prevented the development of EAE in rats,[7,11] guinea pigs,[35,38] and rhesus monkeys.[34] In addition to this prophylactic effect, CS also has a strong therapeutic effect in this model; that is, when administration is started at the onset of the paralytic symptoms. The treated animals recovered more quickly than the controls, but there was often a relapse when treatment was discontinued. Similar results were obtained in the guinea pig.[38]

The above results may occur because a suppressor mechanism fails to develop after the onset of the disease since CS prevents the initial step of antigen sensitization in this model. Additional evidence for CS preventing the occurrence of a suppressor mechanism has been gained from a recently developed relapsing EAE model in the rat.[39] A therapeutic treatment with CS rapidly induced a complete remission in this special model, but soon after discontinuing the drug, the rats relapsed and, in contrast to solvent-treated controls, never recovered from the disease (C. Feurer, Basel, Switzerland; personal communication).

On the other hand, though, if the donor cells are activated in vitro with specific antigen or mitogen, EAE can be adoptively transferred from sensitized animals to isologous recipients. If CS was present during the whole of the 72-hour incubation period, proliferation of the donor cells was considerably suppressed and passive transfer of EAE with such cells in the rat proved impossible.[11,36,37] In addition, another form of EAE—hyperacute EAE induced by the simultaneous injection of B. pertussis vaccine—was suppressed by CS when used preventively.[40]

Sensitization of most species of laboratory animals with peripheral nerve tissues produces an autoimmune demyelinating disease—experimental allergic neuritis. When given prophylactically to rats and guinea pigs, CS totally suppressed the development of neuritis during the period of its administration. Although therapeutic treatment did not produce such a marked effect, the administration of CS prevented further deterioration in the animals' condition almost immediately. In fact, after two days, they were noticeably less affected than the controls.

Another model is experimental autoimmune uveitis, which can be induced in certain strains of rats using the retinal S-antigen and CFA. At a dose of 10 mg/kg/day, CS effectively prevented the expression of uveitis when the medication was begun on the day of immunization. At a higher dose of 40 mg/kg/day, CS also prevented this disease when administered one week after sensitization.[43]

Drachman et al.,[45] though, studied the effects of CS in the rat model of experimental autoimmune myasthenia gravis, which is an autoimmune disorder of neuromuscular functions mediated by antibodies directed against the acetylcholine receptors. They reported that the drug was capable of suppressing the antibody responses both to the hetero- (torpedo) and auto-antigens (rat acetylcholine receptor) during primary, ongoing, and secondary immune responses. Similar results were also obtained independently by P. Hiestand (Basel, Switzerland; personal communication).

Induction of experimental autoimmune thyroid disease in rats by early thymectomy and subsequent whole body irradiation induces a reproducible model of Graves' disease and Hashimoto's thyroiditis. The disease is characterized by progressive thyroid-gland lymphocytic infiltration leading to follicular obliteration and associated circulation of antithyroglobulin antibodies. CS given preventively for several weeks at the beginning of the disease and therapeutically eight weeks after disease induction markedly reduced severity of symptoms, but did not prevent further relapses after its discontinuation. The same type of disease can also be induced in many strains of mice by immunizing them with thyroglobulin emulsified in CFA. CS decreased the severity of this murine thyroiditis only when it was administered preventively; that is, before or at the time of sensitization.[48]

Both early (0–14 days) and late treatment (21–35 days) produced marked detrimental effects in the encephalomyocarditis virus-induced diabetes model in mice. Though clearly inhibiting the pancreatotropic immune reaction, the drug strongly enhanced the diabetogenic action of the virus, as demonstrated by an increased incidence of diabetic females, although females are known to be much more resistant than males.[49] Detrimental effects of CS were also found in the streptozotocin-induced diabetes model in mice.[50]

Cox et al.[51] also reported some interesting data from a model of autoimmune hemolytic anemia. Mice injected with rat erythrocytes produce antierythrocyte autoantibodies as well as suppressor cells that selectively inhibit autoantibody production, but not the net production of antibodies against rat erythrocytes. They showed that CS administration during the induction phase of the response significantly inhibited autoantibody production. The CS-treated mice that failed to synthesize autoantibodies, though, produced suppressor cells that specifically inhibited autoantibodies. However, these suppressor cells did not suppress antirat erythrocyte antibodies in adoptive transfer experiments.

Finally, CS has been tested in two induction models of rat glomerulonephritis where the renal damage has an autoimmune etiology. In Heymann's nephritis,[52] CS had to be given at the time of sensitization to alter the disease. In contrast, Baran et al.[53] reported that CS had preventive as well as curative effects on mercuric chloride-induced nephritis.

Genetic Models

The effect of CS has also been investigated in various spontaneous, hereditary autoimmune animal models (see below).

The obese strain (OS) of chicken develops a spontaneous autoimmune thyroiditis that mimics human Hashimoto's thyroiditis in most clinical, histopathological, and immunological aspects. Wick et al.[54] found that CS did not prevent the development of the OS chicken thyroiditis nor did it improve the already established disease. When given to OS embryos, CS led to significantly more severe thyroiditis and higher titers and frequencies of antithyroglobulin antibodies as compared to controls.

The spontaneously diabetic "BB" Wistar rat demonstrates multiple clinical and pathological homologies to human type I insulin-dependent diabetes mellitus. The disease in this particular strain of rats could be prevented by either a long-term[55] or short-term[56] treatment with CS. However, the therapeutic use of the drug seemed not to influence the course of the already established disease (H. Gunn, unpublished observation).

The NZB/W hybrid mouse develops a spontaneous autoimmune lupus-like disease with certain characteristics that resemble systemic lupus erythematosus in humans. When such mice were treated for an interval of 12 weeks with the nontoxic dose of 100 mg/kg/day of CS, the disease was either prevented or a remission was induced depending on the time of treatment. The drug was effective in suppressing autoantibody responses to various autoantigens and in curing the resulting immune complex-mediated glomerulonephritis (H.C. Gunn, unpublished observation). Similar results were also reported by others.[58,59] Jones and Harris[61] reported only an improved survival of long-term CS-treated mice, but, surprisingly, this was without any noticeable effects in other immunological parameters. The reason for these diverging results remains obscure.

The MRL/lpr mouse strain is used as one of the models of systemic lupus erythematosus. These animals also develop other autoimmune manifestations like marked lymphoid hyperplasia, necrotizing polyarteritis, and an arthritis that histologically resembles rheumatoid arthritis. Gozes et al.[62] observed that short-term treatment of these mice significantly reduced serum levels of anti-DNA antibodies, but had no effect on the spontaneous massive T-cell proliferation. In contrast, our findings (H.C. Gunn, unpublished data) indicated the lack of suppression of anti-DNA antibodies, but with a reduction of T-cell proliferation.

CONCLUSIONS

Studies on the clinical effects of CS on autoimmune diseases are still at an early stage. Many of these diseases have an ill-defined, presumably immunological etiology. Animal models of these diseases suffer from the disadvantage that many are artificially induced and that the correlation with the human counterpart of even the genetic models remains in dispute. Though these models are helping us to understand autoimmunity, their extrapolation to the human condition must be made with caution.

Autoimmunity can be achieved by breaking tolerance through bypassing various immunoregulatory pathways. This can be achieved in most normal strains of animals by introducing an autoantigen rendered more immunogenic (e.g., by the addition of CFA). However, in most cases, such diseases are self-limiting and closely resemble the normal immune response to other heterologous antigens. The prerequisite to maintain a state of autoimmunity is to create some inherent (i.e., the genetic susceptibility of selected strains of animals to immune dysregulation) or induced (e.g., thymectomy and whole body irradiation) abnormalities of the immune system. The genetic models, however, should not be regarded as the only ones relevant to the investigation of immunomodulatory drugs for the human conditions. The induction models may be useful not only to elucidate certain mechanisms involved in autoimmune pathology, but also to study the effects resulting from therapeutic modifications. Because the current thinking is that human autoimmune diseases might be due to multiple causes in genetically susceptible individuals, the most appropriate approach would still command the use of both induced and genetic models.

TABLE 1 suggests that there does not seem to be a trend that would predict what type of autoimmune diseases may benefit from CS treatment. For instance, beneficial or negative examples are found in organ and nonorgan specific models, induced and genetic models, and humoral and cell-mediated models. We will therefore discuss the findings under preventive and therapeutic treatments because the former are of interest to scientists interested in the mechanisms of disease induction and the latter, to clinicians concerned with treating patients with established disease.

The preventive treatment with CS in the experimental models tested gave results essentially in agreement with those to be expected from its use in transplantation. When CS was administered during the sensitization phase or at an early stage in animals spontaneously developing autoimmunity, the onset of the diseases were suppressed as long as the treatment lasted. Once the drug was withdrawn, the disease occurred in some cases. This may be due mainly to the result of a continuing slow release of antigen mixed with CFA, thus forming a depot.

There were, however, two examples where the prophylactic use of CS failed to prevent the symptoms: the thyroiditis in OS chicken[54] and the streptozotocin-induced diabetes in mice.[50] Although the onset of the disease could be prevented in the relapsing EAE in Lewis rats, discontinuation of the drug soon led to the development of an acute and severe form of EAE (C. Feurer, Basel, Switzerland; personal communication). This may be due to an inhibitory effect of CS on some suppressor mechanism of the immune system[54] or a direct effect of the drug on the disease itself.[50]

The therapeutic use of CS in established autoimmune responses produced clear-cut beneficial effects in most induction models where the antigen was mixed with CFA, as well as in the genetic lupus model in the NZB/W mouse. However, in all diabetes models, including the BB/W-rat, and in the thyroiditis models in both OS chicken and mice, the course of the ongoing disease was not altered by CS.

These negative findings raise several questions. For instance, were the CS doses adequate; for how long a period does CS have to be administered in an ongoing autoimmune disease to produce a suppressive effect; can CS still induce a remission once the pathological damage has progressed beyond a certain limit? Because CS is known to be effective in controlling a rejection crisis, what is the main immunological difference between the former and an established autoimmune response? In addition, due to the particular spectrum of most autoimmune disorders, each disease might give a different answer. The results presented in TABLE 1 demonstrate that CS can in a number of cases suppress an ongoing autoimmune response; however, there is no convincing evidence that it does by itself "cure" the disease. Drug-induced remissions are frequently followed by relapses once the drug is discontinued. While immunosuppression by CS may give the body "breathing space" from pathological damage, additional immunomodulatory measures appear to be required to restore the immune system to normal.

Recently, substantial progress has been achieved concerning the mechanism of action of CS. This should allow a more targeted use of this drug, which lacks myelotoxicity and theoretically might positively influence the recovery of a disturbed immune system. However, the disorders underlying autoimmune diseases must also be disclosed in order to better evaluate the conditions in which immunoregulatory drugs like CS are used optimally. The clinical experience up to the beginning of 1985 has been reviewed elsewhere.[12] It will suffice to say here that the outlook of CS in clinical autoimmunity is promising at present.

REFERENCES

1. PETCHER, T. J., H. P. WEBER & A. RUEGGER. 1976. Helv. Chim. Acta 59: 1480–1488.
2. BOREL, J. F. 1982. In Cyclosporin. A. D. J. G. White, Ed.: 5–17. Elsevier Biomedical Press. Amsterdam.
3. BOREL, J. F. 1983. Transplant. Proc. 15(suppl. 1): 2219–2229.
4. BOREL, J. F. 1976. Immunology 31: 631–641.
5. BOREL, J. F., C. FEURER, H. U. GUBLER & H. STAEHELIN. 1976. Agents Actions 4: 468–475.

6. BOREL, J. F., C. FEURER, C. MAGNEE & H. STAEHELIN. 1977. Immunology **32:** 1017–1025.
7. BOREL, J. F., D. WIESINGER & H. U. GUBLER. 1978. Eur. J. Rheum. Inflamm. **1:** 237–241.
8. BOREL, J. F. & B. RYFFEL. 1985. *In* Ciclosporin in Autoimmune Diseases. R. Schindler, Ed.: 24–32. Springer-Verlag. Berlin/Heidelberg.
9. BEVERIDGE, T. 1986. Prog. Allergy **38:** 270–293.
10. BOREL, J. F. & B. V. GRAFFENRIED. 1984. *In* Recent Advances in Systemic Lupus Erythematosus. P. H. Lambert, L. Perrin & S. Izui, Eds.: 313–331.
11. RYFFEL, B., C. FEURER, B. HEUBERGER & J. F. BOREL. 1982. Immunobiology **163:** 470–483.
12. SCHINDLER, R., Ed. 1985. Proc. 1st Int. Symposium on Ciclosporin in Autoimmune Diseases. Springer-Verlag. Heidelberg.
13. BOREL, J. F. & K. J. LAFFERTY. 1983. Transplant. Proc. **15:** 1881–1885.
14. WIESINGER, D. & J. F. BOREL. 1979. Immunobiology **156:** 454–463.
15. MIYAWAKI, T., A. YACHIE, S. OHZEKI, T. NAGOAKI & N. TANIGUCHI. 1983. J. Immunol. **130:** 2737–2742.
16. RUSSELL, D. H., D. F. LARSON, S. B. CARDON & J. G. COPELAND. 1984. Mol. Cell. Endocrinol. **35:** 159–166.
17. RUSSELL, D. H., L. MATRISIAN, R. KIBLER, D. F. LARSON, B. POULOS & B. E. MAGUN. 1984. Biochem. Biophys. Res. Commun. **121:** 899–906.
18. HANDSCHUMACHER, R. E., M. W. HARDING, J. RICE, R. J. DRUGGE & D. W. SPEICHER. 1984. Science **226:** 544–547.
19. ELLIOTT, J. F., Y. LIN, S. B. MIZEL, R. BLEACKLEY, D. G. HARNISH & V. PAETKAU. 1984. Science **226:** 1439–1441.
20. GRANELLI-PIPERNO, A., K. INABA & R. M. STEINMAN. 1984. **160:** 1792–1802.
21. KRONKE, M., W. J. LEONARD, J. M. DEPPER, S. K. ARYA, F. WONG STAAL & R. C. GALLO. 1984. Proc. Natl. Acad. Sci. USA **81:** 5214–5281.
22. PROWSE, S. J., K. J. LAFFERTY & K. SELLINS. 1985. Transplant. Proc. **17:** 1552–1554.
23. LAFFERTY, K. J., J. F. BOREL & P. HODGKIN. 1983. Transplant. Proc. **15**(suppl. 1): 2242–2247.
24. HESS, A. D., P. J. TUTSCHKA & G. W. SANTOS. 1983. Transplant. Proc. **15**(suppl. 1): 2248–2258.
25. BERGER, R., J. G. MEINGASSNER & W. KNAPP. 1983. Scand. J. Immunol. **17:** 241–249.
26. KLAUS, G. C. B. & C. M. HAWRYLOWICZ. 1984. Eur. J. Immunol. **14:** 250–254.
27. MURAGUCHI, A., J. L. BUTLER, J. H. KEHRL, R. J. M. FALKOFF & A. S. FAUCI. 1983. J. Exp. Med. **158:** 690–702.
28. BOREL, J. F., H. U. GUBLER, P. C. HIESTAND & R. M. WENGER. 1986. Adv. Inflammation Res. **11:** 277–291.
29. KAIBARA, N., T. HOTOKEBUCHI, K. TAKAGISHI & I. KATSUKI. 1983. J. Exp. Med. **158:** 2007–2015.
30. HENDERSON, B., N. A. STAINS, I. BURRAI & J. H. COX. 1984. Clin. Exp. Immunol. **57:** 51–56.
31. BOWLES, C. A., P. H. WOLLEY, H. S. LUTHRA & B. S. HANDWERGER. 1983. Arthritis Rheum. **26**(no. 4, suppl. S52): abstr. no. B14.
32. YOCUM, D. E., J. B. ALLEN, S. M. WAHL, G. B. CALANDRA & R. L. WILDER. 1985. Arthritis Rheum. **28**(no. 4, suppl. S82): abstr. no. D40.
33. BOREL, J. F. 1981. Triangle Engl. Ed. **20:** 97–105.
34. BOREL, J. F. 1981. Transplant. Clin. Immunol. **13:** 3–6.
35. BOLTON, C., J. F. BOREL, M. L. CUZNER, A. N. DAVISON & A. M. TURNER. 1982. J. Neurol. Sci. **56:** 147–153.
36. BOLTON, C., G. ALLSOPP & M. L. CUZNER. 1982. Clin. Exp. Immunol. **47:** 127–132.
37. HINRICHS, D. J., K. W. WEGMANN & B. A. PETERS. 1983. Cell. Immunol. **77:** 202–209.
38. FREDANE, L. M., G. A. HASHIM & R. E. MCCABE. 1983. Transplant. Proc. **15**(suppl. 1): 2909–2913.
39. FEURER, C., D. E. PRENTICE & S. CAMMISULI. 1985. J. Neuroimmunol. **10:** 159–166.
40. LEVINE, S. & R. SOWINSKI. 1977. Arch. Int. Pharmacodyn. Ther. **230:** 309–318.

41. TOMKINS, C., R. H. M. KING & P. K. THOMAS. 1980. Neuropathol. Appl. Neurobiol. **6:** 240.

42. KING, R. H. M., R. I. CRAGGS, M. L. P. GROSS, C. TOMPKINS & P. K. THOMAS. 1983. Acta Neuropathol. **59:** 262–268.

43. NUSSENBLATT, R. B., M. M. RODRIGUES, W. B. WACKER, S. J. CEVARIO, M. C. SALINAS-CARMONA & I. GERY. 1981. J. Clin. Invest. **67:** 1228–1231.

44. NUSSENBLATT, R. B., M. SALINAS-CARMONA, B. H. WAKSMAN & I. GERY. 1983. Int. Arch. Allergy Appl. Immunol. **70:** 289–294.

45. DRACHMAN, D. B., R. N. ADAMS, K. MCINTOSH & A. PESTRONK. 1985. Clin. Immunol. Immunopathol. **34:** 174–188.

46. MCGREGOR, A. M., D. P. RENNIE, A. P. WEETMAN, R. A. HASSMAN, S. M. FOORD & C. DIEGUEZ. 1983. Life Sci. **32:** 97–108.

47. HASSMAN, R. A., C. DIEGUEZ, D. P. RENNIE, A. P. WEETMAN, R. HALL & A. M. MCGREGOR. 1985. Clin. Exp. Immunol. **59:** 10–16.

48. VLADUTIU, A. O. 1983. Transplantation **35:** 518–520.

49. VIALETTES, B., D. BAUME, C. CHARPIN, J. DE MAEYER-GUIGNARD & PH. VAGUE. 1983. J. Clin. Lab. Immunol. **10:** 35–40.

50. KOLB, H., M. OSCHILEWSKI, E. SCHWAB, U. OSCHILEWSKI & U. KIESEL. 1986. Diabetes Res. In press.

51. COX, K. O., A. C. ALLISON & B. SAMCEWICZ. 1983. Clin. Immunol. Immunopathol. **28:** 90–95.

52. CATTRAN, D. C. & G. MOLLER. 1985. Kidney Int. **27:** 207.

53. BARAN, D., B. VENDEVILLE, M. C. VIAL, C. COSSON, C. BASCOU, P. TEYCHENNE & P. DRUET. 1986. Clin. Nephrol. **25**(suppl. 1): 175–180.

54. WICK, G., P. U. MUELLER & S. SCHWARZ. 1982. Eur. J. Immunol. **12:** 877–881.

55. STILLER, C. R., A. LAUPACIS, P. A. KEOWN, C. GARDELL, J. DUPRE, P. THIBERT & W. WALL. 1983. Metabolism **32:** 69–72.

56. LIKE, A. A., V. DIRODI, S. THOMAS, D. L. GUBERSKI & A. A. ROSSINI. 1984. Am. J. Pathol. **117:** 92–97.

57. BOREL, J. F. 1981. Transplant. Proc. **13:** 344–348.

58. BOWLES, C. A., K. E. HOLLEY & B. S. HANDWERGER. 1983. Arthritis Rheum. **26**(no. 4, suppl. S76): abstr. no. D45.

59. ISRAEL-BIET, D., L-H. NOEL, M-A. BACH, M. DARDENNE & J. F. BACH. 1983. Clin. Exp. Immunol. **54:** 359–365.

60. JONES, M. G., G. HARRIS & G. COWING. 1983. Transplant. Proc. **15**(suppl. 1): 2904–2908.

61. JONES, M. G. & G. HARRIS. 1985. Clin. Exp. Immunol. **59:** 1–9.

62. GOZES, Y., A. N. THEOFILOPOULOS, C. H. PARK, J. H. SLACK, R. S. BALDERAS & F. J. DIXON. 1982. Fed. Proc. Fed. Am. Soc. Exp. Biol. **41:** 547 (abstr. no. 1619).

DISCUSSION OF THE PAPER

UNIDENTIFIED DISCUSSANT: You showed that cyclosporine treatment suppresses antiacetylcholine receptor antibodies, but what effect does it have on the pathology of myasthenia?

D. B. DRACHMAN (*John Hopkins University, Baltimore, MD*): When you give cyclosporine only at the time of primary immunization, it has no permanent suppressive effect. Cyclosporine has to be used at rather high doses to suppress the antibody response and prevent the disease. Therefore, it may not be the ideal immunosuppressive for this disease.

UNIDENTIFIED DISCUSSANT: Does cyclosporine affect established disease?

DRACHMAN: We have given it during established disease. It lowers the antibody titer for as long as you give it, but when you stop, the antibody titer rises again. When administered just prior to an antigen boost in primed animals for a relatively long time, the anamnestic response is blocked and the existing antibody titers decline unless—and this is a key point—you give a very large antigenic boost, in which case you can overcome the cyclosporine effect.

J. F. BOREL (*Sandoz Limited, Basel, Switzerland*): You need much more cyclosporine to lower the antibody response than to lower a T-cell mediated response.

UNIDENTIFIED DISCUSSANT: What about the toxicity of cyclosporine?

DRACHMAN: It is fairly toxic. However, some of those animals were merely killed by anesthetizing them prior to bleeding.

Hormonal Approaches to Immunotherapy of Autoimmune Disease[a]

NORMAN TALAL, S. ANSAR AHMED,
AND MICHAEL DAUPHINEE

Department of Medicine
Division of Clinical Immunology
The University of Texas Health Science Center at San Antonio
and
Clinical Immunology Section
Audie L. Murphy Memorial Veterans Hospital
San Antonio, Texas 78284

INTRODUCTION

Autoimmune diseases are multifactorial, with genetic, environmental, hormonal, viral, and psychoneurological influences all playing a role in pathogenesis.[1] A striking feature of almost all autoimmune diseases is the marked female predominance. SLE is a good example. The female to male ratio in this disease is 10:1 when one considers patients in the childbearing age. This ratio falls to 3:1 when patients are premenopausal children or postmenopausal women. This simple clinical observation alerts one to a possible important sex hormone influence related to the menstruating reproductive years of a woman's lifetime.

Other clinical facts support this suggestion. For example, Klinefelter's syndrome (an XXY condition in men associated with feminizing features such as gynecomastia) is often accompanied by autoimmunity, including SLE and myasthenia gravis.[2-4] The medical literature includes a pair of monozygotic twins, only one of whom developed SLE some years after oophorectomy.[5] We are also following a patient with Noonan's syndrome (male Turner's syndrome) whose male hypogonadism is associated with SLE and lupus nephritis. SLE patients appear to be under a hyperestrogenic influence.[6,7] Furthermore, the use of estrogen-containing contraceptive pills can result in exacerbations of SLE and is generally contraindicated.[8,9]

In both experimental animals and in humans, normal immunologic reactivity is greater in females than in males.[10] The basis for this difference and the probable explanation for the influence of sex on autoimmune disease lie in the ability of sex hormones to modulate the immune response.[11] Early evidence suggested that sex hormones act on the thymus to influence lymphocyte development and on the reticuloendothelial system to regulate immune complex clearance. For example, suppressor T cells are one of the sensitive target sites for sex hormone action.[12,13] However, the picture now is more complicated with the recent findings in the field of neuroimmunomodulation and the known influence of sex hormones on the central nervous system (CNS).[14]

Our published studies on the ability of sex hormones to modulate the lupus-like

[a]These studies were supported by the General Medical Research Service of the Veterans Administration.

disease of autoimmune mice are briefly reviewed in this report.[15-17] We present further evidence for the ability of estrogen to deplete suppressor T cells, along with recent findings on the ability of sex hormones to modulate the developing fetal immune system (a phenomenon that we call immunologic imprinting).

MATERIALS AND METHODS

Animals

Four- to seventeen-week-old normal C57BL/6 (B6) and eight- to ten-week-old NZW mice were purchased from Jackson Laboratories, Maine. Autoimmune mice are from our own colonies.

Sex Hormone Preparations

Estrogen (E_2-Ayerst Labs) and Depo-testosterone (Te-Upjohn) were used in these studies. Various doses of E_2 (100 ng and 10 μg/100 gram body weight) or Te (100 μg to 1000 μg/100 gram body weight) in sterile peanut oil were administered subcutaneously in a final volume of 0.2–0.25 ml. Te or E_2 were also prepared in the form of capsules as described earlier.[16]

Orchidectomy

A group of mice (C57BL/10) were prepubertally orchidectomized by procedures described earlier.[18]

Sex Hormone Administration

Orchidectomized C57BL/10 or intact C57BL/6 were given either Te or E_2 implants for 3–8 months. Adult female mice were given various doses of Te or E_2 in oil on an alternate day basis for a period of two to four weeks.

Fourteen-day-old pregnant NZW, B/W, or B6-lpr mice were given three separate subcutaneous injections of sex hormones on alternate days until term. The offsprings of these mice were sacrificed at different ages and selected immunological parameters known to be influenced by sex hormones were studied.

Collection of Tissue Materials

Animals were weighed and bled by orbital exsanguination. The serum was collected and stored at $-70°C$ for the analysis of serum autoantibodies. Thymus, spleen, and lymph nodes were collected under aseptic conditions and single cell suspensions were prepared as described earlier.[12] The detailed methodologies for FACS analysis, IL-2 production, and enumeration of serum autoantibodies to DNA have been described earlier.[12,16]

Autoantibody Plaque-Forming Cells to Bromelin-Treated Mouse Red Blood Cells (Br-APFC)

Syngeneic mouse red blood cells (MRBC) obtained from young mice (less than three months old) were washed repeatedly in cold RPMI medium. Equal volumes of washed packed MRBC and 20 mg/ml Bromelin (Br) (Calbiochem-Behring) were mixed and incubated at 37°C in a CO_2 incubator for 45 minutes. The cells were washed three times and a final suspension (20%) was made in complete RPMI.

Spleen cells were treated with ammonium chloride to lyse red blood cells and were either incubated in complete RPMI for four days or used directly. The cell concentration was adjusted to 4×10^7 cells/ml in complete media. Lymphocytes (100 μl) were admixed with 50 μl of Br-MRBC, 20 ml of MRBC absorbed complement (Gibco), and 30 μl of RPMI-1640 complete media. The mixture (100 μl) was loaded into a Cunningham-type glass slide chamber with the aid of a micropipet and the edges were sealed with a paraffin-vaseline mixture. These slides were incubated for three hours at 37°C and the number of IgM plaques formed in each chamber were enumerated.

Ly1$^+$ B-Cell Enumeration

Splenic Ly1$^+$ B cells were visualized and quantitated by flow cytometry after staining spleen lymphocytes with dual antibodies, FITC-F(ab')$_2$ fragments of rabbit anti-mouse IgM (RAM; Zymed Labs), and biotinylated anti-Ly1 (Becton-Dickinson). The methodology for staining was essentially similar to single-color staining as reported earlier.[12] Briefly, 2×10^7 cells/ml were stained with FITC-F(ab')$_2$ RAM for 30–45 minutes in the cold. After appropriate washing procedures, cells were stained with biotinylated anti-Ly1 (30 minutes) followed by Texas red avidin (30 minutes). Controls were as follows: (1) biotinylated anti-Lyt-1 plus Texas red avidin, (2) FITC-F(ab')$_2$ RAM, (3) Texas red avidin alone, and (4) unstained cells. The data were visualized as contour plots and analyzed with a PDP/11 computer by procedures standardized in this laboratory.

RESULTS

Modulation of Lupus in B/W Mice by Sex Hormones

We have reported on the ability of sex steroid hormones to modulate the spontaneous SLE-like disease that occurs in NZB/NZW (B/W) mice.[15–17] In this lupus model, the disorder appears first in female mice and then several months later in males. Androgens suppress the disease in females, even when administered later in life when clinical features are already present. Depletion of androgen by orchidectomy results in an accelerated disease expression comparable to that seen in females (TABLE 1). Estrogen worsens the disease, as evidenced by early mortality when administered to B/W mice of either sex (TABLE 1).

Mechanism of Action of Sex Hormones

We next investigated the mechanism underlying sex hormone action. Studies from several laboratories suggest that there are multiple mechanisms by which sex hormones can modulate immune responses in general and autoimmune diseases in

TABLE 1. Effect of Sex Hormones on Survival of B/W Mice[a]

Experimental Procedure	% Mortality at 8 Months
Males	
Sham surgery	8
Orchidectomized	60[b]
Orchidectomized + E$_2$	95[b]
Orchidectomized + DHT	10
Females	
Sham surgery	78
Ovariectomized	87
Ovariectomized + E$_2$	95
Ovariectomized + DHT	15

[a]B/W mice were prepubertally gonadectomized and given either 17β-estradiol (E$_2$), Dihydro-testosterone (DHT), or empty implants.
[b]$p < 0.05$.

particular.[10] This is not surprising since receptors for sex hormones are present in many different cells in these lymphoid organs. These include lymphocytes, macrophages, epithelial cells, and reticular cells.[19,20] In addition, sex hormone receptors are present in the brain and pituitary. We have recently suggested that sex hormones may also act via the CNS to influence or modulate autoimmune disease.[19]

Available data suggest that T cells are the primary targets for sex hormone action. Evidence in support of this view includes the profound effects of sex hormones on the thymus and T cells.[10] We and others have recently reported that sex hormones affect a subset of T cells, namely, suppressor T cells. For example, E$_2$ depletes Lyt-2 positive cells, while Te or DHT maintains it.[12,21] As shown in TABLE 2, the administration of E$_2$ to either C57BL/10 orchidectomized mice or B6 intact mice reduced Lyt-2 positive cells in the spleen. By contrast, Te treatment had no such effect. Furthermore, E$_2$, but not Te treatment, reduced suppressor cell activity (TABLE 3). This was assessed by the ability of Con-A induced suppressor cells from sex hormone treated mice to inhibit the lymphoproliferative response to PHA. A decrease in suppressor function might contribute to autoimmunity through failure to control emergent B-cell clones capable of producing autoantibodies.

TABLE 2. Estrogen Depletes Lyt-2 Positive Cells

Strain	Experiment No.	Treatment	Tissue	% Positive	% Decrease
C57BL/10	1[a]	Intact	Spleen	22	—
		Orchidectomized	Spleen	14	—
		Orchidectomized + testosterone	Spleen	18	0
		Orchidectomized + estrogen	Spleen	2	86
C57BL/6	2[b]	Intact	Spleen	28	—
		Intact + estrogen	Spleen	15	46
		Intact	Lymph nodes	54	—
		Intact + estrogen	Lymph nodes	26	52

[a]Four-week-old mice were prepubertally orchidectomized and given testosterone or estrogen capsules for three months.
[b]Four-week-old mice were given estrogen capsules, which remained in place for three months.

TABLE 3. Effects of Sex Hormones on Suppressor Cell Activity

Strain	Treatment[a]	Percent Suppression $(1:1)$[b]
C57BL/6	Oil	17
	100 μg Te	36
	100 ng E_2	0
	10 μg E_2	0
C57BL/6-lpr	Oil	59
	100 ng E_2	55
	10 μg E_2	24

[a]Five-week-old mice were given sex hormones for two weeks.

[b]Splenic responder to splenic suppressor cell ratio of 1:1. Fifty microliters of splenic responder cells (plus PHA) were cocultured with 50 μg of Con-A induced splenic suppressor cells for 24 hours in the presence of PHA (3 μg/ml).

Prenatal Effects of Sex Hormones

We have recently investigated the influence of sex steroid hormones on the developing fetal immune system by administering Te or E_2 to pregnant murine mothers in the final week of gestation (day 14). We looked for long-term immunologic effects in the offspring of these mothers that were similar to those that occurred spontaneously in autoimmune mice. A variety of immunoregulatory abnormalities or immunopathologic effects was seen. Autoimmune mice, for example, spontaneously produce significantly greater numbers of plaque-forming cells (APFC) to bromelin-treated mouse red blood cells (Br-MRBC) (TABLE 4). These APFCs are thought to represent a subset of B cells bearing the Ly1 antigen.[22,23] Indeed, in addition to the augmentation in APFCs to Br-MRBC, we also observed marked increases in Ly1+ B cells in autoimmune mice (TABLE 5). Both APFCs and Ly1+ B cells are increased by the administration of estrogen to autoimmune mice starting at four weeks of age (Ansar Ahmed, Dauphinee, and Talal, to be published). Moreover, a similar increase in APFCs and Ly1+ B cells could be induced in mice following in utero exposure to estrogen (TABLE 6).

DISCUSSION

Extensive investigations in mice over the past decade have unequivocally established the involvement of sex hormones in the pathogenesis of autoimmune disease.[10,24] Evidence is also accumulating to indicate that sex hormones profoundly modulate a wide range of experimental autoimmune diseases in animals.[10,24] Overall, the data strongly suggest that male sex hormones prevent or delay the expression of autoimmunity, whereas female sex hormones accelerate autoimmune diseases.

TABLE 4. Increased APFC to Br-MRBC in Spleens of Autoimmune-Prone Mice

Strain	APFC to Br-MRBC $(\times 10^7)$
C3H	650
C3H/lpr	1680
C57BL/6	220
C57BL/6-lpr	1130

TABLE 5. Increased Ly1$^+$ B Cells in Autoimmune-Prone C3H/lpr Mice

Strain	% Ly1$^+$ B	% Ly1$^+$ B of Total B Cells
C3H	6.1	19.1
C3H/lpr	11.6	31.4

The suppression of autoimmunity by male sex hormones is of clinical significance because these agents can be exploited therapeutically. We have shown that male sex hormones have significant therapeutic effect in mice with lupus.[17] Clinically, the attenuated male hormone Danazol has been successfully used in the treatment of autoimmune idiopathic thrombocytopenic purpura and may hold some promise in the management of SLE.[25,26] Thus, one can view sex hormonal modulation of autoimmune disease in two directions: (1) the suppressive properties of male hormones, their therapeutic value in murine lupus, and their potential therapeutic value in patients; (2) the enhancing properties of estrogen, the potential dangers of a hyperestrogenic state, and its significance for the initiation of the lupus diathesis.

This paper demonstrates the long-term effect of estrogen on the developing immune system when administered *in utero* by injection into pregnant murine mothers late in gestation. These mothers gave birth to offspring who showed features later in life that were characteristic of spontaneously autoimmune mice. These features included the presence of APFCs to autologous erythrocytes and an increase in the Lyt-1$^+$ subset of B cells. Both findings are usually associated with B/W and other autoimmune mice,[22,23] and they are considered characteristic features of immune dysregulation and autoimmune disease.

Our studies suggest that permanent alterations can be induced by estrogen at a critical stage in the development of the fetal immune system. This may have biologic importance for the subsequent emergence of SLE, as well as for abnormalities that occur in children born to mothers with symptomatic or asymptomatic SLE.

There are now several studies that demonstrate a deficiency of androgen[27] and/or a hyperestrogenic state[28] in SLE patients. Thus, it is reasonable to presume that a human fetus growing in the uterus of a pregnant SLE patient could be exposed to hormonal alterations similar to those that we have induced experimentally in pregnant mice. The offspring of these lupus mothers might be born with a permanently altered immune system that is predisposed to latent or overt autoimmunity analogous to our findings of immune abnormalities in mice born to hyperestrogenized mothers. Thus, the tendency for autoimmune diseases to occur in families might be explained not only by direct genetic inheritance (e.g., MHC genes), but also by hormonal influences acting upon the developing fetus resident *in utero*.

Indeed, children born to autoimmune mothers producing anti-Ro (SS-A) antibodies may develop the neonatal lupus syndrome characterized by skin rash, congenital heart block, and other congenital cardiac malformations. The skin rash generally disappears upon clearing of maternal immunoglobulins from the newborn's circulation, but the cardiac lesions persist.[29,30] Since the heart, like the central nervous system and immune system, contains receptors for sex hormones, it is possible that hormonal factors may contribute to the cardiac lesions in neonatal lupus.

TABLE 6. Prenatal Exposure of Male B/W Mice to Estrogen

Group	APFC/Spleen	Ly1$^+$ B cells (%)
Oil	300	6.7
Estrogen	3045	12.0

It is well recognized that early exposure to sex hormones induces permanent neurological and behavioral changes. For example, injection of androgen into female rats in the first 24 hours of life results in an aggressive malelike behavior. These permanent changes in the CNS induced by sex hormones are referred to as "imprinting." Accordingly, we suggest the term "immunologic imprinting" to refer to permanent changes induced in the immune system as a consequence of exposure to sex hormones *in utero*.[19]

Finally, autoimmune disorders, like malignant diseases, develop as a consequence of a sequential process that, by analogy with carcinogenesis, can be divided into three stages called initiation, promotion, and progression. Aside from a relatively weak genetic predisposition linked to the MHC, particularly to the class II genes and HLA B8 DR3, little is known about the initiation stage. Almost all therapeutic attempts to date have concentrated on suppressing the immune inflammatory features that characterize the last two stages of disease. A nonvirilizing, but immunologically restorative sex hormone might prove a valuable adjunct to conventional therapy and might also have possibilities as a prophylactic agent in high risk individuals, particularly young women born into families with a high incidence of SLE.

REFERENCES

1. TALAL, N. 1985. The etiology of systemic lupus erythematosus. *In* Third Edition of Monograph on Lupus Erythematosus. E. Dubois & D. Wallace, Eds. Lea & Febiger. Philadelphia. In press.
2. ORTIZ-NEU, C. & E. C. LEROY. 1969. The coincidence of Klinefelter's syndrome and systemic lupus erythematosus. Arthritis Rheum. **12:** 241–246.
3. STERN, R., J. FISHMAN, H. BRUSMAN. & H. G. KUNKEL. 1973. Systemic lupus erythematosus associated with Klinefelter's syndrome. Arthritis Rheum. **20:** 18–22.
4. MICHALSKI, J. P., S. M. SNYDER, R. L. MCLEOD & N. TALAL. 1978. Monozygotic twins with Klinefelter's syndrome discordant for systemic lupus erythematosus and symptomatic myasthenia gravis. Arthritis Rheum. **21:** 306–309.
5. YOCUM, M. W., J. GROSSMAN, C. WATERHOUSE, G. N. ABRAHAM, A. G. MAY & J. J. CONDEMI. 1975. Monozygotic twins discordant for systemic lupus erythematosus. Arthritis Rheum. **18:** 193–199.
6. LAHITA, R. G., H. L. BRADLOW, J. FISHMAN *et al.* 1982. Estrogen metabolism in systemic lupus erythematosus. Arthritis Rheum. **25:** 843–846.
7. INMAN, R. D., L. JOVANOVIC, J. A. MARKENSON, C. LONGCOPE, M. Y. DAWOOD & M. D. LOCKSHIN. 1982. Systemic lupus erythematosus in men. Genetic and endocrine features. Arch. Intern. Med. **142:** 1813–1815.
8. CHAPEL, T. A. & R. E. BURNS. 1971. Oral contraceptives and exacerbations of lupus erythematosus. Am. J. Obstet. Gynecol. **110:** 366–369.
9. JUNGERS, P., M. DOUGADOS, C. PELISSIER *et al.* 1982. Influence of oral contraceptive therapy on the activity of systemic lupus erythematosus. Arthritis Rheum. **25:** 618–623.
10. ANSAR AHMED, S., W. J. PENHALE & N. TALAL. 1985. Sex hormones, immune responses, and autoimmune diseases: Mechanisms of sex hormone action. Am. J. Pathol. **121:** 531–551.
11. TALAL, N. 1979. Proceedings of the Kroc Foundation Conference on Sex Factors, Steroid Hormones, and the Host Response. Arthritis Rheum. **22:** 1153–1320.
12. ANSAR AHMED, S., M. J. DAUPHINEE & N. TALAL. 1985. Effects of short-term administration of sex hormones on normal and autoimmune mice. J. Immunol. **134:** 204–210.
13. COHEN, J. H. M., L. DANIEL, G. CORDIER, S. SAEZ & J. P. REVILLARD. 1983. Sex steroid receptors in peripheral T cells: absence of androgen receptors and restriction of estrogen receptors to OKT8-positive cells. J. Immunol. **131:** 2767–2771.
14. BLALOCK, J. E. & E. M. SMITH. 1985. The immune system: our mobile brain. Immunol. Today **6:** 115.

15. ROUBINIAN, J. R., R. PAPOIAN & N. TALAL. 1977. Androgenic hormones modulate autoantibody responses and improve survival in murine lupus. J. Clin. Invest. **59:** 1066–1077.
16. ROUBINIAN, J. R., N. TALAL, J. S. GREENSPAN, J. R. GOODMAN & P. K. SIITERI. 1978. Effect of castration and sex hormone treatment on survival, anti-nucleic acid antibodies, and glomerulonephritis in NZB × NZW F_1 mice. J. Exp. Med. **147:** 1568–1583.
17. ROUBINIAN, J. R., N. TALAL, J. S. GREENSPAN, J. R. GOODMAN & P. K. SIITERI. 1979. Delayed androgen treatment prolongs survival in murine lupus. J. Clin. Invest. **63:** 902–911.
18. ANSAR AHMED, S. & W. J. PENHALE. 1982. The influence of testosterone on the development of autoimmune thyroiditis in thymectomized and irradiated rats. Clin. Exp. Immunol. **48:** 367–374.
19. ANSAR AHMED, S. & N. TALAL. 1985. The survival value of non-classic target sites for sex hormone action in the immune and central nervous system. Clin. Immunol. Newsletter **6:** 97–99.
20. STUMPF, W. E. & M. SAR. 1976. Autoradiographic localization of estrogen, androgen, progestin, and glucoricosteroid in "target and nontarget tissues." *In* Receptors and Mechanism of Action of Steroid Hormones. J. R. Pasquelini, Ed.: 41–84. Dekker. New York.
21. NOVOTNY, E. A., E. S. RAVECHE, S. SHARROW, M. OTTINGER & A. D. STEINBERG. 1983. Analysis of thymocyte subpopulations following treatment with sex hormones. Clin. Immunol. Immunopathol. **28:** 205–217.
22. HAYAKAWA, K., R. R. HARDY, L. A. HERZNEBERG & A. D. STEINBERG. 1983. Ly1B: A functional distinct B cell subpopulation. *In* Progress in Immunology, V. Y. Yamamura & T. Tada Eds.: 661–665. Academic Press. Tokyo.
23. SMITH, H. R., L. J. YAFFE, T. M. CHUSED, E. S. RAVECHE, O. M. KLINMAN & A. D. STEINBERG. 1985. Analysis of B cell subpopulations. Cell. Immunol. **92:** 190–196.
24. TALAL, N., M. DAUPHINEE, S. ANSAR AHMED & P. CHRISTADOSS. 1983. Sex factors in immunity and autoimmunity. *In* Progress in Immunology, V. Y. Yamamura & T. Tada, Eds.: 1589–1600. Academic Press. Tokyo.
25. AHN, Y. S., W. J. HARRINGTON, S. R. SIMON, R. MYLIAGANAM, L. M. DALL & A. G. SO. 1982. Danazol for the treatment of idiopathic thrombocytopenic purpurs. N. Engl. J. Med. **808:** 1396–1399..
26. MORLEY, K. D., A. PARKE & C. R. V. HUGHES. 1982. Systemic lupus erythematosus: Two patients treated with Danazol. Br. Med. J. **284:** 1431.
27. JUNGERS, P., K. NAHOUL, C. PELISSIER, M. DOUGADOS, F. TRON & J. F. BACH. 1982. Low plasma androgens in women with active or quiescent SLE. Arthritis Rheum. **25:** 454–457.
28. LAHITA, R. G., H. L. BRADLOW, H. G. KUNKEL & J. FISHMAN. 1979. Alterations of estrogen metabolism in systemic lupus erythematosus. Arthritis Rheum. **22:** 1195–1198.
29. LITSEY, S. E., J. A. NOONAN, W. N. O'CONNOR, C. M. COTIRILL & B. MITCHELL. 1985. Maternal connective tissue disease and congenital heart block: demonstration of immuno-globulin in cardiac tissue. N. Engl. J. Med. **312:** 98–100.
30. CHAMEIDES, L., R. C. TRUEX, V. VETTER, W. J. RASHKIND, F. M. GALIOTO, JR. & J. A. NOONAN. 1977. Association of maternal systemic lupus erythematosus with congenital complete heart block. N. Engl. J. Med. **297:** 1201–1207.

DISCUSSION OF THE PAPER

R. S. SCHWARTZ (*Tufts University School of Medicine, Boston, MA*): What do you think about the difference in the results with Danazol in autoimmune diseases of the blood, such as immune thrombocytopenia, where beneficial effects have been obtained, whereas the drug seems to be only marginally effective in systemic lupus?

Another point I would like you to comment on is the evidence of estrogen receptors in human lymphocytes.

N. TALAL (*University of Texas Health Science Center, San Antonio, TX*): I would not say that the effect of Danazol in hematologic autoimmune diseases represents a discrepancy, but rather a reason to be optimistic. There is some evidence that ITP is a disease very closely related to lupus. You are correct about estrogen receptors in human lymphocytes; they occur particularly on the OKT8 suppressor cells, which is a finding that fits very nicely with the data we are getting in mice.

UNIDENTIFIED DISCUSSANT: Do you think that the immunological imprinting is strictly a peripheral phenomenon within the immune system itself or might it be mediated by neural changes?

TALAL: We do not know. I think that the dramatic effects we are seeing suggest some effect on the immune system; however, whether there are additional effects on the central nervous system is certainly a possibility.

Experimental Autoimmune Uveitis (EAU)

An Anti-Idiotypic Antibody Study

CARMEN F. MERRYMAN[a] AND LARRY A. DONOSO[b]

[a]Department of Biochemistry
Thomas Jefferson University
Philadelphia, Pennsylvania 19107

[b]Wills Eye Hospital
Research Division
Philadelphia, Pennsylvania 19107

S-antigen, a highly pathogenic retinal protein for the induction of experimental autoimmune uveitis, has been characterized in the photoreceptor cells of mammalian retinas and in the pinealocytes of the pineal gland.[1,2] Monoclonal antibodies that define different epitopes of S-antigen were produced by conventional hybridoma techniques.[3] One of the monoclonal antibodies, MAbA9-C6 (IgG2a), was useful for studying the embryological development of the rat retina and pineal gland.

In the developing rat retina, S-antigen could first be detected in the three-day-old rat. At this time, S-antigen reactivity was restricted to isolated cells of the outermost portion of the retinal neuroblastic cell layer. In the five-day-old rat, a distinct band of S-antigen immunoreactivity within the outermost portion of the neuroblastic cell layer could be observed before rod outer segment maturation and separation into the various retinal layers. S-antigen was localized to the entire photoreceptor cell in the seven-day-old rat retina and at all stages examined thereafter. In the rat pineal gland,

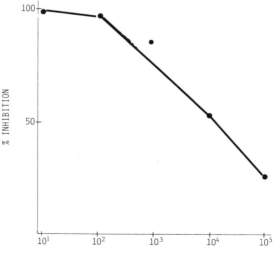

FIGURE 1. Radioimmunoassay showing inhibition of binding of MAbA9-C6 to S-antigen by a polyclonal anti-idiotypic antiserum.

% INHIBITION

DILUTIONS OF INHIBITOR

S-antigen immunoreactivity was observed on the third day after birth and at all stages examined thereafter. These studies indicate that antigenic differentiation with regard to S-antigen occurs prior to anatomic differentiation in the developing rat retina as assessed by conventional light microscopy.

Because MAbA9-C6 defined a unique epitope of S-antigen (individual antigenic specificity), it was also used to immunize rabbits. A rabbit anti-idiotypic antiserum has been obtained that competitively inhibits the idiotype–anti-idiotype interaction with the ligand in two different assays. As seen in the radioimmunoassay in FIGURE 1, the anti-idiotypic antiserum (used in dilutions ranging from 1:80 to 1:80,000) inhibited the binding of the ^{125}I MAbA9-C6 to S-antigen. Normal rabbit IgG, as control, was not inhibitory (not shown).

Immunoperoxidase staining of sections of rat eye were done with purified MAbA9-C6 alone, rabbit anti-idiotype antiserum alone, or MAbA9-C6 preincubated for one

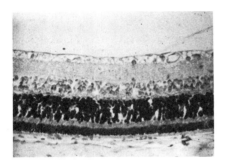 

FIGURE 2. (Left) Indirect immunoperoxidase stain (×100) of human retina with MAbA9-C6. The immune reaction is localized to the photoreceptor cell layer; (right) inhibition of the immune reaction by polyclonal anti-idiotype antiserum (immunoperoxidase, ×100).

hour with rabbit anti-idiotype antiserum. MAbA9-C6 alone bound to the photoreceptor cell layer of the rat retina, but the reactivity was abolished when the monoclonal antibody was incubated in the presence of rabbit anti-idiotypic antibody as seen in FIGURE 2. The rabbit anti-MAbA9-C6 serum alone did not bind to the retinal tissue (not shown). These results indicate that the rabbit anti-idiotype antibody is directed towards an epitope(s) in MAbA9-C6 that combines with S-antigen.

REFERENCES

1. WACKER, W. B., L. A. DONOSO, C. M. KALSOW, V. A. YANKEELOV & D. T. ORGANISCIAK. 1977. J. Immunol. **119:** 1949–1958.
2. BENESKI, D. A., L. A. DONOSO, K. E. EDELBERG, L. E. MAGARGAL, R. FOLBERG & C. MERRYMAN. 1984. Invest. Ophthalmol. Vis. Sci. **25:** 686–690.
3. DONOSO, L. A., C. F. MERRYMAN, K. E. EDELBERG, R. K. NAIDS & C. KALSOW. 1985. Invest. Ophthalmol. Vis. Sci. **26:** 561–567.

BALB/c Substrain Differences in Susceptibility to Experimental Allergic Encephalomyelitis (EAE)[a]

WILLIAM F. HICKEY, WILLIAM M. KIRBY,
AND CORY TEUSCHER

Departments of Pathology and Gynecology Obstetrics
School of Medicine
University of Pennsylvania
Philadelphia, Pennsylvania 19104

Experimental allergic encephalomyelitis (EAE) is currently the best animal model for multiple sclerosis (MS). As an experimental system, murine EAE promises to be a fertile area for study since its natural course after either active or passive induction and its demyelinative histopathology closely mimic MS.[1] In addition, the mouse immune system is the most completely understood of all mammalian systems; thus, basic immunological, immunogenetic, and molecular biological analyses should be able to progress rapidly in the murine EAE model. However, one block to progress has been the lack of a homozygous, inbred strain of mouse that offers features relative to EAE that would permit dissection of the system. With hope of identifying such a strain, we undertook the present study.

Various substrains of BALB/c mice were obtained from a number of independent sources (TABLE 1). The mice were injected in each rear footpad with 0.05 ml of the encephalitogenic emulsion. Controls received the same amount of a saline complete Freund's adjuvant (CFA) emulsion. On the day of injection, or the third day after injection, the mice were inoculated with 0.1 ml of crude pertussigen[2] intravenously and 0.05 ml intraperitoneally. The mice were then observed for the appearance of clinical signs of EAE for a period up to thirty days. At the termination of the observation period, the mice were sacrificed and their central nervous systems were studied histologically for EAE infiltrates.

Encephalitogenic emulsion: a 0.9 N solution containing 40 mg/ml of homogenized, lyophilized mouse (SWR) CNS tissue was prepared.[2] Incomplete Freund's adjuvant (DIFCO, Detroit, Michigan) was supplemented with 4.0 mg/ml of killed mycobacterium (H37Ra, DIFCO). Equal volumes of these two fluids were mixed through a fine bore needle to form a nonseparating emulsion. Thus, each mouse received 2.0 mg of CNS tissue in adjuvant containing 0.2 mg of mycobacterium.

The available results of this ongoing study are shown in TABLE 1 and the apparent relative substrain susceptibility is shown in TABLE 2. Of interest is the apparent intermediate degree of susceptibility exhibited by some of the substrains; however, the small numbers in certain groups do not permit an exact assignment of relative susceptibility. No control animals showed signs of EAE and a smaller percentage of controls died within seven days of pertussigen administration.

Our study produces some interesting points. The BALB/c mouse has been

[a]This work was supported by NIH grant nos. K07-NS00888 and HD-21100, and a grant from the National Multiple Sclerosis Society (RG-1685-A1).

331

TABLE 1. Induction of EAE in BALB/c Substrains

Substrains[b]	Number of Animals Injected	Day of Pertussigen Injection	Number of Animals Dying in First 7 Days	Evaluation of Clinical EAE[a]			Percentage of Mice with Signs of EAE
				No Symptoms	Flaccid Tail and Weakness	Paralysis or Moribund State	
BALB/c J[1]	10	0	4	6	0	0	0
	5	3	0	5	0	0	0
BALB/c AnN[2]	11	0	9	1	1	0	50
	15	3	2	3	1	9	77
BALB/c Ka[3]	14	0	5	2	4	3	77
BALB/c ORNL[4]	8	3	4	2	1	1	50
BALB/c ByJ[1]	20	0	1	9	1	9	50
BALB/c SKFla[5]	8	0	1	7	0	0	0
BALB/c WtJ[1]	10	0	0	10	0	0	0
Wt[4]	8	3	5	1	1	1	66

[a]Histological evaluation revealed that all mice with clinical signs of EAE had inflammatory CNS infiltrates. In addition, in the "susceptible substrains," some asymptomatic mice also had mild infiltration. No control mice and none of the substrains without any clinical evidence of EAE had CNS infiltrates.

[b]Source of mice: 1 = Jackson Laboratories, Bar Harbor, Maine; 2 = National Cancer Institute, N.I.H., Bethesda, Maryland; 3 = Department of Radiology, c/o Division of Laboratory Animal Medicine, Stanford University, Palo Alto, California; 4 = Michael Potter, National Cancer Institute, N.I.H., Bethesda, Maryland; 5 = Lorraine Flaherty, Mouse Genetics Laboratory, State of New York Department of Health, Empire State Plaza, Albany, New York.

characteristically reported as resistant to EAE induction.[3] However, it now appears that all BALB/c substrains differ in this regard. Whether this is due to genetic drift, point mutations, differences in vasoactive amine sensitivity, or undetected genetic contamination from another strain is currently unknown. Skin-grafting experiments, breeding studies, and immunogenetic analyses can be performed to distinguish between the possibilities. At this time, our data permit these conclusions: (1) The BALB/c mouse provides a new EAE system in which homozygous, inbred, potentially MHC syngeneic animals exhibit both susceptibility and resistance; (2) Immunogenetic studies of the BALB/c regarding EAE susceptibility should elucidate subtle genetic factors controlling disease induction; (3) The role of pertussigen and vasoactive amines and their relationship to EAE-induction/blood-brain-barrier alterations can be easily studied in the BALB/c mouse.

TABLE 2. Relative EAE Susceptibility of BALB/c Substrains

Highly Susceptible
BALB/c AnN
BALB/c Ka

Moderately Susceptible
BALB/c ByJ
BALB/c ORNL
BALB/c Wt

Resistant
BALB/c J
BALB/c SKFla
BALB/c WtJ

REFERENCES

1. DOHERTY, P. & E. SIMPSON. 1982. Murine models of multiple sclerosis. Nature **299:** 106–107.
2. MUNOZ, J. J., C. C. A. BERNARD & I. R. MACKAY. 1984. Elicitation of EAE in mice with the aid of pertussigen. Cell. Immunol. **83:** 92–100.
3. LINTHICUM, D. S. & J. A. FRELINGER. 1982. Acute autoimmune encephalomyelitis in mice. J. Exp. Med. **155:** 31–40.

Experimental Allergic Orchitis in Mice

Linkage of Disease Susceptibility to the Locus Controlling *Bordetella pertussis* Induced Sensitivity to Histamine[a]

CORY TEUSCHER

Division of Reproductive Biology and Endocrinology
Department of Obstetrics and Gynecology
The University of Pennsylvania School of Medicine
Philadelphia, Pennsylvania 19104

Susceptibility to experimental allergic orchitis in the mouse is controlled in part by a gene(s) linked to the H-2 complex.[1] BALB/cByJ and B10.D2/nSnJ mice (H-2^d) are highly susceptible to the induction of autoimmune orchitis, whereas H-2^k and H-2^b congeneic strains are resistant. However, not all H-2^d strains of mice are susceptible to disease induction. DBA/2J, NZB/N,[1] and certain BALB/c substrains[2] are disease resistant. Since the use of *Bordetella pertussis* is an absolute requirement for eliciting autoimmune orchitis in responder strains of mice,[1] a genetic analysis of the role of the single non-H-2 linked locus controlling *B. pertussis* induced sensitivity to histamine[3] in governing disease susceptibility was undertaken.

Mice were immunized with 10 mg dry weight of allogeneic mouse testicular homogenate in 0.05 ml of phosphate buffered saline (PBS) emulsified with an equal volume of complete Freund's adjuvant containing 0.45 mg *M. tuberculosis* (H37Ra). Each animal received 0.1 ml of the emulsion distributed equally in both hind footpads. Immediately thereafter, each animal received 10.0 μg of crude pertussigen (P) i.p. and 5.0 μg again 24 hours later. All animals were killed 20–25 days after immunization. Orchitis was graded histologically from 0–10 according to the degree of severity and a PI ± SD calculated as previously described.[1,2] Increased sensitivity to histamine was assessed by the i.p. injection of various doses (mg free base) of histamine in 0.2 ml PBS 3–4 days after the initial immunization. Backcross mice were studied at the time of sacrifice. Deaths were recorded at two hours. Mice challenged with histamine immunized without P served as negative controls.

BALB/cByJ, C57BL/10J, B10.D2/nSnJ, and (B10.D2/nSnJ × DBA/2J)F$_1$ hybrid mice were susceptible to histamine sensitization, whereas DBA/2J mice were not (TABLE 1). A comparison of the disease susceptibilities of the various strains studied with their susceptibilities to histamine sensitization indicates that only those strains of mice that process both the H-2^d haplotypes and that are susceptible to histamine sensitization develop significant autoimmune orchitis [i.e., BALB/cByJ, B10.D2/nSnJ, and (B10.D2/nSnJ × DBA/2J)F$_1$ hybrids]. Since (B10.D2/nSnJ × DBA/2J)F$_1$ hybrids (H-2$^{d/d}$) are susceptible to both histamine sensitization and autoimmune orchitis, (B10.D2/nSnJ × DBA/2J) × DBA/2J backcross mice were studied for both susceptibility to disease and histamine sensitization (TABLE 2). A high degree of correlation between disease susceptibility and histamine sensitization was observed ($\chi^2 = 7.17$, $0.005 < p < 0.01$), indicating that disease susceptibility is indeed

[a]This work was supported by NIH grant no. HD-21100.

334

TABLE 1. Association of *B. pertussis* Induced Histamine Sensitization with Susceptibility to Murine Autoimmune Orchitis[a]

		Histamine				Autoimmune Orchitis
		(−) P	(+) P			
H-2	Strain	10 mg	10 mg	1 mg	0.1 mg	PI ± SD (n)
d	BALB/cByJ	0/5	7/11[b]	3/14[b]	0/12[b]	4.9 ± 4.6 (5)
b	C57BL/10J	0/5	5/5	5/5	—	0.8 ± 0.5 (4)
d	DBA/2J	0/5	0/5	0/5	—	0 ± 0 (5)
d	B10.D2/nSnJ	0/5	5/5	3/10[b]	0/6	3.5 ± 3.0 (5)
d/d	(B10.D2/nSnJ × DBA/2J)F$_1$[c]	0/5	5/5	3/5	0/4	5.5 ± 2.0 (6)

[a]Histamine sensitivity was determined by i.p. injection of histamine three days following initial immunization. Deaths were determined two hours after challenge and the data are expressed as the number of animals that died over the total number of animals studied.
[b]Data represent the total of two independent experiments.
[c]Data include both male and female animals.

TABLE 2. Distribution of Histamine Sensitive and Insensitive Mice in the (B10.D2/nSnJ × DBA/2J) × DBA/2J Backcross Generation according to Disease Susceptibility

Autoimmune Orchitis[a]	Histamine Sensitive (+/−)[b]	Histamine Insensitive (−/−)	Total
Susceptible	16	9	25
Resistant	1	10	11
Total	17	19	36

[a]Disease susceptibility was determined histologically. All animals were classified as either susceptible or resistant depending on the presence or absence of inflammatory infiltrates.
[b]Histamine sensitivity was determined by i.p. injections of 5 mg histamine free base in 0.2 ml PBS 20 days following initial immunization. Deaths were determined at two hours after histamine challenge.

linked to the locus controlling *B. pertussis* induced sensitivity to histamine. In addition, the ratio of disease susceptible to resistant mice in the backcross generation (25:11 or 2.3:1.0) is indicative of additional multigene control.

REFERENCES

1. TUNG, K. S. K., C. TEUSCHER, S. M. SMITH, L. ELLIS & M. L. DUFAU. 1984. Factors that regulate the development of testicular autoimmune diseases. Ann. N.Y. Acad. Sci. **438:** 171–188.
2. TEUSCHER, C., M. POTTER & K. S. K. TUNG. 1985. Differential susceptibility to experimental autoimmune orchitis in BALB/c substrains. Curr. Top. Microbiol. Immunol. **122:** 181–188.
3. OVARY, Z., T. W. VRIS, C. D. SZALAY, N. M. VAZ & C. A. IRITANI. 1973. Independent segregation of the H-2 locus and the locus for responsiveness to histamine-sensitizing factor. Proc. Natl. Acad. Sci. USA **70:** 2500–2501.

Characterization of the Antigen of Human Antitubular Basement Membrane Antibody-Associated Interstitial Nephritis

M. CLAYMAN,[a] L. MICHAUD,[a] J. BRENTJENS,[b]
G. ANDRES,[b] AND E. G. NEILSON[a]

[a]Department of Medicine
University of Pennsylvania
Philadelphia, Pennsylvania 19104

[b]Department of Pathology
State University of New York at Buffalo
Buffalo, New York 14222

Autoimmune interstitial nephritis associated with antibodies to the tubular basement membrane (anti-TBM disease) is a well characterized renal lesion in experimental animals. This is typically induced with a single injection of a heterologous (e.g., rabbit) renal tubular antigen (RTA) preparation [comprised of at least 15 components by SDS-polyacrylamide gel electrophoresis (SDS-PAGE)]. We have recently reported on the isolation of a single disease-causing component from rabbit RTA of MW 48,000 (referred to as R3M-1) using immunoaffinity column chromatography with a relevant monoclonal anti-TBM antibody.[1]

A similar renal lesion is also well described in humans. This has been reported in association with drugs, after renal transplantation, and in idiopathic form. In addition, the majority of patients with antiglomerular basement membrane (anti-GBM) disease also have anti-TBM antibodies. We now report that a determinant from human RTA that is similar to R3M-1 is the target antigen of human anti-TBM antibody-associated interstitial nephritis. After bacterial collagenase digestion, human RTA was passed over the monoclonal affinity column and specifically bound material was reverse eluted in low pH, high molarity buffer. SDS-PAGE evaluation revealed a predominantly single component (referred to as H3M-1) with molecular weight of approximately 48,000. This was similar to R3M-1 and was markedly purified compared with the starting human RTA preparation. Sera from two patients with well-documented anti-TBM disease (which had indirect immunofluorescent titers against the tubular basement membrane of 1:64–1:128) were then analyzed. By solid-phase radioimmunoassay (RIA), these sera recognized H3M-1 at dilutions to 1:10,000. Neither normal human sera nor sera from patients with renal disease, but no anti-TBM antibodies (two with anti-GBM disease, two with interstitial nephritis, two with SLE, and one with membranous glomerulonephritis) were reactive with this moiety. Furthermore, while both sera had strong reactivity with H3M-1, they had only modest reactivity with collagenase solubilized human RTA and almost no reactivity with filtrate from the affinity column. Finally, whereas the human sera recognized R3M-1, 50–75% of this recognition could be blocked with sera from experimental animals with anti-TBM disease, thus suggesting common epitopic recognition.

We conclude that the target antigen of anti-TBM antibodies from patients with anti-TBM disease is H3M-1 and that this moiety is similar to the nephritogenic antigen of experimental anti-TBM disease.

REFERENCE

1. CLAYMAN, M. D. *et al.* 1985. J. Exp. Med. **161:** 290–295.

The Induction of Antigen-Specific Suppressor Cells (Ts) Diminishes Disease Expression in Mice with Interstitial Nephritis

R. MANN AND E. G. NEILSON

Renal-Electrolyte Section
Hospital of the University of Pennsylvania
Philadelphia, Pennsylvania 19104

Within ten days of immunization with renal tubular antigen (RTA) in adjuvant, all strains of mice develop antitubular basement membrane antibodies (αTBM-Ab) and a L3T4$^+$, I-A restricted, antigen-specific helper/inducer cell.[1] Six to ten weeks following immunization in disease-susceptible strains, a renal lesion appears that is characterized by tubular atrophy, mononuclear cellular infiltrates, and interstitial fibrosis.[1] In these susceptible mice, the L3T4$^+$ cell can adoptively transfer disease (disease expression follows cell transfer by 4–6 weeks).[2] This L3T4$^+$ cell is not itself an effector cell for delayed-type hypersensitivity (DTH) to RTA, but will induce, *in vitro,* an Lyt-2$^+$, H-2K restricted, antigen-specific effector cell for DTH to RTA. This Lyt-2$^+$ cell will acutely transfer disease (causing severe lesions within five days of having been placed beneath the kidney capsule).[3] In nonsusceptible strains, a T suppressor cell prevents the emergence of this Lyt-2$^+$ DTH effector cell and may in this way afford protection from disease. We now report the *in vivo* induction of such suppressor cells in immunized disease-susceptible mice and the subsequent diminution in disease expression.

SJL mice, which are disease susceptible, were immunized so as to induce disease. Thereafter, at various times, they received three weekly injections of RTA-coupled syngeneic spleen cells. Antigen presentation in this context has been demonstrated to induce antigen-specific suppressor cells.[4] Controls within each group received cells that had, in the absence of antigen, been subjected to antigen-coupling conditions. After 12 weeks, the mice were sacrificed and bled, and their kidneys were harvested for histologic evaluation. Peripheral node lymphocytes were tested for their ability to suppress a DTH response by transferring them, along with antigen, to the footpads of recipient mice. Footpad swelling 24 hours later has previously been shown to accurately predict nephritogenic potential.

The data presented in TABLE 1 indicate that control cells harvested from immunized mice that had received three weekly injections of uncoupled spleen cells contained a DTH effector cell, but no suppressor cell. Cells from mice primed with RTA-coupled cells, when transferred, suppressed the DTH response to RTA. As shown, lymphocyte subset depletion demonstrated that the induced suppressor cell was an Lyt-2$^+$, I-J$^+$, T cell. Depletion of the suppressor cell by αI-J^s incubation demonstrated the presence of a functionally suppressed DTH effector cell. Incubation with αLyt-2 eliminated both suppressor and effector cell, thus suggesting that the DTH effector cell was of appropriate phenotype to induce disease.

In subsequent experiments, the induced suppressor cell was shown to be antigen-

TABLE 1. The Effect of Induced Suppressor Cells on the DTH Response to RTA and the Phenotypic Characterization of These Cells

Prior Recipient Immunization (RTA/CFA)[a]	Footpad Challenge (Cells + RTA)[b]	Treatment of Cells Prior to Footpad Challenge	DTH Response to RTA (10^{-3} inches)[c]
−	control cells	−	16.5 ± 1.2[d]
+	control cells	−	16.3 ± 1.2[d]
−	Ts cells	−	3.5 ± 0.6
+	Ts cells	−	5.0 ± 0.6
−	Ts cells	C′	5.3 ± 1.4
+	Ts cells	C′	6.3 ± 0.9
−	Ts cells	αI-J^k + C′	5.8 ± 1.2
+	Ts cells	αI-J^s + C′	16.8 ± 0.5[d]
−	Ts cells	αThy-1.2 + C′	5.8 ± 1.1
+	Ts cells	αThy-1.2 + C′	15.3 ± 0.3[d]
−	Ts cells	αLyt-2 + C′	5.8 ± 0.8
+	Ts cells	αLyt-2 + C′	17.3 ± 0.5[d]
−	Ts cells	αL3T4 + C′	5.5 ± 1.0
+	Ts cells	αL3T4 + C′	5.0 ± 1.7
−	no cells	−	6.0 ± 1.0
+	no cells	−	18.0 ± 2.0[d]

[a]Recipient mice were either naive or had been immunized with renal tubular antigen in complete Freund's adjuvant five days prior to footpad challenge.

[b]Control cells were harvested from the peripheral nodes of mice that had been immunized on day 0 and subsequently primed with three weekly injections of 50×10^6 uncoupled syngeneic cells. Ts cells were harvested from the nodes of immunized mice that had been primed with three injections of RTA-coupled cells.

[c]Values expressed are the mean of 4–6 mice $\pm$ SEM. These values represent the incremental difference in footpad swelling, measured 24 hours after challenge, between the pad that received 1×10^6 cells + RTA and that which received 1×10^6 cells + PBS.

[d]$p < 0.001$ compared to control.

TABLE 2. Inhibition of Interstitial Nephritis by Induced Suppressor T Cells

Experimental Group[a]	Injection of RTA-Coupled Spleen Cells[b]	Weeks in Which Cells Were Injected	Histologic Severity at Week 12[c]
Positive Control (RTA/CFA)	−	—	2.7 ± 0.3
Group I	−		2.5 ± 0.9
	+	2, 3, 4	0.3 ± 0.1
Group II	−		2.5 ± 0.5
	+	4, 5, 6	0.1 ± 0.1
Group III	−		2.3 ± 0.8
	+	6, 7, 8	0.3 ± 0.2
Negative Control (CFA)	−	—	0.0 ± 0.0

[a]Negative controls were immunized with complete Freund's adjuvant alone on day 0. All others received RTA in CFA on day 0.

[b]A "+" indicates the intravenous injection of 50×10^6 RTA-coupled spleen cells once a week for three consecutive weeks. A "−" indicates the intravenous injection of 50×10^6 cells subjected to antigen-coupling conditions in the absence of RTA.

[c]Cortical interstitial injury was graded on a scale of 0 to 4. Each group contained 4–6 animals and the values expressed represent the mean $\pm$ SEM.

specific and to be restricted by I-J and Igh-1 gene products. Despite the induction of such suppressor cells, antibody production was comparable to that in immunized controls.

In TABLE 2, we see the result of suppressor cell induction on disease expression. Even in Group III, in which RTA-coupled cells were first introduced six weeks following immunization, disease expression was markedly diminished. The ability to induce an antigen-specific suppressor cell and to thereby alter an immune response already in progress has important therapeutic implications in this and other forms of immune-mediated disease.

REFERENCES

1. NEILSON, E. G., E. MCCAFFERTY, R. MANN, L. MICHAUD & M. CLAYMAN. 1985. J. Immunol. **134:** 2375–2382.
2. MANN, R., B. ZAKHEIM, M. CLAYMAN, E. MCCAFFERTY, L. MICHAUD & E. G. NEILSON. 1985. J. Immunol. **135:** 286.
3. MANN, R., M. CLAYMAN & E. G. NEILSON. 1985. Kidney Int. **27:** 217A.
4. NEILSON, E. G., E. MCCAFFERTY, R. MANN, L. MICHAUD & M. CLAYMAN. 1985. J. Exp. Med. **162:** 215.

Induction of Type II Collagen Autoimmune Arthritis and Ear Disease in Monkey[a]

T. J. YOO, J. M. STUART, T. TAKEDA, N. SUDO,
R. A. FLOYD, T. ISHIBE, G. OLSON, D. ORCHIK,
J. J. SHEA, AND A. H. KANG

Department of Medicine
University of Tennessee
Center for the Health Science
Memphis, Tennessee 38163

INTRODUCTION

The concept of autoimmune sensorineural hearing loss is relatively recent. Yoo *et al.* have suggested that immunity to type II collagen may be a major factor in this disease.[1-4] The present study was conducted to examine this hypothesis in nonhuman primates.

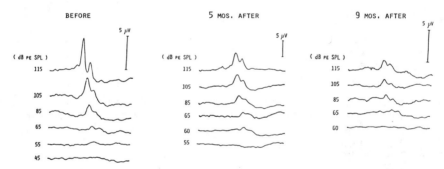

FIGURE 1. Immunization with native bovine type II collagen. Note the elevation of threshold and the marked decrease of amplitude in the immunized monkey. The prolongation of latencies is not recognized.

MATERIALS AND METHODS

Three *Macaca mulatta* and five *Macaca fascicularis* monkeys were used in this study. Two nonimmunized monkeys and one monkey immunized with bovine type I collagen served as the controls. Five monkeys were immunized with 1–2 mg of bovine type II collagen in CFA and boosted several times. The auditory function of these monkeys was followed by the measurement of electrocochleogram and auditory brain

[a]This research was supported by grants from the Deafness Research Foundation, the National Hearing Association, the American Otological Society, and the Veterans Administration.

response. The antibody levels were measured using the ELISA method. The animals were sacrificed at two time points after initial immunization. The joints and temporal bones were immediately fixed in 10% buffered formalin, decalcified, and embedded in paraffin and celloidin. Sections were cut at 10 μ horizontally and stained with hematoxylin and eosin.

RESULTS AND CONCLUSIONS

The immunized monkeys developed polyarthritis seven weeks following the primary immunization. They also showed weight loss that was presumably secondary to the difficulties in feeding themselves due to arthritis. Histological examination of involved joints showed thickening of the synovial membrane with infiltration by a large number of mononuclear cells and giant cells. The animals also developed imbalance. Electrocochleogram and brain stem evoked potential studies showed some shift of action potential threshold, thus indicating hearing loss (FIGURE 1). Histologic examination of the inner ear apparatus showed vacuolated degeneration of the spiral

TABLE 1. Antibody Titer to Type II Collagen Measured by ELISA

Monkey	Dilution of Serum	
	1:100	1:1000
Control	0.019	0.007
BI[a]	0.005	0.001
BII[b]	1.095	0.736

[a]BI = monkey immunized with bovine type I collagen.
[b]BII = monkeys immunized with bovine type II collagen.

ganglion, degeneration of the organ of Corti, vacuolar degeneration of the crista ampullaris, and cochlear vasculitis. These changes were associated with high levels of anti–type II collagen antibodies as measured by ELISA (TABLE 1). These results show that type II collagen autoimmunity could induce hearing loss and arthritis in nonhuman primates.

REFERENCES

1. YOO, T. J., K. TOMODA, J. M. STUART, A. H. KANG & A. S. TOWNES. 1983. Type II collagen-induced autoimmune otospongiosis: a preliminary report. Ann. Otol. Rhinol. Laryngol. **92**(2): 103–8.
2. YOO, T. J., K. TOMODA, J. M. STUART, M. A. CREMER, A. S. TOWNES & A. H. KANG. 1983. Type II collagen-induced autoimmune sensorineural hearing loss and vestibular dysfunction in rats. Ann. Otol. Rhinol. Laryngol. **92**(3): 267–271.
3. YOO, T. J., Y. YAZAWA, K. TOMODA & R. FLOYD. 1983. Type II collagen-induced autoimmune endolymphatic hydrops in guinea pig. Science **222**: 65–67.
4. YOO, T. J., K. TOMODA & A. D. HERNANDEZ. 1984. Type II collagen-induced autoimmune inner ear lesions in guinea pigs. Ann. Otol. Rhinol. Laryngol. **93**(suppl. 113): 3–5.

A Guinea Pig Model of Autoimmune Endolymphatic Hydrops[a]

T. J. YOO,[b] N. SUDO,[b] Y. YAZAWA,[c] R. A. FLOYD,[b]
T. ISHIBE,[d] AND T. TAKEDA[b]

[b]Department of Medicine
University of Tennessee
and
Veterans Administration Medical Center
Memphis, Tennessee 38163

[c]Shiga University of Medical Science
Otsu, Japan

[d]Kansai Medical University
Osaka, Japan

INTRODUCTION

Yoo *et al.* developed a guinea pig model of autoimmune endolymphatic hydrops by immunizing guinea pigs with type II collagen.[1] This study was designed to define the factors that influence the production of type II collagen-induced autoimmune endolymphatic hydrops. The factors used to aid in refining the guinea pig endolymphatic

TABLE 1. Incidence of Hydrops in Guinea Pigs Immunized with Native Bovine Type II Collagen

Degree of Hydrops[a]	Days Postimmunization						
	3	5	7	14	21	28	180
+ +	0	0	0	1	0	0	0
+	2	0	1	8	0	2	2
±	0	0	0	3	0	1	2
0	2	4	3	15	0	16	1

[a]The degree of hydrops was scored by the following scale: ±, very mild; +, mild; + +, moderate.

hydrops model included modification of immunization schedule, monitoring disease progression at earlier time intervals, and lengthening the period of time to study the development and progress of the disease. We also examined whether endolymphatic hydrops could be acquired by transferring cells from immunized animals to nonimmunized controls.

[a]This research was supported by grants from the Deafness Research Foundation, the National Hearing Association, the American Otological Society, and the Veterans Administration.

MATERIALS AND METHODS

Hartley, strain 13, and strain 2 guinea pigs were immunized with 400 μg of native bovine type II collagen in incomplete Freund's adjuvant and boosted one week later. The guinea pigs were sacrificed 3, 5, 7, 14, 21, 28, and 180 days postimmunization. For cell transfer study, guinea pigs received 1×10^7, 2×10^7, or 2×10^8 spleen or lymph-node cells intravenously from guinea pigs sensitized with type II collagen. These recipient guinea pigs were sacrificed one month later. The temporal bones were immediately fixed in 10% buffered formalin, decalcified, and embedded in paraffin and celloidin. Sections were cut at 8 μ horizontally and stained with hematoxylin and eosin.

RESULTS AND CONCLUSIONS

The results of the relationship between hydrops incidence and time sequence are shown in TABLE 1. A high incidence of hydrops was observed in immunized animals

TABLE 2. Cell Transfer of Native Bovine Type II Collagen-Induced Hydrops in Guinea Pigs

Cells Transferred[a]	Time Post-Transfer	Incidence of Hydrops	Degree of Hydrops[b]
2×10^7 LN	4 weeks	1/3	$\pm$
2×10^8 S	4 weeks	1/4	$++$
1×10^7 S	4 weeks	1/7	$\pm$
2×10^7 LN	8 weeks	1/2	$\pm$
2×10^7 S	8 weeks	1/4	$\pm$

[a] Guinea pigs received various numbers of spleen (S) or lymph-node (LN) cells from donor guinea pigs immunized with native bovine type II collagen.
[b] The degree of hydrops was scored by the following scale: $\pm$, very mild; $+$, mild; $++$, moderate.

sacrificed 14 days and 6 months postimmunization. Other histopathological findings in the immunized guinea pigs were as follows: spiral ganglion degeneration, atrophied organ of Corti, cystic lesions of the stria vascularis, mild atrophy of surface epithelium of the endolymphatic duct, and macrophages and precipitates in the endolymph. In addition, 5 out of 20 cell-transferred guinea pigs showed mild to moderate hydrops and the degree and the incidence of hydrops seemed to depend on the cell dosage (TABLE 2).

The results of these experiments show that the production of collagen-induced hydrops depends on the immunization schedule, the antigen dosage, and the postimmunization sacrifice date. Furthermore, the results of the cell-transfer experiment indicate that autoimmune hydrops is transferable by immune cells. Thus, hydrops appears to be another manifestation of immunologic injury resulting in an accumulation of mediator rather than any specific pathologic entity.

REFERENCES

1. Yoo, T. J., Y. Yazawa, K. Tomoda & R. Floyd. 1983. Type II collagen-induced autoimmune endolymphatic hydrops in guinea pig. Science 222: 55–67.
2. Yoo, T. J., K. Tomoda & A. D. Hernandez. 1984. Type II collagen-induced autoimmune inner ear lesions in guinea pigs. Ann. Otol. Rhinol. Laryngol. 93(suppl. 113): 3–5.

Increased Thromboplastin Production in Multiple Sclerosis: An Immunologic Defect?

CHARLES R. SPILLERT,[a] MARINO P. HAFSTEIN,[b]
VENKATA LANKA,[c] AND ERIC J. LAZARO[a]

[a]Department of Surgery
[b]Department of Neurosciences
[c]Department of Radiology
University of Medicine and Dentistry of New Jersey
New Jersey Medical School
Newark, New Jersey 07103

The problem of multiple sclerosis (MS) is a real one. Since there is no laboratory test to suggest the diagnosis in the majority of cases, the diagnosis of MS is largely based on the exclusion of other conditions that mimic the clinical features of this disease process.

It has been well established that the monocyte is the only circulating blood cell capable of producing thromboplastin. This thromboplastin generation is a marker of monocyte activation and has been found to be elevated in cancer.[1] We have, therefore, devised a simple test that enables the detection of thromboplastin generated when endotoxin is added to citrated whole blood followed by incubation, along with the determination of the recalcification time. In disease states in which thromboplastin generation is greater than that in healthy controls, the values of the recalcification

TABLE 1. Mean Recalcification Times (RT ± SD) of Saline- and Endotoxin-Incubated Citrated Whole Bloods of Patients with Chronic Progressive Multiple Sclerosis and Healthy Volunteers

Group	RT Saline (min)	RT Endotoxin (min)
Normal ($N = 19$)	6.55 ± 0.82	5.69 ± 0.75
MS ($N = 33$)	4.99 ± 0.93	3.67 ± 1.3
Significance (unpaired t)	$p < 0.001$	$p < 0.001$

times in the former are significantly lower than those of the latter because thromboplastin accelerates clotting.[1] Whether this also occurs in MS was the purpose of this study.

After obtaining informed consent, 5 cc of blood were obtained via a citrated vacutainer. One cc of citrated whole blood was transferred to two 12 × 75 mm test tubes. One tube contained 10 μl of saline (control tube) and the other tube contained 10 μl of 1 mg/cc solution of *E. coli* endotoxin (055:B5) in saline. These tubes were capped, gently mixed, and incubated at 37 degrees for two hours. Calcium ions (10 μl of 0.5 M CaCl$_2$) were then added to a 0.5-cc aliquot from each tube and the recalcification times were determined using a Sonoclot® Coagulation Analyzer.

All studies were performed in a blinded manner. The values obtained for RT saline and RT endotoxin are found in TABLE 1. In the MS patients, 22/33 (67%) RT saline values and 29/33 (88%) RT endotoxin values were below the lowest normal values.

The results of this study indicate that:

(1) The monocytes of MS patients generate large quantities of thromboplastin when stimulated by endotoxin;
(2) This generation of thromboplastin may represent a marker for measuring immune dysfunction.

REFERENCE

1. SPILLERT, C. R., W. D. SUVAL, E. J. CAFRUNY & E. J. LAZARO. 1984. Antigen-induced change in recalcification time in patients with carcinoma. Clin. Res. **32:** 707.

Immunological Studies of the Prostate

RICHARD J. ABLIN,[a] RACHEL STEIN,[b] JOHN M.
BARTKUS,[a] AND MAURICE J. GONDER[a]

[a]Department of Urology
State University of New York at Stony Brook
Stony Brook, New York 11794

[b]4 Harav Chen
Jerusalem, Israel

Benign prostatic hypertrophy (BPH) and prostate cancer (PCa) are significant medical problems for the aging male. Diversity in the natural history of PCa is characterized by a high incidence of occult foci found on routine autopsy; wide variation in the age of onset of clinical disease and demonstration of experimental autosensitization to prostatic tissue[1] have directed attention to factors of host resistance (i.e., immunological responsiveness) in its pathogenesis.

Recent reviews[2–5] on immunologic studies of the prostate and its secretion in various laboratory animal species and man have demonstrated tissue-specific immunogenicity and development of autoantibodies following parenteral- and cryo- (freezing *in situ*) immunization. Studies in patients with BPH and PCa have provided evidence of perturbations of immunocompetency, immunological responsiveness toward putative tumor-associated antigens, alterations of responsiveness following conventional therapy, and the rationale for implementation of adjuvant immunotherapy.[6]

Relevant to these observations and a basis of subsequent immunological studies of the prostate have been the demonstration of: (i) the development of autoantibodies and their elucidation following cryoimmunization (FIGURE 1), and the remission of metastatic PCa following cryoprostatectomy, thus, cryoimmunotherapy, and (ii) tissue- and species-specific antigens of the normal and pathological human prostate (FIGURE 2). As one proceeds from the normal to the malignant state, there is a loss or deficiency in prostatic tissue-specific acid phosphatase (PSAP) antigens. Immunohistologic localization of prostate antibodies (e.g., those to PSAP) to prostatic epithelial cells has provided a cell-type specific marker for prostate epithelial cells and the prostatic histogenesis of unknown metastases.

Concomitant studies have demonstrated modulation of humoral- and cell-mediated immunity in PCa patients by prostatic and seminal fluids.[8] Intraprostatic suppression of local immunological responsiveness by endogenous prostatic secretions may permit activation of quiescent tumors. In addition, it may compromise the host's ability to control activated tumor cells. The unique milieu of the prostate may provide the necessary microenvironmental conditions to explain: (i) the predilection for the development of BPH and PCa when compared to the rare occurrence of other male accessory sexual gland tumors; (ii) the failure of the PCa patient to develop a substantial clinical response to his malignancy in the early stages of disease; and (iii) the inordinate number of patients found on autopsy to have latent PCa. From a more general point of view, immunomodulation by prostatic and seminal fluids may further contribute to our understanding of what may otherwise appear as antithetical aspects of insemination, pregnancy, and malignancy.

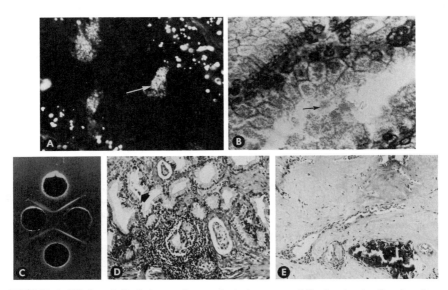

FIGURE 1. "Hallmarks" of the cryoimmunological response following *in situ* freezing (i.e., cryoimmunization) of the prostate (coagulating gland). (A) and (B) Photomicrographs of the rabbit prostate illustrating secretory granules comprising coaguloprostatic fluid (CPF) and their release following freezing. (A) Direct immunofluorescence demonstrating *in vivo* binding of fluorescein-labeled antiserum to rabbit IgG to focal accumulations of secretory granules (arrow) in prostatic epithelial cells. Larger fluorescing granules are lipofuscin granules ($\times 600$ with oil). (B) Hematoxylin and eosin preparation of rabbit prostate illustrating the liberation of secretory granules (arrow) shown in (A) ($\times 400$ with oil). Liberation of this normally sequestered secretory product, CPF, after freezing damage, into the circulation, results in the development of humoral- and cell-mediated cryoimmunological responses illustrated in (C) and (D). (C) Gel precipitation reactions demonstrating antibodies to autologous antigens of the frozen prostate following cryoimmunization and identification of the source of antigen as CPF. Left and right wells: Rabbit antisera resulting from cryoimmunization of the prostate and from parenteral immunization with CPF, respectively. Upper and lower wells: CPF from cryoimmunized and parenterally immunized rabbits, respectively. (D) and (E) Photomicrographs of the monkey prostate (caudal lobe) 41 days following the third of three independent *in situ* freezings of the prostate. (D) Initiation of cellular processes leading to destruction of prostatic acini. Large foci of cellular infiltrates, predominantly lymphocytes, may be seen concentrically around a prostatic acinus. Smaller lymphocytic foci contributing to the destruction of other acini may be seen to the left and right of center. Neutrophilic exudates (arrow), possibly proteinaceous material admixed with neutrophils [observed in the section of rabbit prostate shown in (A)], were observed in the lumina of some acini. (E) End result of the process initiated in (D) illustrates almost complete replacement of glandular elements. Focal squamous metaplasia, calcifications, and markedly hyalinized stroma may be seen. Hematoxylin and eosin, $\times 160$. (Note: This figure was reduced to 45% in magnification.)

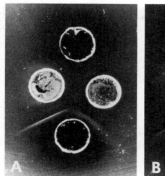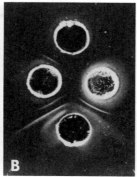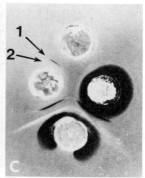

FIGURE 2. Application of adjunct specificity of antigen-antibody interaction in gel diffusion precipitation and enzymatic analysis for identification and characterization of prostate tissue-specific antigens. Reactants are identical in (A), (B), and (C). Lower well: antiserum to normal human prostatic tissue extract (NHPE) absorbed with normal human serum, kidney, and liver; upper well: same antiserum, but further absorbed with human prostatic fluid (HPF). Left and right wells: NHPE and HPF. Precipitation reactions are shown following (A) 48 hours at room temperature, (B) incubation in buffer-substrate mixture incorporating lead nitrate and sodium-β-glycerophosphate, and (c) staining for acid phosphatase with ammonium sulfide. Lines of precipitation, designated as 1 and 2, identify a prostate tissue-specific antigen characterized as prostatic tissue-specific acid phosphatase (PSAP) (1) and a non-PSAP antigen (2); that is, these antigens are prostate tissue-specific because they are not found in PF or seminal fluid, with the latter as demonstrated (not here shown) by further absorption of anti-NHPE serum with human seminal plasma. (From Ablin *et al.*[7])

REFERENCES

1. SHULMAN, S., C. YANTORNO, G. W. BARNES, M. J. GONDER, W. A. SOANES & E. WITEBSKY. 1965. Ann. N.Y. Acad. Sci. **124:** 279–291.
2. ABLIN, R. J. 1977. *In* Urologic Pathology. M. Tannenbaum, Ed.: 33–98. Lea & Febiger. Philadelphia.
3. ABLIN, R. J. 1983. *In* Benign Prostatic Hypertrophy. F. Hinman, Jr., Ed.: 73–98. Springer-Verlag. New York.
4. ABLIN, R. J. & R. A. BHATTI. 1981. *In* Prostatic Cancer. R. J. Ablin, Ed.: 183–204. Marcel Dekker. New York.
5. ABLIN, R. J. 1975. *In* Normal and Abnormal Growth of the Prostate. M. Goland, Ed.: 788–832. Thomas. Springfield, Illinois.
6. ABLIN, R. J. 1981. *In* Prostatic Cancer. R. J. Ablin, Ed.: 251–283. Marcel Dekker. New York.
7. ABLIN, R. J., P. BRONSON, W. A. SOANES & E. WITEBSKY. 1970. J. Immunol. **104:** 1329–1339.
8. ABLIN, R. J. & M. J. GONDER. 1985. *In* Protides of the Biological Fluids. H. Peeters, Ed.: 271–276. Pergamon. Oxford, United Kingdom.

Suppression of Collagen Arthritis by Ly1⁻2⁺ Antigen-Specific T Suppressor Cells[a]

THOMAS F. KRESINA

Division of Rheumatology
Department of Medicine and Pathology
Case Western Reserve University
Cleveland, Ohio 44106

This present study summarizes a previous report[1] that details the adoptive transfer and cell depletion studies utilized to establish the cellular populations required for antigen-specific suppression of collagen-induced arthritis. The data indicate that Thy1⁺ Ly1⁻2⁺ type II collagen-specific splenic cells are generated on intravenous preinoculation with native heterologous type II collagen. These T suppressor cells functionally suppress the erythema and edema of synovitis associated with collagen-induced arthritis, as well as *in vitro* cell-mediated immune responses to type II collagen and serum antibodies specific for type II collagen. This study, therefore, suggests that specific suppression of immune responses to type II collagen by T suppressor cells may be immunotherapeutic in certain forms of arthritis.

ADOPTIVE TRANSFER EXPERIMENTS

Adoptive transfer of whole splenic cell preparations, splenic subpopulations, or thymocytes was utilized to establish the subpopulation required for suppression of collagen arthritis. As shown in TABLE 1, splenic cells from animals inoculated intravenously with native type I collagen and adoptively transferred to naive animals were not capable of suppression of collagen arthritis. However, splenic cells from animals that were administered intravenously with native type II collagen prior to adoptive transfer to naive mice suppressed collagen arthritis, as observed by the gross inflammation score of the recipients ($p < 0.007$). Adoptive transfer of enriched subpopulations of lymphoid cells (either B or T cells) revealed that thymocytes and not subpopulations devoid of functional T cells were capable of suppression of arthritis, as determined by the gross inflammation scores ($p < 0.005$).

CELL DEPLETION STUDIES

Further studies elucidated the cellular phenotype of the T cells capable of suppression of the erythema and edema associated with collagen arthritis. Utilization of anti-Ly antisera, as shown in TABLE 2, resolved that the cellular subpopulation responding to *in vitro* incubation to native type II collagen was Ly1⁻2⁺. These cells, which were not observed in the arthritis animals, were phenotypically T suppressor cells.

[a]This work was supported by NIH grant no. AM-36040 and the Revco D.S. Foundation.

TABLE 1. Adoptive Transfer of Suppression of Collagen Arthritis: Gross Pathology[a]

| | | Inflammation Score[d] | | | |
| | | Hind Paw | | Fore Paw | |
Cell Transferred[b]	Incidence of Inflammation[c]	Left	Right	Left	Right
Spleen cells from type I collagen preinoculated mice	8/8	2.3	1.9	0.5	1.3
Spleen cells from type II collagen preinoculated mice	5/16	0.7	0.8	0.4	0.7
"B" cells from type II collagen preinoculated mice[e]	13/13	1.9	1.4	0.6	1.3
Thymocytes from type II collagen preinoculated mice	3/15	0.9	0.9	0.3	0.4

[a]Animal paws have been individually scored for arthritis on a scale of 1–5 based on the amount of erythema and edema, distortion, or ankylosis of the joint.

[b]Mice were administered intravenous injections three days prior to sacrifice. Spleens were removed and minced into a single cell suspension, and 1×10^7 cells were adoptively transferred four days before immunization.

[c]Number of animals with a recorded pathology score >1 by day 50 divided by the total number of mice per group at day 50.

[d]Average pathology score for the individual paw of each mouse in the designated group.

[e]Single cell suspension of splenic cells treated with anti-Thy-1.2 and complement to remove functional T cells.

DISCUSSION

Previous observations[2-5] have noted that the immune responses to collagen, as well as the arthritic responses in rats with collagen arthritis, can be modulated by administration of either free native collagen, collagen-coupled spleen cells, specific constituent collagenous cyanogen-bromide peptides, or collagen-coupled erythrocytes prior to immunization. The present study shows that the mechanism of this modulation

TABLE 2. Cellular Phenotype of Splenic Subpopulations in Arthritis and Suppressed Mice Responding to *in Vitro* Incubation with Native Type II Collagen

| | Cell-Mediated Immune Response[b] | | | |
Group[a]	Diluent	αThy	αLy1	αLy2
	Stimulation Index ± SD			
Arthritis	4.0 ± 1.6	0.9 ± 1.4	1.5 ± 0.7	3.9 ± 0.5
Suppressed	2.1 ± 0.4	1.1 ± 0.2	1.7 ± 0.4	0.9 ± 0.2

[a]Arthritis group—animals administered 1×10^7 whole spleen cells from mice previously inoculated with saline; suppressed mice—animals administered 1×10^7 whole spleen cells from mice inoculated with native type II collagen.

[b]*In vitro* cell-mediated immune response of pooled splenic cells derived from the designated group before incubation with native type II collagen. Single cell suspensions were aliquoted and treated with either saline, anti-Ly1, anti-Ly2, or anti-Thy-1.2 antisera and complement. Data recorded as a stimulation index defined as:

$$\frac{\text{average CPM } ^3\text{H-thymidine incorporation stimulated cultures}}{\text{average CPM } ^3\text{H-thymidine incorporation of nonstimulated cultures}}.$$

is the generation of collagen type-specific suppressor T cells. Furthermore, a recent report[6] has indicated that collagen arthritis can be abrogated by type II collagen reactive cloned T cells. This study and the latter report suggest that the generation of T cells that modulate the immune response to type II collagen can be immunotherapeutic in certain forms of arthritis.

REFERENCES

1. KRESINA, T. F. & R. W. MOSKOWITZ. 1985. J. Clin. Invest. **75**: 1990–1998.
2. STAINES, N. A., T. HARDINGHAM, M. SMITH & B. HENDERSON. 1981. Immunology **44**: 737–744.
3. SCHOEN, R. T., M. I. GREENE & D. E. TRENTHAM. 1982. J. Immunol. **128**: 717–719.
4. CREMER, M. A., A. D. HERNANDEZ, A. S. TOWNES, J. M. STUART & A. H. KANG. 1983. J. Immunol. **131**: 2995–3000.
5. BRAHN, E. & D. E. TRENTHAM. 1984. Clin. Immunol. Immunopathol. **31**: 124–131.
6. BRAHN, E. & D. E. TRENTHAM. 1985. Arthritis Rheum. **28**: S26.

Treatment of Diabetic (db/db) Mice with Anti-Class-II MHC Monoclonal Antibodies[a]

BHAGIRATH SINGH AND WILLIAM J. CLIFFE

Department of Immunology
and
MRC Group on Immunoregulation
University of Alberta
Edmonton, Alberta, Canada T6G 2H7

INTRODUCTION

Although the initial lesion in the development of diabetes remains largely unknown, C57BL/KsJ (db/db) (H-2d) mice provide a good model for understanding human diabetes.[1] These animals exhibit a severe diabetes-obesity syndrome that in its early stages has similarities to the noninsulin-dependent (type II) diabetes (NIDDM), but in later stages may resemble insulin-dependent (type I) diabetes mellitus (IDDM). The disease is associated with marked histological changes in the islets of Langerhans and in the thymus.[2,3] Necrosis of beta cells is followed by insulinopenia, hyperglycemia, and death around 5–8 months of age. The thymus becomes involuted and lymphopenia is observed in both thymus and spleen. Immunologically, anti-islet antibodies and

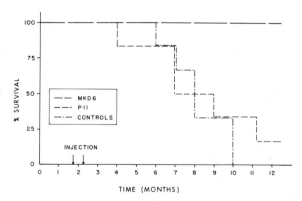

FIGURE 1. Effect of anti-class-II MHC monoclonal antibody MK-D6 (anti-I-Ad) on the life span of diabetic C57BL/KsJ (db/db) mice. Five hundred μl of ascites fluid containing MK-D6 monoclonal antibody or an unrelated antibody (P.1.1) were injected at six weeks of age. The same amount of ascites fluid was again injected two weeks later. Control animals remained uninjected.

[a]This work was supported by the Medical Research Council of Canada and the Alberta Heritage Foundation for Medical Research. Bhagirath Singh is a Scholar of the Alberta Heritage Foundation for Medical Research.

decreased T-cell-mediated immune reactivity is associated with the onset of the disease. Both serum and spleen cells are capable of blocking insulin release from the cultured islet cells. The anti-islet antibody in the sera is cytotoxic and can be detected as early as day 10 after birth.[2] Taken together, these observations point to an autoimmune etiology for the disease. Because of the immunoregulatory role of class-II major-histocompatibility-complex (MHC) antigens, particularly in T-cell-mediated immunity, we have used anti-class-II MHC monoclonal antibodies (anti-Ia) *in vivo* to block the disease in C57BL/KsJ (db/db) mice.[4]

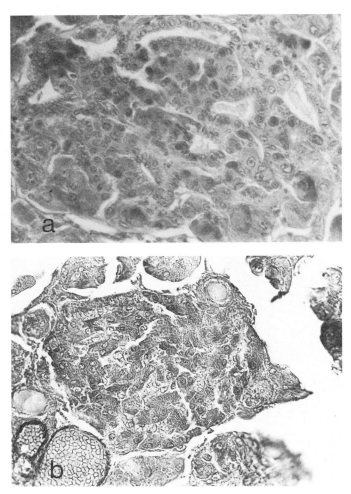

FIGURE 2. Histology of the pancreas of (a) untreated control and (b) MK-D6-treated C57BL/KsJ (db/db) mice at eight months of age stained with aldehyde-fuchsin. (All magnification ×200; this figure was reduced to 70% though). (a) State of late necrosis can be seen with infiltration of acinular cuboidal cells in the beta-cell mass of the islets; (b) necrosis as well as infiltration of acinular cuboidal cells are absent.

RESULTS AND DISCUSSION

Prediabetic C57BL/KsJ (db/db) mice were treated at six weeks of age twice with anti-I-Ad monoclonal antibody[5] MK-D6 (isotype IgG2a) or with a control antibody. This treatment had a profound effect on the disease process. All the anti-I-Ad-treated animals were still alive at 12 months of age, whereas the untreated controls or controls treated with unrelated antibody were dead (FIGURE 1). Histological examination of the pancreas of the untreated animals revealed necrosis and degradation of the beta cells in the islets of Langerhans with the infiltration of acinular cuboidal cells (FIGURE 2). The anti-I-Ad-treated animals, on the other hand, showed no changes in their islet morphology from the animals at the prediabetic stage. High blood glucose levels were unaffected by the treatment with anti-Ia antibodies and may be a reflection of the obesity syndrome of these animals.[1] Anti-Ia antibody had prolonged effects on the disease even though it was only administered twice at the beginning of the experiment. This treatment may work by (i) suppressing the production of anti-islet antibody from Ia-positive B cells, (ii) generating anti-idiotypic antibodies that may regulate autoreactive cells, and (iii) interfering with the recognition of relevant antigen by T lymphocytes in the context of class-II MHC molecules. Therefore, we conclude that Ia antigens may play an important role in the effector phase of the disease process in C57BL/KsJ (db/db) animals.

REFERENCES

1. COLEMAN, D. L. 1982. Diabetes-obesity syndrome in mice. Diabetes **31** (suppl. 1): 1–6.
2. DEBRAY-SACHS, M., M. DARDENNE, P. SAI, W. SAVINO, M. C. RUINIOU, D. BOILLOT, W. GEPTS & R. ASSAN. 1983. Anti-islet immunity and thymic dysfunction in the mutant diabetic C57BL/KsJ db/db mouse. Diabetes **32:** 1048–1054.
3. DARDENNE, M., W. SAVINO, L. N. GASTINEL, B. NABARRA & J. F. BACH. 1983. Thymic dysfunction in the mutant diabetic (db/db) mice. J. Immunol. **130:** 1195–1199.
4. STEINMAN, L., J. T. ROSENBAUM, S. SRIRAM & H. O. MCDEVITT. 1981. *In vivo* effects of antibodies to immune response gene products: prevention of experimental allergic encephalomyelitis. Proc. Natl. Acad. Sci. USA **78:** 7111–7114.
5. KAPPLER, J. W., B. SKIDMORE, J. WHITE & P. MARRACK. 1981. Antigen-inducible, H-2-restricted, interleukin-2-producing T-cell hybridomas: lack of independent antigen and H-2 recognition. J. Exp. Med. **153:** 1198–1214.

In Insulin-Dependent Diabetes, the Expression of an HLA-DR4-Related Susceptibility Gene Is Dominant, but Expression of a DR3-Related Gene Is Dependent on the DR4-Related Gene

MICHAEL J. MacDONALD,[a] JERRY GOTTSCHALL,[b]
JAY B. HUNTER,[b] KAREN L. WINTER,[b]
STEVEN D. JOHNSON,[a] JUDITH L. BLANK,[c]
ELIZABETH P. MASON,[c] AND SHARON MABY[d]

[a]Department of Pediatrics
University of Wisconsin Medical School
Madison, Wisconsin 53706

[b]Blood Center of Southeastern Wisconsin
Milwaukee, Wisconsin 53233

[c]University of Wisconsin Hospital
Madison, Wisconsin 53792

[d]Marshfield Clinic
Marshfield, Wisconsin 54449

In insulin-dependent diabetes mellitus (IDDM), HLA genes are probably involved in an autoimmune-mediated destruction of the pancreatic islet beta cells—the insulin-producing cells. HLA data have been used in many ingenious ways in attempts to discern the mode of inheritance of IDDM. However, due to the complexity and looseness of these HLA associations, this has been a difficult task. The HLA region is highly polymorphic. For example, the HLA-DR locus, which has shown the strongest association with IDDM, has more than ten alleles. Furthermore, unlike most other HLA-associated disorders, not one, but two DR alleles, DR3 and DR4, are associated with IDDM, which raises the question of whether IDDM has more than one etiology. DR3 and DR4 each has a frequency of about 20–30% in the general population, whereas only 50–60% of subjects with IDDM are DR3 positive and 60–80% are DR4 positive. However, more than 95% of subjects with IDDM are DR3 and/or DR4 positive, and of even more complexity, the genotype DR3DR4 is associated with a higher risk for IDDM than any other genotype, including the DR3 and DR4 homozygotes.

The high relative risk for IDDM associated with the DR3DR4 genotype suggests an interaction between a gene associated with DR3 and another gene associated with DR4. To learn more about this possible interaction, two sets of HLA data were analyzed. First, families with one parent with IDDM and at least one offspring with IDDM were studied to find out if the transmission of DR alleles fits any pattern. Surprisingly, the DR4 allele was transmitted from the diabetic parent to the diabetic offspring in 15 of 17 families and the allele for DR3 was transmitted twice. Considering the relative gene frequencies of DR3 (0.30), DR4 (0.42), and other DR alleles (0.28) in the overall IDDM population, this finding is quite surprising. The highly significant rate of transmission of DR4 ($p < 0.001$) raised the possibility that a single dose of a DR4-associated gene (as in dominant inheritance) could give susceptibility to IDDM and suggested another question not previously asked: What is the risk of IDDM associated with DR3 or DR4 in the absence of the other allele? Data on 94 unrelated subjects with IDDM and on 158 nondiabetics showed that DR4 is associated with a risk for IDDM in the absence of DR3 ($p < 0.002$), but that DR3 is associated with a risk mainly in the presence of DR4 (TABLE 1). This is a finding confirmed by performing this same analysis on seven sets of published data (data not shown). These results suggest that DR4 is associated with a primary or independent diabetes susceptibility gene, while the DR3 is associated with a gene that enhances susceptibility mainly in the presence of the DR4-associated gene.

The above concept encompasses hypotheses of dominant inheritance[1] and intermediate inheritance of IDDM [one dose of an HLA-linked allele is sufficient to give susceptibility, but two doses of the allele (as in recessive inheritance) increase susceptibility markedly].[2] In fact, it reconciles these hypotheses with the genetic

TABLE 1. Frequencies, Relative Risks, and Statistical Probability Values for Various Phenotypes Containing DR3 and/or DR4 in IDDM versus Controls[a]

DR Phenotype	Number and Percent of Subjects with a Phenotype		Relative Risk	p Value
	Controls $n = 158$	IDDM $n = 94$		
DR3DR*	45 (28)	51 (54)	2.9	10^{-4}
DR4DR*	47 (30)	74 (79)	8.6	10^{-9}
DR3DR4	8 (5)	33 (35)	9.8	$<2 \times 10^{-9}$
DR3DRblank	5 (3)	5 (5)	1.7	N.S.
DR4DRblank	7 (4)	6 (6)	1.5	N.S.
DR3$^+$DR4$^-$	37 (23)	18 (19)	0.8	N.S.
DR3$^-$DR4$^+$	39 (25)	41 (44)	2.4	$<2 \times 10^{-3}$

[a]DR* represents any DR antigen, including DR3, DR4, or DRblank. DRblank represents the presence of an unidentifiable antigen. The superscript plus and minus signs represent the presence and absence of an antigen, respectively. The numbers in the parentheses represent the percent of the total number of subjects. N.S. means not significant.

heterogeneity hypothesis.[3] Individuals with two doses of susceptibility alleles could have the DR4-associated determinant plus the DR3-associated determinant, which is a situation similar to recessive inheritance, except that the susceptibility alleles are not identical. The heterogeneity hypothesis predicts three forms of IDDM: a form associated with DR3, a form associated with DR4, and a form associated with both alleles. The results of the current study suggest that the two latter forms are the major forms of IDDM. However, the data do not suggest any major differences between the two genetic forms. Instead, the data suggest that the form of IDDM associated with both the DR3- and the DR4-related genes is merely a subset of a major form determined by the primary IDDM susceptibility gene associated with DR4.

REFERENCES

1. MacDONALD, M. J. 1980. Hypothesis: The frequencies of juvenile diabetes in American Blacks and Caucasians are consistent with dominant inheritance. Diabetes **29**(2): 110–114.

2. SPIELMAN, R. S., L. BAKER & C. M. ZMIJEWSKI. 1980. Gene dosage and susceptibility to insulin-dependent diabetes. Ann. Hum. Genet. (London) **34:** 135–150.
3. ROTTER, J. I. 1982. The question of one or two HLA-linked diabetes susceptibility genes is resolved by a heterogeneity model. *In* The Genetics of Diabetes Mellitus. J. Kobberling & R. Tattersall, Eds.: 144–145. Academic Press. London.

Aberrant Expression of HLA-DR Determinants on Human Thyroid Cells Treated with Phytohemagglutinin and γ-Interferon and on Human Melanoma Cells

Demonstration with a Binding Assay Using a New Potent ^{125}I-Monoclonal Antibody against the HLA-DR β-Chain (MAb 03-D7)

P. DE MEYTS,[a] S. HALLEZ,[a] J. L. GU,[a] M. MERCHEZ,[a]
I. ECONOMIDIS,[a] G. G. ROUSSEAU,[a] J. VAN SNICK,[b]
C. SPINEL,[c] J. P. SQUIFFLET,[d] A. M. RAVOET,[e]
M. DE BRUYERE,[e] K. WILLARD,[f] F. VESSIERE,[f]
C. LEMOINE,[f] T. BOON,[f] H. TOYODA,[g]
F. CHEN,[h] AND J. SHIVELY[h]

[a]Hormone and Metabolic Research Unit
[b]Experimental Medicine Unit
International Institute of Cellular and Molecular Pathology
Avenue Hippocrate, 75
B-1200, Brussels, Belgium

[c]Department of Histology,
[d]Department of Experimental Surgery
[e]Department of Hematology
Catholic University of Louvain Medical School
B-1200 Brussels, Belgium

[f]Ludwig Cancer Institute
B-1200 Brussels, Belgium

[g]Department of Molecular Genetics
[h]Department of Immunology
Beckman Research Institute of the City of Hope
Duarte, California 91010

A monoclonal antibody, MAb 03-D7, with an extraordinary affinity for the human class II histocompatibility antigen HLA-DR was obtained by immunizing BALB/c mice with whole human-cultured lymphoblastoid cells of the IM-9 line and fusing the mice spleen lymphocytes with SP 2/0-Ag-14 mouse myeloma cells. MAb immunoprecipitation of lysed ^{35}S-pulsed IM-9 cells showed a doublet around 31K on SDS-polyacrylamide gels identical to that obtained with OKIa, which is a well characterized monoclonal against HLA-DR.

The MAb reacted in Western blots with the purified β-chain of HLA-DR.

359

Preliminary experiments showed that recognition of human lymphocytes was independent of haplotype. MAb 03-D7 does not bind to mice spleen cells. Two-dimensional gels show a strong reaction with HLA-DR and a weaker reaction with two related molecules, possibly DQ(DC) and DP(SB). Further work is in progress to better define the MAb reactivity with HLA-D subregion loci products.

Monoclonal 03-D7 was stoichiometrically labeled with ^{125}I and retained up to 80% binding ability to IM-9 cells. Binding to IM-9 cells was rapid and irreversible, with neither dilution, addition of an excess unlabeled MAb, or dropping of pH to 5.0 removing the bound ^{125}I-MAb. Binding, however, was rapidly reversed at pH 3.0. Scatchard plots were concave upwards with a vertical portion when MAb exceeds the HLA-DR concentration on the surface; this is consistent with irreversible binding. The apparent binding affinity was $>10^9$ M^{-1}. Binding of ^{125}I-MAb-03-D7 was competed for by MAb OKIa, but not by M704 or L243.

When normal thyrocytes in primary cultures were incubated with phytohemagglutinin (PHA), there was a dramatic and transient appearance of ^{125}I-MAb binding, with a maximum around three days after initiation of PHA treatment. Recombinant human γ-interferon (gift from Genentech) at 500 U/ml produced a similar expression of ^{125}I-MAb binding after 48 hours of incubation. Untreated cultures showed a small degree of initial binding, possibly to immunocompetent (dentritic?) cells contaminating the thyrocytes; this binding faded within a few days in the absence of PHA.

These data are in agreement with those of Bottazo's group[1-5] obtained with an immunofluorescence technique and with their hypothesis that aberrant expression of DR determinants on epithelial cells may play a crucial role in autoimmunity.[2]

We have also studied ^{125}I-MAb 03-D7 binding to twelve cloned melanoma cell lines.[6] Nine of these expressed MAb binding sites in variable numbers (3×10^5 to 10^7 per cell)—interestingly, with variable affinity (10^8–10^{10} M^{-1}) and Scatchard plots of various shapes—suggesting that the structure of the expressed DR determinants may vary between cell lines.

The unusual binding properties of MAb 03-D7 should make it a useful tool in the investigation of the mechanisms of autoimmunity, as well as the mechanisms by which melanoma cells escape immune detection. Its potent binding may make it an MAb of choice if it becomes feasible to test the use of anti-DR monoclonals as immunotherapeutic agents.

REFERENCES

1. PUJOL-BORREL, R., T. HANAFUSA, L. CHIOVATO & G. F. BOTTAZZO. 1983. Lectin-induced expression of DR antigen on human cultured follicular thyroid cells. Nature **304:** 71–73.
2. BOTTAZZO, G. F., R. PUJOL-BORREL, T. HANAFUSA & M. FELDMANN. 1983. Role of aberrant HLA-DR expression and antigen presentation in induction of endocrine autoimmunity. Lancet **ii:** 1115–1119.
3. LONDEI, M., J. R. LAMB, G. F. BOTTAZZO & M. FELDMANN. 1984. Epithelial cells expressing aberrant MHC class II determinants can present antigens to cloned human T cells. Nature **312:** 639–641.
4. LONDEI, M., G. F. BOTTAZZO & M. FELDMANN. 1985. Human T-cell clones from autoimmune thyroid glands: Specific recognition of autologous thyroid cells. Science **228:** 85–88.
5. TODD, I., R. PUJOL-BORRELL, L. J. HAMMOND, G. F. BOTTAZZO & M. FELDMANN. 1985. Interferon-γ induces HLA-DR expression by thyroid epithelium. Clin. Exp. Immunol. **61:** 265–273.
6. WINCHESTER, R. J., C-Y. WANG, A. GIBOFSKY, H. G. KUNKEL, K. O. LLOYD & J. O. LLOYD. 1978. Expression of Ia-like antigens on cultured human malignant melanoma cell lines. Proc. Natl. Acad. Sci. USA **75:** 6235–6239.

Immunogenetics of Collagen-Induced Arthritis (CIA) in Mice

A Model of Autoimmune Disease

H. S. LUTHRA,[a] P. H. WOOLEY,[b] A. DILLON,[a]
S. K. SINGH,[a] W. P. LAFUSE,[a] C. J. KRCO,[a]
A. HUSE,[a] J. M. STUART,[c] M. M. GRIFFITHS,[d]
AND C. S. DAVID[a]

[a]Department of Internal Medicine
Mayo Medical School
Rochester, Minnesota 55905

[b]Ayerst Laboratories Research
Princeton, New Jersey 08540

[c]VA Medical Center
Memphis, Tennessee 38163

[d]University of Utah Medical Center
Salt Lake City, Utah 84112

The immune response to native type II collagen has been used to establish an experimental model of arthritis with a number of histological and pathological features resembling human rheumatoid arthritis. Our studies have been aimed at elucidating the role of genetic factors in this disease and at finding potential new treatments.

The genetic control of collagen-induced arthritis was associated with the H-2^q and H-2^r haplotypes. Type II collagen from chicken (CII), rat (RII), deer (DII), bovine (BII), and human (HII) sources was observed to cause arthritis in animals of the H-2^q haplotype, while BII and PII collagen caused arthritis in B10.RIII(H-2^r) animals. These results suggest the possibility of at least two arthritogenic epitopes.[1,2] Use of recombinant strains has mapped the susceptibility to be dependent on genes of the H-2 I region, particularly the I-A subregion.[4]

F_1 mice (susceptible × resistant) were studied in hybrids congeneic to the C57BL/10 background. CIA susceptibility was inherited as a codominant trait dependent upon the second MHC haplotype and it varied from 70% susceptibility in (B10.Q × B10.M)F_1 to complete resistance in (B10.2 × B10.SM)F_1.[1] Susceptibility of F_1 hybrids (B10.AQR × B10.AKM) suggests complementation between K and D region genes.

Recent studies have also been performed to elucidate the role, if any, of non-H-2 genes (TABLE 1). F_1 (SWR/J × B10.Q or DBA-1) mice of (resistant × susceptible) strains with homozygous H-2 genes demonstrated that resistance was a dominant phenomenon. F_1, F_2, and backcross analysis implicated multiple gene involvement (TABLE 2).[5]

Our studies, therefore, suggest a role of H-2 and non-H-2 genes in CIA susceptibility. In the H-2 region, genes at the I-A subregion play a role in susceptibility to disease (H-2^r and H-2^q). Susceptibility of B10.AQR(K^q) × B10.AKM(D^q)F_1 animals suggests complementation between K and D region genes. Non-H-2 genes, on the other hand, play a role in disease resistance.

TABLE 1. Role of Non-H-2 Genes on Collagen-Induced Arthritis

Strain	Background	H-2	Arthritis (%)	
			CII	PII
B.10Q	C57BL	q	75	11
DBA/1	DBA	q	71	70
BZH	Biozzi High	q?	0	43
SWR/J	Swiss	q	0	0
BUB	BUB	q	77	66

TABLE 2. Collagen-Induced Arthritis in H-2 Heterozygous and Homozygous Mice from an F_2 Population Segregating for Non-H-2 Genes[a]

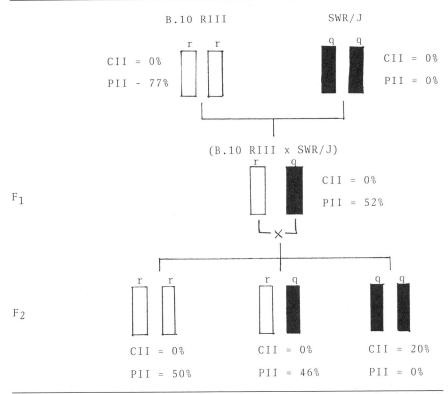

[a]CII = incidence of arthritis with chick type II collagen; PII = incidence of arthritis with porcine type II collagen

Transfer of mild transient disease has been possible using sera (but not cells) from the arthritogenic mice and injecting that sera into nonimmunized susceptible and resistant mice.[6] Recently, disease was transferred into mice from H-II affinity column purified IgG from a patient with seronegative RA. The human and mouse Ig share common idiotypes.[7]

Modification of the disease has been observed by pretreatment of animals with I.V. collagen, polyclonal and monoclonal anti-type II collagen antibody, and polyclonal and monoclonal anti-Ia antisera.[3] This animal model has proven to be a significant resource for studies of autoimmune disease and approach to treatment.

REFERENCES

1. WOOLEY, P. H., A. M. DILLON & H. S. LUTHRA. 1983. Transplant. Proc. **XV**(1): 180.
2. WOOLEY, P. H., H. S. LUTHRA *et al.* 1981. J. Exp. Med. **154:** 688.
3. WOOLEY, P. H., H. S. LUTHRA *et al.* 1985. J. Immunol. **134:** 2366–2374.
4. HUSE, A., P. H. WOOLEY, H. S. LUTHRA *et al.* 1984. Fed. Proc. **43:** 1820.
5. WOOLEY, P. H., H. S. LUTHRA *et al.* 1985. Arthritis Rheum. **28:** S–42.
6. WOOLEY, P. H., H. S. LUTHRA *et al.* 1985. J. Immunol. **134**(4): 2366.
7. WOOLEY, P. H., H. S. LUTHRA *et al.* 1984. Mayo Clin. Proc. **59:** 737.

A Prototype Anti-DNA Autoantibody Appears to Define a New V_H Gene That Is Conserved in Many Strains of Mice

KATHLEEN J. BARRETT AND WILLIAM TREPICCHIO, JR.

Cancer Research Center
Tufts University School of Medicine
Boston, Massachusetts 02111

A spontaneously arising monoclonal anti-DNA autoantibody derived from the lupus-prone mouse strain, MRL/*lpr*, defines a high frequency idiotype found in the sera of all MRL/*lpr* mice, but not in the sera of normal mice.[1,2] We have cloned the two rearranged V_H genes from hybridoma H130 and identified and sequenced the expressed V_H gene (V_H, D, and J_H genes). This sequence is most closely related to that of J558, a myeloma protein that binds α-1,3-dextran,[3] and to two unexpressed V_H genes, 108a and 108b, that were isolated from a BALB/c germline library.[4] The homology between these sequences at the nucleic acid and amino acid levels is 86–90%. These four V regions differ from each other by 12–14 amino acids. The magnitude of this difference suggests that H130 is encoded by a new V_H gene that has not yet been described; however, extensive somatic mutation cannot be excluded until germline genes have been sequenced.

Hybridization at high stringency to cloned H130 probes that contained coding sequences, 5'-flanking sequences, or both, showed that the MLR/*lpr* mouse has two EcoRI fragments that are highly homologous to the expressed V_H gene from H130 in both the coding and 5'-flanking regions. The same two fragments are conserved in normal and autoimmune strains that are haplotype *j* at the Igh-V locus.[5,6] Several strains of different haplotypes have at least one fragment that is highly homologous to the coding and flanking regions. These results suggest that the H130 V_H gene or highly related V_H genes are conserved in many strains of mice, but are not normally expressed.[2] Rigorous proof of such a conclusion demands isolation and sequencing of these germline genes and examination of their expression.

We have found that a panel of MRL/*lpr* anti-DNA autoantibodies are encoded by a minimum of ten different genes that belong to four of the known V_H gene families. Some members of these four V_H gene families might be especially well suited to code for anti-DNA autoantibodies. Thirty percent of these antibodies were encoded by members of the 7183 family, which has been shown to be preferentially rearranged in pre-B cells.[7,8] The distribution is consistent with that found in immature B cells from adult bone marrow and neonatal day-1 hybridomas.[7,8] However, the distribution of V genes expressed by this panel of autoantibodies could also be due to the stochastic use of V genes because of the size of the sample. Taken together, these results suggest that autoantibodies arise from multiple V_H genes, either by direct activation of an immature population of B cells or by polyclonal activation of all B cells.

REFERENCES

1. RAUCH, J., E. MURPHY, J. B. ROTHS, B. D. STOLLAR & R. S. SCHWARTZ. 1982. J. Immunol. **129:** 236.

2. DATTA, S. K., B. D. STOLLAR & R. S. SCHWARTZ. 1983. Proc. Natl. Acad. Sci. USA
   80: 2723.
3. SCHILLING, J., B. CLEVINGER, J. M. DAVIE & L. HOOD. 1980. Nature 283: 35–40.
4. GIVOL, G., R. ZAKUT, K. EFFRON, G. RECHAVI, D. RAM & J. B. COHEN. 1981. Nature
   292: 426–430.
5. BRODEUR, P. H. & R. RIBLET. 1984. Eur. J. Immunol. 14: 922.
6. TREPICCHIO, W., JR. & K. J. BARRETT. 1985. J. Immunol. 134: 2734.
7. YANCOPOULOS, G. D., S. V. DESIDERIO, M. PASKIND, J. F. KEARNEY, D. BALTIMORE & F.
   W. ALT. 1984. Nature 311: 727.
8. PERLMUTTER, R. M., J. F. KEARNEY, S. P. CHANG & L. E. HOOD. 1985. Science 227: 1597.

Hybridoma Lupus Anticoagulants Distinguish between Bilayer and Nonbilayer Phase Lipid Systems[a]

J. RAUCH,[b] M. TANNENBAUM,[b]
H. TANNENBAUM,[b] H. RAMELSON,[b] P. R. CULLIS,[c]
C. P. S. TILCOCK,[c] M. J. HOPE,[c] AND A. S. JANOFF [d]

[b]Rheumatic Disease Unit
Montreal General Hospital Research Institute
McGill University
Montreal, Quebec, Canada

[c]Department of Biochemistry
University of British Columbia
Vancouver, British Columbia, Canada

[d]The Liposome Company
Princeton, New Jersey

Antibodies to phospholipids represent a group of poorly characterized antibodies that may have important physiological and biological functions.[1] The mechanism(s) responsible for the production of these autoantibodies remains unknown. One possible mechanism for the induction and/or pathogenesis of these antibodies involves alterations in the phospholipid architecture of the cell membrane. Such an explanation would seem plausible in light of the ability of membrane lipids to assume a variety of structures in addition to the bilayer phase.[2] This possibility requires a clear demonstration that antiphospholipid antibodies exist that are able to distinguish different polymorphic forms of the same lipid.

Our approach to this problem has involved the use of human hybridoma lupus anticoagulant antibodies (LAA) derived from patients with SLE. LAAs are antiphospholipid antibodies[3] that are defined by their ability to prolong the normal clotting time in *in vitro* coagulation assays measuring the partial thromboplastin time (PTT). In this study, we show that the ability of LAA to prolong PTT values can be inhibited by the presence of hexagonal phase (but not bilayer phase) phosphatidylethanolamine (PE). This finding indicates an ability of these antibodies to distinguish between different structural configurations of the same chemical species of phospholipid.

METHODS

Human hybridoma LAAs were produced by fusing peripheral blood lymphocytes from SLE patients with the GM 4672 lymphoblastoid line.[4] The effects of different phospholipid systems on the partial thromboplastin times of 11 LAAs were assessed in

[a]This work will be published in an extended form in the *Journal of Biological Chemistry* (August–Sept. issue, 1986).

366

the PTT assay following preincubation of the LAAs with phospholipids for ten minutes at 37°C. The polymorphic phase preferences of the phospholipids were determined by employing the ^{31}P NMR technique.[2]

RESULTS

Eleven of the 68 hybridoma IgM antibodies analyzed showed LAA activity. FIGURE 1 shows a titration curve of the inhibition of LAA activity of hybridoma

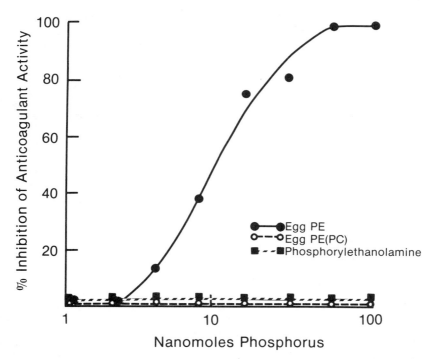

FIGURE 1. Titration of the inhibition of the anticoagulant activity of antibody 824 after preincubation with egg PE, egg PE(PC), or phosphorylethanolamine at 37°C for ten minutes. At this temperature, egg PE is hexagonal and egg PE(PC) is lamellar.

antibody 824. Complete inhibition of anticoagulant activity was obtained with the addition of egg PE (nonbilayer at 37°C) at 68 nmoles phosphorus, while no inhibition occurred with egg phosphatidylethanolamine derived from phosphatidylcholine [PE(PC)] (bilayer at 37°C) and phosphorylethanolamine, the polar-head group of PE.

The effects of different PE phospholipid phase structures on the PTT of 11 LAAs and a control IgM antibody (1500) are shown in FIGURE 2. Hybridoma LAAs incubated with buffer had PTT values ranging between 66–72 sec, representing a prolongation of 6–12 sec over the IgM control (PTT = 60 sec). Bovine PE, egg PE, and dioleoylphosphatidylethanolamine (DOPE) (which are all hexagonal at 37°C) did not affect the PTT of the control 1500 IgM, but reduced the PTT values of the 11 hybridoma LAAs to the control value ($p < 0.0005$), thereby showing complete inhibition of lupus anticoagulant activity. In contrast, dipalmitoylphosphatidylethanolamine (DPPE) and egg PE(PC) (which are both lamellar at 37°C) caused no inhibition of LAA activity at concentrations 1.5–48-fold that of DOPE.

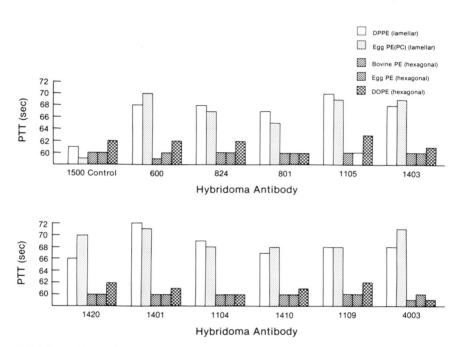

FIGURE 2. Effects of preincubation of different phospholipid phase systems with hybridoma lupus anticoagulants at 37°C. Incubation of the 11 hybridoma lupus anticoagulants with lamellar phospholipids [such as DPPE and egg PE(PC)] resulted in PTT values equivalent to the PTT values of the antibodies plus buffer. They, therefore, represent the maximum PTT values for each antibody. In contrast, incubation of the 11 lupus anticoagulant antibodies with hexagonal phospholipids (bovine PE, egg PE, and DOPE) caused a significant decrease ($p < 0.0005$) in the PTT to values equivalent to the 1500 IgM control.

DISCUSSION

Our results indicate that LAAs react preferentially with hexagonal phase lipid structures. The possibility of antibodies against nonbilayer lipid structures may initially appear surprising. However, whereas the normal function of a cell membrane relies on the presence of a largely (if not exclusively) bilayer lipid organization, many membrane lipids preferentially adopt nonbilayer hexagonal phase or lipidic particle[5] structure. The long-term presence of such structures *in vivo* could well represent lesions requiring antibody recognition and clearance.

REFERENCES

1. ALVING, C. R. 1984. Biochem. Soc. Trans. **12:** 342.
2. CULLIS, P. R. & B. DE KRUIJFF. 1979. Biochim. Biophys. Acta **559:** 399.
3. THIAGARAJAN, P., S. S. SHAPIRO *et al.* 1980. J. Clin. Invest. **66:** 397.
4. MASSICOTTE, H., J. RAUCH *et al.* 1984. Hybridoma **3:** 215.
5. VERKLEIJ, A. J., C. MOMBERS *et al.* 1979. Nature **279:** 162.

Demonstration of Lupus Anticoagulant Antigens Using an Enzyme-Linked Immunoadsorbent Assay (ELISA)

D. WARE BRANCH, NEAL S. ROTE, AND
JAMES R. SCOTT

*Departments of Obstetrics and Gynecology
and Pathology
University of Utah School of Medicine
Salt Lake City, Utah 84132*

Lupus anticoagulant (LAC) is an autoantibody that is associated with thromboembolic disease and recurrent pregnancy loss.[1] It is termed an "anticoagulant" because it prolongs phospholipid-dependent coagulation tests [such as the activated partial thromboplastin time (APTT)] by binding to the phospholipid portion of the prothrombin-prothrombinase complex.[2] Carreras has demonstrated that LAC-containing plasma fractions inhibit the generation of prostacyclin by vascular tissues and has hypothesized that this is the mechanism of the associated thrombosis and pregnancy loss.[3] It has been suggested that the antiphospholipid activity of LAC, which is demonstrable in coagulation assays, is also involved in the inhibition of prostacyclin generation. However, the specific phospholipid(s) against which LAC is directed is unknown. In order to evaluate LAC-antigen interactions, we have developed an ELISA for the detection of LAC[4] and have used it to study the antigenic specificity of LAC by binding-inhibition assays.

MATERIALS AND METHODS

Sera from 14 women with LAC were tested.[4] The partial thromboplastin ELISA used in the LAC-binding inhibition assays has been previously described.[4] Basically, it uses partial thromboplastin as the solid phase in an ELISA; sera are tested at 1:2 dilutions. The ELISA has been shown to be 100% sensitive and specific for the detection of IgG-LAC in serum.[4]

ELISA inhibition with specific phospholipids: A 1-mg sample of purified phospholipid was dried under nitrogen to remove the organic solvents. The residual phospholipid was resuspended in PBS-Tween and bubbled with nitrogen for 40 minutes. The phospholipid suspension was thoroughly mixed and placed in a sonication bath for one hour (20°–25°C). After sonication, the phospholipid suspension was centrifuged at 10,000 g for ten minutes at room temperature. The supernatant, which contained unilamellar phospholipid vesicles, was serially diluted in PBS-Tween. To each well of a microtiter plate that was sensitized with partial thromboplastin, 0.025 ml of sera and 0.025 ml of phospholipid solution (0.025 mg) were added and allowed to incubate for one hour. The microtiter plate was then washed four times with PBS-Tween and developed as described for the partial thromboplastin ELISA.[4] All dilutions were run in duplicate.

RESULTS

As shown in FIGURE 1, both cardiolipin (CL) and phosphatidylserine (PS) preparations demonstrated significant inhibition of LAC binding ($p < 0.001$). None of the other phospholipids tested showed any inhibition of binding. Enhancement of binding was seen with PE, PG, and PI, but a similar percentage of enhancement was also seen with control sera. These results suggest that the antigenic determinant of LAC resides within the polar-head groups of the phospholipids, cardiolipin and phosphatidylserine, as they are arranged on the surface of unilamellar vesicles.

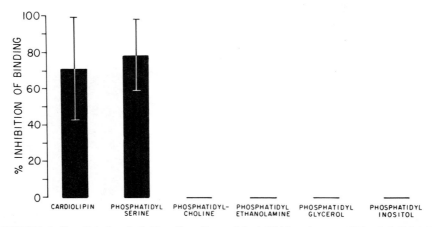

FIGURE 1. Specific phospholipid unilamellar vesicle inhibition (mean ± SD) of IgG-LAC binding to partial thromboplastin using the sera of 14 patients with LAC. Cardiolipin and phosphatidylserine showed significant inhibition compared to the other phospholipids. None of the other phospholipids shown in the figure demonstrated any inhibition of binding. The specificity control involved the addition of the phospholipid vesicles to an ELISA that measured the binding of antihuman IgG to IgG; no inhibition was seen with any phospholipid in this control.

CONCLUSIONS

Cardiolipin is not a component of the partial thromboplastin used in our coagulation laboratory. Thus, our data indicated that the phospholipid antigen of LAC in coagulation assays is phosphatidylserine. Furthermore, because cardiolipin is not found in the cell plasma membrane, our data suggest that the inhibition of cellular prostacyclin generation may occur through LAC binding to cell membrane phosphatidylserine.

REFERENCES

1. LUBBE, W. F., W. S. BUTLER, S. J. PALMER & G. C. LIGGINS. 1984. Lupus anticoagulant in pregnancy. Br. J. Obstet. Gynecol. **91:** 357.

2. THIAGARAJAN, P., S. S. SHAPIRO & L. DE MARCO. 1980. Monoclonal immunoglobulin M-lambda coagulation inhibitor with phospholipid specificity. J. Clin. Invest. **66:** 397.
3. CARRERAS, L. O., S. J. MACHIN, R. DEMAN *et al.* 1981. Arterial thrombosis, intrauterine death, and lupus anticoagulant: Detection of immunoglobulin interfering with prostacyclin formation. Lancet **1:** 244.
4. BRANCH, D. W., N. S. ROTE & J. R. SCOTT. 1986. The demonstration of lupus anticoagulant by an enzyme-linked immunoadsorbant assay (ELISA). J. Clin. Exp. Immunol. **39:** 296.

Thrombocytopenia in Pregnancy-Induced Hypertension

IgG and IgM on Maternal and Umbilical Cord Platelets

NEAL S. ROTE,[a,b] MARK HARRISON,[a] R. JANE LAU,[a]
AND JAMES R. SCOTT[a]

[a]Department of Obstetrics and Gynecology
[b]Department of Pathology
University of Utah School of Medicine
Salt Lake City, Utah 84132

In pregnancy-induced hypertension (PIH), a significant percentage of women (10% to 25%) have thrombocytopenia in association with their disease.[1] As in autoimmune thrombocytopenia (ATP), transient neonatal thrombocytopenia has also been reported in some children born to these mothers.[1] The mechanisms involved in the induction of maternal thrombocytopenia and the associated neonatal thrombocytopenia remain unexplained. Because of these similarities between ATP and PIH, we have begun to explore the potential immunologic etiology of maternal and fetal thrombocytopenia associated with PIH. To investigate possible immunologic factors, platelet-associated IgG (PAIgG) and IgM (PAIgM) were measured in PIH mothers and their infants.

METHODS

Participants in this study had developed PIH as defined by the Committee on Terminology of the American College of Obstetricians and Gynecologists. Women with normal pregnancy and no history of PIH or thrombocytopenia, as well as women with documented ATP, were used as controls. Maternal blood samples were obtained near the time of delivery and from umbilical cords upon delivery. For platelet recovery, blood was collected in tubes containing the anticoagulant acid-citrate-dextrose. An ELISA procedure was used to measure platelet-associated immunoglobulin (PAIg) directly on maternal and cord blood platelets.[1]

RESULTS

We compared PAIgG levels on three groups of subjects (FIGURE 1). None of the pregnant controls had elevated PAIgG, while 15 (68.1%) pregnant ATP patients and 10 (34.5%) PIH patients had elevated amounts of PAIgG. Only one umbilical cord sample from normal pregnancies had slightly elevated PAIgG and none had elevated PAIgM (FIGURE 2). PAIgM was also never observed on umbilical cord samples from ATP patients. In pregnancies complicated by PIH and thrombocytopenia, on the other hand, 6 (45.1%) had elevated PAIgG and 7 (58.3%) had elevated PAIgM.

373

DISCUSSION

Recent reports of thrombocytopenia in some infants born to mothers with PIH are compatible with the concept of an immune mechanism for both maternal and fetal thrombocytopenia.[1] This would be a situation analogous to ATP in which a maternal IgG antiplatelet antibody crosses the placenta and combines with fetal platelets to result in fetal thrombocytopenia. This is supported by the increased amount of IgG on maternal platelets from both ATP and PIH patients. However, our results have shown that the antibody associated with fetal platelets in PIH can be of both the IgM and IgG classes. No placental transport mechanism is known to exist for IgM. In addition, PAIgM has been documented in neonates when only IgG or no PAIg were found in

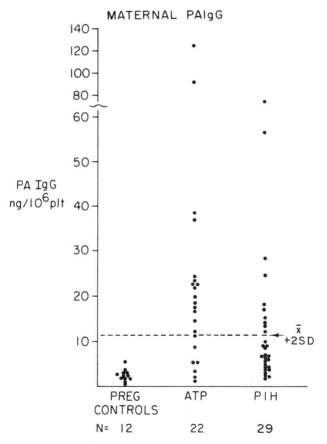

FIGURE 1. Incidence and quantity of PAIgG in normal pregnancy and pregnancies complicated by ATP and PIH. The mean for normal nonthrombocytopenic controls is 4.49 ± 2.84 ng PAIgG/10^6 platelets and 4.38 ± 3.24 ng PAIgM/10^6 platelets. Two standard deviations above the mean (10.16 ng PAIgG/10^6 platelets and 10.86 ng PAIgM/10^6 platelets) is used as a cutoff to distinguish elevated levels of platelet-associated antibody.

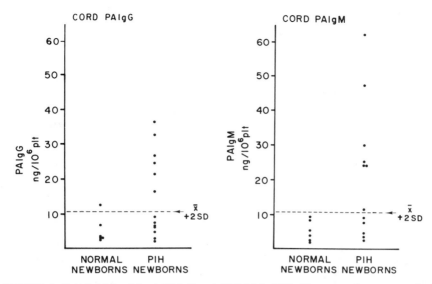

FIGURE 2. Relationship of fetal PAIgG and PAIgM in PIH. The mean plus two standard deviations is as described in FIGURE 1.

their PIH mothers. In our experience, IgM has never been observed on umbilical cord platelets during normal pregnancies or pregnancies complicated by ATP.

The source and specificity of the PAIgM remain mysteries. These exciting, but perplexing results suggest the possibility of a fetal immune response in the development of thrombocytopenia associated with PIH. Such a response has not been previously documented in any other maternal or fetal autoimmune disorder. The PAIgM could theoretically be nonspecifically-adsorbed immunoglobulin, rheumatoid factor, or IgM-containing immune complexes, but umbilical cord sera from these individuals did not contain any elevated total IgM, IgM rheumatoid factors, or IgM-containing immune complexes.

REFERENCE

1.   ROTE, N. S. & R. J. LAU. 1985. Clin. Obstet. Gynecol. **28:** 84–100.

Cross-Reactive Idiotypes in IgA-Deficient Sera

C. CUNNINGHAM-RUNDLES,[a] M. K. L. CHEUNG,[a]
AND J. KOISTINEN[b]

[a]Memorial Sloan-Kettering Cancer Center
and
Cornell University Graduate School of Medical Sciences
Sloan-Kettering Division
Department of Immunology
New York, New York 10021

[b]Finnish Red Cross Blood Transfusion Service
Helsinki, Finland

Selective IgA deficiency is a common immunodeficiency disease in which levels of serum and secretory IgA are low or absent. About one-half of the individuals having this deficiency can be demonstrated to have an excessive absorption of food protein from the intestinal tract and high levels of antibodies to these substances, presumably due to the absence of secretory IgA.[1,2] Further antigen ingestion in these individuals can lead to the formation of circulating immune complexes.[3-5] In previous studies, we have shown that bovine antigens are important constituents of these complexes.[4] Since systemic immunization with antigen-antibody complexes has been shown to be a very effective means of producing anti-idiotypic antibodies in animal systems,[6] we previously sought anti-antibovine casein antibodies in the sera of IgA-deficient patients. Antibodies with specific activity for the casein binding site of anticasein antibodies were subsequently isolated.[1] In these studies, we demonstrate that an autologous anti-idiotype, anti-anticasein, and a specifically raised heterologous anti-anticasein can be used to show that the anticaseins of unrelated IgA-deficient donors share common antigenic determinants.

Sera of plasma of 16 adult patients with selective IgA deficiency were obtained from the Immunodeficiency Clinic of the Memorial Sloan-Kettering Cancer Center (12 donors) and the Finnish Red Cross (4 donors). Anticasein antibodies were isolated from sera by affinity chromatography as previously described.[1] The plasma of the IgA-deficient Finnish donor, Rei, having the highest anticasein activity, was used as a source of anticasein used in rabbit immunizations and for isolation of an autologous anti-anticasein.[1] Two white male Hartley rabbits were tolerized to pooled human IgG and then given three i.v. injections of Rei anticasein-casein immune complexes.[7] Potential antibodies to Rei anticasein were isolated from the resulting sera and were tested for anti-idiotypic activity by an inhibition ELISA.[7]

To test the possibility that antigenic cross-reactivity might exist between the isolated anticasein antibodies of different IgA-deficient donors, we determined the degree of inhibition that a panel of isolated anticaseins produced on the binding of alkaline-phosphatase-labeled Rei anticasein to either autologous Rei-anti-anticasein or rabbit anti-anticasein. For these experiments, equal amounts of isolated anticasein IgG of the 17 donors were used.

The results for experiments using the autologous anti-anticasein are shown in

FIGURE 1A and those for the heterologous anti-anticasein are shown in FIGURE 1B. For each anticasein IgG, the relative amount of inhibition produced was expressed as a percentage of the inhibition produced by nonlabeled Rei anticasein IgG, which in both experiments was found to produce maximum inhibition. Using the autologous reagent,

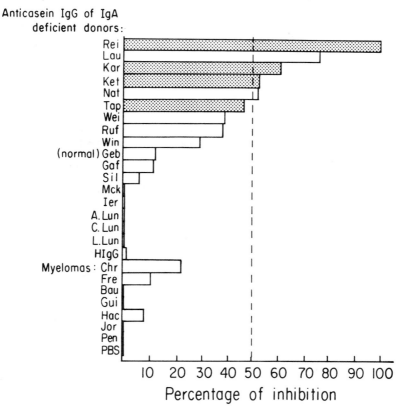

FIGURE 1A. The percentage of cross-reactivity between various anticaseins was determined by an inhibition ELISA in which 10 μg of anticaseins (or control IgG) were permitted to interfere with the binding of AP-Rei anticaseins and its corresponding (A) autologous or (B) heterologous anti-anticasein. Maximum inhibition occurred with the addition of Rei-anticasein and no inhibition by the PBS control. Shaded anticaseins were derived from the blood of Finnish donors. (Reproduced from *The Journal of Clinical Investigation*, 1985, **75:** 1722–1728, by copyright permission of The American Society for Clinical Investigation.)

we found that 5 anticaseins produced >50% inhibition, while using the heterologous reagent, 12 produced >50% inhibition; thus, this indicated the presence of substantial cross-reactivity. In each test, Finnish anticaseins (shaded) displayed more cross-reactivity. Therefore, using these anti-idiotypes in an assay used to identify cross-reactive idiotypes between the isolated anticaseins of unrelated and ethnically diverse

IgA-deficient donors, we found that 6 of 16 were cross-reactive using the autologous anti-idiotype and that the same 6, plus an additional 6 anticaseins, were cross-reactive using the heterologous anti-idiotype. These findings indicate that anticaseins share several common idiotypes, with the rabbit antisera having the capacity to recognize a broader spectrum of cross-reactive determinants than the autologous anti-anticasein.

Cross-reactive idiotypes have been described in the sera of mice, rabbits, guinea pigs, and man. Although there are numerous reports in animals for such cross-reactivities, in man, fewer reports exist, and these have been shown predominantly among antibodies isolated from sera of individuals having autoimmune disease. The results of this study affirm the possibility that antibodies directed to external antigens, found in sera of IgA-deficient individuals, may also share cross-reactive idiotypes.

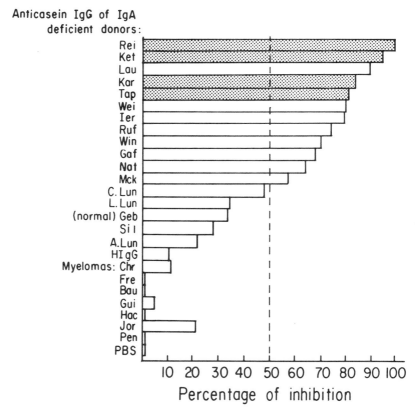

FIGURE 1B. The percentage of cross-reactivity between various anticaseins was determined by an inhibition ELISA in which 10 μg of anticaseins (or control IgG) were permitted to interfere with the binding of AP-Rei anticaseins and its corresponding (A) autologous or (B) heterologous anti-anticasein. Maximum inhibition occurred with the addition of Rei-anticasein and no inhibition by the PBS control. Shaded anticaseins were derived from the blood of Finnish donors. (Reproduced from *The Journal of Clinical Investigation,* 1985, **75:** 1722–1728, by copyright permission of The American Society for Clinical Investigation.)

REFERENCES

1. CUNNINGHAM-RUNDLES, C. 1982. Naturally occurring autologous antiidiotypic antibodies. J. Exp. Med. **155:** 711–719.
2. BUCKLEY, R. H. & S. C. DEES. 1969. Correlation of milk precipitins with IgA deficiency. N. Engl. J. Med. **281:** 465–469.
3. CUNNINGHAM-RUNDLES, C., W. E. BRANDEIS, R. A. GOOD & N. K. DAY. 1978. Milk precipitins and circulating immune complexes and IgA deficiency. Proc. Natl. Acad. Sci. USA **15:** 3387–3389.
4. CUNNINGHAM-RUNDLES, C., W. E. BRANDEIS, R. A. GOOD & N. K. DAY. 1979. Bovine proteins and the formation of circulating immune complexes in selective IgA deficiency. J. Clin. Invest. **64:** 272–279.
5. CUNNINGHAM-RUNDLES, C., W. E. BRANDEIS, R. SAFAI, R. O'REILLY, N. K. DAY & R. A. GOOD. 1979. Selective IgA deficiency and circulating immune complexes containing bovine proteins in a child with chronic graft vs. host disease. Am. J. Med. **67:** 883–889.
6. KLAUS, G. G. B. 1978. Antigen-antibody complexes elicit anti-idiotypes. Nature (London) **272:** 255–256.
7. CHEUNG, M. K. L., C. CUNNINGHAM-RUNDLES & J. KOISTINEN. 1985. Cross-reactive idiotypes in immunoglobulin A-deficient sera. J. Clin. Invest. **75:** 1722–1728.

Divergence of the Role of Acute Phase Protein Responses in Autoimmune Strains of Mice

MARY JO STARUCH AND FRANCIS J. DUMONT

Department of Immunology and Inflammation Research
Merck Sharp & Dohme Research Laboratories
Rahway, New Jersey 07065

Endogenous levels of the acute phase protein, serum amyloid A (SAA), were monitored over a period of several months in autoimmunity-prone mouse strains. SAA is an apolipoprotein of hepatic origin whose levels are greatly elevated in response to tissue damage, infection, or inflammation, and may be the precursor of amyloid A fibrils of secondary amyloidosis. Increased serum levels of SAA have been found in patients with active chronic inflammatory disease, particularly those who develop secondary amyloidosis, such as rheumatoid arthritis (RA). However, patients with low incidence of amyloidosis, such as those with SLE, generally do not exhibit increased levels of SAA even during active phases.[1]

Previous reports have indicated a role for acute phase proteins in autoimmune mouse strains. Rordorf et al.[2] have shown that MRL-*lpr/lpr* mice, which exhibit symptoms similar to RA, develop high levels of the acute phase protein, SAP. Also, Hara et al.[3] reported that the serum protein gp70, which forms immune complexes in later stages of disease, behaves as an inducible acute phase reactant in SLE-prone NZB and (NZB × NZW)F$_1$ mice. We have confirmed the acute phase response in MRL/1 mice by measuring SAA levels over a period of 1–7 months. SAA begins to rise at 4–5 months and remains high until death (FIGURE 1). The rise in SAA closely follows the kinetics of disease progression, including such parameters as increases in anti-dsDNA antibodies and blood urea nitrogen levels.

In contrast to the MRL/1, male BXSB and (NZW × BXSB)F$_1$ mice, which develop an accelerated form of SLE, were found to have a different pattern of endogenous SAA levels. These mice exhibited a very early increase at 4–8 weeks old, which was then followed by declining levels as the disease progressed (FIGURE 1). The female F$_1$ mice, which only develop a mild form of SLE later in life, did not show this early peak response; SAA remained at normal levels throughout with a slight increase at 12 months (FIGURE 2).

This lack of SAA in the females was not due to an inability to produce SAA since the serum protein could be induced by treatment with an inflammatory stimulus (LPS). SAA levels measured 20 hours after i.p. injection of 10 μg of LPS increased from 89 ± 43 u/ml for controls to 11,267 ± 973 for treated females. This pattern in the F$_1$ strains is similar to human SLE where SAA is not generally observed during active phases, but can be induced by episodes of infection.[1]

Anti-dsDNA antibody titers were also monitored in the autoimmune strains. The antibody levels closely followed those of SAA except for female (NZW × BXSB)F$_1$. High antibody titers were found early (2 months) and very late (12 months) in female F$_1$ mice. The association of SAA levels, and not that of anti-dsDNA antibody titers, with severity of autoimmunity in the (NZW × BXSB)F$_1$ indicates that acute phase proteins may be a more relevant parameter for monitoring or predicting autoimmune disease than anti-dsDNA antibodies.

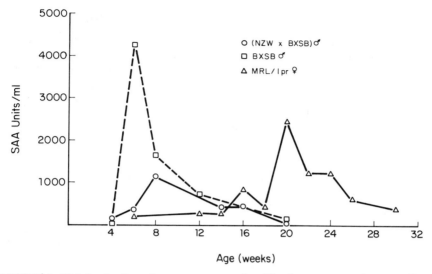

FIGURE 1. SAA levels of autoimmune mouse strains. The data represent the mean SAA units/ml of serum of 8–15 mice per time point. SAA was measured by a competitive ELISA using a monoclonal anti-SAA antibody and an enzyme-labeled AA.

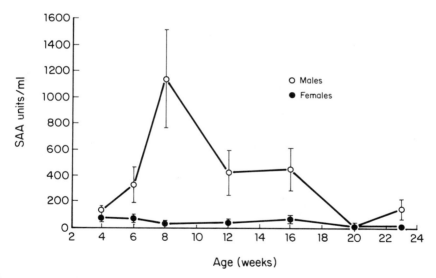

FIGURE 2. Comparison of SAA levels of male and female (NZW × BXSB)F_1 mice. The F_1 mice were bred at Merck Sharp & Dohme Research Laboratories. The data represent the mean ± SEM of eight mice per time point. The males and females were littermates.

The difference in endogenous levels of SAA among autoimmune strains of mice suggests contrasting roles for the acute phase response in the disease process. The late occurrence of the response in MRL-*lpr/lpr* is most likely a consequence of disease symptoms and tissue damage. On the other hand, since SAA appears early in BXSB and (NZW × BXSB)F$_1$ males, and not at all in females, it may contribute to the development of autoimmunity or it may indicate the presence of a disease-related pathogenic agent.

REFERENCES

1. DE BEER, F. C., R. K. MALLYA, E. A. FAGAN, J. G. LANHAM, G. R. HUGHES & M. B. PEPYS. 1982. Lancet 2: 231.
2. RORDORF, C., H. P. SCHNEBLI, M. L. BALTZ, G. A. TENNENT & M. B. PEPYS. 1982. J. Exp. Med. 156: 1268.
3. HARA, I., S. IZUI & F. J. DIXON. 1982. J. Exp. Med. 155: 345.

Alterations of the Lyt-2$^+$ T-Cell Population in Murine Systemic Autoimmunity

FRANCIS J. DUMONT, ROBERT C. HABBERSETT, AND
JACQUELINE A. TREFFINGER

Department of Cellular Immunology
Merck Sharp & Dohme Research Laboratories
Rahway, New Jersey 07065

Systemic autoimmunity arises as a result of multiple abnormalities of the immune system. Extensive studies in murine SLE models have demonstrated that one of these abnormalities is B-cell hyperactivity.[1] However, the possible T-cell defects that may underlie or amplify this B-cell hyperactivity are still unclear.[2,3] A better understanding of such defects may offer ways to modulate autoantibody production and should be facilitated by defining immunoregulatory T-cell circuit components in autoimmune mouse strains. The present investigations were conducted for that purpose. We focused our attention on Lyt-2$^+$ cells since they play a crucial role in immunoregulation.[4]

Two subsets of Lyt-2$^+$ cells could be distinguished using the 9F3 monoclonal antibody (MAb) and two-color flow cytofluorometry analysis.[5,6] In normal strains (e.g., C57B1/6, C3H), 9F3$^+$ cells accounted for 25–35% of the peripheral Lyt-2$^+$ population.[6] In mice homozygous for the *lpr* mutation, which induces generalized lymphadenopathy and severe SLE syndrome,[1] the frequency of 9F3$^+$ cells within the Lyt-2$^+$ population increased up to 90% (FIGURES 1a,b).[6] Most interestingly, a similar elevated frequency of 9F3$^+$ cells was disclosed in other lupus-prone strains. Thus, BXSB males that develop SLE by 6–8 months of age due to an Y-linked autoimmunity accelerating gene[1] exhibited increased 9F3$^+$ cells already at 4 months (FIGURE 1c). BXSB females, known to suffer from milder SLE later in life,[1] showed 50–60% 9F3$^+$ cells by 10–12 months of age. In females of the late onset SLE MRL-+/+ strain,[1] 9F3$^+$ cell frequency reached an average of 85% at 10–12 months (FIGURE 1d). MRL-+/+ males usually displayed less than 40% 9F3$^+$ cells at this age. In C57B1/6 and C3H mice, aging was accompanied by only a modest rise (5–15%) of 9F3$^+$ cells. Therefore, a dramatic increase of the relative frequency of the 9F3$^+$ Lyt-2$^+$ subset appears associated with the propensity to develop SLE.

A clue to the significance of these alterations was provided by the study of adult thymectomized mice. Thymectomy of two-month-old C57B1/6 mice resulted six months later in an augmentation of the 9F3$^+$ Lyt-2$^+$ subset (FIGURE 1e). The 9F3 staining profile then resembled that of C57B1/6-*lpr/lpr* mice (FIGURE 1b). Adult thymectomy of BXSB females also led to increased 9F3$^+$ cell frequency, giving rise to a "male-like" pattern (FIGURE 1f). This suggested that the Lyt-2$^+$ subset imbalance spontaneously occurring in autoimmune mice reflects some thymus dysfunction. To support this idea, we found that in old MRL-+/+ females, the degree of 9F3$^-$ Lyt-2$^+$ cell depletion in lymph nodes correlates with cortical atrophy and B-cell infiltration of the thymus. Such thymic lesions were uncommon in MRL-+/+ males.

Preliminary characterization of 9F3-defined Lyt-2$^+$ subsets separated on the FACS was performed. FIGURE 2a shows that 9F3$^-$, but not 9F3$^+$ cells proliferated vigorously in presence of Con-A. However, both Lyt-2$^+$ subsets produced IL-2

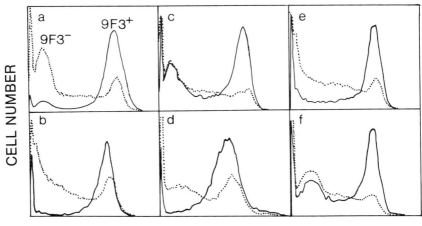

FIGURE 1. Fluorescence distribution profiles (logarithmic amplification, three decades) of the 9F3 staining of Lyt-2⁺ cells from the lymph nodes of various normal and autoimmune strains. These curves were generated by computer-assisted slice analysis of two-color fluorescence 9F3 versus Lyt-2 staining patterns of 100,000 cells per sample. (a) 4-month-old MRL-*lpr/lpr* (-----) and MRL-+/+ (·····) mice; (b) 8-month-old C57B1/6-*lpr/lpr* (-----) and C57B1/6-+/+ (·····) mice, (c) 4-month-old BXSB male (-----) and female (·····) mice; (d) 12-month-old MRL-+/+ female (-----) and male (·····) mice; (e) 8-month-old adult thymectomized (-----) or sham-thymectomized (·····) C57B1/6 mice, six months after thymectomy, (f) 5-month-old thymectomized (----) or sham-thymectomized (·····) BXSB females, three months after thymectomy. Note the increased proportion of 9F3⁺ cells in lupus-prone mice and in thymectomized mice.

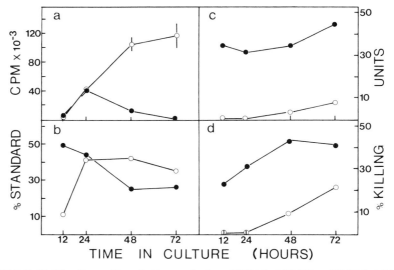

FIGURE 2. Proliferation and lymphokine production of 9F3⁺ Lyt-2⁺ (●) and 9F3⁻ Lyt-2⁺ (○) cells from 4-month-old BXSB males sorted on the FACS and cultured *in vitro* in the presence of Concanavalin A (5 μg/ml). (a) ³H-Thymidine uptake after four hour pulses; (b) Interleukin-2 levels measured in culture supernatants (1:8 dilutions) by the CTLL assay and expressed as percent of the maximum response given by a standard IL-2 preparation; (c) Interleukin-3/CSF-2 activity in culture supernatants assessed with the FDCP-2 cell line and converted to arbitrary units using WEHI-3b culture supernatant as a standard; (d) Interferon-gamma levels in culture supernatants (1:80 dilutions) measured with the MAF macrophage tumoricidal assay and expressed as percent killing of P815 cells by macrophages.

(FIGURE 2b). Thus, the abortive mitogenic response of 9F3$^+$ cells is probably not due to an IL-2 deficiency. Perhaps, 9F3$^+$ cells cannot utilize optimally IL-2 because of low IL-2 receptor expression and/or these cells produce other lymphokines (e.g., SIRS, lymphotoxin) that inhibit their own proliferation. In fact, despite the low mitogenic response, 9F3$^+$ cells secreted higher amounts of IL-3/CSF-2 and of Interferon-γ (measured by Gloria Koo) than 9F3$^-$ cells. Therefore, the 9F3-defined phenotypic delineation of Lyt-2$^+$ subsets has functional relevance.

Together, these data demonstrate the existence of a common T-cell alteration, manifested by an excess of 9F3$^+$ cells within the Lyt-2$^+$ population, in several SLE-prone strains. Because the primary genetic defects in these strains are different, such an anomaly is likely to represent a secondary phenomenon. It may itself, then, result from some common thymus dysfunction. However, since the 9F3-defined Lyt-2$^+$ subsets differ functionally, their imbalance may be of etiopathogenic significance. Conceivably, this imbalance could lead to deranged immunoregulation and contribute to the self-sustaining of the autoimmune condition.

REFERENCES

1. THEOFILOPOULOS, A. N. & F. J. DIXON. 1985. Adv. Immunol. **37:** 269–390.
2. SMITH, H. R., T. M. CHUSED, P. A. SMATHERS & A. D. STEINBERG. 1983. J. Immunol. **130:** 1200–1205.
3. HANG, L. M., A. N. THEOFILOPOULOS, R. S. BALDERAS, S. J. FRANCIS & F. J. DIXON. 1984. J. Immunol. **132:** 1809–1813.
4. DORF, M. E. & B. BENACERRAF. 1984. Ann. Rev. Immunol. **2:** 127–157.
5. DUMONT, F. J., R. C. HABBERSETT & E. A. NICHOLS. 1984. J. Immunol. **133:** 809–815.
6. DUMONT, F. J., R. C. HABBERSETT & L. Z. COKER. 1985. J. Immunol. **134:** 196–203.

Restricted Heterogeneity and T-Cell Dependence of Human Thyroid Autoantibody IgG Subclasses[a]

T. F. DAVIES,[b] C. M. WEBER,[c] P. WALLACK,[b]
AND M. PLATZER[c]

[b]Department of Medicine
Mount Sinai School of Medicine
New York, New York 10029

[c]St. Vincent's Hospital
New York, New York 10011

INTRODUCTION

The autoimmune thyroid diseases encompass both thyroid atrophy secondary to autoimmune destruction and thyroid hypertrophy secondary to autoimmune stimulation. Both are associated with local and circulating thyroid autoantibodies, principally of the IgG class, and a variety of reported T-cell defects. We have examined the IgG subclass distribution of thyroid autoantibodies and their *in vitro* T-cell dependence in randomly chosen patients with autoimmune thyroiditis and in euthyroid individuals with detectable serum thyroid autoantibodies.

METHODOLOGY

Subclass ELISAs

Noncompetitive assays for human thyroglobulin (hTg) and thyroid microsomal (M) antibody (Ab) were as described,[1] but they included murine monoclonal antibodies NL16 (IgG1), GOM2 (IgG2), ZG4 (IgG3), and RJ4 (IgG4) (Seward Laboratories, Bedford, United Kingdom) as an intermediate step. Sera were assayed at 1:100 dilution and results were expressed as the percent that a subclass contributed to the total specific absorbance.

T-Cell Function Testing

Here, 2×10^5 non–T cells were combined with increasing numbers of AET-SRBC rosetted autologous T cells to provide ratios from 1:0 to 1:10 as previously described.[2,3] After seven days with PWM (1:100), supernatants were assayed for IgG subclass secretion.

[a]This work was supported in part by grant no. AM28243 from NIADDKD, the Irma T. Hirschl Charitable Trust, and the IBM Corporation.

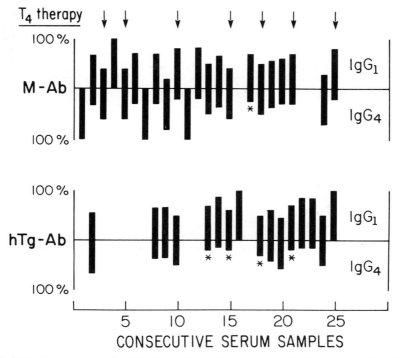

FIGURE 1. Subclass analysis of hTg-Ab and M-Ab for the sera positive in the standard ELISAs. Data are expressed as the percent contributions of IgG1 and IgG4 to the total absorbance obtained. * = sera with IgG2 and/or IgG3 contributions.

RESULTS

Twenty-five out of 75 sera examined had detectable hTg or M-Ab, 7 were patients on T4 replacement, and 18 were euthyroid individuals. Twenty-two were positive for M-Ab and all, but one sample, showed restricted heterogeneity confined to the IgG1 and/or IgG4 subclass. The contribution of each subclass to an individual autoantibody titer varied from 100% IgG1 to 100% IgG4. Sixteen of the 25 sera had hTg-Ab and the

TABLE 1. IgG1 Subclass Response to T-Cell Help and Suppression

Sample	Normal IgG1 (% maximum)	Patients IgG1 (% maximum)
T cells only	<1	<1
Non–T cells only	<1	<1
Ratio		
1:1	49.0 ± 5.9	100.0
2:1	77.0 ± 1.2	94.0 ± 6.8
4:1	100.0	92.0 ± 5.8
8:1	35.0 ± 4.2	87.0 ± 7.2
10:1	26.3 ± 5.1	67.0 ± 5.0

majority showed restriction to IgG1 and IgG4 with similar distributions occurring between subclasses. Only 5 sera showed hTg/M-Ab in IgG subclasses 2 and/or 3 (FIGURE 1). In normal controls, IgG1, but not subclasses 2, 3, or 4, exhibited T-cell dependence as evidenced by enhancement and inhibition of IgG1 secretion as the number of T cells increased. T-cell suppressor dysfunction was apparent in patients with autoimmune thyroiditis as demonstrated by the reduced ability of patient T cells ($n = 6$), compared to normal T cells ($n = 6$), to suppress total IgG1 subclass secretion (TABLE 1).

DISCUSSION

These data demonstrate restricted heterogeneity of human thyroid autoantibodies and T-cell dependence of IgG1 thyroid autoantibody secretion. They confirm our previous observations that the T-cell suppressor defect in patients with autoimmune thyroid disease is not thyroid-specific. In addition, the concept of certain thyroid autoantibodies (for example, IgG4) being outside T-cell regulatory control adds further weight to our questioning of the importance of thyroid-specific suppressor T-cell function in the etiology of autoimmune thyroid disease.

REFERENCES

1. ROMAN, S. H., F. KORN & T. F. DAVIES. 1984. Enzyme-linked immunosorbent microassay and hemagglutination compared for detection of thyroglobulin and thyroid microsomal autoantibodies. Clin. Chem. **30:** 246–251.
2. DAVIES, T. F., B. BERMAS, M. PLATZER & S. H. ROMAN. 1985. T cell sensitization to autologous thyroid cells and normal nonspecific suppressor T cell function in Graves' disease. Clin. Endocrinol. **22:** 155–167.
3. DAVIES, T. F. & M. PLATZER. 1986. The suppressor T cell defect in Hashimoto's disease is not thyroid specific. Clin. Exp. Immunol. **63:** 73–79.

Production of Antibodies against S_m and RNP Antigens in Rabbits

M. ISHAQ[a] AND R. ALI

Department of Biochemistry
J.N. Medical College
A.M.U. Aligarth, India

Antibodies against S_m and RNP small nuclear ribonucleoproteins are characteristic of certain rheumatic diseases.[1] We reported the purification of these antigens from goat liver and identified the reactive polypeptides.[2] In recent years, growing interest in the development of monoclonal antibodies against S_m and RNP determinants has been emphasized. However, no report concerning the experimental immunization of animals with these antigens has appeared, although antibodies against other nuclear antigens, like nucleosomes,[3] histones,[4] and some nonhistone proteins,[5] have been developed in experimental animals. Here, we report the production of specific antisera against S_m and RNP antigens in rabbits and characterize the antigenic specificity of the immune sera.

Rabbits immunized weekly for six weeks with purified S_m/RNP (1 mg protein and 200 Ug RNA per injection) in Freund's complete adjuvant produced precipitating and hemagglutinating antibodies against these antigens. The immune sera exhibited two precipitin bands with S_m/RNP reacting in complete immunological identity with precipitin lines obtained with an SLE serum containing antibodies to both S_m and RNP antigens (FIGURE 1). Further evidence concerning the nature of rabbit immune

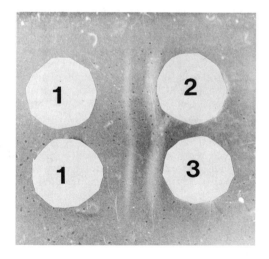

FIGURE 1. Counterimmunoelectrophoresis with SLE and rabbit immune sera using purified S_m/RNP. (1) S_m/RNP 1 mg protein/ml; (2) rabbit immune serum; (3) anti-S_m/RNP SLE serum.

[a]Present Address: Department of Clinical Biochemistry, Sher-i-Kashmir Institute of Medical Sciences, Srinagar—190011, India

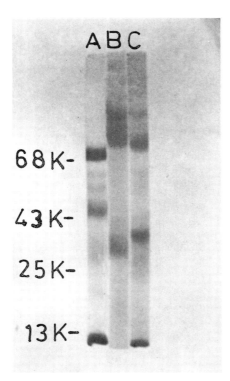

FIGURE 2. SDS-PAGE of S_m/RNP polypeptides. Lane B and C represent, respectively, polypeptides of S_m/RNP isolated from rabbit and SLE immunoaffinity columns. Lane A represents the molecular weight markers.

antibodies came from the studies on the purification of S_m/RNP antigens using rabbit immune IgG-linked Sepharose 4B column. The antigen eluted from the column exhibited properties similar to those shown by S_m/RNP isolated from an SLE IgG affinity column. FIGURE 2 shows the polypeptide profile of affinity purified antigens in sodium dodecyl sulfate polyacrylamide gel electrophoresis (SDS-PAGE). The number and molecular weights of rabbit immune IgG-purified polypeptides (lane B) was identical to the SLE IgG-purified S_m/RNP antigen (lane C). In both cases, four major polypeptides of 14 K, 30 K, 70 K, and 80 K were obtained. (70 K and 80 K are RNP-specific, whereas 14 K and 30 K are S_m-specific polypeptides.)[2]

On the basis of the above results, we conclude that the antibodies elicited by rabbits as a result of immunization with S_m/RNP antigens are identical with respect to antigenic specificity to the naturally occurring SLE S_m/RNP autoantibodies. It is felt that such antisera might be useful as a source of anti-S_m and anti-RNP antibodies with specificity identical to SLE autoantibodies.

REFERENCES

1. MOORE, T. L., T. D. WEISS, S. H. NEUCKS, A. R. BALDASSERA & J. ZUCKNER. 1981. Semin. Arthritis Rheum. **10:** 309–318.
2. ISHAQ, M. & R. ALI. 1983. Biochem. Biophys. Res. Commun. **114:** 564–570.
3. TAHOURDIN, C. S. & M. BUSTIN. 1980. Biochemistry **19:** 4387–4394.
4. BUSTIN, M. 1978. Cell Nucleus **4:** 195–238.
5. BUSTIN, M. 1976. FEBS Lett. **70:** 1–10.

HLA-DR Gene Expression in Human Thyroid Tissue and Cultured Human Thyroid Cells[a]

L. A. PICCININI,[b] B. S. SCHACHTER,[c]
S. DURGERIAN,[c] AND T. F. DAVIES[b]

[b]*Department of Medicine*
[c]*Department of Obstetrics, Gynecology, and Reproductive Science*
Mount Sinai School of Medicine
New York, New York 10029

INTRODUCTION

HLA class II antigens (DR, DQ, and DP) are expressed primarily on the surface of lymphocytes (B and activated T cells) and cells of the monocyte-macrophage lineage. They may also be expressed, though, in a variety of tissues that contain immune infiltration with local release of lymphokines (i.e., gamma interferon) that are potent inducers of class II antigen expression. HLA-DR antigen has been found on the surface of human thyroid cells in cases of autoimmune thyroid disease (i.e., Graves' hyperthyroidism), but normal thyroid tissue has been found negative for DR antigen.[1,2] However, the expression of class II antigens (HLA-DR) may by induced in normal thyroid cells that have been exposed to lectin or gamma interferon.[1,3] We have extended these observations on the role of class II antigens and thyroid disease to the study of the levels of HLA-DR gene expression in human thyroid tissue and human thyrocytes in culture.

METHODOLOGY

Tissue and Cell Culture

Postoperative human tissue was quick-frozen and stored at $-70°C$ prior to RNA preparation. Thyroid cell cultures were prepared by collagenase digestion (1.25 mg/ml) of thyroid tissue, followed by culture for five days $\pm$ lectin (leucoagglutinin, 10 μg/ml).

Detection of DR Antigen

Thyroid cell cultures were harvested using trypsin-EDTA and stained for DR antigen by indirect immunofluorescence using anti-DR monoclonal antibody L-243 (Becton Dickenson, California).

[a]This work was supported in part by grant no. AM28243 from NIADDKD, the Irma T. Hirschl Charitable Trust, and the IBM Corporation.

Total Cellular RNA Analysis

Total cellular RNA was prepared from tissues and cells according to guanidinium isothiocyanate extraction and cesium chloride centrifugation. RNA preparations were transferred to Gene Screen (DUPONT) membrane filters for Northern blot analysis or dot blot analysis, both according to the method of Thomas.[4]

Cytoplasmic RNA Analysis

Cytoplasmic extracts were prepared from cells according to the method of White and Bancroft[5] before application to Gene Screen using a Minifold dot or slot blot apparatus (Schleicher & Schvell).

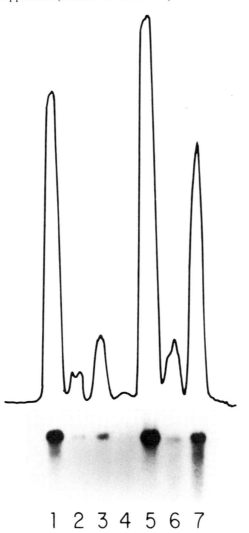

FIGURE 1. Northern blot analysis of DR-alpha transcripts. Densitometric tracing of the relative signal intensity is depicted above a Northern blot analysis of DR-alpha transcripts in total cellular RNA isolated from human tissues and the Raji cell line and probed with DR-alpha cDNA as described. RNA samples (25 μg per lane) were from the following sources: lane 1, Graves' thyroid tissue (patient N); lane 2, thyroid adenoma tissue; lane 3, Graves' thyroid tissue (patient S); lane 4, testicular tissue; lane 5, Raji cell line; lane 6, normal thyroid tissue; lane 7, Graves' thyroid tissue (patient M).

TABLE 1. Relative DR-Alpha Transcript Levels in Normal and Abnormal Human Thyrocytes

Sample[a]	DR-Alpha Transcript Levels[b] (% DR-positive control)
Raji	100
Normal human thyrocyte	16.3 ± 9.3
Human thyroid adenoma	15.3 ± 5.3
Graves' thyrocyte	61.5 ± 13.4
Human testis	0.0
Fisher rat thyroid cell line	0.0

[a]All samples were isolated from cultured cells except for human testis, which represented total cellular RNA from tissue.

[b]DR-alpha transcript levels were determined by densitometric scans of RNA or cytoplasmic dot/slot blots and were normalized for amounts of RNA or cell number. Levels were expressed as % DR-positive Raji cell line (100%).

Northern, Dot, and Slot Blot Hybridization

Blots were baked, prehybridized under standard conditions, and hybridized to an HLA-DR alpha-chain-specific cDNA probe (DR alpha-10) cloned into the Pst-1 site of pBR322 by GC tailing (from E. Long, NIAID). The cDNA probe was ^{32}P-labeled by nick-translation to a specific activity of $(5-8) \times 10^8$ cpm per μg of DNA.

RESULTS

Northern blot analysis (FIGURE 1) of total cellular RNA revealed a single DR alpha-chain transcript less than 2 kb in size in all human thyroid tissues examined. This DR-alpha transcript comigrated with the species present in the Raji human B lymphoblastoid cell line, which constitutively expresses HLA-DR antigen. Human testicular tissue (FIGURE 1, lane 4) appeared negative for DR alpha-chain transcripts. Dot blot analysis indicated that mRNA-DR alpha levels were variable among normal and abnormal thyroid tissues, as well as thyroid cells in culture. The highest mRNA-DR alpha levels relative to the Raji cell line control were found in cases of Graves' hyperthyroidism (TABLE 1). Furthermore, eight out of eight samples of normal human thyrocytes cultured in the presence of lectin demonstrated significant, though variable increases in mRNA-DR alpha levels relative to control cultures. Such increases at the level of DR-alpha gene transcription were correlated with increased levels of DR antigen as demonstrated in thyrocyte cultures by indirect immunofluorescence (data not included).

DISCUSSION

Normal human thyroid tissue, as well as thyroid adenomata, express low, but detectable levels of DR alpha-chain transcripts in contrast to the high levels present in Graves' thyroid tissue. Moreover, this DR-alpha-chain transcript appears identical in size to the mRNA species present in DR-positive lymphoid cells. This variation in DR alpha-chain gene expression noted in thyroid tissue is also detected at the level of thyroid cells in culture. High levels of DR gene expression in the human thyrocyte suggest its capacity to act directly in antigen presentation. Such quantitative differences in thyrocyte HLA class II antigen expression may be critical in the genesis and/or maintenance of autoimmune thyroid disease.

REFERENCES

1. DAVIES, T. F. 1985. J. Clin. Endocrinol. Metabol. 1985. **61:** 418.
2. HANAFUSA, T., L. CHIOVATO, D. DONIACH, R. PUJOL-BORRELL, R. C. G. RUSSELL & G. F. BOTTAZZO. 1983. Lancet **ii:** 1111.
3. PUJOL-BORRELL, R., T. HANAFUSA, L. CHIOVATO & G. F. BOTTAZZO. 1983. Nature **304:** 71.
4. THOMAS, P. S. 1980. Proc. Natl. Acad. Sci. USA **77:** 5201.
5. WHITE, B. A. & F. C. BANCROFT. 1982. J. Biol. Chem. **257:** 8569.

Functional Properties of the A3 and B1 Allotypes of Human C4 and Their Possible Relationship to Systemic Lupus Erythematosus[a]

YUN-HUA WONG,[b] CHOONG Y. HAN,[b]
PAMELA D. HALE,[b] VERNA M. SKANES,[c]
AND PAUL LEVINE[b]

[b]James S. McDonnell Department of Genetics
Washington University School of Medicine
St. Louis, Missouri 63110

[c]Division of Immunology
Faculty of Medicine
Memorial University of Newfoundland
St. John's, Newfoundland, Canada

Human C4 is specified by two gene loci, A and B, that lie within the major histocompatibility complex.[1] There is an array of C4A and C4B alleles, including a null allele at each locus. At physiological pH, C4A gene products form amide bonds, whereas C4B gene products form acyl-ester bonds.[2] With the possible exception of C4A6, the C4A gene products are more reactive than the C4B gene products. For example, the efficiency of amide bond formation can approach 90%, while that of acyl-ester bond formation is around 10%.[2,3]

Fielder et al.[4] and more recently Revielle et al.[5] have observed an association between the C4A-null B1 phenotype (A*QOB1) and systemic lupus erythematosus (SLE). The frequency of the A*QOB1 phenotype in the general population is around 1%, whereas among SLE patients, it is around 15%.

In 1980, Nussenzweig[6] proposed that deficiencies in the complement system could "aggravate and even contribute to the development of immune complex diseases." Recently, Porter[7] has suggested that lower than average C4 activity could lead to insufficient clearance of immune complexes. Thus, we hypothesize here that the association between the C4B*QOB1 phenotype and SLE may not be fortuitous, but rather that in the absence of the more reactive, amide-bond-forming C4A3, the processing and clearance of immune complexes composed of nucleic acids and antibodies directed against them are impaired. In order to test this hypothesis, we have initiated a series of experiments concerned with the effects of nucleotides and DNA on the covalent binding properties of C4.

RESULTS

The results of fluid-phase binding experiments[3] concerned with the effects of nucleotides on the covalent binding reaction between radiolabeled putrescine and C4

[a]The research reported here was supported by NIH grant nos. AI16543 and AM20579.

395

TABLE 1. Effects of Nucleotides on the Covalent Binding between C4 and [^{3}H]-Putrescine

	Binding Efficiency
Cl	1.00
Control ($-$Cl)	0.18
Cl plus	
(1) ATP (2 mM)	0.57
(2) ATP (10 mM)	0.67
(3) GTP (2 mM)	0.72
(4) GTP (10 mM)	0.42
(5) 5'-pd(GG)-3' (1.2 mM)	0.77
(6) Oligo-G(dG)$_6$ (0.55 mM)	0.38
(7) Poly-dG (1.83 mg/ml)	0.51

from pooled human serum show that both ATP and GTP and certain homopolymers of G inhibit the binding reaction to various degrees (TABLE 1). FIGURE 1 shows that ATP has a marked effect on the covalent binding reaction of C4A3, but its effect on C4B1 is marginal.

The effects of human DNA on the fluid-phase binding of C4 to radiolabeled putrescine are shown in TABLE 2. High molecular weight DNA does not appear to have a marked effect on the binding efficiency between C4 and putrescine (Table 2, columns 2 and 3). On the other hand, the reverse is true of DNA that has been fragmented by

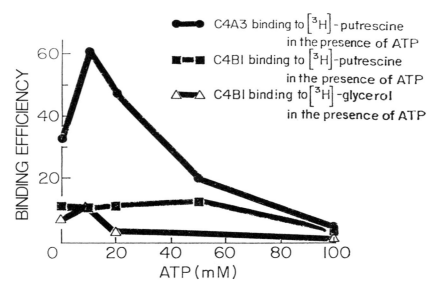

FIGURE 1. Inhibition of [^{3}H]-putrescine binding to C4A3 and C4B1 and inhibition of [^{3}H]-glycerol binding to C4B1 by ATP. Different concentrations of ATP were used to inhibit the binding of either [^{3}H]-putrescine or [^{3}H]-glycerol to C4A3 and C4B1 in the presence of Cl. The concentration of putrescine was 5 mM; glycerol was 25 mM. The reaction mixtures were incubated at pH 7.4 for 30 minutes at 37°C.

sonication (column 4). DNA that has been fragmented and then heated at 100 degrees and then cooled immediately on ice in order to produce a preparation that is enriched for single-stranded DNA appears to have less of an effect than double-stranded, fragmented DNA (column 5). DNA in any form or size did not inhibit the activation of C4. No effort was made in this experiment to characterize the molecular sizes of the DNA that are effective in inhibiting the covalent binding reaction nor was an effort made to determine the extent to which the melting procedure produced single-stranded DNA. Experiments currently under way entail the use of DNAs of known molecular size, structure, and base sequence.

SUMMARY OF OBSERVATIONS

The experiments described here are of an exploratory nature designed to ascertain whether nucleotides and DNA affect the covalent binding reaction of C4. The results of these experiments show: (1) Nucleotides and DNA affect the binding efficiency of C4 by competing in the covalent binding reaction between C4 and putrescine; (2) The

TABLE 2. Effect of DNA on the Covalent Binding Reaction between C4 and [^{3}H]-Putresine[a]

DNA Concentration (mg/ml)	Intact DNA	Intact DNA (Heat Treated)	Fragmented DNA	Fragmented DNA (Heat Treated)
1	—	—	0.60	0.60
2	—	—	0.34	0.71
3	0.73	0.69	0.05	0.47

[a]All the data were expressed as binding efficiencies. Binding efficiency for the control sample lacking DNA was 0.60.

competitive effect of the nucleotides is on C4A3, not on C4B1; (3) Fragments of double-stranded human DNA, but not high molecular weight DNA, compete in the covalent binding reaction between C4 and putrescine.

REFERENCES

1. O'NEILL, G. J., S. Y. YANG & B. DUPONT. 1978. Two HLA-linked loci controlling the fourth component of human complement. Proc. Natl. Acad. Sci. USA **75**: 5165.
2. LAW, S. K., A. W. DODDS & R. R. PORTER. 1984. A comparison of the properties of two classes, C4A and C4B, of the human complement component C4. EMBO J. **3**: 1819.
3. LAW, S. K., T. M. MINICH & R. P. LEVINE. 1984. The covalent binding efficiency of the third and fourth complement proteins in relation to pH, nucleophilicity, and availability of hydroxyl groups. Biochemistry **23**: 3267.
4. FIELDER, A. H. L., M. J. WALPORT, J. R. BATCHELOR, R. I. RYNES, C. M. BLACK, I. A. DODI & G. R. V. HUGHES. 1983. Family study of the major histocompatibility complex in patients with systemic lupus erythematosus: Importance of null alleles of C4A and C4B in determining disease susceptibility. Br. Med. J. **286**: 425.
5. REVIELLE, J. D., F. C. ARNETT, R. W. WILSON, W. B. BIAS & R. H. MCLEAN. 1985. Null alleles of the fourth component of complement and HLA haplotypes in familial systemic lupus erythematosus. Immmunogenetics **21**: 425.

6. NUSSENZWEIG, V. 1980. Interaction between complement and immune complexes: Role of complement in containing immune complex damage. Prog. Immunol. 4th Int. Congr. Immunol. (Paris), pp. 1044–1061.
7. PORTER, R. R. 1983. Complement polymorphism, the major histocompatibility complex and associated disease: A speculation. Mol. Biol. Med. 1: 161.

Interaction between Autoaggressive T Lymphocyte Lines and Their Target Tissues

Encephalitogenic T Lymphocytes Destroy Astrocytes Presenting Myelin Basic Protein

DEMING SUN AND HARTMUT WEKERLE

Max-Planck-Gesellschaft
Clinical Research Unit for Multiple Sclerosis
D-8700 Würzburg, Federal Republic of Germany

Autoimmune diseases are the result of pathological interactions between autoaggressive lymphocytes and the relevant target tissues. At least in experimentally induced autoimmune diseases of the nervous system, highly defined molecular structures are the target epitopes of genetically controlled T-cell autoimmune responses and these epitopes must be immunogenically presented by specialized cellular components within the attacked tissues.

Work from our laboratory has recently established that astrocytes, the main glial components of the central nervous system, have the capacity to present self and foreign

TABLE 1. Cytolytic Activity of Antigen-Specific Encephalitogenic and Nonencephalitogenic T Line Cells (^{51}Cr release assay, 9 hours)

Code	T Line Target Antigen	EAE	Antigen (10 µg/ml)	Blocking mAB (dilution 1:4000)	Net ^{51}Cr Release (%)
Z1a	(MBP, 68–88)	+	MBP	0	67, 3
			Ovalbumin	0	0, 6
			MBP	OX3	6, 2
			MBP	OX18	72, 1
L.BP644	(MBP, 68–88)	+	0	0	1, 8
			MBP	0	57, 2
L.C2	(MBP, 48–67)	0	MPB	0	25, 9
L.OA	(Ovalbumin)	0	MBP	0	9, 2
			Ovalbumin	0	8, 4

antigens to immunocompetent T lymphocytes. We found that Lewis rat astrocytes activate syngeneic MBP-specific, encephalitogenic T line lymphocytes in the presence of the antigen and that antigen presentation is enhanced by prior induction of Ia antigens on the astrocytes.[1,2] All T lines expressed the "helper/inducer" phenotype of W3/25+, OX8−.

We now report that recognition of the encephalitogenic determinant of MBP by encephalitogenic T line cells leads to complete lysis of the antigen-presenting astrocytes within a few hours. Target cell lysis is strictly antigen-specific and Ia restricted, and it seems to require direct effector-target contact (TABLE 1).

Target lysis is neither a long-term culture artifact nor the property of one individual T line because all our encephalitogenic lines (in culture from four weeks up to five years) had the same activity. Target lysis seems, however, to depend on the antigenic epitope to be recognized: target lysis was seen only with MBP-specific encephalitogenic T line cells, but not with any of the other lines recognizing other proteins. Even within the different MBP epitopes, there is a hierarchy of "lysogenicity": lines recognizing the encephalitogenic sequence 68–88 are highly lytic, whereas lines against the adjacent epitope 48–67 have much lower, if any lytic capacity. So far, there is an excellent correlation between target lysis and the capacity to transfer EAE *in vivo*.

Our results suggest that the membrane phenotype of a T lymphocyte may not reliably reflect the actual immunological function and that the structural quality of an (auto-)antigen may codetermine the quality of the resulting immune response. These data furthermore indicate that encephalitogenic T cells, although of the "helper/inducer" phenotype, may mediate disease by interfering with the function of CNS astrocytes.

REFERENCES

1. FONTANA, A., W. FIERZ & H. WEKERLE. 1984. Nature **307:** 273–276.
2. FIERZ, W., B. ENDLER, K. RESKE, H. WEKERLE & A. FONTANA. 1985. J. Immunol. **134:** 3785–3793.

Suppression of T-Cell Mediated Autoimmune Disease with Antibodies against the Interleukin-2 Receptor

Effect of Hybridoma ART-18 on T Line Mediated Experimental Autoimmune Encephalomyelitis

HARTMUT WEKERLE[a] AND TIBOR DIAMANTSTEIN[b]

[a]Max-Planck-Gesellschaft
Clinical Research Unit for Multiple Sclerosis[c]
D-8700 Würzburg, Federal Republic of Germany

[b]Immunology Research Unit
Klinikum Steglitz
Freie Universität Berlin
1000 Berlin, Federal Republic of Germany

Immunotherapy of autoimmune disease should be efficient and specific. It should eliminate the pathogenic lymphocyte clones, but spare the rest of the immune repertoire. We have applied a monoclonal hybridoma antibody against rat T lymphocyte receptor for interleukin-2 (IL2R)[1] to treat T line lymphocyte mediated experimental autoimmune encephalomyelitis (EAE) in vivo. We found that at a dose of 1 mg/kg, the antibodies of hybridoma ART-18 protect Lewis rats from lethal doses of a syngeneic T-cell line recognizing the encephalitogenic peptide sequence of myelin basic protein (MBP). It was also found that this treatment has no demonstrable effect on the general immune reactivity of the recipients.

MBP-specific permanent T lymphocyte lines derived from Lewis rats[2] mediate lethal EAE to adult syngeneic recipients at doses as low as 1×10^6 cells/rat. These cells are autoaggressive only after reactivation by antigen or mitogens; resting stages of the lines do not transfer disease. We injected young adult Lewis rats with doses of 4×10^6 freshly activated MBP-specific T line cells. Control rats, which were injected i.p. with 1 mg/kg of hybridoma antibodies of irrelevant specificity, died without exception within six days. In contrast, all rats that were treated with anti-IL2R hybridoma ART-18 (1 mg/kg i.p. on three or four consecutive days) survived either without any symptoms (6/9) or with mild, transient EAE (3/9). Most animals that received only one single injection of ART-18 were also well: one animal died, but the other two were without any symptoms (FIGURE 1). Therefore, treatment with ART-18 had to take place early after tranfer of the pathogenic T line cells. Delay of the first injection of ART-18 (1 mg/kg i.p.) by one or two days after T line transfer markedly reduced the therapeutic effect: 4/6 rats died, while 2/6 had mild or no EAE.

Possible side effects of anti-IL2R therapy were studied in rats that survived the transfer of encephalitogenic T line cells due to injection of ART-18 antibodies. Such rats were immunized with ovalbumin emulsified in Freund's complete adjuvant. After ten days, the regional lymph nodes were harvested and their cells challenged in vitro

[c]The Clinical Research Unit for Multiple Sclerosis is supported by funds of the Hermann-und-Lilly-Schilling-Stiftung.

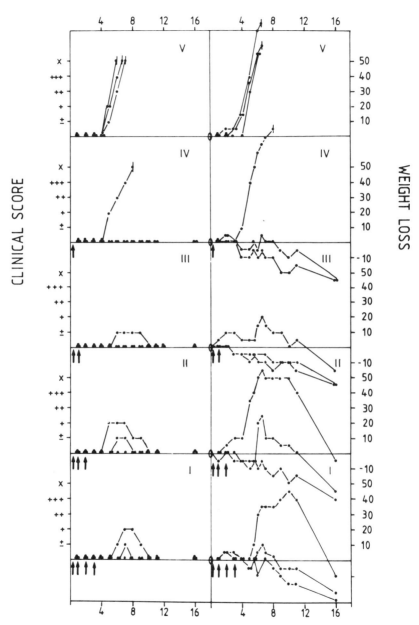

FIGURE 1. Protective effect of anti-IL2R mAB ART-18 on Lewis rats injected with lethal doses of encephalitogenic T line cells. Time course of weight loss is shown in the right panel and clinical status is shown in the left. Rating: ±: tail flaccidity only; +: hind-limb paralysis; + +: paralysis ascending to forelimbs; + + +: moribund state with convulsions and coma; ×: death.

against ovalbumin, tuberculin, and concanavalin A. In other experiments, the lymphocyte subset composition of lymph nodes was assessed by immunofluorescence and cytofluometric analysis using a standard panel of monoclonal antibodies. No immune abnormalities were found in these experiments. Thus, treatment with anti-IL2R monoclonal antibody ART-18 seems to be selective and efficient because: (a) only activated, but not resting autoreactive T lymphocytes are known to mediate organ-specific autoimmune dieases and (b) in the rat, IL2R is expressed only on activated, but not on resting T lymphocytes.

REFERENCES

1. OSAWA, H. & T. DIAMANTSTEIN. 1983. J. Immunol. **130:** 51–55.
2. BEN-NUN, A., H. WEKERLE & I. R. COHEN. 1981. Eur. J. Immunol. **11:** 195–199.

Anti-Myelin Basic Protein Autoreactive T Lymphocytes in Healthy Subjects and Multiple Sclerosis Patients

ELISABETH TOURNIER-LASSERVE,[a] CLAUDE JACQUE,[b]
DIDIER FRADELIZI,[c] AND MARIE-ANNE BACH[a]

[a]Unité de Pathologie de l'Immunité
Institut Pasteur
75724 Paris, France

[b]Unité INSERM 134
Hôpital de la Salpêtrière
Paris, France

[c]Institut Gustave Roussy
Villejuif, France

INTRODUCTION

Multiple sclerosis (MS) is widely thought to result from an autoimmune process because it shares several clinical, histopathological, and immunological features with the animal models of experimental allergic encephalomyelitis (EAE).[1,2] Its etiology is, however, unknown, but a viral agent is likely to be involved. Moreover, at variance with EAE where the autoimmune process has been shown to be elicited by myelin basic protein (MBP),[2,3] the autoantigen towards which autoimmunity is directed in MS is still a matter of debate. Indeed, although most authors did find some evidences of T-cell sensitization to MBP in MS patients,[1] the pathophysiological relevance of such a phenomenon was questionable because T-cell reactivity as assessed *in vitro* by the assays so far available was relatively low, was not detectable in all MS patients, and was sometimes observed in patients suffering other neurological diseases or in healthy subjects. We have taken advantage of the development of new techniques based on the use of interleukin-2 (IL2) for isolation and long-term culture of antigen-specific T cells to further explore T-cell reactivity to MBP in MS patients and healthy subjects.

MATERIALS AND METHODS

Patients suffering MS were followed in Hôpital de la Salpêtrière, Paris, France. Healthy subjects were staff members or blood-bank donors. The proliferative response of peripheral blood mononuclear cells (PBMC) to human MBP was assessed by culturing 10^5 cells for six days with or without human MBP (100 μg/ml) in 0.2 ml RPMI 1640 supplemented with 10% human AB serum. ^{3}H-thymidine incorporation was measured after an 18-hour pulse. In some cultures, the proliferative response was assessed after a further two days incubation in the presence of IL2 (HPLC purified IL2 prepared by one of us or lymphocult TLF, Biotest, Federal Republic of Germany). Results were expressed as:

$$\text{stimulation indexes (SI)} = \frac{\text{cpm with MBP}}{\text{cpm without MBP}}.$$

404

MBP-specific T-cell lines were obtained by restimulating the primary MBP-triggered cultures of PBMC described above after 7 to 14 days with the MBP plus irradiated autologous PBMC used as antigen-presenting cells (APC), and then by adding IL2 2 to 5 days later. Such T-cell lines were further propagated in the presence of IL2 by weekly restimulation with MBP plus APC. MBP-triggered T-cell clones were obtained by a limiting dilution technique and were further expanded as for the T-cell lines. Proliferative response of T-cell lines and clones was assayed by culturing 10^4 to 5×10^4 T-cells with MBP plus 5×10^4 APC in the absence of IL2 for 48 to 72 hours and measuring ^{3}H-thymidine incorporation after an 18-hour pulse. T-cell marker phenotype of T-cell lines and clones was studied in an immunofluorescence assay using monoclonal antibodies, OKT4 and OKT8 (Ortho Pharmaceuticals, Raritan, New Jersey).

RESULTS AND DISCUSSION

When assayed in the absence of IL2 (TABLE 1), a significant proliferative response of PBMC as defined by an SI ≥ 2 was observed in 8 out of 14 MS patients and in 2 out of 10 healthy subjects, with a mean SI significantly higher ($p < 0.05$) in the former

TABLE 1. Proliferative Response of PBMC from MS Patients and Healthy Subjects to MBP

	^{3}H-Thymidine Incorporation (SI)[a]	
Subjects	without IL2	with IL2
MS patients	2.95 (8/14)[b] ± 0.61	10.2 (9/11) ± 5.14
Healthy subjects	1.84 (2/10) ± 0.59	2.77 (5/7) ± 1.35

[a]Proliferative response to human MBP was assayed either after six days of culture without IL2 or after an additional incubation of two days with IL2.
[b]Mean ± SEM. In parentheses: number of subjects with SI $\geq$ 2/number of subjects tested.

group than in the latter. MBP-induced proliferative response was increased in both groups after IL2 addition, which resulted in a significant proliferation in 9 out of 11 MS patients, but also in 5 out of 7 healthy subjects. These data may indicate that a majority of healthy subjects do harbor low numbers of circulating anti-MBP autoreactive T cells, which can be evidenced at best when MBP-triggered proliferation is amplified by IL2 addition. In MS patients, the frequency of such MBP-reactive T cells in blood would be increased (leading to a higher proliferative response of the bulk T-cell population), which could be due to an *in vivo* presensitization to MBP. The relevance of such a phenomenon to the pathophysiology of MS is unknown.

In order to further analyze T-cell responsiveness to MBP, MBP-triggered T-cell lines were developed from two MS patients and one healthy subject. All three T-cell lines exhibited a strong proliferative response to human MBP in the presence of autologous APC and not to PPD, thus demonstrating the specificity of these lines to the triggering antigen. The fine specificity of the normal T-cell line was further investigated by measuring the proliferative response of these cells to MBP from other species (kindly given by N. Gonatas and G.A. Hashim). As shown in TABLE 2, a strong proliferative response to nonhuman MBP was also noted, which was not unexpected in view of the close sequence homology of these various proteins. The T-cell line was mainly composed of OKT4+ cells (82% versus 2% OKT8+ cells). Burns *et al.*[4] also reported recently the observation of guinea pig MBP-triggered T-cell lines from normal subjects that cross-reacted with human MBP and expressed the OKT4 phenotype.

Six clones also were obtained from the normal MBP-specific T-cell line, with three of them only displaying a specific proliferative response to MBP. One of these clones (C8) was tested for proliferative response to MBP from other species and showed broad cross-reactivity with these proteins. T-cells from this clone all expressed the OKT4 + / OKT8 − phenotype.

In the experimental models of EAE, each species was found exquisitely sensitive to a limited number of peptide fragments of MBP.[2,3] More importantly, the T-cell sensitizing epitope may differ from a strain to another within the same species in relation to the strain susceptibility to MBP-induced EAE.[5] The development of

TABLE 2. Proliferative Response of Normal MBP-Reactive T-Cell Lines and Clones to MBP from Various Species

MBP	T-Cell Line	Clone C8
	^{3}H-Thymidine Incorporation (cpm)^a	
None	1655	165
Human	3329	7185
Bovine	5884	9345
Rat	6244	3402
Mouse	7900	ND
Guinea pig	ND	3902
Monkey	3689	ND

^{a}In this study, 10^4 cells were cultured for 48 hours with MBP from various species plus 5×10^4 autologous irradiated PBMC.

MBP-specific T-cell lines and clones in humans will allow us to study the human T-cell repertoire to MBP epitopes and to search for a peculiar T-cell responsiveness to MBP in MS patients.

REFERENCES

1. LISAK, R. P. 1980. Neurology (Minneapolis) **30:** 99–105.
2. PATERSON, P. Y., E. D. DAY & C. WHITACRE. 1981. Immunol. Rev. **55:** 89–120.
3. HASHIM, G. A. 1978. Immunol. Rev. **39:** 60.
4. BURNS, J., A. ROSENZWEIG, B. ZWEIMAN & R. P. LISAK. 1983. Cell. Immunol. **81:** 435–440.
5. FRITZ, R. B., C. H. JEN CHOU & D. E. McFARLIN. 1983. J. Immunol. **130:** 191–194.

Studies on Collagen II Induced Arthritis in Mice and Rats

LARS KLARESKOG,[a] RIKARD HOLMDAHL,[a]
KRISTOFER RUBIN,[a] AND HANS WIGZELL[b]

[a]Department of Medical and Physiological Chemistry
Uppsala University
S-751 23 Uppsala, Sweden

[b]Karolinska Institutet
Stockholm, Sweden

Collagen II induced arthritis in mice and rats was studied in regard to disease course after immunization with native type II collagens from different species, in regard to cell composition of inflammatory lesions, and in regard to the possibilities to induce the disease *in vivo* with the help of cloned antigen-specific T helper cells and with monoclonal antibodies. It was demonstrated that:

(1) The disease course after immunization of male DBA/1 mice with native mouse collagen II is characterized by a slow and progressive onset of disease and by frequent exacerbations of disease in both previously affected and previously nonaffected joints. On the other hand, after immunization with heterologous native collagen II, there is seen a rapid and aggressive onset of disease with few exacerbations (as has been described by other authors).[1] More than 50% of all immunized male mice acquired arthritis within 20 weeks, whereas none of the similarly immunized female littermates demonstrated arthritis within this time.

(2) Antibody titers against mouse collagen II do not correlate with arthritis development, neither after immunization with mouse collagen nor after immunization with collagen of rat, cow, chick, and human origin. Instead, the amounts of autoantibodies towards collagen II were dependent on the immunogen used for immunization. Thus, in general, immunization with heterologous collagens gave higher autoantibody titers than immunization with mouse collagen, irrespective of the development of arthritis.

(3) Immunohistochemical studies on the synovial tissue, particularly the pannus region, of arthritis rats immunized with native bovine collagen II showed that T "helper" cells dominate the lymphoid infiltrates, that many class II transplantation antigen-expressing cells are present in the synovial lining and in the pannus close to the damaged cartilage, and that few, if any, B cells/plasma cells are present within the synovial tissue early in the course of arthritis.[2,3]

(4) Lines and clones of collagen II specific T helper cells grown *in vitro* induce an aggressive synovitis in both untreated and irradiated (750 rad) syngeneic recipient DBA/1 mice.[4] Injection of purified monoclonal antibodies reactive with native mouse collagen II in amounts of up to 5 mg per mouse did, however, only give rise to a relatively mild synovitis.

It is concluded, therefore, that experimental arthritis in mice induced with homologous collagen II resembles human rheumatoid arthritis more than experimental arthritis induced with heterologous collagens. In addition, collagen arthritis, as has been suggested for human rheumatoid arthritis,[5] is probably induced mainly via a T-cell-mediated delayed type hypersensitivity reaction.

REFERENCES

1. WOOLEY, G. A., H. S. LUTHRA, J. M. STUART & C. S. DAVID. 1981. J. Exp. Med. **154:** 688-700.
2. KLARESKOG, L. R., R. HOLMDAHL, E. LARSSON & H. WIGZELL. 1983. Clin. Exp. Immunol. **51:** 117–125.
3. HOLMDAHL, R., K. RUBIN, L. KLARESKOG, L. DENCKER, G. GUSTAFSON & E. LARSSON. 1985. Scand. J. Immunol. **21:** 197–204.
4. HOLMDAHL, R., L. KLARESKOG, K. RUBIN, E. LARSSON & H. WIGZELL. 1985. Scand. J. Immunol. **22:** 295–306.
5. KLARESKOG, L., U. FORSUM, A. SCHEYNIUS, D. KABELITZ & H. WIGZELL. 1982. Proc. Natl. Acad. Sci. USA **79:** 3632–3636.

Autoantibody Inducing T-Cell Lines with Atypical MHC Restriction

Y. NAPARSTEK, M. P. MADAIO, K. BAUR, L. BREITMAN,
AND R. S. SCHWARTZ

Tufts New England Medical Center
Boston, Massachusetts 02111

Polyclonal B-cell activation associated with the spontaneous production of anti-DNA and other autoantibodies is characteristic of both human and murine systemic lupus erythematosus (SLE).[1,2] The importance of polyclonal B-cell activation in SLE is further supported by the observation that exogenously administered B-cell activators to normal mice lead to both autoantibody production and a lupus-like syndrome.[3] The precise sequence of events and pathogens that spontaneously occur in individuals with SLE, though, are not fully understood.

In the present study, we have isolated T cells from lupus mice that have unique requirements for activation. Moreover, these cells induce B-cell activation and autoantibody production. Since these cells were derived from nonimmunized mice, they may be important participants in the pathways leading to the production of autoantibodies *in vivo*.

Autoreactive T cells (AR-TC) were derived from the splenocytes of nonimmunized MRL-*lpr/lpr* mice. Splenocytes were cultured with alternating cycles of either T-cell growth factor (TCGF) or irradiated syngeneic antigen-presenting cells (APCs). AR-TCs were found to have the helper/inducer phenotype, and they responded to APCs from both MRL mice and mice with syngeneic class II antigens.

The MHC restriction was further studied by the use of APCs from recombinant mice. It was found that both I-A^k and I-E^k encoded antigens were required in order to stimulate AR-TC. AR-TC activated by syngeneic APCs secreted factors that induced B-cell proliferation, as well as hematopoietic growth-promoting factors, as measured by the proliferation of FDC-Pl cells (IL-3, GM-CSF dependent cell line[3]). B cells from both lupus strains of mice and normal mice incubated in medium conditioned by the activated AR-TC produced immunoglobulins and anti-DNA antibodies.

In summary:

(1) Autoreactive T-cell lines from MRL-*lpr/lpr* mice can be established without exogenous immunization.
(2) The proliferative responses of these AR-TCs require both I-A and I-E self-MHC-antigens.
(3) Activated AR-TCs produce factors that promote B-cell proliferation, immunoglobulin synthesis, and autoantibody production.

If unregulated, therefore, AR-TCs could lead to polyclonal B-cell activation and autoantibody production *in vivo*.

REFERENCES

1. KOFFLER, D., R. CARR, V. ANGELLO *et al.* 1971. Antibodies to polynucleotides in human sera: antigenic specificity and relation to disease. J. Exp. Med. **134:** 294–312.

2. ANDREWS, B. S., R. A. EISENBERG, A. N. THEOFILOPOULOS *et al.* 1978. Spontaneous murine lupus-like syndrome. Clinical and immunopathological manifestations in several strains. J. Exp. Med. **148:** 1198–1215.
3. HANG, L., M. T. AGUADO, F. J. DIXON & A. N. THEOFILOPOULOS. 1985. Induction of severe autoimmune disease in normal mice by simultaneous action of multiple immunostimulants. J. Exp. Med. **161:** 423–428.

Is There a Role for Antibody in the Pathogenesis of Spontaneous Diabetes in the BB Rat?

STEPHEN J. PROWSE, DONALD BELLGRAU,
AND KEVIN J. LAFFERTY

Barbara Davis Center for Childhood Diabetes
Department of Microbiology and Immunology and Pediatrics
University of Colorado Health Sciences Center
Denver, Colorado 80262

Type I diabetes in the BB rat is thought to be an autoimmune disease mediated by T-cell recognition of an islet beta-cell antigen.[1] It is now established that T cells recognize antigens in association with major histocompatibility complex (MHC) gene products.[2] Therefore, T cells that purportedly destroy beta cells by a direct interaction would be recognizing a beta-cell antigen in association with an MHC product of the BB rat. According to this hypothesis, transplants of MHC compatible islet tissue would be less likely to survive in nonimmunosuppressed animals than an allogeneic islet graft

TABLE 1. BB/D Rats Destroy Cultured PVG Islet, but Not Cultured PVG Pituitary Grafts[a]

Recipient Rat no.	Histologic Score		
	Pancreas	Islet Graft	Pituitary Graft
1	3	1	0
2	3	1	0
3	4	3	0
4	2	3	1
5	1	3	0
6	4	4	0
7	3	3	0

[a]Diabetes-prone, but nondiabetic BB/D rats were transplanted under the kidney capsule with a cluster of PVG islet tissue or anterior pituitary, both of which had been cultured for 14 days in 95% oxygen at 37°C.[4] The animals were killed 18 days after transplantation and the pancreas, islet graft, and pituitary graft were analyzed by histology. The diabetic state of the animals was tested at the time they were killed; nos. 3, 6, and 7 were diabetic. Histology scores: 0, no infiltration; 1, minor infiltration; 2, major focal infiltration; 3, generalized infiltration and destruction; 4, total destruction.

that has been treated to reduce its immunogenicity; this is because of a likely recurrence of disease in the MHC compatible tissue.

Previous studies[3] have shown that islet grafts are destroyed in diabetic BB rats. To differentiate between graft destruction mediated by disease occurrence in the transplanted tissue or an allograft response, we tested the tissue specificity of the response. A group of seven nondiabetic, diabetes-prone BB/D rats were transplanted with a cluster of cultured PVG islets and one PVG anterior pituitary that had been cultured

411

under identical conditions.[4] A control group of diabetes-prone BB animals were transplanted with uncultured pituitary to investigate the capacity of these animals to reject a pituitary allograft. After 18 days, both grafts and the recipient's pancreas were removed and examined histologically.

Inflammatory tissue damage occurred in the islet graft, but not in the adjacent pituitary allograft (TABLE 1), suggesting that islet damage did not result from the activation of an allograft response. The cellular infiltrate in the graft was characterized by eosinophilia, giant cell formation, and mast cell accumulation. No cell infiltrate was seen in six out of seven cultured pituitary grafts. One cultured pituitary transplant had a minor focal mononuclear cell accumulation between intact pituitary tissue and kidney parenchyma. Uncultured pituitary tissue was rejected by BB rats in 18 days. A typical mononuclear cell infiltrate was seen in these grafts. No eosinophils were seen. This indicates that eosinophilia is not typical of an inflammatory response in BB rats. Eosinophils were also seen in association with some inflammatory foci in the recipient's pancreas. Multinucleate giant cells were also seen in some islets and mast cells were present in the pancreatic parenchyma. The eosinophilia is transitory and is not a

TABLE 2. The Incidence of ICA in BB Rats Aged <100 Days or ≥100 Days[a]

	Age	
	<100 Days	≥100 Days
ICA positive	5	8
ICA negative	28	5

[a]Sera from rats were tested on Bouin's fixed normal rat pancreas with a second antibody, fluorescent goat anti-rat IgG, used to detect binding. Normal sera do not have islet cell antibody.

long-term feature of islet pathology in BB rats. These results suggest that an antibody-mediated reaction may be responsible for the disease process. A study of serum from BB rats of various ages revealed the presence of islet cell antibody (ICA) (TABLE 2). Peripheral blood eosinophilia was also seen in animals aged 85 days or older.

Taken together, the pathology, the lack of MHC restriction in the disease process, and the presence of ICA and eosinophilia suggest that some form of antibody-mediated damage is occurring in the pancreas of the BB rats.

REFERENCES

1. KOEVARY, S., A. ROSSINI, W. STOLLER, W. CHICK & R. M. WILLIAMS. 1983. Science **220:** 727–729.
2. ZINKERNAGEL, R. M. & P. C. DOHERTY 1974. Nature **248:** 701–703.
3. NAJI, A., W. K. SILVERS, S. J. BARTLETT, J. FRANCFORT & C. F. BARKER. 1984. World J. Surg. **8:** 214–220.
4. LAFFERTY, K. J. & S. J. PROWSE. 1984. World J. Surg. **8:** 187–197.

Antibodies to the Acetylcholine Receptor in Myasthenia Gravis

Comparison between Human and Fetal Calf Antigen

ROBIN KAUFMAN AND JOEL OGER

Department of Medicine
University of British Columbia
Vancouver, British Columbia, Canada V6T 1WS

INTRODUCTION

Myasthenia gravis (MG) is an autoimmune disorder of the neuromuscular junction. It is characterized by circulating antibodies directed against the nicotinic acetylcholine receptor (AchR) on the muscle end plate. Anti-AchR antibodies have been shown to mediate immune injury to the postsynaptic membrane and to be responsible for an increased degradation of AchR. Although quantitative measures of anti-AchR titers in the serum of MG patients have not shown a good correlation with disease activity,[1] the presence of antibodies is an excellent diagnostic indicator for MG.

Muscle preparations from various species have been tested for use as antigen in the assay for anti-AchR antibodies. However, low levels of cross-reactivity have been observed.[2] Recently, it has been proposed that antigen prepared from fetal calf muscle

TABLE 1. Results of Antibody Detection Using Human Antigen

	+	±	−
Generalized MG (21)	20	0	1
Remission (4)	0	0	4
Ocular MG (6)	4	0	2
Other Neurological Diseases (16)	0	1	15
Healthy Controls (40)	0	0	40

is an acceptable alternative to that prepared from human tissue. Gotti *et al.*[3] reported an excellent correlation between levels of antibodies against human and against fetal calf antigens. Only 3/52 (6%) sera positive for human antigen antibodies were found not to be positive for fetal calf antigen.

Using a modification of the assay described by Lindstrom,[4] we have tested the serum of 87 individuals for antibodies against human AchR. In addition, we have compared human and fetal calf muscles as antigen sources.

TECHNIQUES

Briefly, AchR was solubilized from human or fetal calf muscle by homogenization in the presence of Triton X (2%). AchR was labeled by specific binding of ^{125}I-

alpha-bungarotoxin. Ten μl of serum to be tested was incubated overnight at 4°C with 100 μl of homogenate containing labeled AchR. In the final step, 100 μl of 7% Staph A was used to precipitate IgG. The pellet was washed and counted. Results are expressed as cpm and compared with results obtained for sera from healthy individuals run in parallel. Values greater than 2 SD above the mean of the controls are considered positive in the assay. Values of 1 to 2 SD above the control mean are considered borderline.

RESULTS

Using human antigen, we have found 20/21 (95%) generalized MG, 4/6 ocular MG, 0/4 patients in clinical remission, and 0/56 nonmyasthenics to be positive with this assay (TABLE 1).

A comparison of results obtained using human and fetal calf muscle antigen in the assay has shown that 6/21 (29%) of the myasthenic sera positive with human antigen

TABLE 2. Comparison of Results Obtained Using Human and Fetal Calf Muscle Antigen

		Human AchR	
		Positive	Negative
Fetal Calf AchR	Positive	15	0
	Negative	6	45

are negative with fetal calf antigen. Among 45 sera negative with human antigens, none were found to be positive using fetal calf antigen (TABLE 2).

CONCLUSION

We found a good correlation between results obtained with the human and fetal calf antigens. However, we think that the number of discrepancies that we have seen precludes the use of fetal calf muscle as a source of antigen in the diagnosis of myasthenia gravis.

REFERENCES

1. LINDSTROM, J. 1977. Clin. Immunol. Immunopathol. **7:** 36.
2. ABRAMSKY, O. *et al.* 1981. Ann. N.Y. Acad. Sci. **377:** 806.
3. GOTTI, C. *et al.* 1984. Neurology **34:** 374.
4. LINDSTROM, J. 1976. Neurology **26:** 1054.

Antibodies to an M_r 64,000 Human Islet Cell Protein in the Prediabetic Period of IDDM Patients

S. BÆKKESKOV,[a] J. BRUINING,[b] S. SRIKANTA,[c]
T. MANDRUP-POULSEN,[d] C. DE BEAUFORT,[b]
G. EISENBARTH,[c] J. NERUP,[d] AND Å. LERNMARK,[a]

[a]Hagedorn Research Laboratory
Niels Steensensvej 6, DK-2820
Gentofte, Denmark

[b]Sophia Children's Hospital
Rotterdam, the Netherlands

[c]Joslin Diabetes Center
Boston, Massachusetts

[d]Steno Memorial Hospital
Gentofte, Denmark

Autoantibodies in insulin-dependent diabetic (IDDM) patients recognize an M_r 64,000 human islet cell protein.[1] In the spontaneously diabetic BB-rat, which develops IDDM in many ways similar to human IDDM, antibodies to an M_r 64,000 rat islet cell protein were found to be a very early sign of an aberrant immunological reaction to islet cells and were associated with the development of IDDM.[2,3]

The appearance of M_r 64,000 antibodies was studied in the prediabetic period of 12 IDDM patients (nos. 1–12), including 7 positive and 5 negative for islet cell cytoplasmic antibodies (ICCA). Serum samples from different time points were tested in immunoprecipitation experiments using detergent lysates of ^{35}S-methionine-labeled human islets. Immunoprecipitates were analyzed by SDS-PAGE and fluorography. FIGURE 1 shows the immunoprecipitation of human islet cell proteins with sera from patient no. 6. Antibodies to the M_r 64,000 protein were consistently detected in nine IDDM patients (FIGURE 2), including the seven that were ICCA positive. The M_r 64,000 antibodies appeared before ICCA in one patient and preceded the clinical onset in two ICCA negative patients. In eight of the nine consistently positive patients, the antibodies were present already in the first sample obtained ($4 \leq t \leq 91$ months before the clinical onset).

It is, therefore, not known how early the antibodies developed. In one patient (no. 1) who was negative in the first two samples (78 and 70 months before the onset of IDDM), antibodies appeared 55 months before the onset of IDDM (FIGURE 2). Three patients, all ICCA negative, were negative or weakly positive for M_r 64,000 antibodies (FIGURE 2). Seven first-degree relatives to IDDM patients having signs of altered β-cell function were tested in parallel and found to be M_r 64,000 antibody positive. Sera from the control group, which comprised six healthy IDDM relatives and three healthy laboratory personnel, were all negative. The results indicate that antibodies to the M_r 64,000 protein may be associated with β-cell destruction and signify a later development of IDDM.

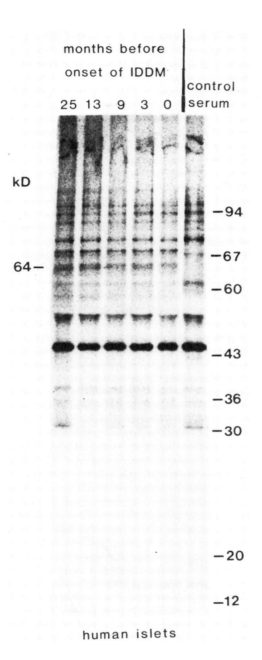

FIGURE 1. Fluorograph showing immunoprecipitation of the M_r 64,000 antigen with sera obtained before and at the clinical onset of IDDM in patient no. 6, who is a monozygotic twin originally discordant for IDDM. ^{35}S-Methionine-labeled human islet cell lysates were immunoprecipitated with serum samples obtained at different time points before or at the clinical onset of IDDM. The first sample was obtained when the twin brother developed IDDM, which was approximately two years before the diagnosis of the patient's own IDDM.

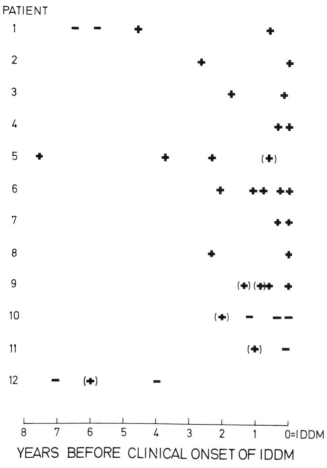

FIGURE 2. Appearance of M_r 64,000 antibodies in the prediabetic period of 12 IDDM patients. ^{35}S-Methionine-labeled human islet cell lysates were immunoprecipitated with serum samples obtained at different time points before or at the clinical onset of IDDM. Immunoprecipitates were analyzed by SDS-PAGE and fluorography, and sera were designated positive, +, weakly positive, (+), or negative, −, according to intensity of the M_r 64,000 antigen on fluorograms.

REFERENCES

1.   BÆKKESKOV, S., J. H. NIELSEN, B. MARNER, T. BILDE, J. LUDVIGSSON & Å LERNMARK. 1982. Nature **298:** 167–169.
2.   BÆKKESKOV, S., T. DYRBERG & Å LERNMARK. 1984. Science **224:** 1348–1350.
3.   BÆKKESKOV, S. & Å LERNMARK. 1985. Diabetes **34**(suppl 1): 68A.

Modulation of a Subset of CD4+ (T4) "T Helper" Cells in Active Multiple Sclerosis (MS) and Experimental Allergic Encephalomyelitis (EAE) in Macaques[a]

L. M. ROSE,[b] E. A. CLARK,[b] A. GINSBERG,[c]
J. A. LEDBETTER,[d] S. HRUBY,[e] AND E. C. ALVORD, JR.[e]

[b]Department of Microbiology and Immunology
University of Washington
Seattle, Washington 98195

[c]Northwest Hospital
Seattle, Washington

[d]Genetic Systems Corporation
Seattle, Washington 98121

[e]Department of Pathology
University of Washington
Seattle, Washington 98195

A number of studies have suggested that CD4+ (T4, Leu3a) T helper/inducer (T_h) cells play a role in the pathogenesis of MS. Lesion progression in MS is associated with large numbers of CD4+ cells at the lesion margins.[1] Similarly, a selective migration of Lyt-1+ cells into the CNS from the peripheral blood has been detected in mice developing EAE.[2] Our own analysis of patients with active MS has revealed a selective loss of a subset of T_h cells that is detectable only by two-color fluorescence-activated cell sorter analysis.[3] Using monoclonal antibodies (MAb) to the CD4+ T-cell subset marker and the common leukocyte marker p220, CD4+ cells can be divided into two subsets: p220+ and p220−. We have measured the frequencies of these two subsets both in patients with MS and in long-tailed macaques (*M. fascicularis*) developing EAE. Chronic EAE was induced in macaques by inoculating animals with homologous myelin basic protein (BP) in complete Freund's adjuvant according to the method of Alvord et al.[4] Blood was drawn once a week for complete blood counts and FACS cell sorter analyses of lymphocyte subsets.

A comparison of the frequencies of p220+CD4+ cells and p220-CD4+ cells revealed that the p220+ subset was depleted in both patients with active MS and in animals induced to develop EAE. The p220+CD4+ cells were not depleted in patients with inactive MS or other neurologic diseases. Of ten animals inoculated with BP, six developed overt clinical signs and four developed subclinical EAE (TABLE 1). All of the animals with clinically active EAE had a selective depletion of p220+CD4+ cells. Two of four animals with subclinical EAE also had a loss of p220+CD4+ cells. This specific loss of p220+ cells is of interest because the p220 molecule is thought to play a role in

[a]This work was supported by NIH grant no. CA-39935, the National Multiple Sclerosis Society, and the Genetic Systems Corporation.

418

T-cell activation.[5] MAb to p220 in the presence of submitogenic doses of PHA or anti-CD3 (T3) antibodies enhances T-cell proliferation by upregulating IL-2 receptor levels.

Fluctuations in CD8$^+$ (T8) "T suppressor" subsets were also observed in both MS and EAE, but these fluctuations were not specific. For example, a subset of CD8$^+$ cells (CD8^{bri}, Lp95–150^{bri}) was elevated in many MS patients, but this subset was also increased in patients with other neurologic diseases and in older healthy controls. In some animals developing EAE, a clear decrease of CD8$^+$ cells was observed, but this was not as consistently observed as depletion of CD4$^+$ cells (TABLE 1). In both MS and EAE, T_h/T_s ratios were not informative. Our results demonstrate that a subset of T_h cells is depleted both in MS and EAE. Furthermore, CD4$^+$ cells have been found at the margins of MS lesions and recently, Waldor *et al.* (*Science.* 1985. **227:** 415) have found that administration of rat L3T4 anti-mouse T_h antibodies can prevent and cure

TABLE 1. Summary of Immunologic Findings in Macaques Induced to Develop Clinical or Subclinical EAE with Myelin Basic Protein

	CFA Controls	Clinical EAE	Subclinical EAE
No. of Animals	4	6	4
WBC Count	Constant (4/4)	Constant (6/6)	Constant (4/4)
Lymphocyte Count	↑↓ (4/4)	↓ (5/6)	↑↓ (2/4)
No. T Cells	Constant (3/4)	Constant (1/6)	Constant (2/4)
No. B Cells	Constant (3/4)	Constant (5/6)	Constant (2/4)
Decrease in no. CD4$^+$ Cells	0/4	6/6	2/4
Decrease in no. CD8$^+$ Cells	1/4	5/6	2/4
$T_h > T_s$	1/4	1/6	1/4
Decrease in NK Cell Activity	0/3	2/2	4/5

EAE in mice. Together, these results suggest that anti-CD4$^+$ antibodies may have a therapeutic effect in MS or EAE.

REFERENCES

1. TRAUGOTT, U., E. R. REINHERZ & C. E. RAINE. 1982. Science **219:** 308–310.
2. HAUSER, S. L., A. K. BAHN, M. CHI, F. GILLES & H. L. WEINER. 1984. J. Immunol. **133:** 3037–3042.
3. ROSE, L. M., A. H. GINSBERG, T. L. ROTHSTEIN, J. A. LEDBETTER & E. A. CLARK. 1985. Proc. Natl. Acad. Sci. USA. **82:** 7389–7393.
4. ALVORD, E. C., JR., S. HRUBY, C. M. SHAW & J. C. SLIMP. 1984. *In* Experimental Allergic Encephalomyelitis: A Useful Model for Multiple Sclerosis. E. C. Alvord, M. W. Kies & A. J. Suckling, Eds.: 359–363. Alan Liss. New York.
5. LEDBETTER, J. A., L. M. ROSE, C. E. SPOONER P. B. BEATTY, P. J. MARTIN & E. A. CLARK. 1985. J. Immunol. **135:** 1819–1825.

IgM-Associated Polyneuropathy

An Expression of Monoclonal Autoimmunity

ALBERTO M. MARMONT

Department of Hematology and Clinical Immunology
S. Martino Hospital
16132 Genova, Italy

A chronic sensimotor polyneuropathy (CSP) is known to be associated with a spectrum of B-cell proliferative disorders, including IgG monoclonal immunoglobulins of uncertain significance (MGUS)[1] and myeloma, IgA myeloma, IgM MGUS, and Waldenström's macroglobulinemia.[2] The IgM monoclonal diseases are by far the most frequent paraproteinemic conditions associated with a CSP;[2-4] however, a distinction has been made between "group I" patients with low levels of monoclonal IgM and no important lymphoid infiltration of the bone marrow (MGUS) and "group II" patients with overt macroglobulinemia.[5] The first group was characterized by immune binding of the monoclonal IgM to the myelin sheaths mediated by the F(ab') fragments and by the clinical priority of the sensimotor disturbances. An integral membrane glycoprotein called MAG has been defined as the target antigen of the monoclonal IgM antibodies.[6,7]

A high proportion of monoclonal immunoglobulins, especially IgM, has been found to possess antibody activity against cytoskeleton proteins,[8,9] generally unassociated with clinical disturbances; however, two patients with neuropathy and macroglobulinemia were shown to have antivimentin antibodies, perhaps cross-reacting with a Schwann cell surface antigen(s).[10]

CASE REPORTS

Two patients with chronic sensimotor neuropathy were studied. They were both males, aged 72 and 45, respectively. The history was neurological in both cases. A monoclonal IgM-K was found in both cases—2100 and 927 mg%, respectively. In both cases, there were 5% lymphoplasmacytoid cells in the bone marrow; 90% were IgM-K. Both patients were treated with plasma exchange and cyclophosphamide; in both, IgM levels declined (2100 to 500, 900 to 300), but no clinical amelioration of the neuropathy followed.

SPECIAL STUDIES

In both cases, sural nerve biopsy showed severe myelin rarefaction and "onion bulb" images. By transmission electron microscopy (TEM), a marked detachment of myelin sheaths was evident (FIGURE 1). By direct double staining immunofluorescence (IF), a characteristic binary pattern (FIGURE 2) with specific IgM-K reactivity was evident. Anti-C3 IF was also elicited. Indirect IF using frog sciatic nerve and patient no. 2's serum was also positive with IgM-K reactivity.

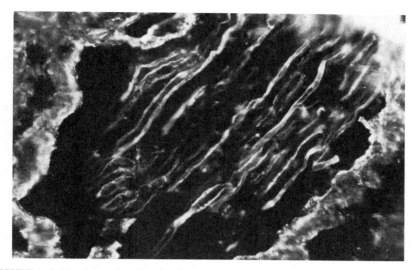

FIGURE 1. IgM staining of myelin sheaths in case no. 2. Direct immunofluorescence of cryostat sections of sural nerve biopsy.

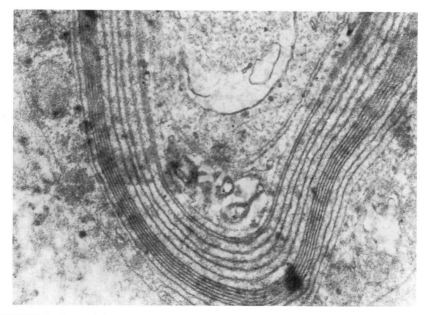

FIGURE 2. Transmission electron microscopy of the same sural nerve biopsy in FIGURE 1. Detachment of external and internal strata of myelin sheaths is evident.

DISCUSSION

Whether MAG-binding monoclonal paraproteins (IgM, IgG, IgA) may mediate myelin damage by their immune (type 2) activity against peripheral nerve antigens has been a point widely discussed. The passive transfer of myeloma (IgG) neuropathy from man to mouse, though, has provided experimental evidence for humoral-induced demyelination.[11]
Whether MAG antibodies are, or are not, species-specific is a moot point; along with cases in which the monoclonal IgM was bound exclusively with human peripheral nerve myelin,[6] others have been reported in which there was strong binding with teleost and avian myelin.[2] In addition, while no damage was elicited by means of intraneural injections of the offending immunoglobulin in the rat,[12] positive results have been obtained, as already remarked, in the mouse.[11]
The demonstration that MAG and natural killer (NK) cells share an antigenic determinant[13] has led to the hypothesis of a two-stage process that involves first sensitization against the autoantigen and then loss of homeostatic down-regulation of antibody response by NK cells.[13] However, although cross-reactions to endogenous, generally neoplastic, antigens may be at the origin of certain autoimmune paraneoplastic syndromes of the nervous system,[14] this does not appear to be the case for this kind of monoclonal immunoglobulin-determined peripheral neuropathy (MIDPN). Here, primary transformation of a B lymphoplasmacytic clonogenic cell, which synthesizes "natural" antibodies against MAG, may well be the original event.[15] Similarly to chronic cold agglutinin disease[16] and type II mixed cryoglobulinemia[17] (in which a monoclonal IgM binds to the I antigen in the former case and to IgG in the latter), MIDPN is most probably the expression of an anhomeostatically expanded clone of immunocytes. In conclusion, then, the definition of "monoclonal autoimmunity" seems best to indicate this group of autoimmune conditions.[18]

REFERENCES

1. KYLE, R. A. 1978. Am. J. Med. **64**: 814–826.
2. SMITH, I. S., S. N. KAHN, B. W. LACEY, R. H. M. KING, R. E. EAMES, D. J. WHYBREW & P. K. THOMAS. 1983. Brain **106**: 169–195.
3. KELLY, J. J., R. A. KYLE, P. C. O'BRIEN & P. J. DYCK. 1981. Neurology (Minneap.) **31**: 1480–1483.
4. ULDRY, P. A., A. J. STECK & F. REGLI. 1984. Schweiz. Med. Wochenschr. **114**: 1678–1685.
5. DELLAGI, K., P. DUPOUEY, J. C. BROUET, A. BILLECOCQ, D. GOMEZ, J. P. CLAUVEL & M. SELIGMANN. 1983. Blood **62**: 280–285.
6. LATOV, N., P. E. BRAUN, R. B. GROSS, W. H. SHERMAN & L. CHESS. 1981. Proc. Natl. Acad. Sci. USA **78**: 139–142.
7. NOBILE-ORAZIO, E., A. P. HAYS, N. LATOV, G. PERMAN, J. GOLIER, M. E. SHY & L. FREDDO. 1984. Neurology **34**: 1336–1342.
8. DIGHIERO, G., B. GUILBERT, J. P. FERMAND, P. LYMBERI, F. DANON & S. AVRAMEAS. 1983. Blood **62**: 264–270.
9. TOUSCO, F., G. CORBASCIO, M. BERTINI & F. MARMONT. 1985. Haematologica **70**: 106–109.
10. DELLAGI, K., F. CHEDRU, J. P. CLAUVEL & J. C. BROUET. 1984. Presse Med. **19**: 1199–1201.
11. BESINGER, V. A., K. V. TOYKA, A. P. ANZIL, D. FATEH-MOGHADAM, R. NEUMEIER, R. RAUSCHER & K. HEININGER. 1981. Science **213**: 1027–1030.
12. BOSCH, E. P., L. E. ANSBACHER, J. A. GOEKEN & P. A. CANCILLA. 1982. J. Neuropathol. Exp. Neurol. **41**: 446–459.

13. MURRAY, N. & A. J. STECK. 1984. Lancet 1: 711–712.
14. WAKSMAN, B. H. 1984. Immunol. Today 5: 346–347.
15. STEFANSSON, K., L. MARTON, J. P. ANTEL, R. L. WOLLMANN, R. P. ROOS, G. CHEJFFE & B. G. W. ARNASON. 1983. Acta Neuropathol. 39: 255–261.
16. SCHUBOTHE, H. 1966. Semin. Hematol. 3: 27–45.
17. GREY, H. M. & P. F. KOHLER. 1973. Semin. Hematol. 10: 87–92.
18. MARMONT, A. M., G. L. MANCARDI, M. TABATON, M. SICCARDI, L. GRASSIA, A. SCHENONE & M. REPETTO. 1985. Haematologica 70: 471–476.

Index of Contributors